Libraries and Information Services in the United Kingdom and the Republic of Ireland 2007–2008

facet publishing

Published by Facet Publishing
7 Ridgmount Street
London
WC1E 7AE

Facet Publishing (formerly Library Association Publishing) is wholly owned by CILIP: the Chartered Institute of Library and Information Professionals.

First published as *Libraries in the United Kingdom and the Republic of Ireland* by The Library Association, 1960 and thereafter annually.

Twenty-ninth edition published as *Libraries and Information Services in the United Kingdom and the Republic of Ireland* by Facet Publishing, 2002.
This thirty-fourth edition 2007

ISBN 978-1-85604-621-3
ISSN 1741-7120 (*Libraries in the United Kingdom and the Republic of Ireland* 1369-9687)

This thirty-fourth edition has been compiled by Lin Franklin and June York.

Typeset in 8/10pt Humanist 521 by Facet Publishing.
Printed and bound in Great Britain by MPG Books Ltd, Bodmin, Cornwall.

CONTENTS

PREFACE

How this book is organized

Libraries and Information Services in the United Kingdom and the Republic of Ireland is published annually, and is a listing of organizations falling into the four categories below.

1 Public library authorities

- All public library authorities in the UK and the Republic of Ireland, arranged under home countries
  - Public Libraries in England, Northern Ireland, Scotland, Wales and Crown Dependencies
  - Public Libraries in the Republic of Ireland

  Service managers and officers, including those for children's services, are listed, as supplied by the individual authorities.

  It is clearly impossible to list here all branch libraries, mobile bases and so on, so each entry includes headquarters/central library details, together with major branches and area/regional/group libraries, as supplied by each individual library. Libraries in this section are arranged by name of authority.

A listing of the nine Government regions in England, indicating which public library authorities fall in their areas, is given on page 443.

2 Academic libraries (arranged by name of institution)

- University libraries in the UK and the Republic of Ireland, together with major department and site/campus libraries
- College libraries at the universities of Oxford, Cambridge and London

  Please note: potential users of the Oxford and Cambridge libraries should be aware that their use is restricted to members of the college, and to bona fide scholars on application to the Librarian; any additional information about their use is given with each entry.
- The university-equivalent colleges in the Republic of Ireland
- Other degree-awarding institutions in the UK

  All colleges of higher education funded by HEFCE, SHEFC and HEFCW are included.

3 Selected government, national and special libraries in the UK and the Republic of Ireland

- Special libraries are included if they are one of the main libraries or organizations in their subject field. For example, the British Architectural Library at the Royal Institute of

British Architects is included for architecture, the Institution of Civil Engineers for civil engineering.

Many of the libraries in this section require a prior appointment to be made before visiting.

4 Schools and departments of information and library studies

- Each academic institution offering courses in information and library studies, with full contact details of the departments concerned.

5 Key library agencies and other relevant organizations

- This section lists the **key national and regional agencies, professional organizations and other relevant bodies**. It provides contact details for each body together with a short description of its function within the library profession.

6 Index

- Organizations are fully indexed by name and place.

Updating Libraries and Information Services in the UK

The directory is compiled by mailing questionnaires or entries for updating to libraries already listed in this book, and to others that have been suggested for inclusion. We would like to thank all the libraries for taking the time to reply to yet another mailing. With their assistance we received a 100% return rate. This means that every entry has been approved by the institution concerned.

We are dependent upon libraries to keep us informed of changes throughout the year. In this way we shall be able to ensure that our mailing label service is as current as possible. Libraries will, of course, be contacted afresh for the preparation of the next edition.

Mailing list

The data in this directory is also available to rent in a variety of formats including .csv files via e-mail, on disk/CD or as laser-quality adhesive labels. Visit the Facet Publishing website at www.facetpublishing. co.uk/listrental.shtml for further information.

Full set

Named Chief Librarian	ISBN 978 1 85604 026 6
Acquisitions Librarian	ISBN 978 1 85604 198 0

Public libraries (main headquarters)

Named Chief Librarian	ISBN 978 0 85365 587 9
Acquisitions Librarian	ISBN 978 1 85604 199 7

Public libraries (main headquarters and branches)

Named Chief Librarian	ISBN 978 1 85604 025 9

Academic and special libraries

Named Chief Librarian	ISBN 978 0 85365 959 4
Acquisitions Librarian	ISBN 978 1 85604 201 7

Key library agencies

Named Chief Officer	ISBN 978 1 85604 447 9

Please help us to improve this directory

Any comments about additions or other changes to *Libraries and Information Services in the United Kingdom and the Republic of Ireland* will be welcomed. Please address them to:

The Editor, Libraries and Information Services in the UK, Facet Publishing,
7 Ridgmount Street, London WC1E 7AE

Tel: 020 7255 0590
e-mail: info@facetpublishing.co.uk

Public Libraries in the United Kingdom, the Channel Islands and the Isle of Man

England
Northern Ireland
Scotland
Wales
Crown Dependencies

Service managers and officers, including those for children's services, are listed, as supplied by the individual authorities

BARKING AND DAGENHAM

Authority: London Borough of Barking and Dagenham
HQ Library Services HQ, 18 Muirhead Quay, Fresh Wharf, Barking, Essex IG11 7BD
☎020 8724 8530 (enquiries and administration)
e-mail: libraries@lbbd.gov.uk
url: www.lbbd.gov.uk/4-libraries/libraries-menu.html
Head of Library Services Trevor Brown MCLIP (e-mail: trevor.brown@lbbd.gov.uk)
Principal Librarian (Learning & Development) Mrs Susan Leighton MA MCLIP (e-mail: susan.leighton@lbbd.gov.uk)
Principal Librarian (Information & Resources) Tony Clifford BA MCLIP (e-mail: tony.clifford@lbbd.gov.uk)
Principal Librarian (Customer & Professional Services) Ms Vashti Thorne BA MCLIP (e-mail: vashti.thorne@lbbd.gov.uk)
Principal Librarian (Quality & Standards) David Bailey BSc MCLIP (e-mail: david.bailey@lbbd.gov.uk)

Community libraries

- Castle Green Library, Gale Street, Dagenham, Essex RM9 4UN
  ☎020 8270 4166
- Fanshawe Library, Fanshawe Community Centre, Barnmead Road, Dagenham, Essex RM9 5DX
  ☎020 8270 4244
- Marks Gate Library, Rose Lane, Chadwell Heath, Essex RM6 5NJ
  ☎020 8270 4165
- Markyate Library, Markyate Road, Dagenham, Essex RM8 2LD
  ☎020 8270 4137
- Rectory Library, Rectory Road, Dagenham, Dagenham, Essex RM9 5DX
  ☎020 8270 6233
- Robert Jeyes Library, High Road, Chadwell Heath, Essex RM6 6AS
  ☎020 8270 4305
- Rush Green Library, Dagenham Road, Rush Green, Essex RM7 0TL
  ☎020 8270 4304
- Thames View Library, Bastable Avenue, Barking, Essex IG11 0LG
  ☎020 8270 4164
- Valence Library, Becontree Avenue, Dagenham, Essex RM8 3HS
  ☎020 8270 6864
- Wantz Library, Rainham Road North, Dagenham, Essex RM10 7DX
  ☎020 8270 4169

BARNET

Authority: London Borough of Barnet
HQ Children's Service – Libraries, Museums & Local Studies, Building 4, North London Business Park, Oakleigh Road South, London N11 1NP

☎020 8359 7770
Fax 0870 889 6804
url: www.barnet.gov.uk/libraries
Head of Libraries, Museums & Local Studies Ms Tricia Little BA MCLIP (e-mail: tricia.little@barnet.gov.uk)
Libraries Strategic Development Manager Richard Nurse BA(Hons) MA MCLIP (e-mail: richard.nurse@barnet.gov.uk)
Heritage and Support Manager Bob Carter BA(Hons) MCLIP (e-mail: bob.carter@barnet.gov.uk)
Development Manager, Children and Education Ms Hannah Richens BA(Hons) DipILM MCLIP (e-mail: hannah.richens@barnet.gov.uk)

Area libraries

- Chipping Barnet Library, 3 Stapylton Road, Barnet, Herts EN5 4QT
  ☎020 8359 4040
  e-mail: chipping.barnet.library@barnet.gov.uk
  Area Manager Ms Veronica Padwick BA MCLIP (e-mail: veronica.padwick@barnet.gov.uk)
- Hendon Library, The Burroughs, London NW4 4BQ
  ☎020 8359 2628
  e-mail: hendon.library@barnet.gov.uk
  Area Manager Mrs Gill Harvey MCLIP (e-mail: gill.harvey@barnet.gov.uk)

BARNSLEY

Authority: Barnsley Metropolitan Borough Council
HQ Central Library, Shambles Street, Barnsley S70 2JF
☎(01226) 773911/30 (enquiries), (01226) 773926 (administration)
Fax (01226) 773955
e-mail: barnsleylibraryenquiries@barnsley.gov.uk
url: www.barnsley.gov.uk/libraries
Chief Libraries Officer Mrs Kathryn Green BA(Hons) MCLIP DMS
Libraries Operations Officer Ms Wendy Mann BSc(Hons) MCLIP
Information and Resources Officer Ms Jane Lee BA(Hons) MCLIP DMS
Children's Services Officer Mrs Jane E Matthews BLib(Hons) MCLIP (e-mail: JaneMatthews@barnsley.gov.uk), Ms Ceri Worman BA DipLib PGCE MCLIP (job share)
Archives and Local Studies Officer Ms Louise Whitworth BA(Hons) MArAd

Central/largest library

Central Library, Shambles Street, Barnsley, Barnsley, South Yorks S70 2JF
☎(01226) 773940 (enquiries)
Fax (01226) 773955

BATH AND NORTH EAST SOMERSET

Authority: Bath and North East Somerset Council
HQ HQ Customer Service, Libraries and Information, Bath Central Library, 19a The Podium, Northgate Street, Bath BA1 5AN

☎(01225) 394041
url: www.bathnes.gov.uk/libraries
Library Services Manager Mrs June Brassington MCLIP (01225 396424; e-mail: june_brassington@bathnes.gov.uk)

Central/largest library

Bath Library and Information Centre, 19a The Podium, Northgate Street, Bath BA1 5AN
☎(01225) 394041 (enquiries), (01225) 396082 (administration)
Fax (01225) 477809
e-mail: libraries@bathnes.gov.uk
SMS (text): (07797) 806545; Minicom: (01225) 477309
Libraries Development Manager Ms Julia Burton BLib MCLIP (01225 396078; e-mail: julia_burton@bathnes.gov.uk)
Libraries Operational Manager Mrs Susan Holmes (e-mail: susan_holmes@bathnes.gov.uk)
Libraries Customer Services Manager Peter Moth (e-mail: peter_moth@bathnes.gov.uk)

Group libraries

- Keynsham Library, The Centre, Keynsham, Bristol BS31 1ED
  ☎(01225) 394041
  Fax (01225) 477809
  e-mail: keynsham_library@bathnes.gov.uk
- Midsomer Norton Library, 119 High Street, Midsomer Norton, Bath BA3 2DA
  ☎(01225) 394041
  Fax (01225) 477809
  e-mail: midsomernorton_library@bathnes.gov.uk

BEDFORDSHIRE

Authority: Bedfordshire County Council
HQ Libraries, County Hall, Cauldwell Street, Bedford MK42 9AP
☎(01234) 228752
Fax (01234) 276387
url: www.bedfordshire.gov.uk
Head of Libraries Barry S George MCLIP (01234 228752; e-mail: barry.george@bedscc.gov.uk)
Library Resources Manager Andy Baker MCLIP (01234 228785)
Library Services Manager Ms Jenny Poad BA DMS MCLIP (01234 350931)

Central/largest library

Bedford Central Library, Harpur Street, Bedford MK40 1PG
☎(01234) 350931 (enquiries/administration)
Fax (01234) 342163
e-mail: bedford.library@bedscc.gov.uk
Central Library Manager Ms Joanne Smith

Gateway libraries

- Dunstable Library, Vernon Place, Dunstable, Beds LU5 4HA

☎(01582) 608441
Fax (01582) 471290
e-mail: dunstable.library@bedscc.gov.uk
Library Manager Ms Ruth Lambert

- Leighton Buzzard Library, Lake Street, Leighton Buzzard, Beds LU7 1RX
  ☎(01525) 371788
  Fax (01525) 815368
  e-mail: leightonbuzzard.library@bedscc.gov.uk
  Library Manager Ms Hazel Kerr

Area libraries

- Biggleswade Library, Chestnut Avenue, Biggleswade, Beds SG18 0LL
  ☎(01767) 312324
  Fax (01767) 601802
  e-mail: biggleswade.library@bedscc.gov.uk
  Library Manager Ms Sue Townsend
- Flitwick Library, Conniston Road, Flitwick, Beds MK45 1QJ
  ☎(01525) 715268
  Fax (01525) 713897
  e-mail: flitwick.library@bedscc.gov.uk
  Library Manager John Booth
- Shefford Library, High Street, Shefford, Beds SG17 5DD
  ☎(01462) 639070
  Fax (01462) 639071
  e-mail: shefford.library@bedscc.gov.uk
  Library Manager Ms Carol Forse

Neighbourhood libraries

- Houghton Regis Library, Bedford Square, Houghton Regis, Beds LU5 5ES
  ☎(01582) 865473
  Fax (01582) 868466
  e-mail: houghtonregis.library@bedscc.gov.uk
  Library Manager Ms Sue Bishop
- Kempston Library, Halsey Road, Kempston, Beds MK42 8AU
  ☎(01234) 853092
  Fax (01234) 841476
  e-mail: kempston.library@bedscc.gov.uk
  Library Manager Ms Ros Willis
- Putnoe Library, Library Walk, Putnoe, Bedford MK41 8HQ
  ☎(01234) 353422
  Fax (01234) 272833
  e-mail: putnoe.library@bedscc.gov.uk
  Library Manager Ms Coral Clarke

BEXLEY

Authority: London Borough of Bexley
HQ Directorate of Environment and Regeneration Services, Libraries and Community Information, Ground Floor, Footscray Offices, Maidstone Road, Sidcup, Kent DA14 5HS
☎020 8309 4100
Fax 020 8309 4142
url: www.bexley.gov.uk
Acting Library Services Manager Ms Judith Mitlin BSc PLD DMS (020 8309 4131; e-mail: judith.mitlin@bexley.gov.uk)
Development & Support Services Manager H C M Paton BA DipLib MCLIP (020 8309 4134; e-mail: hugh.paton@bexley.gov.uk)
Senior Group Manager Philip Ware BA MCLIP (020 8309 4166; e-mail: philip.ware@bexley.gov.uk)
Corporate Archivist & Records Manager Simon McKeon BA MA (020 8303 7777 ext 3470; e-mail: simon.mckeon@bexley.gov.uk)

Central/largest library

Central Library, Townley Road, Bexleyheath, Kent DA6 7HJ
☎020 8303 7777
Fax 020 8304 7058

BIRMINGHAM

Authority: Birmingham City Council
HQ Central Library, Chamberlain Square, Birmingham B3 3HQ
☎0121 303 4511 (enquiries), 0121 303 2449 management
Fax 0121 233 9695 (enquiries), 0121 233 9702 (management)
e-mail: libraries@birmingham.gov.uk
url: www.birmingham.gov.uk
Head of Library and Archive Services Brian Gambles MA DipLib (e-mail: brian.gambles@birmingham.gov.uk)
Senior Manager – Library Services Geoff Mills MSc BA DipLib MCLIP (e-mail: geoff.mills@birmingham.gov.uk)
Senior Manager – Performance and Efficiency Mrs Linda Butler BA MCLIP (e-mail: linda.butler@birmingham.gov.uk)

BLACKBURN WITH DARWEN

Authority: Blackburn with Darwen Borough Council
HQ Central Library, Town Hall Street, Blackburn, Lancashire BB2 1AG
☎(01254) 661221 (enquiries), 01254 587902 (administration)
Fax (01254) 690539
url: www.blackburn.gov.uk/libraries
Head of Cultural Services Mrs Susan Law MBE MCLIP (01254 587906; e-mail: susan.law@blackburn.gov.uk)
Information and Development Manager Ms Ruth Wood BA MCLIP (01254 587901; e-mail: ruth.wood@blackburn.gov.uk)

Operations Manager Mrs Kath Sutton MCLIP (01254 587907; e-mail: kath.sutton@blackburn.gov.uk)
Literacy Development and Resources Manager Miss Jean Gabbatt BLib MCLIP (01254 587937; e-mail: jean.gabbatt@blackburn.gov.uk)
Literacy Development Manager Mrs Geraldine Wilson MCLIP (01254 587236; e-mail: geraldine.wilson@blackburn.gov.uk)
Performance and Quality Manager Miss Adele Karwat BA MCLIP (01254 587954; e-mail: adele.karwat@blackburn.gov.uk)
Central Library Manager Mrs Ada Clinton (01254 587935; e-mail: ada.clinton@blackburn.gov.uk)

BLACKPOOL

Authority: Blackpool Borough Council
HQ Culture and Communities, Progress House, Clifton Road, Blackpool, Lancs FY4 4US
☎(01253) 478080 (enquiries), 01253 478105 (administration)
Fax (01253) 478059
url: www.blackpool.gov.uk
Assistant Director, Lifelong Learning and Cultural Services Mrs P Hansell MBA BA MCLIP (e-mail: pat.hansell@blackpool.gov.uk)
Head of Libraries Mrs A Ellis BA MCLIP DMS (e-mail: anne.ellis@blackpool.gov.uk)
Head of Arts Ms Carolyn Primett BA MA (e-mail: carolyn.primett@blackpool.gov.uk)

Central/largest library

Central Library, Queen Street, Blackpool, Lancashire FY1 1PX
☎(01253) 478080
Fax (01253) 478082

BOLTON

Authority: Bolton Metropolitan Borough Council
HQ Central Library, Le Mans Crescent, Bolton, Lancs BL1 1SE
☎(01204) 333173
Fax (01204) 332225
e-mail: central.library@bolton.gov.uk
Assistant Director, Adult Services (Culture) Mrs Stephanie Crossley BA(Hons) DipLIS MCLIP (e-mail: stephanie.crossley@bolton.gov.uk)
Head of Library Service Mrs Julie Spencer MBE BA(Hons) MBA MCLIP (e-mail: julie.spencer@bolton.gov.uk)
Knowledge and E-Services Manager Mrs Ann Melmoth BA MBA MCLIP (e-mail: ann.melmoth@bolton.gov.uk)
Communities and Learning Manager Ms Mary Keane BA(Hons) DipLib MCLIP (e-mail: mary.keane@bolton.gov.uk)
Customer Services Manager Mrs Judith Rudd MCLIP (e-mail: judith.rudd@bolton.gov.uk)

BOURNEMOUTH

Stock Support Unit, Bournemouth library, 22 The Triangle
B'mth BH2 5RQ
01202454817

Authority: Bournemouth Borough Council
HQ Bournemouth Libraries, Information, Culture and Community Learning Directorate, Town Hall, Bournemouth BH2 6DY
☎(01202) 454848 (general enquiries)
Fax (01202) 454830
e-mail: bournemouth@bournemouthlibraries.org.uk
url: www.bournemouth.gov.uk/libraries
Head of Information, Culture and Community Learning Ms Shelagh Levett BA(Hons) CertEd MCLIP (01202 454615; fax: 01202 454620; e-mail: shelagh.levett@bournemouthlibraries.org.uk)
Principal Area Services Manager Mrs Carolyn Date GradIPD MCLIP (01202 454826)
Principal Development and Support Services Manager Mrs Elaine Arthur BA(Hons) MCLIP DMS (01202 454825), Mrs Linda Constable BA(Hons) MCLIP PGDip(Res) (job share)

Central/largest library

The Bournemouth Library, 22 The Triangle, Bournemouth BH2 5RQ
☎(01202) 454848

BRACKNELL FOREST

Authority: Bracknell Forest Borough Council
HQ Education, Children's Services and Libraries Department, Seymour House, 38 Broadway, Bracknell, Berks RG12 1AU
☎(01344) 354000
Fax (01344) 354001
e-mail: bracknell.library@bracknell-forest.gov.uk
url: www.bracknell-forest.gov.uk/libraries
Head of Libraries and Information Ms Ruth Burgess BLib MCLIP (01344 353134; e-mail: ruth.burgess@bracknell-forest.gov.uk)

Central/largest library

Bracknell Library, Education, Children's Services and Libraries Department, Town Square, Bracknell, Berks RG12 1BH
☎(01344) 423149
Fax (01344) 411392
e-mail: bracknell.library@bracknell-forest.gov.uk
url: www.bracknell-forest.gov.uk/libraries
Community Services Manager Mrs Fiona Atkinson BA(Hons) MA MCLIP (e-mail: fiona.atkinson@bracknell-forest.gov.uk)

BRADFORD

Authority: City of Bradford Metropolitan District Council
HQ Central Library, Prince's Way, Bradford BD1 1NN
☎(01274) 433600
Fax (01274) 395108

e-mail: public.libraries@bradford.gov.uk
url: www.bradford.gov.uk
Strategic Director, Culture, Tourism & Sport Ms Jane Glaister OBE BA FMA PGDipLib (01274 432647; e-mail: jane.glaister@bradford.gov.uk)
Head of Libraries, Archives and Information Service Ian Watson BA MCLIP (01274 433640; e-mail: ian.watson@bradford.gov.uk)

Group libraries

- North Group, c/o Central Library, Prince's Way, Bradford BD1 1NN
  ☎(01274) 433600
  Fax (01274) 395108
  e-mail: public.libraries@bradford.gov.uk
  Principal Libraries Officer: Operations North Ms Jackie Kitwood BA DipLib MCLIP (e-mail: jackie.kitwood@bradford.gov.uk)
- South Group, c/o Central Library, Prince's Way, Bradford BD1 1NN
  ☎(01274) 433600
  Fax (01274) 395108
  e-mail: public.libraries@bradford.gov.uk
  Principal Libraries Officer: Operations South Ms Jane Heap BA(Hons) MCLIP (e-mail: jane.heap@bradford.gov.uk)

BRENT

Authority: London Borough of Brent
HQ Environment and Culture Directorate, Ground Floor, Brent House, 349-357 High Road, Wembley, Middlesex HA9 6BZ
☎020 8937 3144
Fax 020 8937 3008
url: www.brent.gov.uk
Director of Environment and Culture Richard Saunders
Assistant Director (Arts and Learning) Ms Marianne Locke BA MCLIP (020 8937 5415; e-mail: marianne.locke@brent.gov.uk)
Head of Library Services Ms Susan McKenzie BA DAA (020 8937 3149; e-mail: susan.mckenzie@brent.gov.uk)

Area libraries

- Barham Park Library, Harrow Road, Sudbury, Middlesex HA0 2HB
  ☎020 8937 3550
  Fax 020 8937 3553
- Cricklewood Library, 152 Olive Road, Cricklewood, London NW2 6UY
  ☎020 8937 3540
  Fax 020 8450 5211
- Ealing Road Library, Coronet Parade, Wembley, Middlesex HA0 4BR
  ☎020 8937 3560
  Fax 020 8795 3425
- Harlesden Library, Craven Park Road, Harlesden, London NW10 8SE
  ☎020 8965 7132
  Fax 020 8838 2199

- Kensal Rise Library, Bathurst Gardens, Harlesden, London NW10 5JA
  ☎020 8969 0942
  Fax 020 8960 8399
- Kilburn Library, Salusbury Road, Kilburn, London NW6 6NN
  ☎020 8937 3530
  Fax 020 7625 6387
- Kingsbury Library, Stag Lane, Kingsbury, London NW9 9AE
  ☎020 8937 3520
  Fax 020 8905 0264
- Neasden Library, 277 Neasden Lane, London NW10 1QJ
  ☎020 8937 3580
  Fax 020 8208 3909
- Outreach Library Service, 2-12 Grange Road, Willesden, London NW10 2QY
  ☎020 8452 6941
- Preston Library, Carlton Avenue East, Wembley, Middlesex HA9 8PL
  ☎020 8937 3510
  Fax 020 8908 6220
- Tokyngton Library, Monks Park, Wembley, Middlesex HA9 6JE
  ☎020 8937 3590
  Fax 020 8795 3440
- Town Hall Library, Brent Town Hall, Forty Lane, Wembley, Middlesex HA9 9HV
  ☎020 8937 3500
  Fax 020 8937 3504
- Willesden Green Library, 95 High Road, Willesden, London NW10 2ST
  ☎020 8937 3400
  Fax 020 8937 3401

BRIGHTON AND HOVE

Authority: Brighton and Hove City Council
HQ Royal Pavilion Libraries and Museums Divisions, Cultural Services, Jubilee Library, Jubilee Street, Brighton BN1 1GE
☎(01273) 290800
Fax (01273) 296976
url: www.citylibraries.info
Head of Libraries and Information Services Ms Sally McMahon BA DipLib MCLIP (01273 296963)
Principal Library Manager: Operations & Performance Ms Julia Hugall BA DipLib MCLIP (01273 296933)
Principal Library Manager: Collections & Learning Nigel Imi BA DipLib MCLIP
Principal Library Manager: Community & Development Alan Issler BA MCLIP (e-mail: alan.issler@brighton-hove.gov.uk)
Principal Library Manager: Information & E-services Ms Kate Rouse MSc (e-mail: kate.rouse@brighton-hove.gov.uk)

Central libraries

- Jubilee Library, Jubilee Street, Brighton BN1 1GE
  ☎(01273) 290800

- Hove Library, 182-186 Church Road, Hove, East Sussex BN3 2EG
  ☎(01273) 290700 (minicom)

BRISTOL

Authority: Bristol City Council
HQ Central Library, College Green, Bristol BS1 5TL
☎0117 903 7200 (all enquiries)
Fax 0117 922 1081
e-mail: bristol.library.service@bristol.gov.uk
url: www.bristol.gov.uk
Head of Libraries Ms Kate Davenport MA MCLIP DMS (e-mail: kate.davenport@bristol.gov.uk)
Business Support Manager Ms Kate Cole BA MCLIP (e-mail: kate.cole@bristol.gov.uk)
Central Library Manager Ms Janet Bremner BA MCLIP (e-mail: janet.bremner@bristol.gov.uk), Ms Julie Bowie BA MCLIP (e-mail: julie.bowie@bristol.gov.uk)
Special Projects Manager Ms Julie York BA MCLIP (e-mail: julie.york@bristol.gov.uk)

BROMLEY

Authority: London Borough of Bromley
HQ Central Library, High Street, Bromley, Kent BR1 1EX
☎020 8460 9955 (enquiries and administration)
Fax 020 8313 9975
e-mail: reference.library@bromley.gov.uk
url: www.bromley.gov.uk
Assistant Director, Libraries and Lifelong Learning Ms Linda Simpson (e-mail: linda.simpson@bromley.gov.uk)
Principal Library Services Manager David Brockhurst BA (e-mail: david.brockhurst@bromley.gov.uk)
Service Manager, Development Ian Dodds BSc(Hons) MA MCLIP (e-mail: ian.dodds@bromley.gov.uk)
Service Manager, Resources John Wilkins BSc (e-mail: john.wilkins@bromley.gov.uk)
Customer Services Manager Tim Woolgar MCLIP (e-mail: tim.woolgar@bromley.gov.uk)

Central/largest library

Central Library, High Street, Bromley, Kent BR1 1EX
☎Tel/fax etc. as HQ

District libraries

- Beckenham Library, Beckenham Road, Beckenham, Kent BR3 4PE
  ☎020 8650 7292/3
- Orpington Library, The Priory, Church Hill, Orpington, Kent BR6 0HH
  ☎(01689) 831551

BUCKINGHAMSHIRE

Authority: Buckinghamshire County Council
HQ Culture and Learning, County Hall, Walton Street, Aylesbury, Bucks HP20 1UU
☎(0845) 370 8090
e-mail: library@buckscc.gov.uk
url: www.buckscc.gov.uk/libraries
Head of Culture and Learning Services Ms Amanda Brooke-Webb (01296 383549)
Senior Operations Manager Peter Mussett MCLIP (01296 382254; fax: 01296 382259; e-mail: pmussett@buckscc.gov.uk)

Main group libraries

- Amersham Library, Chiltern Avenue, Amersham, Bucks HP6 5AH
  ☎(0845) 370 8090
  Fax (01494) 586870
  Library Manager Ms Glenys Brown
- Aylesbury Central Library, Walton Street, Aylesbury, Bucks HP20 1UU
  ☎(0845) 370 8090
  Library Manager Ms Sarah Townsend PGDipIM MCLIP
- Beaconsfield Library, Reynolds Road, Beaconsfield, Bucks HP9 2NJ
  ☎(0845) 370 8090
  Fax (01494) 678772
  Library Manager Ms Judy Williamson BA PGDipLib MC MCLIP
- Buckingham Library, Verney Close, Buckingham MK18 1JP
  ☎(0845) 370 8090
  Fax (01280) 823597
  Library Manager Ms Steph Gassor MCLIP
- Chesham Library, Elgiva Lane, Chesham, Bucks HP5 2JD
  ☎(0845) 370 8090
  Fax (01494) 773074
  Library Manager Ms Jenny Mainwaring MCLIP
- Hazlemere Library, 312 Amersham Road, Hazlemere, Bucks HP15 7PY
  ☎(0845) 370 8090
  Fax (01494) 533086
  Library Manager Ms Janet Webb
- High Wycombe Library, Queen Victoria Road, High Wycombe, Bucks HP11 1BD
  ☎(0845) 370 8090
  Fax (01494) 533086
  Library Manager Ms Helen Goreham BLib MCLIP
- Marlow Library, Institute Road, Marlow, Bucks SL7 1BL
  ☎(0845) 370 8090
  Library Manager Ms Harlene Semmens

BURY

Authority: Bury Metropolitan Borough Council
HQ Arts, Libraries and Adult Learning, Craig House, Bank Street, Bury, Lancs BL9 0DN
☎0161 253 5861 (administration)

Fax 0161 253 55757
e-mail: information@bury.gov.uk
url: www.bury.gov.uk/culture.htm
Head of Libraries and Adult Learning Mrs Diana Sorrigan BA MCLIP (0161 253 6077; e-mail: d.sorrigan@bury.gov.uk)
Assistant Head of Libraries & Adult Learning (Branches/Centres & Staff Development) Mrs Lesley Kelly BA MA MCLIP (0161 253 7579; e-mail: s.l.kelly@bury.gov.uk)
Assistant Head of Libraries & Adult Learning (Central Services & Social Inclusion) Tony Jowett BA MA MCLIP (0161 253 5876; e-mail: t.jowett@bury.gov.uk)

Central/largest library

Central Library, Manchester Road, Bury, Lancs BL9 0DG
☎0161 253 5873
Fax 0161 253 5857
e-mail: information@bury.gov.uk
Principal Librarian Tony Jowett BA MA MCLIP (e-mail: t.jowett@bury.gov.uk)

Branch libraries

- Prestwich Library & Adult Learning Centre, Longfield Centre, Prestwich, Manchester M25 1AY
  ☎0161 253 7214/7216
  Fax 0161 798 9981
  e-mail: prestwich.lib@bury.gov.uk
  Library & Adult Learning Centre Supervisors Ms Joan Watkiss BA DipLib (0161 253 7219) David Galloway BA DipLib (0161 253 7219)
- Radcliffe Library, Stand Lane, Radcliffe, Manchester M26 1NW
  ☎0161 253 7161
  Fax 0161 724 6087
  e-mail: radcliffe.lib@bury.gov.uk
  Library Supervisor Ms Joanne Smillie NEBS (0161 253 7160)
- Ramsbottom Library & Adult Learning Centre, Carr Street, Ramsbottom, Bury, Lancs BL0 9AE
  ☎0161 253 5352/5425
  e-mail: ramsbottom.lib@bury.gov.uk
  Library & Adult Learning Centre Supervisor Miss Deborah Smith NEBS
- Tottington Library, Market Street, Tottington, Bury, Lancs BL8 3LN
  ☎0161 253 6652
  Fax (01204) 886517
  e-mail: tottington.lib@bury.gov.uk
  Library Supervisors Mrs Lynsay Snape NEBS, Mrs Stephanie Lamb NEBS
- Unsworth Library, Sunnybank Road, Unsworth, Bury, Lancs BL9 8ED
  ☎0161 253 7560
  Fax 0161 272 1931
  e-mail: unsworth.lib@bury.gov.uk
  Library Supervisor Mrs Louise Guilfoyle NEBS
- Whitefield Library & Adult Learning Centre, Pinfold Lane, Whitefield, Manchester M45 7NY

☎0161 253 5548
Fax 0161 796 1780
e-mail: whitefield.lib@bury.gov.uk
Library & Adult Learning Centre Supervisor Mrs Janet Moores

Outreach libraries

- Ainsworth Library, Church Street, Ainsworth, Lancs BL2 5RP
  ☎0161 253 5886
  e-mail: ainsworth.lib@bury.gov.uk
- Brandlesholme Community Library, 375 Brandlesholme Road, Bury, Lancs BL8 1HS
  ☎0161 764 2731
- Castle Sport and Leisure Library, Castle Leisure Centre, Bolton Street, Bury, Lancs BL9 0EZ
  ☎0161 253 5560
  e-mail: castle.lib@bury.gov.uk
- Moorside Community Library, St John's Church Hall, Parkinson Street, Bury, Lancs BL9 6NY
  ☎0161 253 6471
  e-mail: moorside.lib@bury.gov.uk
- New Kershaw Centre, Deal Street, Bury, Lancs BL9 7PZ
  ☎0161 253 6400
  e-mail: kershaw.lib@bury.gov.uk
- Sedgeley Park Community Library, St Gabriel's Community Rooms, Bishops Road, Prestwich, Manchester M25 0HT
  ☎0161 798 9420
- South Cross Street Community Library, 90 South Cross Street, Bury, Lancs BL9 0RS
  ☎0161 253 6079
- Topping Fold Library, Topping Fold Road, Bury, Lancs BL9 7NG
  ☎0161 253 6361
  e-mail: topping.lib@bury.gov.uk

CALDERDALE

Authority: Calderdale Metropolitan Borough Council
HQ Central Library, Northgate, Halifax, Yorks HX1 1UN
☎(01422) 392630 (enquiries), 392605 (administration)
Fax (01422) 392615
e-mail: libraries@calderdale.gov.uk
url: www.calderdale.gov.uk
Head of Libraries, Museums and Arts Gary Borrows MCLIP
Collections and Service Development Manager David Duffy BA MCLIP (01422 392602)
Operations and Customer Services Manager Ms Carole Heaton MA MCLIP

CAMBRIDGESHIRE

Authority: Cambridgeshire County Council
HQ Cambridgeshire Libraries, Archives and Information, ET1042, C305 Castle Court, Shire Hall, Cambridge CB3 0AP

☎(01223) 717023 (administration)
Fax (01223) 717079
e-mail: your.library@cambridgeshire.gov.uk
url: www.cambridgeshire.gov.uk/library
Head of Libraries, Archives and Information Mrs Lesley Noblett MA MCLIP (01223 717292; e-mail: lesley.noblett@cambridgeshire.gov.uk)
Head of Development and Support Services Chris Heaton MA MCLIP (01223 717839; e-mail: chris.heaton@cambridgeshire.gov.uk)

Central/largest library

Central Library, 7 Lion Yard, Cambridge CB2 3QD
☎0845 045 5225
(Closed for redevelopment – due to reopen Spring 2008)

Hub libraries

- Ely Library, 6 The Cloisters, Ely, Cambs CB7 4ZH
  ☎0845 045 5225
  Fax (01353) 616164
- Huntingdon Library, Dryden House, St Johns Street, Huntingdon, Cambs PE29 3NU
  ☎0845 045 5225
  Fax (01480) 459563
- March Library, City Road, March, Cambs PE15 9LT
  ☎0845 045 5225
  Fax (01354) 754760
- St Ives Library, Station Road, St Ives, Huntingdon, Cambs PE27 5BW
  ☎0845 045 5225
  Fax (01480) 375496
- St Neots Library, Priory Lane, St Neots, Huntingdon, Cambs PE19 2BH
  ☎0845 045 5225
  Fax (01480) 396006
- Wisbech Library, 1 Ely Place, Wisbech, Cambs PE13 1EU
  ☎0845 045 5225
  Fax (01945) 582784

CAMDEN

Authority: London Borough of Camden
HQ Libraries, Information and Community Learning, Culture and Environment Directorate, 7th Floor, Camden Town Hall Extension, Argyle Street, London WC1H 8EQ
☎020 7974 4001
Fax 020 7974 4801
url: www.camden.gov.uk
Head of Libraries and Information Services David Jones BA(Hons) DipLib (020 7974 4058; e-mail: david.jones@camden.gov.uk)

Central/largest library

Swiss Cottage Library, 88 Avenue Road, London NW3 3HA
☎020 7974 6522 (general enquiries)

Fax 020 7974 6532
e-mail: swisscottagelibrary@camden.gov.uk
Library Manager Bob Gryspeerdt BA MCLIP (020 7974 6509)

Other libraries

- Belsize Library, Antrim Road, London NW3 4XN
  ☎020 7974 6518
  Fax 020 7974 6508
  e-mail: belsizelibrary@camden.gov.uk
  Library Manager Bob Gryspeerdt BA MCLIP
- Camden Town Library, Crowndale Centre, 218 Eversholt Street, London NW1 1BD
  ☎020 7974 1563
  Fax 020 7974 1582
  e-mail: camdentownlibrary@camden.gov.uk
  Library Manager Mrs Gloria Keys (020 7974 1563/1531))
- Chalk Farm Library, Sharpleshall Street, London NW1 8YN
  ☎020 7974 6526
  Fax 020 7974 6502
  e-mail: chalkfarmlibrary@camden.gov.uk
  Library Manager Roberto Cioccari
- Heath Library, Keats Grove, London NW3 2RR
  ☎020 7974 6520 (tel/fax)
  e-mail: heathlibrary@camden.gov.uk
  Library Manager Ms Katharine Chasey
- Highgate Library, Chester Road, London N19 5DH
  ☎020 7974 5752, 020 7281 2546 (home library service)
  Fax 020 7974 5555
  e-mail: highgatelibrary@camden.gov.uk
  Library Manager Ms Katharine Chasey
- Holborn Library, 32-38 Theobalds Road, London WC1X 8PA
  ☎020 7974 6345/6, 020 7974 6342 (Local studies)
  Fax 020 7974 6356
  e-mail: holbornlibrary@camden.gov.uk
  Library Manager Ms Shirley Jacobs (020 7974 6353)
- Kentish Town Library, 262-266 Kentish Town Road, London NW5 2AA
  ☎020 7974 6253
  Fax 020 7974 5650
  e-mail: kentishtownlibrary@camden.gov.uk
  Library Manager Roberto Cioccari (020 7974 6261/6253)
- Kilburn Library Centre, 12-22 Kilburn High Road, London NW6 5UH
  ☎020 7974 1965
  Fax 020 7974 6524
  e-mail: culturallibrarycentre@camden.gov.uk
  Library Manager Mrs Gloria Keys
- Queen's Crescent Library, 165 Queen's Crescent, London NW5 4HH
  ☎020 7974 6243 (tel/fax)
  e-mail: queenscrescentlibrary@camden.gov.uk
  Library Manager Roberto Cioccari (020 7974 6252)

- Regent's Park Library, Compton Close, Robert Street, London NW1 3QT
  ☎020 7974 1530
  Fax 020 7974 1531
  e-mail: regentsparklibrary@camden.gov.uk
  Library Manager Ms Shirley Jacobs
- St Pancras Library, Town Hall Extension, Argyle Street, London WC1H 8NN
  ☎020 7974 5833
  Fax 020 7974 5963
  e-mail: stpancraslibrary@camden.gov.uk
  Library Manager Mrs Gloria Keys (020 7974 5865)
- West Hampstead Library, Dennington Park Road, London NW6 1AU
  ☎020 7974 6610
  Fax 020 7974 6539
  e-mail: westhampsteadlibrary@camden.gov.uk
  Library Manager Ms Katharine Chasey (020 7974 6620)

CHESHIRE

Authority: Cheshire County Council
HQ Community Services Department, County Hall, Chester CH1 1SF
☎(01244) 602424 (County Hall switchboard)
url: www.cheshire.gov.uk/library/
County Manager Cultural Services Guy Kilminster BA(Hons) FMA (01244 606020; e-mail: guy.kilminster@cheshire.gov.uk)
Manager of Public Libraries Ms Linda Morris DipLib (01244 606024; e-mail: linda.morris@cheshire.gov.uk)
Resources and Development Manager Roy Walker DLIS (01244 606023; e-mail: roy.walker@cheshire.gov.uk)

Group HQs

- Business Information Service, Ellesmere Port Library, Civic Way, Ellesmere Port, Cheshire CH65 0BG
  ☎0151 357 4695
  Fax 0151 355 6849
  e-mail: bisep@cheshire.gov.uk
  url: www.cheshire.gov.uk/bis
  Community and Business Information Manager Ms Sue Eddison
- Chester Library, Northgate Street, Chester CH1 2EF
  ☎(01244) 312935
  Fax (01244) 315534
  e-mail: chester.infopoint@cheshire.gov.uk
  Group Librarian Angus Madders MCLIP (e-mail: angus.madders@cheshire.gov.uk)
- Congleton Library, Market Square, Congleton, Cheshire CW12 1BU
  ☎(01260) 285550
  Fax (01260) 285551
  e-mail: congleton.infopoint@cheshire.gov.uk
  Group Librarian Miss Sheila M Kane MCLIP (e-mail: sheila.kane@cheshire.gov.uk)
- Crewe Library, Prince Albert Street, Crewe, Cheshire CW1 2DH

☎(01270) 505250
Fax (01270) 505293
e-mail: crewe.infopoint@cheshire.gov.uk
Group Librarian Mrs Jo Norton BA MCLIP (e-mail: nortonrowland@cheshire.gov.uk), Mrs Caroline Balabil BA MA MCLIP (e-mail: nortonrowland@cheshire.gov.uk)

- Ellesmere Port Library, Civic Way, Ellesmere Port, Cheshire L65 0BG
  ☎0151 357 4684
  Fax 0151 355 6849
  e-mail: eport.infopoint@cheshire.gov.uk
  Group Librarian Roger D Booth BSc DipLib MCLIP (e-mail: roger.booth@cheshire.gov.uk)
- Macclesfield Library, 2 Jordangate, Macclesfield, Cheshire SK10 1EE
  ☎(01625) 422512
  Fax (01625) 612818
  e-mail: macclesfield.infopoint@cheshire.gov.uk
  Group Librarian Paul Everitt MCLIP (e-mail: paul.everitt@cheshire.gov.uk)
- Northwich Library, Witton Street, Northwich, Cheshire CW9 5DR
  ☎(01606) 44221
  Fax (01606) 48396
  e-mail: northwich.infopoint@cheshire.gov.uk
  Group Librarian Mrs Rachel Foster BA(Hons) MCLIP (e-mail: rachel.foster@cheshire.gov.uk)
- Wilmslow Library, South Drive, Wilmslow, Cheshire SK9 1NW
  ☎(01625) 415037
  Fax (01625) 548401
  Group Librarian Mrs Lynda Cotterill BA MCLIP (e-mail: lynda.cotterill@cheshire.gov.uk)

CORNWALL

Authority: Cornwall County Council
HQ Chief Executive's Department, Unit 17, Threemilestone Industrial Estate, Threemilestone, Truro, Cornwall TR4 9LD
☎(01872) 324316 (enquiries)
Fax (01872) 223509
e-mail: library@cornwall.gov.uk
url: www.cornwall.gov.uk
Assistant Chief Executive, Communications and Libraries Chris Ramsey BSc(Hons) MA AdvDipBFM(CIPFA)(based at Room 202, New County Hall, Truro TR1 3AY)

Additional libraries

- Bodmin Library, Lower Bore Street, Bodmin, Cornwall PL31 2LX
  ☎(01208) 72286
- Bude Library, The Wharf, Bude, Cornwall EX23 8LG
  ☎(01288) 352527
- Callington Library, Launceston Road, Callington, Cornwall PL17 7DR
  ☎(01579) 383236
- Camborne Library, The Cross, Camborne, Cornwall TR14 8HA

☎(01209) 713544

- Camelford Library, Town Hall, Market Place, Camelford, Cornwall PL32 9PD
☎(01840) 212409
- Falmouth Library, The Moor, Falmouth, Cornwall TR11 3QA
☎(01326) 314901
- Fowey Library, Caffa Mill House, 2 Passage Lane, Fowey, Cornwall PL23 1JS
☎(01726) 832332
- Hayle Library, Commercial Road, Hayle, Cornwall TR27 4DE
☎(01736) 753196
- Helston Library, Trengrouse Way, Helston, Cornwall TR13 8AG
☎(01326) 572321
- Launceston Library, Bounsalls Lane, Launceston, Cornwall PL15 9AB
☎(01566) 773306
- Liskeard Library, Barras Street, Liskeard, Cornwall PL14 6AB
☎(01579) 343285
- Looe Library, Sea Front Court, Looe, Cornwall PL13 1AL
☎(01503) 262365
- Lostwithiel Library, Taprell House, North Street, Lostwithiel, Cornwall PL22 0BL
☎(01208) 872747
- Newquay Library, Marcus Hill, Newquay, Cornwall TR7 1BD
☎(01637) 873538
- Padstow Library, The Institute, Padstow, Cornwall PL28 8AL
☎(01841) 532387
- Par Library, Hamley's Corner, Eastcliffe Road, Par, Cornwall PL24 2AH
☎(01726) 814853
- Penryn Library, St Thomas Street, Penryn, Cornwall TR10 8JN
☎(01326) 372203
- Penzance Library, Morrab Road, Penzance, Cornwall TR18 4EY
☎(01736) 363954
- Perranporth Library, Oddfellows Hall, Ponsmere Road, Perranporth, Cornwall TR6 0BW
☎(01872) 572590
- Redruth Library, Clinton Road, Redruth, Cornwall TR15 2QE
☎(01209) 219111
- St Agnes Library, The Car Park, St Agnes, Cornwall TR5 0TP
☎(01872) 553245
- St Austell Library, 2 Carlyon Road, St Austell, Cornwall PL25 4LD
☎(01726) 73348
- St Columb Library, The Town Hall, St Columb, Cornwall TR9 6AN
☎(01637) 881480
- St Dennis Library, St Dennis CP School, Carne Hill, St Dennis, Cornwall PL26 8AY
☎(01726) 823149
- St Ives Library, Gabriel Street, St Ives, Cornwall TR26 2LU
☎(01736) 795377
- St Just Library, Market Street, St Just, Cornwall TR19 7HX
☎(01736) 788669
- St Keverne Library, St Keverne CP School, School Hill, St Keverne, Cornwall TR12 6NQ
☎(01326) 281218

- Saltash Library, Callington Road, Saltash, Cornwall PL12 6DX
  ☎(01752) 842478
- Torpoint Library, Fore Street, Torpoint, Cornwall PL11 2AG
  ☎(01752) 812207
- Truro Library, Union Place, Truro, Cornwall TR1 1EP
  ☎(01872) 279205
- Upton Cross Library, Upton Cross School, Liskeard, Cornwall PL14 5AX
  ☎(01579) 363878 (tel/fax)
- Wadebridge Library, Southern Way, Wadebridge, Cornwall PL27 7BX
  ☎(01208) 812202

COVENTRY

Authority: Coventry City Council
HQ Coventry Libraries and Information Services, 2nd Floor, West Orchard House, 28-34 Corporation Street, Coventry CV1 1GF
☎024 7683 1579
Fax 024 7683 2470
url: url: www.coventry.gov.uk
Director of Community Services Directorate John Bolton
Head of Libraries and Information Services Andrew Green BA MLS DMS MCLIP (024 7683 1579; fax: 024 7683 1584; e-mail: andrew.green@coventry.gov.uk)
Assistant Head of Libraries and Information Services: East Area, Media and Cultural Development Ms Sorrelle Clements (024 7683 2800; fax: 024 7683 1584; e-mail: sorrelle.clements@coventry.gov.uk)
Assistant Head of Libraries and Information Services: West Area, Equalities and Young People Colin Scott (024 7683 2457; fax: 024 7683 1584; e-mail: colin.scott@coventry.gov.uk)
Assistant Head of Libraries and Information Services: Central Library, Information and Learning Simon Rice (024 7683 1707; fax: 024 7683 1584; e-mail: simon.rice@coventry.gov.uk)
Business Manager Bob Parsons (024 7683 3649; fax: 024 7683 1584; e-mail: bob.parsons@coventry.gov.uk)

Central/largest library

Central Library, Smithford Way, Coventry CV1 1FY
☎024 7683 2314 (enquiries), 024 7683 2321 (library office)
Fax 024 7683 2440 (enquiries), 024 7683 2315 (library office)
e-mail: library.office@coventry.gov.uk; central.library@coventry.gov.uk (enquiries)

East Area Libraries

- Aldermoor Farm Library, Aldermoor Farm School, Pinley Fields, Stoke Aldermoor, Coventry CV3 1DD
  ☎024 7644 2840
  Fax 024 7644 2840
  e-mail: aldermoorfarm.library@coventry.gov.uk
- Arena Park Library, Coventry Arena Shopping Park, Classic Drive, Rowley's Green, Coventry CV6 6AF

☎024 7678 5181
Fax 024 7670 0329
e-mail: arenapark.library@coventry.gov.uk

- Bell Green Library and Learning Centre, 17-23 Riley Square, Bell Green, Coventry CV2 1LS
  ☎024 7668 8986
  Fax 024 7666 3468
  e-mail: bellgreen.library@coventry.gov.uk
- Cheylesmore Community Library, Poitiers Road, Cheylesmore, Coventry CV3 5JX
  ☎024 7650 2106
  Fax 024 7650 5287
  e-mail: cheylesmore.library@coventry.gov.uk
- Foleshill Library, Broad Street, Foleshill, Coventry CV6 5BG
  ☎024 7668 9154
  Fax 024 7666 7461
  e-mail: foleshill.library@coventry.gov.uk
- Hillfields Community Library, St Peter's Centre, Charles Street, Coventry CV1 5NP
  ☎024 7663 3878
  Fax 024 7623 1970
  e-mail: library.hillfields@coventry.gov.uk
- Stoke Library, Kingsway, Stoke, Coventry CV2 4EA
  ☎024 7645 2059
  Fax 024 7645 2567
  e-mail: stoke.library@coventry.gov.uk
- Willenhall Library, 106 Remembrance Road, Willenhall, Coventry CV3 3DN
  ☎024 7630 2383
  Fax 024 7630 2151
  e-mail: willenhall.library@coventry.gov.uk
- Wyken Community Library, Wyken Community Centre, Westmorland Road, Coventry CV2 5BY
  ☎024 7670 9348
  Fax 024 7670 9348
  e-mail: wyken.library@coventry.gov.uk

West Area Libraries

- Canley Library, Prior Deram Walk, Canley, Coventry CV4 8FT
  ☎024 7667 3041
  Fax 024 7671 7361
  e-mail: canley.library@coventry.gov.uk
- Coundon Library, Moseley Avenue, Radford, Coventry CV6 1HT
  ☎024 7659 3496
  Fax 024 7659 8768
  e-mail: coundon.library@coventry.gov.uk
- Earlsdon Library, Earlsdon Avenue North, Earlsdon, Coventry CV5 6FZ
  ☎024 7667 5359
  Fax 024 7671 7958
  e-mail: earlsdon.library@coventry.gov.uk
- Finham Library, Droylsdon Park Road, Finham, Coventry CV3 6EQ

☎024 7641 4050
Fax 024 7641 9524
e-mail: finham.library@coventry.gov.uk

- Jubilee Library, Jubilee Crescent, Radford, Coventry CV6 3EX
  ☎024 7659 6762
  Fax 024 7659 5728
  e-mail: jubileecrescent.library@coventry.gov.uk
- Tile Hill Library, Jardine Crescent, Tile Hill, Coventry CV4 9PL
  ☎024 7646 4994
  Fax 024 7669 5774
  e-mail: tilehill.library@coventry.gov.uk
- Whoberley Community Library, St John's School, Winsford Avenue, Allesley Park, Coventry CV5 9HZ
  ☎(07903) 749521

CROYDON

Authority: London Borough of Croydon
HQ Central Library, Katharine Street, Croydon CR9 1ET
☎020 8760 5400
Fax 020 8253 1004
url: www.croydon.gov.uk
Head of Libraries Ms Adie Batt BA MCLIP (020 8253 1001; e-mail: adie.batt@croydon.gov.uk)

CUMBRIA

Authority: Cumbria County Council
HQ Economy, Culture and Environment, Arroyo Block, The Castle, Carlisle CA3 8UR
☎(01228) 607295 (enquiries), (01228) 607296 (management)
Fax (01228) 607299
url: www.cumbria.gov.uk/libraries/
Corporate Director of Economy, Culture and Environment Ralph Howard
Head of Culture Jim Grisenthwaite (01228 607282; e-mail: jim.grisenthwaite@cumbriacc.gov.uk)
Library Services Manager Alan Welton BA MCLIP (01228 607292; e-mail: alan.welton@cumbriacc.gov.uk)
Library Operations Manager Mrs Liz Bowe MCLIP (01228 607338; e-mail: liz.bowe@cumbriacc.gov.uk)
Principal Administrative Officer Paul Graham (01228 607294; e-mail: paul.graham@cumbriacc.gov.uk)

Group libraries

- Barrow-in-Furness Library, Ramsden Square, Barrow-in-Furness, Cumbria LA14 1LL
  ☎(01229) 894370
  Fax (01229) 894371
  e-mail: barrow.library@cumbriacc.gov.uk
  Area Library Manager Ms Bernadette Maine MCLIP

- Carlisle Library, 11 Globe Lane, Carlisle CA3 8NX
  ☎(01228) 607310
  Fax (01228) 607333
  e-mail: carlisle.library@cumbriacc.gov.uk
  Area Library Manager Mike Lister MCLIP
- Daniel Hay Library, Lowther Street, Whitehaven, Cumbria CA28 7QZ
  ☎(01946) 852900
  Fax (01946) 852911
  e-mail: whitehaven.library@cumbriacc.gov.uk
  Area Library Manager Mrs Alayne Cowling MCLIP
- Kendal Library, Stricklandgate, Kendal, Cumbria LA9 4PY
  ☎(01539) 773520
  Fax (01539) 773544
  e-mail: kendal.library@cumbriacc.gov.uk
  Area Library Manager Tom Holliday MCLIP
- Penrith Library, St Andrews Churchyard, Penrith, Cumbria CA11 7YA
  ☎(01768) 242100
  Fax (01768) 242101
  e-mail: penrith.library@cumbriacc.gov.uk
  Area Library Manager Mike Lister MCLIP
- Workington Library, Vulcans Lane, Workington, Cumbria CA14 2ND
  ☎(01900) 325170
  Fax (01900) 325181
  e-mail: workington.library@cumbriacc.gov.uk
  Area Library Manager Mrs Alayne Cowling MCLIP

DARLINGTON

ILL 01325 349635

Authority: Darlington Borough Council
HQ Central Library, Crown Street, Darlington DL1 1ND
☎(01325) 462034 (enquiries)
Fax (01325) 381556
e-mail: crown.street.library@darlington.gov.uk
url: www.darlington.gov.uk/library
Head of Libraries and Community Learning Mrs Ruth Bernstein
Library Manager Mrs Lynne Litchfield
Audience Development – Young People James Hedge
Audience Development Mrs Jeannie Bishop
Stock Services Librarian Mrs Jean Longstaff MCLIP
Local Studies Librarian Miss Katherine Williamson

Branch library

- Cockerton Library, Cockerton Green, Darlington DL3 9AA
  ☎(01325) 461320
  Community Librarian Ms Carole Houghton

DERBY

Authority: Derby City Council
HQ Derby City Libraries, Regeneration and Community, Roman House, Friar Gate, Derby DE1 1XB
☎(01332) 716607
Fax (01332) 715549
e-mail: libraries@derby.gov.uk
url: www.derby.gov.uk/libraries
Head of Library Services David Potton MA DipLib MCLIP (01332 716602; e-mail: david.potton@derby.gov.uk)
Assistant Head of Library Services (Resources and Learning) Mark Elliott BLib(Hons) MCLIP PGC(Man) (01332 716609; e-mail: mark.elliott@derby.gov.uk)
Assistant Head of Library Services (Operations and Community) Ms Fran Renwick MA MCLIP (01332 716610; e-mail: fran.renwick@derby.gov.uk)

Central/largest library

Central Library, The Wardwick, Derby DE1 1HS
☎(01332) 255398/9 (enquiries), 255400/1 (renewals), 255390 (administration)
Fax (01332) 369570
Operations Manager (Central Library Services) Ms Julie Topham (01332 255307; e-mail: julie.topham@derby.gov.uk)

DERBYSHIRE

Authority: Derbyshire County Council
HQ Cultural and Community Services Department, County Hall, Matlock, Derbyshire DE4 3AG
☎(01629) 580000 ext 6591 (enquiries), ext 6590 (administration)
Fax (01629) 585363
e-mail: derbyshire.libraries@derbyshire.gov.uk
url: www.derbyshire.gov.uk
Strategic Director of Cultural and Community Services Martin Molloy OBE BA DipLib MCLIP (e-mail: martin.molloy@derbyshire.gov.uk)
Deputy Director of Cultural and Community Services and Head of Libraries and Heritage Division Miss Jaci Brumwell MCLIP (e-mail: jaci.brumwell@derbyshire.gov.uk)
Assistant Director, Policy, Information and Partnership Robert Gent BA DMS MIMgt MCLIP (e-mail: robert.gent@derbyshire.gov.uk)
Assistant Director of Libraries and Heritage Divison Don Gibbs BA MCLIP (e-mail: don.gibbs@derbyshire.gov.uk)
Operations Manager (North Area) Martyn Shaw BA DipLib MCLIP (e-mail: martyn.shaw@derbyshire.gov.uk)
Operations Manager (South Area) Ms Carol Campbell-Hayes BA FCLIP (e-mail: carol.campbell-hayes@derbyshire.gov.uk)
Operations Manager (West Area) Mrs Ann Ainsworth BA MCLIP (e-mail: ann.ainsworth@derbyshire.gov.uk)

Central/largest library (North Area)

Chesterfield Library, New Beetwell Street, Chesterfield, Derbyshire S40 1QN
☎(01246) 209292
Fax (01246) 209304
e-mail: chesterfield.library@derbyshire.gov.uk
Senior Librarian Ms Janet Scott BA MA MCLIP (e-mail: janet.scott@derbyshire.gov.uk)

North Area

- Chesterfield Library, New Beetwell Street, Chesterfield, Derbyshire S40 1GN
  ☎(01246) 209292
  Fax (01246) 209304
  Principal Librarian Mrs Julie Potton BA MCLIP (e-mail: julie.potton@derbyshire.gov.uk)

South Area

- Ilkeston Library, Market Place, Ilkeston, Derbyshire DE7 5RN
  ☎0115 930 1104
  Fax 0115 944 1226
  e-mail: ilkeston.library@derbyshire.gov.uk
  Principal Librarian Ms Rosina Peberdy BA NSc(Econ) MCLIP (e-mail: rosina.peberdy@derbyshire.gov.uk)

West Area

- Buxton Library, Kents Bank Road, Buxton, Derbyshire SK17 9HJ
  ☎(01298) 25331
  Fax (01298) 73744
  e-mail: buxton.library@derbyshire.gov.uk
  Principal Librarian Ms Catherine Howard BA(Hons) MA MCLIP (e-mail: catherine.howard@derbyshire.gov.uk)

DEVON

ILL 01392 384314
" 381963

Authority: Devon County Council
HQ Devon Library and Information Services, Great Moor House, Bittern Road, Sowton, Exeter, Devon EX2 7NL
☎(01392) 384315
Fax (01392) 384316
e-mail: devlibs@devon.gov.uk
url: www.devon.gov.uk/libraries
Head of Library and Information Services Mrs Lynn Osborne BA MCLIP (e-mail: lynn.osborne@devon.gov.uk)
Policy & Strategy Manager & Deputy Head of Library & Information Services Geraint Hughes MA DipLib (e-mail: geraint.hughes@devon.gov.uk)
Service Development Manager Mike Maguire MCLIP (e-mail: mike.maguire@devon.gov.uk)
Service Support Manager Mike Skinner BLS DipHE (e-mail: mike.skinner@devon.gov.uk)
Operations Manager Ms Liz Alexander MCLIP (e-mail: liz.alexander@devon.gov.uk)

Central/largest libraries

- Barnstaple Central Library, Tuly Street, Barnstaple, Devon EX31 1EL
  ☎(01271) 388619 (tel/fax)
  e-mail: barnstaple.library@devon.gov.uk
  Library Manager Geoff King
- Exeter Central Library, Castle Street, Exeter, Devon EX4 3PQ
  ☎(01392) 384222
  Fax (01392) 384228
  e-mail: exeter.library@devon.gov.uk
  Library Manager Andrew Davey BSc MCLIP

Larger branch libraries

- Bideford Library, 6 New Road, Bideford, Devon EX39 2HR
  ☎(01237) 476075 (tel/fax)
  Librarian i/c Mrs Rose Arno, Mrs Margaret Shambrook
- Exmouth Library, 40 Exeter Road, Exmouth, Devon EX8 1PS
  ☎(01395) 272677
  Fax (01395) 271426
  Librarian i/c Kelvin Crook MCLIP
- Honiton Library, 48 New Street, Honiton, Devon EX14 1BS
  ☎(01404) 42818
  Fax (01404) 45326
  Librarian i/c Miss Jenny Wood MBE
- Kingsbridge Library, Ilbert Road, Kingsbridge, Devon TQ7 1EB
  ☎(01548) 852315
  Fax (01548) 857210
  Librarian i/c Mrs Wendy Bloomer
- Newton Abbot Library, Market Street, Newton Abbot, Devon TQ12 2RJ
  ☎(01626) 206420
  Fax (01626) 206425
  Librarian i/c Mrs Linda Roland-Howe
- St Thomas Library, Cowick Street, Exeter, Devon EX4 1AF
  ☎(01392) 252783
  Librarian i/c Mrs Jill Hughes
- Sidmouth Library, Blackmore Drive, Sidmouth, Devon EX10 8LA
  ☎(01395) 512192
  Librarian i/c Mrs Gill Spence
- Tavistock Library, The Quay, Plymouth Road, Tavistock, Devon PL19 8AB
  ☎(01822) 612218
  Fax (01822) 610690
  Librarian i/c Mrs Moira Andrews
- Teignmouth Library, Fore Street, Teignmouth, Devon TQ14 8DY
  ☎(01626) 774646
  Fax (01626) 870155
  Librarian i/c Mrs Pauline Anderson MCLIP

- Tiverton Library, Phoenix House, Phoenix Lane, Tiverton, Devon EX16 6SA
  ☎(01884) 244644
  Fax (01884) 244645
  Librarian i/c Mrs Hazel Skinner BLS MCLIP

  (Note: This is not the full list of branch libraries)

DONCASTER

Authority: Doncaster Metropolitan Borough Council
HQ Central Library, Waterdale, Doncaster DN1 3JE
☎(01302) 734305
Fax (01302) 734302
e-mail: reference.library@doncaster.gov.uk
url: www.doncaster.gov.uk
Head of Library and Information Services Vacant
Principal Library Manager: Service Development D John L Mellor BA MCLIP (01302 734311; e-mail: john.mellor@doncaster.gov.uk)
Principal Library Manager: Service Delivery Dave Butler BA MCLIP (01302 734298; e-mail: dave.butler@doncaster.gov.uk)

DORSET

ILL 01305 224452

Authority: Dorset County Council
HQ County Library HQ, Colliton Park, Dorchester, Dorset DT1 1XJ
☎(01305) 225000 (enquiries)
Fax (01305) 224344 (administration)
e-mail: dorsetlibraries@dorsetcc.gov.uk
url: www.dorsetcc.gov.uk/libraries

Music Library 01202 485938

Head of Cultural Services, Libraries and Arts Paul Leivers BA MBA MCLIP (e-mail: p.leivers@dorsetcc.gov.uk)
Dorset Library Services Manager Ms Tracy Long BA(Hons) MCLIP (01305 224458; e-mail: t.long@dorsetcc.gov.uk)
Senior Manager, Customer Services Roger J Dale MCLIP (01305 224458; e-mail: r.j.dale@dorsetcc.gov.uk)
Senior Manager, Reading and Learning Ms Sharon Kirkpatrick BLS MCLIP (01305 228529; e-mail: s.d.kirkpatrick@dorsetcc.gov.uk)
Business Support Manager (01305 224449) Ms Val Goose

DUDLEY

Authority: Dudley Metropolitan Borough Council
HQ Directorate of Adult, Community and Housing Services, Ednam House, St James's Road, Dudley, West Midlands DY1 3JJ
☎(01384) 812295 (administration)
Fax (01384) 811995
url: www.dudley.gov.uk/libraries
Head of Service – Library Strategy and Development Ms Jayne Wilkins (01384 812680; e-mail: jayne.wilkins@dudley.gov.uk)

Assistant Director of Libraries, Archives and Adult Learning Mrs Kate Millin BLib MCLIP (01384 812295; e-mail: kate.millin@dudley.gov.uk)
Head of Service – Library Operations Ms Jen Beardsmore (e-mail: jen.beardsmore@dudley.gov.uk)

Town libraries

- Brierley Hill Library, High Street, Brierley Hill, West Midlands DY5 3ET
  ☎(01384) 812865
  Fax (01384) 812866
  e-mail: bhilllib.ed@dudley.gov.uk
  Town Librarian Stephen Masters MCLIP
- Dudley Library, St James's Road, West Midlands DY1 1HR
  ☎(01384) 815560
  Fax (01384) 815543
  e-mail: dudlibref.ed@dudley.gov.uk
  Town Librarian Mrs Hilary Riley MCLIP
- Halesowen Library, Queensway Mall, The Cornbow, Halesowen, West Midlands B63 4AJ
  ☎(01384) 812980
  Fax (01384) 812981
  e-mail: hallib.ed@dudley.gov.uk
  Town Librarian Mrs Angela Horton
- Stourbridge Library, Crown Centre, Crown Lane, Stourbridge, West Midlands DY8 1YE
  ☎(01384) 812945
  Fax (01384) 812946
  e-mail: stourlibref.ed@dudley.gov.uk
  Town Librarian Ms Louise Clark BA MCLIP

Group Libraries Headquarters (North)

- Sedgley Library, Ladies Walk Centre, Ladies Walk, Sedgley, West Midlands DY3 3UA
  ☎(01384) 812790
  e-mail: sedglib.ed@dudley.gov.uk
  Group Librarian Mrs Hazel Birt MCLIP, Mrs Linda Wattis BA (job-share)

Group Libraries Headquarters (South)

- Kingswinford Library, Market Street, Kingswinford, West Midlands DY6 9LG
  ☎(01384) 812740
  e-mail: kfordlib.ed@dudley.gov.uk
  Group Librarian Mrs Sharon Whitehouse BA MCLIP

Archives and Local History Service

- Mount Pleasant Street, Coseley, Dudley, West Midlands WV14 9JR
  ☎(01384) 812770 (tel/fax)
  e-mail: archives.ed@dudley.gov.uk
  Borough Archivist Miss Gillian Roberts BA DAA

DURHAM

Authority: Durham County Council
HQ Libraries, Learning and Culture, Adult and Community Services, The Rivergreen Centre, Aykley Heads, Durham DH1 5TS
☎0191 370 8831 (enquiries), 0191 370 8834 (administration)
Fax 0191 370 8897
e-mail: culture@durham.gov.uk
url: www.durham.gov.uk
Head of Libraries, Learning and Culture Ms Rosemary Laxton MCLIP
Youth Services Manager Peter Burns MCLIP (e-mail: peter.burns@durham.gov.uk)

Divisional libraries

- Eastern Division. Peterlee Library, Burnhope Way, Peterlee, Co Durham SR8 1NT
  ☎0191 586 2279
  Fax 0191 586 6664
  Divisional Manager Ms Sheila Owens BA MCLIP
- Northern Division. Durham Clayport Library, Millennium Place, Durham DH1 1WA
  ☎0191 386 4003
  Fax 0191 386 0379
  Divisional Manager Ms Anne Davison BA MCLIP
- Western Division. Crook Library, Market Place, Crook, Co Durham DL15 8QH
  ☎(01388) 762269
  Fax (01388) 766170
  Divisional Manager Ms June Gowland BA(Hons) MCLIP DipMgt

EALING

Authority: Ealing Council
HQ Library Administrative Office, 4th Floor NE, Perceval House, 14–16 Uxbridge Road, London W5 2HL
☎020 8825 5600
Fax 020 825 6550
e-mail: libuser@ealing.gov.uk
url: www.ealing.gov.uk/libraries/index.htm
Head of Service Mark Bryant (e-mail: mbryant@ealing.gov.uk)

Central/largest library

Central Library, 103 Ealing Broadway Centre, London W5 5JY
☎020 8567 3670 (enquiries), 020 8567 3656 (reference)
Fax 020 8840 2351

Main libraries

- Acton Library, High Street, London W3 6NA
  ☎020 8752 0999
  Fax 020 8992 6086
- Greenford Library, Oldfield Lane South, Greenford, Middlesex UB6 9LG

☎020 8578 1466
Fax 020 8575 7800

- Southall Library, Osterley Park Road, Southall, Middlesex UB2 4BL
☎020 8574 3412
Fax 020 8571 7629

EAST RIDING OF YORKSHIRE

Authority: East Riding of Yorkshire Council
HQ East Riding Libraries, Council Offices, Main Road, Skirlaugh, East Riding of Yorks HU11 5HN
☎(01482) 392702
Fax (01482) 392711
url: www.eastriding.gov.uk
Libraries, Arts and Heritage Group Manager Alan Moir (01482 392701; e-mail: alan.moir@eastriding.gov.uk)
Library Services Manager Ms Libby Herbert (01482 392715; e-mail: libby.herbert@eastriding.gov.uk)

EAST SUSSEX

Authority: East Sussex County Council
HQ Library and Information Services, G-Floor, Centre Block, County Hall, St Anne's Crescent, Lewes, East Sussex BN7 1UE
☎(01273) 481538 (enquiries), (01273) 481870 (administration)
Fax (01273) 481716
url: www.eastsussex.gov.uk
Assistant Director, Libraries and Culture Dr Irene Campbell MA DipLib MCLIP (01273 481347; e-mail: irene.campbell@eastsussex.gov.uk)
Assistant Head of Library and Information Services: Professional Services Mrs Helena Sykes MCLIP (01273 481872; e-mail: helena.sykes@eastsussex.gov.uk)
Assistant Head of Library and Information Services: Strategy and Performance Ms Rhona Drever MA(Hons) DipLib MCLIP (01273 481329; e-mail: rhona.drever@eastsussex.gov.uk)
Assistant Head of Library and Information Services: Customer Services Mrs Valerie Wright MCLIP (01273 482129; e-mail: valerie.wright@eastsussex.gov.uk)

Area offices

East Area

- Hastings Library, Brassey Institute, 13 Claremont, Hastings, East Sussex TN34 1HE
☎(01424) 420501
Fax (01424) 430261
Area Manager Mick Bacon MCLIP (01424 420501; e-mail: mick.bacon@eastsussex.co.uk)

South Area

- Eastbourne Library, Grove Road, Eastbourne, East Sussex BN21 4TL

☎(01323) 434206
Fax (01323) 649174
Area Manager Ms Alison Cairns BA(Hons) DipLib DMS MCLIP (01323 434203; e-mail: alison.cairns@eastsussex.gov.uk)

West Area

- Lewes Library, Albion Street, Lewes, East Sussex BN7 2ND
  ☎(01273) 474232
  Fax (01273) 477881
  Area Manager Barry Forster MCLIP (01273 479729; e-mail: barry.forster@eastsussex.gov.uk)

North Area

- Uckfield Library (Wealden), High Street, Uckfield, Uckfield, East Sussex TN22 1AR
  ☎(01825) 763254
  Fax (01825) 769762
  Area Manager Mrs Joss Makin MCLIP (01825 769761; e-mail: joss.makin@eastsussex.gov.uk)

Branch libraries

- Battle Library, 7 Market Square, Battle, East Sussex TN33 0XA
  ☎(01424) 772250
  e-mail: library.battle@eastsussex.gov.uk
- Bexhill Library, Western Road, Bexhill-on-Sea, East Sussex TN40 1DY
  ☎(01424) 212546
  e-mail: library.bexhill@eastsussex.gov.uk
- Crowborough Library, Pine Grove, Crowborough, East Sussex TN6 1DH
  ☎(01892) 664426
  e-mail: library.crowborough@eastsussex.gov.uk
- Eastbourne Library, Grove Road, Eastbourne, East Sussex BN21 4TL
  ☎(01323) 434206
  e-mail: library.eastbourne@eastsussex.gov.uk
- Forest Row Library, The Community Centre, Hartfield Road, Forest Row, East Sussex RH18 5DZ
  ☎(01342) 825331
  e-mail: library.forestrow@eastsussex.gov.uk
- Hailsham Library, Western Road, Hailsham, East Sussex BN27 3DN
  ☎(01323) 840604
  e-mail: library.hailsham@eastsussex.gov.uk
- Hampden Park Library, Brodrick Close, Hampden Park, Eastbourne, East Sussex BN22 9NQ
  ☎(01323) 502485
  e-mail: library.hampdenpark@eastsussex.gov.uk
- Hastings Children's Library, Robertson Passage, off Robertson Street, Hastings, East Sussex TN34 1HL
  ☎(01424) 722330
  e-mail: hastings.children@eastsussex.gov.uk

- Hastings Library, Brassey Institute, 13 Claremont, Hastings, East Sussex TN34 1HE
  ☎(01424) 420501
  e-mail: library.hastings@eastsussex.gov.uk
- Heathfield Library, 21 High Street, Heathfield, East Sussex TN21 8LU
  ☎(01435) 863975
  e-mail: library.heathfield@eastsussex.gov.uk
- Hollington Library, 96 Battle Road, St Leonards on Sea, East Sussex TN37 7AG
  ☎(01424) 421718
  e-mail: library.hollington@eastsussex.gov.uk
- Langney Library, Unit 4, The Shopping Centre, 110 Kingfisher Drive, Langney, Eastbourne, East Sussex BN23 7DR
  ☎(01323) 761214
  e-mail: library.langney@eastsussex.gov.uk
- Lewes Library, Styles Field, Friars Walk, Lewes, East Sussex BN7 2LZ
  ☎(01273) 474232
  e-mail: library.lewes@eastsussex.gov.uk
- Mayfield Library, Mayfield CE School, Fletching Street, Mayfield, East Sussex TN20 6TA
  ☎(01435) 873195
  e-mail: library.mayfield@eastsussex.gov.uk
- Newhaven Library, 16 High Street, Newhaven, East Sussex BN9 9PD
  ☎(01273) 514468
  e-mail: library.newhaven@eastsussex.gov.uk
- Ore Library, Old London Road, Ore, Hastings, East Sussex TN35 5BP
  ☎(01424) 428316
  e-mail: library.ore@eastsussex.gov.uk
- Peacehaven Library, Meridian Centre, Peacehaven, East Sussex BN10 6AU
  ☎(01273) 583945
  e-mail: library.peacehaven@eastsussex.gov.uk
- Pevensey Bay Library, Wallsend House, Richmond Road, Pevensey Bay, East Sussex BN24 6AU
  ☎(01323) 761708
  e-mail: library.pevenseybay@eastsussex.gov.uk
- Polegate Library, Windsor Way, Eastbourne, East Sussex BN26 6QF
  ☎(01323) 482155
  e-mail: library.polegate@eastsussex.gov.uk
- Ringmer Library, Cecil Gates Room, The Village Hall, Lewes Road, Ringmer, Lewes, East Sussex BN8 5QH
  ☎(01273) 814661
  e-mail: library.ringmer@eastsussex.gov.uk
- Rye Library, Lion Street, Rye, East Sussex TN31 7LB
  ☎(01797) 223355
  e-mail: library.rye@eastsussex.gov.uk
- Seaford Library, 17 Sutton Park Road, Seaford, East Sussex BN25 1QX
  ☎(01323) 893420
  e-mail: library.seaford@eastsussex.gov.uk
- Uckfield Library, Library Way, High Street, Uckfield, East Sussex TN22 1AR
  ☎(01825) 763254

e-mail: library.uckfield@eastsussex.gov.uk

- Wadhurst Library, The Institute, High Street, Wadhurst, East Sussex TN5 6AP
☎(01892) 783649
e-mail: library.wadhurst@eastsussex.gov.uk
- Willingdon Library, Coppice Avenue, Lower Willingdon, Eastbourne, East Sussex BN20 9PN
☎(01323) 482534
e-mail: library.willingdon@eastsussex.gov.uk

Bibliographical Services

- Brookes Road, Lewes, East Sussex BN7 2BY
Head of Information and Local Studies Ms Noreen Finn MCLIP (01273 479816; e-mail: noreen.finn@eastsussex.gov.uk)
Head of Children and Young Studies Mrs Greta Paterson MA DipLib MCLIP DMS (01273 474493; e-mail: greta.paterson@eastsussex.gov.uk)
Reader Development Manager Chris Desmond (01273 481537; e-mail: chris.desmond@eastsussex.gov.uk)
Equal Access Manager Ms Julie Button (01273 479155; e-mail: julie.button@eastsussex.gov.uk)

Schools Library Service

- Hammonds Drive, Lottbridge Drove, Hampden Park, Eastbourne, East Sussex BN23 6PW
Head of Schools Library Service Ms Michele Eaton BA(Hons) MCLIP (01323 416324; e-mail: michele.eaton@eastsussex.gov.uk)

ENFIELD

Authority: London Borough of Enfield
HQ Leisure, Culture and Youth, PO Box 58, Civic Centre, Enfield, Middlesex EN1 3XJ
☎020 8379 3752 (enquiries and administration)
Fax 020 8379 3753
url: www.enfield.gov.uk
Head of Libraries and Museums Ms Julie Gibson MA MCLIP (020 8379 3749; e-mail: julie.gibson@enfield.gov.uk)
Libraries Strategy and Resources Manager Mrs Madeline Barratt BA MCLIP DipLaw (e-mail: madeline.barratt@enfield.gov.uk)

Central/largest library

Central Library, Cecil Road, Enfield, Middlesex EN2 6TW
☎020 8366 2244
Fax 020 8379 8400
Area Library Manager Mrs Sheila Barford MCLIP (020 8379 8301)

Area libraries

- Edmonton Green Library, 36/44 South Mall, London N9 0NX
☎020 8379 2600
Fax 020 8379 2615

Area Library Manager Peter Brown BA MCLIP (020 8379 2605)

- Palmers Green Library, Broomfield Lane, London N13 4EY
  ☎020 8379 2711
  Fax 020 8379 2712
  Area Library Manager Ms Pam Tuttiett BA MCLIP (020 8379 2694)

ESSEX

01245 244940

Authority: Essex County Council
HQ County Library HQ, County Hall, Market Road, Chelmsford, Essex CM1 1QH
☎(01245) 438438 (all enquiries)
Fax (01245) 492780 (general), (01245) 436769 (Management Team)
e-mail: essexlib@essexcc.gov.uk
url: www.essexcc.gov.uk/libraries
Director of Adult, Health and Community Wellbeing Ms Jenny Owen (01245 434806)
Libraries Manager Ms Michele Jones MSc BA(Hons) DipLib MCLIP (01245 436761)

Central/largest library

Chelmsford Library, PO Box 882, Market Road, Chelmsford, Essex CM1 1LH
☎(01245) 492758
Fax (01245) 492536 (enquiries), (01245) 436769 (administration)
e-mail: cfdlib@essexcc.gov.uk

Area Headquarters

- East Area. Colchester Library, Trinity Square, Colchester, Essex CO1 1JB
  ☎(01206) 245900
  Fax (01206) 245901
  e-mail: colchester.library@essexcc.gov.uk
  Strategic Manager, Reading and Learning Mrs Moira Tarrant (e-mail: moira.tarrant@essexcc.gov.uk)
- Mid Area. Chelmsford Library, PO Pox 882, Market Road, Chelmsford, Essex CM1 1LH
  ☎(01245) 492758
  Fax (01245) 492536
  e-mail: cfdlib@essexcc.gov.uk
  Strategic Manager, Transformation and Resources Martin Palmer BA MBA MCLIP MCMI (e-mail: martin.palmer@essexcc.gov.uk)
- South Area. Basildon Central Library, St Martin's Square, Basildon, Essex SS14 1EE
  ☎(01268) 288533
  Fax (01268) 286326
  Strategic Manager, Digital Citizenship Ms Elaine Adams BA MCLIP DMS (e-mail: elaine.adams@essexcc.gov.uk)
- West Area. Harlow Central Library, The High, Harlow, Essex CM20 1HA
  ☎(01279) 413772
  Fax (01279) 424612
  Strategic Manager, Community and Civic Values Ms Jenny Salisbury BLib(Hons) MCLIP (e-mail: jenny.salisbury@essexcc.gov.uk)

GATESHEAD

Authority: Gateshead Metropolitan Borough Council
HQ Libraries and Arts Service, Central Library, Prince Consort Road, Gateshead, Tyne and Wear NE8 4LN
☎0191 433 8400
Fax 0191 477 7454
e-mail: enquiries@gateshead.gov.uk
url: www.gateshead.gov.uk/libraries
Head of Libraries and Arts Ms Ann Borthwick BA MCLIP (e-mail: annborthwick@gateshead.gov.uk)
Principal Libraries Manager Stephen Walters BSc MCLIP (e-mail: stephenwalters@gateshead.gov.uk)
Libraries Operations Manager Ms Angela Parker MCLIP (e-mail: angelaparker@gateshead.gov.uk)

Libraries and Arts Service, Old Town Hall, West Street, Gateshead, Tyne and Wear NE8 1HE
☎0191 433 6929
Head of Libraries and Arts Ms Ann Borthwick BA MCLIP (e-mail: annborthwick@gateshead.gov.uk)

GLOUCESTERSHIRE ILL 01452 425036

Authority: Gloucestershire County Council
HQ Libraries and Information Services, Quayside House, Shire Hall, Gloucester GL1 2HY
☎0845 230 5420 (general enquiries), (01452) 425048 (management)
Fax (01452) 425042
e-mail: libraryhelp@gloucestershire.gov.uk
url: www.libraries.gloucestershire.gov.uk
Head of Libraries and Information David Paynter MCLIP (e-mail: david.paynter@gloucestershire.gov.uk)
Assistant Head of Libraries and Information (Policy and Performance) Ms Sue Laurence BA(Hons) DipLib MCLIP (e-mail: sue.laurence@gloucestershire.gov.uk)
Assistant Head of Libraries and Information (Direct Services) Ms Jo Hand BA DipLib MCLIP (e-mail: jo.hand@gloucestershire.gov.uk)
Assistant Head of Libraries and Information (Business Management and Special Projects) John Holland BA(Hons) DipLib MCLIP (e-mail: john.holland@gloucestershire.gov.uk)
Policy Development Officer, Access and Reader Development Ms Jill Barker BA DipLib MCLIP, Ms Kay Franklin MCLIP (e-mail: pdoaccess&rd@gloucestershire.gov.uk)
Policy Development Officer, Information and Adult Learning Ms Katie Conder BA(Hons) MA MCLIP (e-mail: pdoial@gloucestershire.gov.uk)
Policy Development Officer, Children and Young People Mrs Helen Briggs BA DMS MIMgt MCLIP (e-mail: helen.briggs@gloucestershire.gov.uk)
Stock Manager Ms Helen Dorricott BA DipLib MA MCLIP (e-mail: helen.dorricott@gloucestershire.gov.uk)

Central/largest libraries

- Cheltenham Library, Clarence Street, Cheltenham, Glos GL50 3JT
  ☎(01242) 532688/532685
  Fax (01242) 532684
  Library Service Manager Ms Jane Allen
- Gloucester Library, Brunswick Road, Gloucester GL1 1HT
  ☎(01452) 426973/426977
  Fax (01452) 521468
  Library Service Manager Peter Clark

Area libraries

- Cheltenham and Tewkesbury. Based at Cheltenham Library, Clarence Street, Cheltenham, Glos GL50 3JT
  ☎(01242) 532678
  Fax (01242) 532673
  Area Manager Ms Kathleen Sullivan BA MA (e-mail: kathleen.sullivan@gloucestershire.gov.uk)
- Gloucester and Forest. Based at Gloucester Library, Brunswick Road, Gloucester GL1 1HT
  ☎(01452) 426976
  Fax (01452) 521468
  Area Manager Ms Christiane Nicholson BA MCLIP (e-mail: christiane.nicholson@gloucestershire.gov.uk)
- Stroud and Cotswolds. Based at Stroud Library, Lansdown, Stroud, Glos GL5 1BB
  ☎(01453) 756842
  Fax (01453) 757829
  Area Manager Mrs Mary Tucker BA MLib MCLIP (e-mail: mary.tucker@gloucestershire.gov.uk)

Selected branch libraries

- Cirencester Bingham Library, The Waterloo, Cirencester, Glos GL7 2PZ
  ☎(01285) 659813
  Fax (01285) 640449
  Library Service Manager Ms Carole Summerell
- Tewkesbury Library, Sun Street, Tewkesbury, Glos GL20 5NX
  ☎(01684) 293086
  Fax (01684) 290125
  Library Service Manager Ms Janet Thomson

GREENWICH

Authority: London Borough of Greenwich
HQ Culture and Community Services, Library Support Services, Plumstead Library, 232 Plumstead High Street, London SE18 1JL
☎020 8317 4466
Fax 020 8317 4868
e-mail: libraries@greenwich.gov.uk
url: www.greenwich.gov.uk
Head of Community Services Ms Julia Newton

District libraries

- Blackheath Library, 17-23 Old Dover Road, London SE3 7BT
  ☎020 8858 1131
  Fax 020 8853 3615
- Eltham Library, Eltham High Street, London SE9 1TS
  ☎020 8850 2268
  Fax 020 8850 1368
- Woolwich Library, Calderwood Street, London SE18 6QZ
  ☎020 8921 5750
  Fax 020 8316 1645

HACKNEY

Authority: London Borough of Hackney
HQ Strategic Leadership Team, Homerton Library, Homerton High Street, London E9 6AS
☎020 8356 1697
Fax 020 8356 1692
Head of Libraries, Archives and Information Services Ms Nicola Baker BA MCLIP MBA (020 8356 2560; fax: 020 8356 7575; e-mail: nicola.baker@hackney.gov.uk) (Based at First Floor, Maurice Bishop House, 17 Reading Lane, London E8 1HH)
Archives and Information Manager, Libraries Edward Rogers (e-mail: edward.rogers@hackney.gov.uk)
Development Manager, Libraries Ms Anita Kane BA DipLib MCLIP (020 8356 1696; fax: 020 8356 1693; e-mail: anita.kane@hackney.gov.uk)
Operations Manager, Libraries John Holland (020 8356 1695; fax: 020 8356 1693; e-mail: john.holland@hackney.gov.uk)

Central/largest library

Hackney Central Library, Technology and Learning Centre, 1 Reading Lane, London E8 1GQ
☎020 8356 2562
Library Manager Ms Sue Comitti (e-mail: sue.comitti@hackney.gov.uk)
Knowledge Manager Cyprian Marah (020 8356 2568; e-mail: cyprian.marah@hackney.gov.uk)

Town centre libraries

- C L R James Library, 24-30 Dalston Lane, London E8 3AZ
  ☎020 8356 1665
  Fax 020 7254 4655
  Library Manager Ms Jane Wardlaw
- Clapton Library, Northwold Road, London E5 8RA
  ☎020 8356 1620
  Fax 020 8806 7849
- Community Library Services Team, Stoke Newington Library, Church Street, London N16 0JS
  ☎020 8356 5238
  Manager Ms Edwina Wontner
- Hackney Archives, 43 De Beauvoir Road, London N1 5SQ
  ☎020 7241 2886

Fax 020 7241 6688
e-mail: archives@hackney.gov.uk
url: www.hackney.gov.uk/archives
Principal Archivist Ms Libby Adams

- Homerton Library, Homerton High Street, London E9 6AS
  ☎020 8356 1690
  Fax 020 8525 7945
  Manager Ms Marcia Charles
- Shoreditch Library, 80 Hoxton Street, London N1 6LP
  ☎020 8356 4350
  Library Manager Ms Sarah Scott
- Stamford Hill Library, Portland Avenue, London N16 6SB
  ☎020 8356 1700
  Fax 020 8809 5986
  Library Manager Ms Margaret Sinn
- Stoke Newington Library, Church Street, London N16 0JS
  ☎020 8356 5230
  Fax 020 8356 5237
  Library Manager Ms Jackie Obeney-Williams (020 8356 5238; e-mail: jackie.obeney-williams@hackney.gov.uk)

HALTON

Authority: Halton Borough Council
HQ Halton Lea Library, Halton Lea, Runcorn, Cheshire WA7 2PF
☎(01928) 715351
Fax (01928) 790221
url: www.halton.gov.uk/libraries
Library Services Manager Mrs Paula Reilly-Cooper BSc DipLib MCLIP (0151 424 2061 ext 4096; e-mail: paula.reilly-cooper@halton.gov.uk) (Based at Runcorn Town Hall, Heath Road, Runcorn, Cheshire WA7 5TD)
Specialist Services Manager Philip Cooke BA(Hons) MA (e-mail: philip.cooke@halton.gov.uk)
Stock Specialist Officer Mrs Trudy Jones BA(Hons) MCLIP
Reference and Information Officer Mrs Jean Bradburn MCLIP
Systems Officer Ms Catherine Jones BA(Hons) MA
Young Persons Officer Mrs Allyson Watt BA(Hons) MCLIP (e-mail: allyson.watt@halton.gov.uk), Mrs Jennie Archer MCLIP (e-mail: jennie.archer@halton.gov.uk)
Bibliographical Services Officer Mrs Geraldine Kane BA(Hons) MCLIP

Central/largest library

Halton Lea Library, Halton Lea, Runcorn, Cheshire WA7 2PF
☎Tel/fax etc. as HQ
Senior Librarian Miss Siobhan Kirk BA(Hons) MCLIP

Area libraries

- Ditton Library, Queens Avenue, Ditton, Widnes, Cheshire WA8 8HR

☎0151 424 2459
Senior Librarian Miss Siobhan Kirk BA(Hons) MCLIP (01928 715351)

- Runcorn Library, Egerton Street, Runcorn, Cheshire WA7 1JL
  ☎(01928) 574495
  Senior Librarian Miss Siobhan Kirk BA(Hons) MCLIP (01928 715351)
- Widnes Library, Kingsway Learning Centre, Victoria Square, Widnes, Cheshire WA8 7QY
  ☎0151 907 8383
  Fax 0151 907 8384
  Senior Librarian Miss Siobhan Kirk BA(Hons) MCLIP (01928 715351)

HAMMERSMITH AND FULHAM

Authority: London Borough of Hammersmith and Fulham
HQ Hammersmith Library, Shepherds Bush Road, London W6 7AT
☎020 8753 2400 (24-hr information phoneline), 020 8753 3827 (enquiries), 020 8753 3813 (administration)
Fax 020 8753 3815
url: www.lbhf.gov.uk
Head of Libraries David Herbert BA MLS MCLIP (020 8753 3810; e-mail: david.herbert@lbhf.gov.uk)
Borough Archivist and Local History Manager Ms Jane Kimber BA(Hons) DAA MSc (020 8741 5159; e-mail: jane.kimber@lbhf.gov.uk)
Library Operations Manager Steve Liddle BA(Hons) DipLib (020 8753 3818; e-mail: steven.liddle@lbhf.gov.uk)
Children's & Young People's Librarian Ms Rachel Levy BA(Hons) MA (020 8753 3829; e-mail: rachel.levy@lbhf.gov.uk)

Area libraries

- Fulham Library, 598 Fulham Road, London SW6 5NX
  ☎020 8753 3877
  Senior Librarian Ms Jenny Samuels MCLIP
- Hammersmith Library, Shepherds Bush Road, London W6 7AT
  ☎Tel/fax etc. as HQ
  Senior Librarian Ms Gaynor Lynch MCLIP, Ms Linda Hardman MSc MCLIP (job-share)

Branch libraries

- Askew Road Library, 87/91 Askew Road, London W12 9AS
  ☎020 8753 3863
- Barons Court Library, North End Crescent, London W14 8TG
  ☎020 8753 3888
- Sands End Library, The Community Centre, 59-61 Broughton Road, London SW6 2LE
  ☎020 8753 3885
- Shepherds Bush Library, 7 Uxbridge Road, London W12 8LJ
  ☎020 8753 3842
  Fax 020 8740 1712
- Mobile Library Service and Housebound Readers Service
  ☎020 7610 4251

HAMPSHIRE

ILL 01962 826640.
Music 01962 826637

Authority: Hampshire County Council
HQ ~~Library and Information Service, 81 North Walls, Winchester, Hants SO23 8BY~~
County Store, HCC, Library HQ, 5-6 Moorside Place, Winchester SO23 7FZ
☎(01962) 826600
Fax (01962) 856615
url: www.hants.gov.uk/library
Head of Library and Information Service Richard Ward MLib MCLIP (01962 826621; fax: 01962 850667; e-mail: richard.ward@hants.gov.uk)
Head of Field Services Alasdair Anderson BA DMS MCLIP (01962 826681; e-mail: alasdair.anderson@hants.gov.uk)
Discovery Centres and Capital Programme Manager Chris Edwards (01962 826740; e-mail: chris.edwards@hants.gov.uk)
Head of Performance, Business Manager Miss Sue Greenfield BA MIMgt MCLIP (01962 826684; e-mail: sue.greenfield@hants.gov.uk)
Head of E-Government and ICT Ms Jan Jones BLib MCLIP (01962 826759; e-mail: jan.jones@hants.gov.uk)
Stock Manager Stephen Edwards BA MCLIP (01962 826630; e-mail: stephen.edwards@hants.gov.uk)
Children's and School Services Manager Anne Marley BA MCLIP (01962 826658; e-mail: anne.marley@hants.gov.uk)
Adult Services Manager Miss Mary Franklin BA(Hons) MCLIP (01962 826682; e-mail: mary.franklin@hants.gov.uk)

HARINGEY

Authority: London Borough of Haringey
HQ Haringey Library Services, Central Library, High Road, Wood Green, London N22 6XD
☎020 8489 2754 (enquiries)
Fax 020 8489 2722
url: www.haringey.gov.uk
Assistant Director, Culture, Libraries and Learning Ms Diana Edmonds BA DipLib FCLIP (e-mail: diana.edmonds@haringey.gov.uk)
Library Service Delivery and Development Manager Ms Maria Stephanou BSc(Hons) (020 8489 2736; e-mail: maria.stephanou@haringey.gov.uk)

Central Library

Wood Green Central Library, High Road, Wood Green, London N22 6XD
☎020 8489 2780
Fax 020 8489 2555

Area libraries

- Hornsey Library, Haringey Park, London N8 9JA
  ☎020 8489 1118
  Library Manager Ms Sian Segel BA(Hons)
- Marcus Garvey Library, Tottenham Green Leisure Centre, 1 Philip Lane, London N15 4JA

☎020 8489 5353
Library Manager Ms Anne Doherty BSc(Hons)

HARROW

Authority: London Borough of Harrow
HQ Civic Centre Library, PO Box 4, Civic Centre, Station Road, Harrow, Middlesex HA1 2UU
☎020 8424 1055/6 (enquiries), 020 8424 1059/1970 (administration)
Fax 020 8424 1971
e-mail: library@harrow.gov.uk
url: www.harrow.gov.uk
Group Manager Library Services Bob Mills BSc MCLIP DMS (e-mail: bob.mills@harrow.gov.uk)
Principal Librarian (Stock and Support Services) Ms Nikki Copleston BA MCLIP (020 8424 1046; e-mail: nikki.copleston@harrow.gov.uk)
Principal Librarian (Reference and Information Services) Paul Lane MA DipLib MCLIP (020 8424 1055; e-mail: paul.lane@harrow.gov.uk)
Principal Librarian (Young People's Services and Lifelong Learning) Mrs Gillian Polding MCLIP (020 8424 1052; e-mail: gill.poulding@harrow.gov.uk)

Central/largest library

Gayton Library, Gayton Road, Harrow, Middlesex HA1 2HL
☎020 8427 6012/8986
Service Manager Lending Services John Pennells MCLIP DMS (e-mail: john.pennells@harrow.gov.uk)

HARTLEPOOL

Authority: Hartlepool Borough Council
HQ Central Library, 124 York Road, Hartlepool TS26 9DE
☎(01429) 272905
Fax (01429) 275685
e-mail: infodesk@hartlepool.gov.uk
url: www.hartlepool.gov.uk
Borough Librarian Graham Jarritt BA(Hons) (e-mail: graham.jarritt@hartlepool.gov.uk)

Resources and Development

- Resources and Development Section, Carnegie Building, Northgate, Hartlepool TS24 0LT
  ☎(01429) 523644
  Fax (01429) 275665
  Resources and Development Officer Mrs Kay Tranter BA(Hons) (e-mail: kay.tranter@hartlepool.gov.uk)

HAVERING

Authority: London Borough of Havering
HQ Central Library, St Edwards Way, Romford, Essex RM1 3AR

☎(01708) 432389
Fax (01708) 432391
e-mail: libraryservices@havering.gov.uk
url: www.havering.gov.uk
Acting Library Services Manager Ms Ann Rennie
Children's Services Manager Mrs Ruth Gedalovitch BA(Hons) MCLIP (01708 432380; e-mail: ruth.gedalovitch@havering.gov.uk)

HEREFORDSHIRE

ILL 01432 260686

Authority: Herefordshire Council
HQ Herefordshire Libraries, Shirehall, Hereford HR1 2HY
☎(01432) 359830
Fax (01432) 260744
url: www.libraries.herefordshire.gov.uk
Assistant Cultural Services Manager (Heritage and Libraries) Ms Kate Murray BA MCLIP (01432 263602; e-mail: kmurray@herefordshire.gov.uk)
Principal Libraries Officer James Anthony MA MA (01432 260557; e-mail: janthony@herefordshire.gov.uk)
Senior Stock Librarian Mrs Carolyn Huckfield BA(Hons) MCLIP (01432 261570; e-mail: chuckfield@herefordshire.gov.uk)

Central library

Hereford Library, Broad Street, Hereford HR4 9AU
☎(01432) 383600
Fax (01432) 383607

Largest libraries

- Leominster Library, 8 Buttercross, Leominster, Herefordshire HR6 8BN
  ☎(01432) 383290
  Fax (01568) 616025
- Ross-on-Wye Library, Cantilupe Road, Ross-on-Wye, Herefordshire HR9 7AN
  ☎(01432) 383280
  Fax (01432) 383282

HERTFORDSHIRE

Authority: Hertfordshire County Council
HQ Libraries, Heritage and Arts, New Barnfield, Travellers Lane, Hatfield, Herts AL10 8XG
☎(01438) 737333 (enquiries and administration)
Fax (01707) 281589
e-mail: firstname.lastname@hertscc.gov.uk
url: www.hertsdirect.org/libraries
Head of Libraries, Heritage and Arts Ms Glenda Wood BA(Hons) DipLib MCLIP (01992 555151; e-mail: glenda.wood@hertscc.gov.uk)
Operational Development Manager Derek Knight MCLIP (01707 281584; e-mail: derek.knight@hertscc.gov.uk)

Service Development Manager, Stock, Reader Development & Equalities Ms Sue Valentine BA(Hons) MCLIP (01707 281584; e-mail: sue.valentine@hertscc.gov.uk)
Service Development Manager, Information & Lifelong Learning Andrew Bignell BA DipLib (01707 281584; e-mail: andrew.bignell@hertscc.gov.uk)
Service Development Manager, Children & Schools Ms Sue Jones MA MCLIP (01707 281630; e-mail: sue.jones@herts-sls.org.uk)

Central/largest library

Central Resources Library, New Barnfield, Travellers Lane, Hatfield, Herts AL10 8XG
☎(01438) 737333
Fax (01707) 281514
e-mail: centralresources.library@hertscc.gov.uk
Central Resources Librarian Ms Myra Campbell MA MCLIP

District libraries

- Bishop's Stortford Library, The Causeway, Bishop's Stortford, Herts CM23 2EJ
  ☎(01438) 737333
  Fax (01279) 307471
  e-mail: bishopsstortford.library@hertscc.gov.uk
  District Librarian Ms Jean Holmes BA MCLIP
- Borehamwood Library, Elstree Way, Borehamwood, Herts WD6 1JX
  ☎(01923) 471333
  Fax (01923) 338414
  e-mail: borehamwood.library@hertscc.gov.uk
  District Librarian Ms Rachel Bilton
- Hemel Hempstead Library, Central Library, Combe Street, Hemel Hempstead, Hertfordshire HP1 1HJ
  ☎(01438) 737333
  Fax (01442) 404660
  e-mail: hemelhempstead.library@hertscc.gov.uk
  District Librarian Ms Claire Barraclough BA MCLIP
- Hitchin Library, Paynes Park, Hitchin, Herts SG5 1EW
  ☎(01438) 737333
  Fax (01462) 640529
  e-mail: hitchin.library@hertscc.gov.uk
  District Librarian Ms Iris Oakey BA DipLib MCLIP
- Hoddesdon Library, 98a High Street, Hoddesdon, Herts EN11 8HD
  ☎(01438) 737333
  Fax (01992) 411039
  e-mail: hoddesdon.library@hertscc.gov.uk
  District Librarian Ms Carol Hill BA MCLIP
- Rickmansworth Library, High Street, Rickmansworth, Herts WD3 1EH
  ☎(01923) 471333
  Fax (01923) 710384
  e-mail: rickmansworth.library@hertscc.gov.uk
  District Librarian Ms Marie Staunton BA DipLib MCLIP
- St Albans Library, The Maltings, St Albans, Hertfordshire AL1 3JQ

☎(01438) 737333
Fax (01727) 848613
e-mail: st.albans.library@hertscc.gov.uk
District Librarian Russel Barrow BA(Hons)

- Stevenage Library, Southgate, Stevenage, Hertfordshire SG1 1HD
☎(01438) 737333
Fax (01438) 219026
e-mail: stevenage.library@hertscc.gov.uk
District Librarian Ms Iris Oakey BA DipLib MCLIP
- Watford Library, Hempstead Road, Watford, Hertfordshire WD1 3EU
☎(01923) 471333
Fax (01923) 334688
e-mail: watford.library@hertscc.gov.uk
District Librarian Ms Marie Staunton BA DipLib MCLIP
- Welwyn Garden City Library, Campus West, Welwyn Garden City, Herts AL8 6AJ
☎(01438) 737333
Fax (01707) 897595
e-mail: wgc.library@hertscc.gov.uk
District Librarian Jim Macrae MA MCLIP

HILLINGDON

Authority: London Borough of Hillingdon
HQ Central Library, 14-15 High Street, Uxbridge, Middlesex UB8 1HD
☎(01895) 250600 (enquiries), (01895) 250700 (administration)
Fax (01895) 811164 (administration)
e-mail: clibrary@hillingdon.grid.org
url: www.hillingdon.gov.uk/libraries
Assistant Director, Cultural Services Vacant
Acting Head of Public Service Josie Mitchell MCLIP (01895 250716; e-mail: jmitchell@hillingdongrid.org)
Acting Head of Resources and Development Ms Eileen Smyth MCLIP (01895 250701; e-mail: esmyth@hillingdongrid.org)
Head of ICT Development Derrick Fernandes (01895 250701; e-mail: dfernandes@hillingdon.gov.uk)

Area libraries

- Central Library, 14-15 High Street, Uxbridge, Middlesex UB8 1HD
☎(01895) 250714
Fax (01895) 811164
e-mail: clibrary@hillingdon.grid.org
- Hayes Library, Golden Crescent, Hayes, Middlesex UB3 1AQ
☎020 8573 2855
Fax 020 8848 0269
- Manor Farm Library, Bury Street, Ruislip, Middlesex HA4 7SU
☎(01895) 633651
Fax (01895) 677555

HOUNSLOW

Authority: London Borough of Hounslow
HQ Hounslow Library Network (CIP), CentreSpace, Treaty Centre, High Street, Hounslow, Middlesex TW3 1ES
☎0845 456 2800 (enquiries), 0845 456 2921 (administration)
Fax 0845 456 2880
url: www.cip.com
Head of Library Services Ms Frances Stanbury MCLIP (e-mail: frances-stanbury@cip.org.uk)
Senior Manager (Resources) Ms Elizabeth Lee BA(Hons) MCLIP (e-mail: elizabeth-lee@cip.org.uk)
Library Network Manager Ms Sarah Vass BA(Hons) MSc (e-mail: sarah-vass@cip.org.uk)
Team Leader (Adult Library Services) Michael Clift BA (e-mail: michael-clift@cip.org.uk)
Team Leader (Bibliographical Services) Ms Elizabeth Cutts MCLIP (e-mail: elizabeth-cutts@cip.org.uk)
Team Leaders (Children's Library Services) Ms Carole Thompson, Gavin McQueen (e-mail: cls.tl@cip.org.uk)
Team Leader (Customer Services) Ms Ann Greene (e-mail: ann-greene@cip.org.uk)
Team Leader (Community Services) Ms Gulshan Iqbal BA DipLib (e-mail: gulshan-iqbal@cip.org.uk)

Central/largest library

Hounslow Library, CentreSpace, Treaty Centre, High Street, Hounslow, Middlesex TW3 1ES
☎0845 456 2800
Fax 0845 456 2880
Head of Library Services Ms Frances Stanbury MCLIP (e-mail: frances-stanbury@cip.org.uk)

Branch libraries

- Beavers Library @ The Hub, 103 Salisbury Road, Hounslow, Middlesex TW4 7NW
  ☎020 8572 6995
- Bedfont Library, Staines Road, Bedfont, Middlesex TW14 8BD
  ☎020 8890 6173
- Brentford Library, Boston Manor Road, Brentford, Middlesex TW8 8DW
  ☎020 8560 8801
- Chiswick Library, Duke's Avenue, Chiswick, London W4 2AB
  ☎020 8994 1008
- Cranford Library, Bath Road, Cranford, Middlesex TW5 9TL
  ☎020 8759 0641
- Feltham Library, The Centre, High Street, Feltham, Middlesex TW13 4GU
  ☎020 8890 3506
- Hanworth Library, 2-12 Hampton Road West, Feltham, Middlesex TW13 6AW
  ☎020 8898 0256
- Heston Library, New Heston Road, Heston, Middlesex TW5 0LW
  ☎020 8570 1028
- Isleworth Library, Twickenham Road, Isleworth, Middlesex TW7 7EU

☎020 8560 2934

- Osterley Library, St Mary's Crescent, Osterley, Middlesex TW7 4NB
  ☎020 8560 4295

ISLE OF WIGHT

01983 203881

Authority: Isle of Wight Council
HQ Library Headquarters, 5 Mariners Way, Somerton Industrial Estate, Cowes, Isle of Wight PO31 8PD
☎(01983) 203880 (enquiries and administration)
Fax (01983) 203899
url: www.iwight.com/thelibrary
Libraries Officer Rob Jones BA MCLIP CertEd (e-mail: rob.jones@iow.gov.uk)
Development Librarian – Operations Andrew Walker BA MCLIP (e-mail: andrew.walker@iow.gov.uk)
Development Librarian – Stock and Information John English BLib DMS MCLIP (e-mail: john.english@iow.gov.uk)
Development Librarian – Young People and Lifelong Learning Mrs Elspeth Jackson BA(Hons) DipLIS MCLIP (e-mail: elspeth.jackson@iow.gov.uk)

Central/largest library

Lord Louis Library, Orchard Street, Newport, Isle of Wight PO30 1LL
☎(01983) 527655 (enquiries and administration)
Fax (01983) 825972

Area libraries

- Bembridge Library, Church Road, Bembridge, Isle of Wight PO35 5NA
  ☎(01983) 873102 (tel/fax)
- Brighstone Library, New Road, Brighstone, Newport, Isle of Wight PO30 4BB
  ☎(01983) 740150 (tel/fax)
- Cowes Library, Beckford Road, Cowes, Isle of Wight PO31 7SG
  ☎(01983) 293341 (tel/fax)
- East Cowes Library, The York Centre, 11 York Avenue, East Cowes, Isle of Wight PO32 6QY
  ☎(01983) 293019 (tel/fax)
- Freshwater Library, School Green Road, Freshwater, Isle of Wight PO35 5NA
  ☎(01983) 752377 (tel/fax)
- Niton Library, High Street, Niton, Isle of Wight PO38 2AZ
  ☎(01983) 730863 (tel/fax)
- Ryde Library, George Street, Ryde, Isle of Wight PO33 2JE
  ☎(01983) 562170
  Fax (01983) 615644
- Sandown Library, High Street, Sandown, Isle of Wight PO36 8AF
  ☎(01983) 402748 (tel/fax)
- Shanklin Library, Victoria Avenue, Shanklin, Isle of Wight PO37 6PG
  ☎(01983) 863126 (tel/fax)
- Ventnor Library, High Street, Ventnor, Isle of Wight PO38 1LZ
  ☎(01983) 852039 (tel/fax)

ISLINGTON

Authority: London Borough of Islington
HQ Library and Cultural Services, Central Library, 2 Fieldway Crescent, London N5 1PF
☎020 7527 6900 (enquiries), 020 7527 6905 (administration)
Fax 020 7527 6906
e-mail: library.informationunit@islington.gov.uk
url: www.islington.gov.uk/libraries
Head of Library and Cultural Services Ms Rosemary Doyle MCLIP MBA (020 7527 6903; e-mail: rosemary.doyle@islington.gov.uk)
Assistant Head of Service (Support) Ms Michelle Gannon BSc(Hons) (e-mail: michelle.gannon@islington.gov.uk)
Assistant Head of Service (Public) Brendan Redmond MCLIP (020 7527 6909; e-mail: brendan.redmond@islington.gov.uk)
Children's Services Manager Geoff James BA(Hons) DipLib MCLIP (020 7527 6997; fax: 020 7527 6914; e-mail: geoff.james@islington.gov.uk)

Central/largest library

Central Library, 2 Fieldway Crescent, London N5 1PF
☎020 7527 6900
Fax 020 7527 6902
e-mail: centrallending.lib@islington.gov.uk
Public Services Manager Ms Teresa Gibson (020 7527 6950; e-mail: teresa.gibson@islington.gov.uk)

Other libraries

- Archway Library, Hamlyn House, Highgate Hill, London N19 5PH
  ☎020 7527 7820
  Fax 020 7527 7833
  e-mail: archway.library@islington.gov.uk
- Finsbury Library, 245 St John Street, London EC1V 4NB
  ☎020 7527 7960
  Fax 020 7527 7998
  e-mail: finsbury.library@islington.gov.uk
- John Barnes Library, 275 Camden Road, London N7 0JN
  ☎020 7527 7900
  Fax 020 7527 7907
  e-mail: johnbarnes.library@islington.gov.uk
- Lewis Carroll Library, 180 Copenhagen Street, London N1 0ST
  ☎020 7527 7936
  Fax 020 7527 7935
  e-mail: lewiscarroll.library@islington.gov.uk
- Mildmay Library, 21-23 Mildmay Park, London N1 4NA
  ☎020 7527 7880
  Fax 020 7527 7898
  e-mail: mildmay.library@islington.gov.uk
- N4 Library, 26 Blackstock Road, London N4 2DW
  ☎020 7527 7800

Fax 020 527 7808
e-mail: n4.library@islington.gov.uk

- North Library, Manor Gardens, London N7 6JX
☎020 7527 7840
Fax 020 7527 7854
e-mail: north.library@islington.gov.uk
- South Library, 115-117 Essex Road, London N1 2SL
☎020 7527 7860
Fax 020 7527 7869
e-mail: south.library@islington.gov.uk
- West Library, Bridgeman Road, London N1 1BD
☎020 7527 7920
Fax 020 7527 7929
e-mail: west.library@islington.gov.uk

KENSINGTON AND CHELSEA

Authority: Royal Borough of Kensington and Chelsea
HQ Central Library, Phillimore Walk, London W8 7RX
☎020 7361 3010 (general enquiries), 020 7361 3058 (management)
Fax 020 7361 2976
e-mail: headoflibraryservice@rbkc.gov.uk
url: www.rbkc.gov.uk/libraries
Head of Library Service Ms J E Battye BA MCLIP
Assistant Head of Libraries – Service Delivery & Development Miss Elizabeth Hibbs BA DipLib MCLIP
Assistant Head of Libraries – Resources & Support Mrs Jo Alaimo

Main libraries

- Brompton Library, 210 Old Brompton Road, London SW5 0BS
☎020 7373 3111
- Central Library, Hornton Street, London W8 7RX
☎020 7361 3010
Fax 020 7361 2976
- Chelsea Library, The Old Town Hall, Kings Road, London SW3 5EZ
☎020 7361 3010
- North Kensington Library, 108 Ladbroke Grove, London W11 1PZ
☎020 7361 3010

KENT

Authority: Kent County Council
HQ Libraries and Archives, Springfield, Maidstone, Kent ME14 2LH
☎(01622) 696505
Fax (01622) 696450
e-mail: libraries@kent.gov.uk
url: www.kent.gov.uk
Head of Libraries and Archives Ms Cath Anley

Strategic Manager Ms Lesley Spencer
Strategic Manager Ms Gill Bromley
Strategic Manager Ms Susan Sparks
Stock Services Manager Ken Jarvis
Area Manager, East Kent Ms Lynn Catt
Area Manager, West Kent Ms Jane Setterfield

Central library

County Central Library, Springfield, Maidstone, Kent ME14 2LH
☎(01622) 696511
Fax (01622) 696494
Information Services Manager Ms Christel Pobgee
District Manager Ms Katy Hill

Main town centre libraries

- Ashford Library, Church Street, Ashford, Kent TN23 1QX
  ☎(01233) 620649
  Fax (01233) 620295
  District Manager Ms Joy Pritchard
- Canterbury Library, High Street, Canterbury, Kent CT1 2JF
  ☎(01227) 463608
  Fax (01227) 768338
  District Manager Ms Shirley Sheridan
- Dartford Library, Central Park, Dartford, Kent DA1 1EU
  ☎(01322) 221133
  Fax (01322) 278271
  District Manager Ms Sally Reeve
- Dover Library, Market Square, Dover, Kent CT16 1PB
  ☎(01304) 204241
  Fax (01304) 225914
  District Manager Ms Heather Hilton
- Gravesend Library, Windmill Street, Gravesend, Kent DA12 1BE
  ☎(01474) 352758
  Fax (01474) 320284
  District Manager Christopher Bull
- Maidstone Library, St Faith's Street, Maidstone, Kent ME14 1LH
  ☎(01622) 752344
  Fax (01622) 754980
  District Manager Ms Katy Hill
- Sevenoaks Kaleidoscope, Buckhurst Lane, Sevenoaks, Kent TN13 1LQ
  ☎(01732) 453118
  Fax (01732) 457468
  District Manager Ms Fiona Dutton
- Shepway-Folkestone Library, 2 Grace Hill, Folkestone, Kent CT20 1HD
  ☎(01303) 850123
  Fax (01303) 242907
  District Manager Ms Jan Rudolph

- Sittingbourne Library, Central Avenue, Sittingbourne, Kent ME10 4AH
  ☎(01795) 476545
  Fax (01795) 428376
  District Manager Ms Lesley Rich
- Thanet-Broadstairs Library, The Broadway, Broadstairs, Kent CT10 2BS
  ☎(01843) 862994
  Fax (01843) 861938
  District Manager Ms Jackie Taylor-Smith
- Tonbridge Library, Avebury Avenue, Tonbridge, Kent TN9 1TG
  ☎(01732) 352754
  Fax (01732) 358300
  District Manager Ms Sue Wheeler
- Tunbridge Wells Library, Mount Pleasant Road, Tunbridge Wells, Kent TN1 1NS
  ☎(01892) 522352
  Fax (01892) 514657
  District Manager Ms Rebecca Banks

Other town libraries

- Coldharbour Library, Coldharbour Road, Northfleet, Kent DA11 8AE
  ☎(01843) 862994
- Cranbrook Library, Carriers Road, Cranbrook, Kent TN17 3JT
  ☎(01580) 712463
- Deal Library, Broad Street, Deal, Kent CT14 6ER
  ☎(01304) 374726
- Faversham Library, Newton Road, Faversham, Kent ME13 8DY
  ☎(01795) 532448
- Herne Bay Library, 124 High Street, Herne Bay, Kent CT6 5JY
  ☎(01227) 374896
- Hythe Library, 1 Stade Street, Hythe, Kent CT21 6BQ
  ☎(01303) 267111
- Sheerness Library, Russell Street, Sheerness, Kent ME12 1PL
  ☎(01795) 662618
- Swanley Library, London Road, Swanley, Kent BR8 7AE
  ☎(01322) 662570
- Tenterden Library, 55 High Street, Tenterden, Kent TN30 6BD
  ☎(01580) 762558
- Whitstable Library, 31-33 Oxford Street, Whitstable, Kent CT5 1DB
  ☎(01227) 273309

(Note: these do not represent the full list of branch libraries)

KINGSTON UPON HULL

Authority: Kingston upon Hull City Council
HQ Central Library, Albion Street, Kingston upon Hull HU1 3TF
☎(01482) 210000 (enquiries), (01482) 616822 (administration)
Fax (01482) 616827
url: www.hullcc.gov.uk
City Librarian Vacant

Area libraries

- Anlaby Park Library, The Greenway, Anlaby High Road, Kingston upon Hull HU4 6TX
  ☎(01482) 505506
- Avenues Library, 76 Chanterlands Avenue, Kingston upon Hull HU5 3TS
  ☎(01482) 331280
- Bransholme Library, District Centre, Goodhart Road, Bransholme, Kingston upon Hull HU7 4EF
  ☎(01482) 331234
- Fred Moore Library, Wold Road, Derringham Bank, Kingston upon Hull HU5 5UN
  ☎(01482) 331239
- Freedom Centre Library, 95 Preston Road, Kingston upon Hull HU9 5QB
  ☎(01482) 710100
- Gipsyville Library, 728-730 Hessle High Road, Kingston upon Hull HU4 6JA
  ☎(01482) 616973
- Greenwood Avenue Library, Greenwood Avenue, Kingston upon Hull HU6 9RU
  ☎(01482) 331257
- Holderness Road Customer Service Centre and Library, 1 The Mount, Holderness Road, Kingston upon Hull HU9 2AH
  ☎(01482) 318830
- Ings Customer Service Centre and Library, Savoy Road, Kingston upon Hull HU8 0TY
  ☎(01482) 331250
- Marfleet Library, Marfleet Primary Health Care Centre, Preston Road, Kingston upon Hull HU9 5UZ
  ☎(01482) 331264
- Stadium Library, The Learning Zone, KC Stadium, Walton Street, Kingston upon Hull HU3 6HU
  ☎(01482) 381947
- Walker Street Customer Service Centre, The Octagon, Walker Street, Kingston upon Hull HU3 2RA
  ☎(01482) 318845
- Western Library, The Boulevard, Hessle Road, Kingston upon Hull HU3 3ED
  ☎(01482) 320399

KINGSTON UPON THAMES

Authority: Royal Borough of Kingston upon Thames
HQ Kingston Library, Fairfield Road, Kingston upon Thames, Surrey KT1 2PS
☎020 8547 6413 (administration)
Fax 020 8547 6426
url: www.kingston.gov.uk
Head of Library Service Ms B Lee BA MCLIP (020 8547 6423; e-mail: barbara.lee@rbk.kingston.gov.uk)
ICT Development Manager M O'Brien (020 8547 6420; e-mail: mike.obrien@rbk.kingston.gov.uk)
Senior Team Librarian (Adult Services) Mrs E Ryder MCLIP (020 8547 6409; e-mail: elizabeth.ryder@rbk.kingston.gov.uk)

Branch libraries

- Community Library, Surbiton Library Annexe, Ewell Road, Surbiton, Surrey KT6 6AG
  ☎020 8339 7900
  Fax 020 8339 9805
  Acting Library Manager P Tanter (e-mail: paul.tanter@rbk.kingston.gov.uk)
- Hook and Chessington Library, Hook Road, Chessington, Surrey KT9 1EJ
  ☎020 8397 4931
  Fax 020 8391 4410
  Library Manager Ms M Newman (e-mail: michaela.newman@rbk.kingston.gov.uk)
- Kingston Library, Fairfield Road, Kingston upon Thames, Surrey KT1 2PS
  ☎020 8547 6400
  Fax 020 8547 6401
  Library Manager A Gale (e-mail: alan.gale@rbk.kingston.gov.uk)
- New Malden Library, Kingston Road, New Malden, Surrey KT3 3LY
  ☎020 8547 6540
  Fax 020 8547 6545
  Library Manager Adam Moore (e-mail: adam.moore@rbk.kingston.gov.uk)
- Old Malden Library, Church Road, Worcester Park, Surrey KT4 7RD
  ☎020 8337 6344
  Fax 020 8330 3118
  Library Manager J Plummer (e-mail: john.plummer@rbk.kingston.gov.uk)
- Surbiton Library, Ewell Road, Surbiton, Surrey KT6 6AG
  ☎020 8547 6444
  Fax 020 8339 9805
  Senior Library Manager Mrs J Allum (e-mail: janet.allum@rbk.kingston.gov.uk)
- Tolworth Community Library and IT Learning Centre, The Broadway, Tolworth, Surbiton, Surrey KT6 7DJ
  ☎020 8547 6470
  Fax 020 8339 6955
  e-mail: tolworth.library@rbk.kingston.gov.uk
  Library Manager Ms C Roberts
- Tudor Drive Library, Tudor Drive, Kingston upon Thames, Surrey KT2 5QH
  ☎020 8546 1198
  Fax 020 8547 2295
  Library Manager Ms S Montague (e-mail: sheila.montague@rbk.kingston.gov.uk)

KIRKLEES

Authority: Kirklees Metropolitan Council
HQ Kirklees Culture and Leisure Services, Red Doles Lane, Huddersfield, West Yorks HD2 1YF
☎(01484) 226300
Fax (01484) 226342
url: www.kirklees.gov.uk
Head of Culture and Leisure Services Ms Kimiyo Rickett (01484 234002; e-mail: kimiyo.rickett@kirklees.gov.uk) (based at Stadium Business and Leisure Complex, Stadium Way, Huddersfield, West Yorks HD1 6PG)

Assistant Head of Service (Frontline Services) Ms Catherine Morris BA DLIS MCLIP DMS (01484 226303; e-mail: catherine.morris@kirklees.gov.uk)

Central/largest library

Huddersfield Library, Princess Alexandra Walk, Huddersfield, West Yorks HD1 2SU
☎(01484) 221951
Fax (01484) 221952
Chief Librarian Ms Jan Clark BA MCLIP (e-mail: jan.clark@kirklees.gov.uk)

Area libraries

- Area East. Dewsbury Library, Railway Street, Dewsbury, West Yorks WF12 8EQ
  ☎(01924) 325085
  Librarian i/c Ms Alison Peaden BA MCLIP (e-mail: alison.peaden@kirklees.gov.uk)
- Area North. Cleckheaton Library, Whitcliffe Road, Cleckheaton, West Yorks BD19 3DX
  ☎(01274) 335169
  Librarian i/c Ms Janet Pearson BSc(Hons) PGDipInfStud PGCentMgt (e-mail: janet.pearson@kirklees.gov.uk)
- Area South. Shepley Library, Marsh Lane, Shepley, Huddersfield, West Yorks HD8 8AE
  ☎(01484) 222728
  Librarian i/c Ms Kathryn Harrison BA(Hons) PGDipLib MCLIP (e-mail: kathryn.harrison@kirklees.gov.uk)
- Area West. Holmfirth Library, 47 Huddersfield Road, Holmfirth, West Yorks HD9 3JH
  ☎(01484) 222432
  Librarian i/c Ms Ann Blakeley BA MCLIP DMS (e-mail: ann.blakeley@kirklees.gov.uk)
- Mobiles and Home Service, Cultural Services HQ, Red Doles Lane, Huddersfield, West Yorks HD2 1YF
  ☎(01484) 226350
  Librarian i/c Ms Louise Hazell MSc BEd CertEd MCLIP (e-mail: louise.hazell@kirklees.gov.uk)

KNOWSLEY

Authority: Knowsley Metropolitan Borough Council
HQ Huyton Library, Civic Way, Huyton, Merseyside L36 9GD
☎0151 443 3680
Fax 0151 443 3739
url: www.knowsley.gov.uk/leisure/libraries
Head of Libraries Peter Marchant MA BH(Hons) DipLib DM MCLIP (e-mail: peter.marchant@knowsley.gov.uk)

Central/largest library

Huyton Library, Civic Way, Huyton, Merseyside L36 9GD
☎0151 443 3734
Fax 0151 443 3739
e-mail: huyton.library@knowsley.gov.uk
Library Managers Ms Phyl Carolan, Brian Lester

Branch libraries

- Central Services Unit, 599 Princess Drive, Huyton, Merseyside L14 9ND
  ☎0151 482 1302
  Fax 0151 482 1309
  e-mail: central.services.unit@knowsley.gov.uk
  Central Services Manager Frank Wilson
- Halewood Library, Leathers Lane, Halewood, Merseyside L26 0TS
  ☎0151 486 4442
  Fax 0151 486 8101
  e-mail: halewood.library@knowsley.gov.uk
  Library Manager Philip Perry
- Kirkby Library, Newtown Gardens, Kirkby, Merseyside L32 8RR
  ☎0151 443 4290
  Fax 0151 546 1453
  e-mail: kirkby.library@knowsley.gov.uk
  Library Manager David Birchall
- Page Moss Library, Stockbridge Lane, Huyton, Merseyside L36 3SA
  ☎0151 489 9814
  Fax 0151 480 9284
  e-mail: page.moss.library@knowsley.gov.uk
  Library Manager Ms Angela Arden
- Prescot Library, High Street, Prescot, Merseyside L34 3LD
  ☎0151 426 6449
  Fax 0151 430 7548
  e-mail: prescot.library@knowsley.gov.uk
  Library Managers Mrs Diane Lester, Mrs Erica Jones
- Stockbridge Village Library, The Withens, Stockbridge Village, Merseyside L28 1SU
  ☎0151 480 3925 (tel/fax)
  e-mail: stockbridge.library@knowsley.gov.uk
  Library Managers Ms Michele Hayes, Ms Margaret Wiggins
- Whiston Library, Dragon Lane, Whiston, Merseyside L3 3QW
  ☎0151 426 4757
  Fax 0151 493 0191
  e-mail: whiston.library@knowsley.gov.uk
  Library Manager Ms Trish Fletcher

LAMBETH

Authority: London Borough of Lambeth
HQ Libraries, Archives and Arts Headquarters, 1st Floor, Blue Star House, 234–244 Stockwell Road, London SW9 9SP
☎020 7926 0750 (enquiries)
Fax 020 7926 0751
url: www.lambeth.gov.uk
Head of Libraries, Archives and Arts Ms Lesley Ray MCLIP (e-mail: lray@lambeth.gov.uk)
Deputy Head of Libraries, Archives and Arts Vacant

Development Manager, Learning and Access Ms Susan Doyle MCLIP (e-mail: sdoyle@lambeth.gov.uk)
Development Manager, Information and ICT Vacant
Support Services Manager Vacant

Minet Archives and Lending Library

- Minet Library, 52 Knatchbull Road, London SE5 9QY
  ☎020 7926 6076
  Fax 020 7926 6080
  e-mail: minetlibrary@lambeth.gov.uk/archives@lambeth.gov.uk
  Manager Jon Newman MA DAA (e-mail: jnewman@lambeth.gov.uk) Len Reilly BA DipLib MCLIP (e-mail: ljreilly@lambeth.gov.uk)

North Area

- Clapham Library, 1 Northside, Clapham Common, London SW4 0QW
  ☎020 7926 0717
  Fax 020 7926 4859
  e-mail: claphamlibrary@lambeth.gov.uk
  Area Library Manager Michel Merson (e-mail: mmerson@lambeth.gov.uk)
- Durning Library, 167 Kennington Lane, London SE11 4HF
  ☎020 7926 8682
  Fax 020 7926 8685
  e-mail: durninglibrary@lambeth.gov.uk
- South Lambeth Library, 180 South Lambeth Road, London SW8 1QP
  ☎020 7926 0705
  Fax 020 7926 0708
  e-mail: southlambethlibrary@lambeth.gov.uk
- Waterloo Library, 114–118 Lower Marsh, London SE1 7AG
  ☎020 7926 8750
  Fax 020 7926 8749
  e-mail: waterloolibrary@lambeth.gov.uk

Central Area

- Brixton Library, Brixton Oval, London SW2 1JQ
  ☎020 7926 1056
  Fax 020 7926 1070
  e-mail: brixtonlendinglibrary@lambeth.gov.uk
  Area Library Manager Ms Laura Chrysostomou (e-mail: lchrysostomou@lambeth.gov.uk)
- Carnegie Library, 188 Herne Hill Road, London SE24 0AG
  ☎020 7926 6050
  Fax 020 7926 6072
  e-mail: carnegielibrary@lambeth.gov.uk

South Area

- Streatham Library, 63 Streatham High Road, London SW16 1PL
  ☎020 7926 6768

Fax 020 7926 5804
e-mail: streathamlibrary@lambeth.gov.uk
Area Library Manager Ms Marcia Bogle-Mayne (e-mail: mboglemayne@lambeth.gov.uk)

- West Norwood Library, Norwood High Street, London SE27 9JX
  ☎020 7926 8092
  Fax 020 7926 8032
  e-mail: westnorwoodlibrary@lambeth.gov.uk

Support Services

- Children and Young People Services, Brixton Library, Brixton Oval, London SW2 1JQ
  ☎020 7926 1104
  Fax 020 7926 1070
  Senior Children and Young People Librarian Ms Sandra Davidson (e-mail: sdavidson@lambeth.gov.uk)
- Library Systems, 188 Herne Hill, London SE24 0AG
  ☎020 7926 6090
  Fax 020 7926 6072
  e-mail: librarysystems@lambeth.gov.uk
  Systems Manager (ICT) Ms Michelle Thomas BSc (e-mail: mthomas3@lambeth.gov.uk)
- Stock Services, 188 Herne Hill Road, London SE24 0AG
  ☎020 7926 6069
  Fax 020 7926 6072
  e-mail: stocksupportservices@lambeth.gov.uk
  Stock Services Manager Ms Clare Stockbridge Bland BA MCLIP (e-mail: cstockbridgebland@lambeth.gov.uk)

LANCASHIRE

ILL 01772 534052

Authority: Lancashire County Council
HQ Education and Cultural Services Directorate, County Library and Information Service, County Hall, PO Box 61, Preston, Lancs PR1 8RJ
☎(01772) 524008
Fax (01772) 534880
e-mail: library@lcl.lancscc.gov.uk
url: www.lancashire.gov.uk/libraries
Head of Library and Information Services David G Lightfoot MA DMS MCLIP (01772 534010; e-mail: david.lightfoot@lcl.lancscc.gov.uk)
Assistant County Library Managers David Blackett BA MCLIP (01772 534091; e-mail: david.blackett@lcl.lancscc.gov.uk), Ms Judith Farrell MCLIP (01772 532440; e-mail: judith.farrell@lcl.lancscc.gov.uk)

Divisional libraries

- Central Lancashire Division. Harris Library, Market Square, Preston, Lancs PR1 2PP
  ☎(01772) 532676, (01772) 532409 (administration)
  Fax (01772) 534053
  Interim Divisional Librarian Ms Sheila Burns

- East Lancashire Division. Divisional Library, Grimshaw Street, Burnley, Lancs BB11 2BD
  ☎(01282) 437115
  Fax (01282) 831682
  Divisional Librarian John Hodgkinson BA MCLIP
- North Lancashire Division. Divisional Library, Telephone House, Fenton Street, Lancaster LA1 1AB
  ☎(01524) 585270
  Fax (01524) 845125
  Interim Divisional Librarian Mrs Julie Bell BA(Hons) MCLIP
- South East Lancashire Division. Divisional Library, St James' Street, Accrington, Lancs BB5 1NQ
  ☎(01254) 872385
  Fax (01254) 306912
  Interim Divisional Librarian Mrs Ros Sudworth
- South Lancashire Division. Divisional Library, Union Street, Chorley, Lancs PR7 1EB
  ☎(01257) 277222
  Fax (01257) 231730
  Divisional Librarian Denis Whitham BSc MCLIP

LEEDS

Authority: Leeds City Council
HQ City Development Department, 7th Floor (West), No 110 Merrion Centre, Merrion House, Leeds LS2 8DT
☎0113 247 8330 (management enquiries)
Fax 0113 247 8331
url: www.leeds.gov.uk
Chief Libraries, Arts and Heritage Officer Ms Catherine Blanshard BA MCLIP (e-mail: catherine.blanshard@leeds.gov.uk)

Library headquarters

Library Headquarters, 1 Bowcliffe Road, Off Gibraltar Island Road, Hunslet, Leeds LS10 1HB
☎0113 395 2311/3 (general enquiries)
Fax 0113 395 2362/3
Libraries Development Manager Ms Patricia Carroll BA MCLIP (e-mail: patricia.carroll@leeds.gov.uk)

Central/largest library

Central Library, Municipal Buildings, Calverley Street, Leeds LS1 3AB
☎0113 247 8274
Fax 0113 247 8268
url: www.leeds.gov.uk
Library Service Delivery Manager Ms Bev Rice BA (e-mail: bev.rice@leeds.gov.uk)

LEICESTER

ILL 0116 2995484

Authority: Leicester City Council
HQ Regeneration and Culture Department, 12th Floor, Block A, New Walk Centre, Welford Place, Welford Road, Leicester LE1 6ZG
☎0116 252 6762 (administration)
Fax 0116 255 6048
e-mail: libraries@leicester.gov.uk
url: www.leicester.gov.uk/libraries
Head of Library Services (Strategy) Ms Patricia Flynn BA(Hons) DMS (e-mail: patricia.flynn@leicester.gov.uk)
Acting Head of Library Services (Operations) Adrian Wills BA DMS MCLIP (0116 252 7327; e-mail: adrian.wills@leicester.gov.uk)
Quality & Development Manager Michael Maxwell BA(Hons) DMS MCLIP (0116 252 7334; e-mail: michael.maxwell@leicester.gov.uk)
Inclusion and Diversity Manager Ms Penny Leahy BA(Hons) MCLIP (0116 252 7336; e-mail: penny.leahy@leicester.gov.uk)
Library Services Manager – Children and Young People Paul Gobey BA DipLib MCLIP (0116 225 4997; e-mail: paul.gobey@leicester.gov.uk)

Central/largest libraries

- Central Library – Learning and Information (Reference), Bishop Street, Leicester LE1 6AA
  ☎0116 299 5401
  Fax 0116 299 5444
  e-mail: central.reference@leicester.gov.uk
  Central Reference and Information Services Manager Ms Sally Mitchell
- Central Library – Lending, 54 Belvoir Street, Leicester LE1 6QL
  ☎0116 299 5402 (enquiries)
  Fax 0116 299 5434
  e-mail: central.lending@leicester.gov.uk
  Adult Lending Services Manager Michael Lewis

LEICESTERSHIRE

Authority: Leicestershire County Council
HQ Library Services, County Hall, Glenfield, Leicester LE3 8TD
☎0116 265 7015 (enquiries), 0116 265 7363 (administration)
Fax 0116 265 7370
e-mail: libraries@leics.gov.uk
url: www.leics.gov.uk/libraries
Head of Library Services Ms Margaret Bellamy DMS MBA MCLIP (e-mail: mbellamy@leics.gov.uk)
Service Delivery Manager Nigel Thomas BLib(Hons) MCLIP DPLM (e-mail: nthomas@leics.gov.uk)

Main library group HQs

- Loughborough Library, Granby Street, Loughborough, Leics LE11 3DZ
  ☎(01509) 212985/266436

Fax (01509) 610594
Area Manager Ms Gill Loveridge BA MBA MCLIP (e-mail: gloveridge@leics.gov.uk)
Area Community Manager Ms Lesley Bowell BA MCLIP (e-mail: lbowell@leics.gov.uk)

- Wigston Library, Bull Head Street, Wigston, Leicester LE18 1PA
☎0116 288 7381/257 1891
Fax 0116 281 2985
Area Manager Mrs Lorraine Selby (e-mail: lselby@leics.gov.uk)
Area Community Manager Mrs Dilys Few BSc MCLIP (e-mail: dfew@leics.gov.uk)

Market town libraries

- Coalville Library, High Street, Coalville, Leics LE67 3EA
☎(01530) 835951
Fax (01530) 832019
Area Community Manager Ms Liz Malone LLB(Hons) PGDipLib MCLIP (e-mail: lmalone@leics.gov.uk)
- Hinckley Library, Lancaster Road, Hinckley, Leics LE10 0AT
☎(01455) 635106
Fax (01455) 251385
Area Community Manager Ms Liz Malone LLB(Hons) PGDipLib MCLIP (e-mail: lmalone@leics.gov.uk)
- Melton Mowbray Library, Wilton Road, Melton Mowbray, Leics LE13 0UJ
☎(01664) 560161
Fax (01664) 410199
Area Community Managers Ms Ruth Pointer BA MCLIP (e-mail: rpointer@leics.gov.uk), Mrs Jackie Knight MCLIP (e-mail: jknight@leics.gov.uk)
- Pen Lloyd Library, Adam & Eve Street, Market Harborough, Leics LE16 7LT
☎(01858) 821272
Fax (01858) 821265
Area Community Managers Ms Ruth Pointer BA MCLIP (e-mail: rpointer@leics.gov.uk), Mrs Jackie Knight MCLIP (e-mail: jknight@leics.gov.uk)

LEWISHAM

Authority: London Borough of Lewisham
HQ Community Services, 1st Floor, Town Hall Chambers, Catford, London SE6 4RU
☎020 8314 8024 (enquiries)
Fax 020 8314 3229
url: www.lewisham.gov.uk
Library and Information Service Manager John Hughes BA(Hons) DipLib MCLIP (e-mail: john.hughes1@lewisham.gov.uk)
Children and Young Persons Librarian Ms Joanne Moulton BA DipIM MCLIP (020 8314 7189; e-mail: joanne.moulton@lewisham.gov.uk)

Central/largest library

Lewisham Library, 199-201 Lewisham High Street, London SE13 6LG
☎020 8297 9677
Fax 020 8297 1169

Central Librarian Victor Chapman BLib(Hons) MCLIP (e-mail: victor.chapman@lewisham.gov.uk)

Neighbourhood library

- Catford Library, Laurence House, Catford, London SE6 4RU
  ☎020 8314 6399
  Fax 020 8314 1110
  Neighbourhood Librarian Ms Monica Yarde BA DipLib MCLIP (e-mail: monica.yarde@lewisham.gov.uk)

District library

- Downham Library, Downham Health and Leisure Centre, 7–9 Moorside Road, Bromley, Kent BR1 5EP
  ☎020 8695 8886
  District Librarian Ms Glenys Englert MCLIP (e-mail: glenys.englert@lewisham.gov.uk)

LINCOLNSHIRE

Authority: Lincolnshire County Council
HQ Community Services (Culture and Adult Education), County Offices, Newland, Lincoln LN1 1YL
☎(01522) 553207
Fax (01522) 552811
url: www.lincolnshire.gov.uk
Head of Libraries, Learning and Inclusion John Pateman BA DipLib MBA FCLIP (e-mail: john.pateman@lincolnshire.gov.uk)
Divisional Manager East, Libraries and Learning Ms Toni Franck (01522 550357; e-mail: toni.franck@lincolnshire.gov.uk)
Divisional Manager West, Libraries and Learning Gary Porter (01522 550358; e-mail: gary.porter@lincolnshire.gov.uk)
Divisional Manager East, Heritage and Regeneration Ms Gill Fraser MA MCLIP (01522 552831; e-mail: gill.fraser@lincolnshire.gov.uk)
Divisional Manager West, Heritage and Regeneration Mike Cavanagh (01522 552839; e-mail: mike.cavanagh@lincolnshire.gov.uk)

Central/largest libraries

- Lincoln Central Library, Free School Lane, Lincoln LN2 1EZ
  ☎(01522) 782010
  Fax (01522) 575011
  e-mail: lincoln.library@lincolnshire.gov.uk
- Mobile Library Services, Eastgate Centre, 105 Eastgate, Sleaford, Lincs NG34 7EN
  ☎(01522) 550361
  Fax (01522) 550372

LIVERPOOL

ILL 0151 2335806

Authority: Liverpool City Council
HQ Liverpool Libraries and Information Services, Municipal Buildings, Dale Street, Liverpool L2 2DH
☎0151 233 6346
Fax 0151 233 6399
url: www.liverpool.gov.uk
Head of Libraries and Information Services Miss Joyce Little BA(Hons) MBA MCLIP (e-mail: joyce.little@liverpool.gov.uk)
Customer Services Manager: Information and Digital Citizenship Alan Metcalf BSc DipLib MCLIP (0151 233 5808; e-mail: alan.metcalf@liverpool.gov.uk)
Customer Services Manager: Learning and Social Inclusion John Keane BA(Hons) MCLIP (0151 233 5833; e-mail: john.keane@liverpool.gov.uk)
Manager (Operational Services) Kenneth Kay BA(Hons) DipLib MCLIP (0151 233 5857; e-mail: kenneth.kay@liverpool.gov.uk)
Customer Services Manager: Books and Reading Ron Travis BA(Hons) MA DipLib MCLIP (0151 233 5847; e-mail: ron.travis@liverpool.gov.uk)

Central/largest library

Central Library, William Brown Street, Liverpool L3 8EW
☎0151 233 5835 (enquiries), 0151 233 5851 (administration)
Fax 0151 233 5886 (enquiries), 0151 233 5824 (administration)
e-mail: refbt.central.library@liverpool.gov.uk

Other large libraries

- Allerton Library, Liverpool L18 6HG
  ☎0151 233 3333
  e-mail: allerton.library@liverpool.gov.uk
- Childwall Fiveways Library, Liverpool L15 6QR
  ☎0151 722 3214
  e-mail: childwall.library@liverpool.gov.uk
- Norris Green Library, Townsend Avenue, Liverpool L11 5AF
  ☎0151 233 1090
  e-mail: norrisgreen.library@liverpool.gov.uk

LONDON, CITY OF

Authority: City of London
HQ Libraries, Archives and Guildhall Art Gallery, Aldermanbury, London EC2V 7HH
☎020 7332 1852
Fax 020 7600 3384
url: www.cityoflondon.gov.uk
Director David Bradbury MA MCLIP (e-mail: david.bradbury@cityoflondon.gov.uk)
Assistant Director (Heritage) Ms Deborah Jenkins (e-mail: deborah.jenkins@cityoflondon.gov.uk)
Assistant Director (Libraries) Barry Cropper MA DipLib MCLIP MIMgt (e-mail: barry.cropper@cityoflondon.gov.uk)

Central/largest libraries

- Barbican Library, Barbican Centre, Silk Street, London EC2Y 8DS
  ☎020 7638 0569
  Fax 020 7638 2249
  Librarian i/c John Lake BA MCLIP (e-mail: john.lake@cityoflondon.gov.uk)
- Guildhall Library, Aldermanbury, London EC2V 7HH
  ☎020 7332 1868/1870
  Fax 020 7600 3384
  Librarian i/c Andrew Harper BA MCLIP (e-mail: andrew.harper@cityoflondon.gov.uk)

Regional/district libraries

- Camomile Street Library, 12-20 Camomile Street, London EC3A 7EX
  ☎020 7247 8895
  Fax 020 7377 2972
  Librarian i/c Malcolm Key BA MCLIP (e-mail: malcolm.key@cityoflondon.gov.uk)
- City Business Library, 1 Brewers' Hall Garden, London EC2V 5BX
  ☎020 7332 1812
  Fax 020 7332 1847
  Librarian i/c Ms Goretti Considine (e-mail: goretti.considine@cityoflondon.gov.uk)
- Shoe Lane Library, Hill House, Little New Street, London EC4A 3JR
  ☎020 7583 7178
  Fax 020 7353 0884
  Librarian i/c Leslie King BA MCLIP (e-mail: leslie.king@cityoflondon.gov.uk)

LUTON

Authority: Luton Borough Council
HQ Libraries Service, Central Library, St George's Square, Luton, Beds LU1 2NG
☎(01582) 547440 (enquiries)
Fax (01582) 547461
e-mail: referencelibrary@luton.gov.uk
url: www.luton.gov.uk/library; lutonlibrary.com
Libraries Manager Ms Jean George BA DMS MCLIP (01582 547422; e-mail: jean.george@luton.gov.uk)
Principal Librarian, Adult Services and Reader Development Ms Fiona Marriott BA MCLIP (01582 547417; e-mail: fiona.marriott@luton.gov.uk)
Principal Librarian, Information Services and Electronic Delivery Mrs Lucy Cross BLib MCLIP (01582 547432; e-mail: lucy.cross@luton.gov.uk)

Central/largest library

Central Library, St George's Square, Luton, Beds LU1 2NG
☎(01582) 547440
Library Manager Ms Julie Devine (01582 547424)

Branch libraries

- Leagrave Library, Marsh Road, Luton, Beds LU3 2NL
  ☎(01582) 556650
  Library Manager Mrs Dawn Boother

- Lewsey Library, Landrace Road, Luton, Beds LU4 0SW
  ☎(01582) 696094
  Library Manager Mrs Julie Kelly
- Marsh Farm Library and Luton Home Library Service, Purley Centre, Luton, Beds LU3 3SR
  ☎(01582) 574803
  Library Manager Ms Zoe Ayres
- Stopsley Library, Hitchin Road, Luton, Beds LU2 7UG
  ☎(01582) 706368
  Library Manager Mrs Pip Hipwell
- Sundon Park Library, Hill Rise, Luton, Beds LU3 3EE
  ☎(01582) 574573
  Library Manager Mrs Ann Soan
- Wigmore Library, Wigmore Lane, Luton, Beds LU3 8DJ
  ☎(01582) 706340
  Library Manager Mrs Jane Wigley

MANCHESTER

Authority: Manchester City Council
HQ Central Library, St Peter's Square, Manchester M2 5PD
☎0161 234 1900
Fax 0161 234 1963
e-mail: mcb@libraries.manchester.gov.uk
url: www.manchester.gov.uk/libraries
Head of Library and Information Services Ms Nicola Parker BA(Hons) MCLIP (e-mail: n.parker@manchester.gov.uk)
Head of Service Improvement Neil MacInnes (e-mail: n.macinnes@manchester.gov.uk)
Operations Manager Mrs Eunice Long (e-mail: e.long@manchester.gov.uk)
Central Library Manager Steve Willis BA DipLib MCLIP (e-mail: s.willis@manchester.gov.uk)

Library Operations

- Chorlton Group, Chorlton Library, Manchester Road, Chorlton, Manchester M21 9PN
  ☎0161 881 3179
  Fax 0161 860 0169
  Group Manager David Green (e-mail: d.green1@manchester.gov.uk)
- Crumpsall Group, Crumpsall Library, Abraham Moss Centre, Manchester M8 5UF
  ☎0161 908 1900
  Fax 0161 908 1912
  Group Manager Ms Louise Cunningham (e-mail: l.cunningham@manchester.gov.uk)
- Didsbury Group, Didsbury Library, 692 Wilmslow Road, Didsbury, Manchester M20 2DN
  ☎0161 445 3220
  Group Manager Ms Gail Mallet (e-mail: g.mallet@manchester.gov.uk)
- Forum Group, Forum Library, The Forum, Forum Square, Manchester M22 5RX
  ☎0161 935 4040
  Group Manager Ms Fran Goddard (e-mail: f.goddard@manchester.gov.uk)
- Longsight Group, Longsight Library, 519 Stockport Road, Manchester M12 4NE

☎0161 224 1411
Fax 0161 225 2119
Group Managers Ms Helen Blagborough BSc DipLib MCLIP (e-mail: h.blagborough@manchester.gov.uk) Ms Sue Moores (e-mail: s.moores@manchester.gov.uk)

- Miles Platting Group, East City Library, Whitworth House, Ashton Old Road, Manchester M11 2WH
  ☎0161 234 5501
  Group Manager Ms Maxine Goulding (e-mail: m.goulding@manchester.gov.uk)
- Community Services Co-ordinator Mobiles Services, Hammerstone Road Depot, Gorton, Manchester M18 8EQ
  ☎0161 957 5900
  Fax 0161 957 5901
  Group Manager Ms Hilary Pate (e-mail: h.pate@manchester.gov.uk)

MEDWAY

Authority: Medway Council
HQ Community Services, Civic Centre, Strood, Rochester, Kent ME2 4AU
☎(01634) 306000 (administration)
Fax (01634) 828702
url: www.medway.gov.uk
Assistant Director, Economic Development, Skills and Leisure Ms Kathy Wadsworth
Arts and Libraries Manager Ms Mandy Thwaites
Libraries Development Manager Mrs Lyn Rainbow BA(Hons) MCLIP (01634 338736)

Central/largest libraries

- Chatham Library, Gun Wharf, Dock Road, Chatham, Kent ME4 4TX
  ☎(01634) 337799
  Fax (01634) 337800
  e-mail: chatham.library@medway.gov.uk
- Gillingham Library, High Street, Gillingham, Kent ME7 1BG
  ☎(01634) 337340
  Fax (01634) 283805
  e-mail: gillingham.library@medway.gov.uk
- Medway Archives and Local Studies Centre, Civic Centre, Strood, Rochester, Kent ME2 4AU
  ☎(01634) 332714
  Fax (01634) 297060
  e-mail: local.studies@medway.gov.uk
- Strood Library, 32 Bryant Road, Strood, Rochester, Kent ME2 3EP
  ☎(01634) 335890
  Fax (01634) 297919
  e-mail: strood.library@medway.gov.uk

MERTON

Authority: London Borough of Merton
HQ Libraries and Heritage Services, Merton Civic Centre, London Road, Morden, Surrey SM4 5DX
☎020 8545 3783
Fax 020 8545 3237
url: www.merton.gov.uk
Head of Libraries and Heritage Services Ms Ingrid Lackajis BA MCLIP (020 8545 3770; e-mail: ingrid.lackajis@merton.gov.uk)
Development Manager, Lifelong Learning (Adults) Ms Pam Rew BA DipLib MCLIP (020 8545 4089; fax: 020 8545 3237; e-mail: pam.rew@merton.gov.uk)
Libraries Operations Manager Vacant
Stock Manager Anthony Hopkins (020 8288 6594; e-mail: anthony.hopkins@merton.gov.uk)

Main libraries

- Mitcham Library, London Road, Mitcham, Surrey CR4 7YR
  ☎020 8648 4070
  Fax 020 8646 6360
  e-mail: mitcham.library@merton.gov.uk
  Library Manager Mrs Raihana Ahmad MA
- Morden Library, Civic Centre, London Road, Morden, Surrey SM4 5DX
  ☎020 8545 4040
  Fax 020 8545 4037
  e-mail: morden.library@merton.gov.uk
  Library Manager Ms Sarah Azhar
- Wimbledon Library, Wimbledon Hill Road, London SW19 7NB
  ☎020 8946 7432/7979 (reference and information)
  Fax 020 8944 6804
  e-mail: wimbledon.library@merton.gov.uk
  Library Manager Selladurai Gunasingham MA

Branch libraries

- Donald Hope Library (Colliers Wood), Cavendish House, High Street, London SW19 2HR
  ☎020 8542 1975
  Fax 020 8543 9767
  e-mail: donaldhope.library@merton.gov.uk
  Library Manager Ms Chrysella Holder
- Pollards Hill Library, South Lodge Avenue, Mitcham, Surrey CR4 1LT
  ☎020 8764 5877
  Fax 020 8765 0925
  e-mail: pollardshill.library@merton.gov.uk
  Library Manager Mrs Anne Hutchings
- Raynes Park Library, Approach Road, London SW20 8BA
  ☎020 8274 5718
  Fax 020 8542 1893

e-mail: raynespark.library@merton.gov.uk
Library Manager Ms Elizabeth Smallwood

◗ West Barnes Library, Station Road, New Malden, Surrey KT3 6JF
☎020 8942 2635
Fax 020 8336 0554
e-mail: westbarnes.library@merton.gov.uk
Library Manager Ms Amanda Edmonds

MIDDLESBROUGH

Authority: Middlesbrough Borough Council
HQ Libraries and Information, Central Library, Victoria Square, Middlesbrough TS1 2AY
☎(01642) 729416 (administration)
Fax (01642) 729953
url: www.middlesbrough.gov.uk
Libraries and Information Manager Ms Chrys Mellor BSc(Econ) DipLib MCLIP (01642 729048; fax: 01642 729978; e-mail: chrys_mellor@middlesbrough.gov.uk) (based at PO Box 134, 1st Floor, Civic Centre, Middlesbrough TS1 2YB)

Central/largest library

Central Library, Victoria Square, Middlesbrough TS1 2AY
☎(01642) 729002 (enquiries), (01642) 729416 (administration)
Fax (01642) 729953
Library Manager (Operations) Mrs Jen Brittain BA (e-mail: jen_brittain@middlesbrough.gov.uk)
Library Manager (ICT Development) Ms Julie Tweedy BA MCLIP (e-mail: julie_tweedy@middlesbrough.gov.uk)
Library Manager (Young People) Ms Caryn Annal BA(Hons) (e-mail: caryn_annal@middlesbrough.gov.uk), Ms Rita Wilson BA(Hons) DipLib MCLIP (e-mail: rita_wilson@middlesbrough.gov.uk)

MILTON KEYNES

ILL 0191 277 4100

Authority: Milton Keynes Council
HQ Central Library Services, 555 Silbury Boulevard, Milton Keynes MK9 3HL
☎(01908) 254050
Fax (01908) 254089
e-mail: central.library@milton-keynes.gov.uk
url: www.mkweb.co.uk/libraries
Library Manager (Central Library Services) Mrs Elizabeth Brand BA MCLIP (e-mail: elizabeth.brand@milton-keynes.gov.uk)
Learning and Skills Manager Ms Deborah Cooper (01908 254074; e-mail: deborah.cooper@milton-keynes.gov.uk)
Senior Librarian (Children and Young People) Mrs Emma Carrick BA MCLIP (01908 254081; e-mail: emma.carrick@milton-keynes.gov.uk), Mrs Michelle Herriman BA DipLib MCLIP (e-mail: michelle.herriman@milton-keynes.gov.uk) (job-share)

Community libraries

- Bletchley Library, Westfield Road, Bletchley, Milton Keynes MK2 2RA
  ☎(01908) 372797
  Fax (01908) 645562
  Library Manager (Community Libraries) Ms Michelle Thomas BA DipLib MCLIP (e-mail: michelle.thomas@milton-keynes.gov.uk)

NEWCASTLE UPON TYNE

Authority: Newcastle upon Tyne City Council
HQ Newcastle Libraries and Information Services, PO Box 88, Newcastle upon Tyne NE99 1DX
☎0845 002 0336 (enquiries), 0191 277 4140 (administration)
Fax 0191 277 4137
e-mail: info@newcastle.gov.uk
url: www.newcastle.gov.uk/libraries
Head of Culture, Libraries and Lifelong Learning Tony Durcan BLib MCLIP (e-mail: tony.durcan@newcastle.gov.uk)
Assistant Head of Service (Operations) Allan Wraight BA MCLIP DMS (0191 277 4151; e-mail: allan.wraight@newcastle.gov.uk)
Senior Library and Information Manager (Central Services) Ms Eileen Burt MCLIP (0191 277 4153; e-mail: eileen.burt@newcastle.gov.uk)
Senior Library and Information Manager (Information & E-Libraries) Andrew Fletcher BA MCLIP (0191 277 4154; e-mail: andrew.fletcher@newcastle.gov.uk)
Senior Library and Information Manager (Access & Learning) Mrs Janice Hall MCLIP (0191 277 4203; e-mail: janice.hall@newcastle.gov.uk)
Library and Information Manager (Lending & Customer Services) Mrs Barbara Heathcote (0191 277 4115; e-mail: barbara.heathcote@newcastle.gov.uk)
Library and Information Manager (Reference & Information) Ms Angela Forster (0191 277 4148; e-mail: angela.forster@newcastle.gov.uk)
Libraries PFI Manager Stephen Darby (0191 277 4128; e-mail: stephen.darby@newcastle.gov.uk)

NEWHAM

Authority: London Borough of Newham
HQ Library Management, Culture Department, 292 Barking Road, East Ham, London E6 3BA
☎020 8430 2000 (switchboard), 020 8430 3994 (general enquiries)
Fax 020 8430 3921
url: www.newham.gov.uk
Director David Murray
Acting Head of Libraries Ms Alexis Wainwright

Largest library

Stratford Library, 3 The Grove, Stratford, London E15 1EL
☎020 8430 6890
Library Manager Mark Blair

Branch libraries

- Beckton Globe Library, 1 Kingsford Way, London E6 5JQ
  ☎020 8430 4063
  Library Manager Steve Waltho
- Canning Town Library, Barking Road, Canning Town, London E16 4HQ
  ☎020 7476 2696
  Fax 020 7511 8693
  Library Manager Ms Helen Allsop
- Custom House Library, Prince Regent Lane, London E16 3JJ
  ☎020 7476 1565
  Library Manager David Langham
- East Ham Library, High Street South, London E6 4EL
  ☎020 8430 3648
  Library Manager Ms Angela Conder
- The Gate Library and Local Service Centre, 4–20 Woodgrange Road, Forest Gate, London E7 0QH
  ☎020 8430 3838
  Library Manager Ms Angelina McIntyre
- Green Street Library, 337–341 Green Street, Upton Park, London E13 9AR
  ☎020 8472 4101
  Library Manager Ms Joanne Udall
- Manor Park Library, Romford Road, Manor Park, London E12 5JY
  ☎020 8430 2207
  Library Manager Samuel Olumalegun
- North Woolwich Library, Storey School, Woodman Street, North Woolwich, London E16 2LS
  ☎020 7511 2387
  Library Manager Kris Krisnarajah
- Plaistow Library, North Street, Plaistow, London E13 9HL
  ☎020 8472 0420
  Library Manager Ms Mandy Webb

NORFOLK

Authority: Norfolk County Council
HQ Library and Information Service, County Hall, Martineau Lane, Norwich NR1 2UA
☎(01603) 222049
Fax (01603) 222422
e-mail: libraries@norfolk.gov.uk
url: www.library.norfolk.gov.uk
Head of Libraries Mrs Jennifer Holland BA(Hons) MCLIP MCMI (01603 222272; e-mail: jennifer.holland@norfolk.gov.uk)
Finance and Business Support Manager John Perrott DMF (01603 222054; e-mail: john.perrott@norfolk.gov.uk)
Assistant Head of Service – Development Mrs Lorna Payne MA MCLIP (01603 222273; e-mail: lorna.payne@norfolk.gov.uk)
Assistant Head of Service – Business Development Neil Buxton MCLIP (01603 223406)

Central/largest libraries

- Dereham Library, 59 High Street, Dereham, Norfolk NR19 1DZ
  ☎(01362) 693184
  Fax (01362) 691891
  e-mail: dereham.lib@norfolk.gov.uk
  Assistant Head of Service Ms Sarah Hassan BA(Hons) MA MCLIP
- Gorleston Library, Lowestoft Road, Gorleston, Norfolk NR31 6SG
  ☎(01493) 662156
  Fax (01493) 446010
  e-mail: gorleston.lib@norfolk.gov.uk
  Assistant Head of Service Ms Jan Holden BA(Hons) DipLib MA
- Great Yarmouth Library, Tolhouse Street, Great Yarmouth, Norfolk NR30 2SH
  ☎(01493) 844551
  Fax (01493) 857628
  e-mail: yarmouth.lib@norfolk.gov.uk
  Assistant Head of Service Ms Jan Holden BA(Hons) DipLib MA
- King's Lynn Library, London Road, King's Lynn, Norfolk PE30 5EZ
  ☎(01553) 772568
  Fax (01553) 769832
  e-mail: kings.lynn.lib@norfolk.gov.uk
  Assistant Head of Service Ms Sarah Hassan BA(Hons) MA MCLIP
- Norfolk and Norwich Millennium Library, The Forum, Millennium Plain, Norwich NR2 1AW
  ☎(01603) 774774
  Fax (01603) 774705
  e-mail: millennium.lib@norfolk.gov.uk
  Assistant Head of Service Ms Jan Holden BA(Hons) DipLib MA
- Thetford Library, Raymond Street, Thetford, Norfolk IP24 2EA
  ☎(01842) 752048
  Fax (01842) 750125
  e-mail: thetford.lib@norfolk.gov.uk
  Assistant Head of Service Ms Sarah Hassan BA(Hons) MA MCLIP

Area library HQs

- North, South and West Area HQ, Dereham Library, 59 High Street, Dereham, Norfolk NR19 1DZ
  ☎(01362) 693184
  Fax (01362) 691891
  e-mail: dereham.lib@norfolk.gov.uk
  Assistant Head of Service Ms Sarah Hassan BA(Hons) MA MCLIP
- Norwich and East Area HQ, Norfolk and Norwich Millennium Library, The Forum, Millennium Plain, Norwich NR2 1AW
  ☎(01603) 774774
  Fax (01603) 774705
  e-mail: millennium.lib@norfolk.gov.uk
  Assistant Head of Service Ms Jan Holden BA(Hons) DipLib MA

NORTH EAST LINCOLNSHIRE

Authority: North East Lincolnshire Council
HQ Central Library, Town Hall Square, Grimsby, North East Lincs DN31 1HG
☎(01472) 323600 (enquiries), (01472) 323617 (administration)
Fax (01472) 323618
e-mail: librariesandmuseums@nelincs.gov.uk
url: www.nelincs.gov.uk
Culture and Libraries Manager Steve Hipkins BA(Hons) MA DipLib MCLIP (01472 323611; e-mail: steve.hipkins@nelincs.gov.uk)
Principal Librarian (Strategy) David A H Bell MCLIP (01472 323612; e-mail: david.bell@nelincs.gov.uk)
Principal Librarian (Customer Services) Mrs Joan Sargent BA DipLib (01472 323614; e-mail: joan.sargent@nelincs.gov.uk)
Finance and Administration Manager Mrs Isola Blow (01472 323616; e-mail: isola.blow@nelincs.gov.uk)
E-Library Manager Vacant

Branch libraries

- Cleethorpes Library, Alexandra Road, Cleethorpes, North East Lincs DN35 8LG
  ☎(01472) 323648/323650
  Fax (01472) 323652
- Grant Thorold Library, Durban Road, Grimsby, North East Lincs DN32 8BX
  ☎(01472) 323631
  Fax (01472) 323816
- Humberston Library, Church Lane, Humberston, North East Lincs DN36 4HZ
  ☎(01472) 323682
- Immingham Library, Civic Centre, Pelham Road, Immingham, North East Lincs DN40 1QF
  ☎(01469) 516050
  Fax (01469) 516051
- Laceby Library, The Stanford Centre, Cooper Lane, Laceby, North East Lincs DN37 7AX
  ☎(01472) 323684
- Nunsthorpe Library, Grimsby Institute Community Campus, Sutcliffe Avenue, Grimsby, North East Lincs DN33 1AW
  ☎(01472) 323636
- Scartho Learning Centre and Library, St Giles Avenue, Grimsby, North East Lincs DN33 2HB
  ☎(01472) 323638
- Waltham Library, High Street, Waltham, North East Lincs DN37 0LL
  ☎(01472) 323656
- Willows Library, Binbrook Way, Grimsby, North East Lincs DN37 9AS
  ☎(01472) 323679

NORTH LINCOLNSHIRE

Authority: North Lincolnshire Council
HQ Scunthorpe Central Library, Carlton Street, Scunthorpe, North Lincs DN15 6TX
☎(01724) 860161 (tel/fax)
e-mail: ref.library@northlincs.gov.uk
url: www.northlincs.gov.uk/library/
Head of Library and Information Services Ms Helen Rowe BA DipLib MCLIP (e-mail: helen.rowe@northlincs.gov.uk)

NORTH SOMERSET

Authority: North Somerset Council
HQ Libraries Office, The Winter Gardens, Royal Parade, Weston-super-Mare, Somerset BS23 1AQ
☎(01934) 634820
Fax (01934) 612182
url: www.n-somerset.gov.uk; www.foursite.somerset.gov.uk (online catalogue)
Library and Information Service Manager Andy Brisley BLib MCLIP (e-mail: andy.brisley@n-somerset.gov.uk)
Library Development Manager Nigel Kelly BA MCLIP DMS MIMgt (e-mail: nigel.kelly@n-somerset.gov.uk)
Library Operations Manager Mrs Victoria Flower BA (e-mail: victoria.flower@n-somerset.gov.uk)

Largest library

- Weston Library, The Boulevard, Weston-super-Mare, Somerset BS23 1PL
  ☎(01934) 636638 (enquiries), (01934) 620373 (administration)
  Fax (01934) 413046
  e-mail: weston.library@n-somerset.gov.uk
  Operations Officer Graham Tuckwell BA MCLIP (e-mail: graham.tuckwell@n-somerset.gov.uk)

NORTH TYNESIDE

Authority: North Tyneside Council
HQ Central Library, Northumberland Square, North Shields, Tyne and Wear NE30 1QU
☎0191 200 5424
Fax 0191 200 6118
e-mail: central.library@northtyneside.gov.uk
url: www.northtyneside.gov.uk/libraries/index
Libraries, Information and Museums Manager Mrs Julia Stafford BA MCLIP (e-mail: julia.stafford@northtyneside.gov.uk)
Adult Services and Strategic Support Manager Mrs Gayle Taylor BSc(Hons) MCLIP (e-mail: gayle.taylor@northtyneside.gov.uk)
Children's Services and Reader Development Manager Ms Andrea Stephenson BA (e-mail: andrea.stephenson@northtyneside.gov.uk)

Resources and Finance Manager Mrs Lesley Bird (e-mail: lesley.bird@northtyneside.gov.uk)
Heritage and Service Development Manager Ms Paula Harvey BA(Hons) ILM BSc CBIS MCLIP (e-mail: paula.harvey@northtyneside.gov.uk)

Main libraries

- Wallsend Library, Ferndale Avenue, Wallsend, Tyne and Wear NE28 7NB
  ☎0191 200 6968
  Fax 0191 200 6967
  e-mail: wallsend.library@northtyneside.gov.uk
- Whitley Bay Library, Park Road, Whitley Bay, Tyne and Wear NE26 1EJ
  ☎0191 200 8500
  Fax 0191 200 8536
  e-mail: whitleybay.library@northtyneside.gov.uk

NORTH YORKSHIRE

Authority: North Yorkshire County Council
HQ Adult and Communty Services (Library and Community Services), Library HQ, 21 Grammar School Lane, Northallerton, North Yorks DL6 1DF
☎(01609) 533800 (enquiries and administration)
Fax (01609) 780793
e-mail: libraries@northyorks.gov.uk
url: www.northyorks.gov.uk/libraries
Assistant Director (Library and Community Services) Ms Julie Blaisdale BA(Hons) MCLIP (e-mail: julie.blaisdale@northyorks.gov.uk)
General Manager: Libraries David Fay BA MCLIP (e-mail: david.fay@northyorks.gov.uk)
Support Services Manager Chris Riley DMA ACIS MIPD (e-mail: chris.riley@northyorks.gov.uk)
Management Co-ordinators Miss Barbara Poole BA MCLIP (e-mail: barbara.poole@northyorks.gov.uk), Ms Iris Maynard (e-mail: iris.maynard@northyorks.gov.uk)
General Manager: Archives, Registrations and Coroner's Services Ms Lesley Willetts BA DipLib MCLIP (e-mail: lesley.willetts@northyorks.gov.uk)
Manager: Children and Schools Mrs Brenda Hooper BSc MCLIP (e-mail: brenda.hooper@northyorks.gov.uk)

Larger libraries

- Library and Information Centre Harrogate, Victoria Avenue, Harrogate, North Yorks HG1 1EG
  ☎(01423) 720300 (Lending), 720305 (Reference)
  Fax (01423) 523158
  e-mail: harrogate.library@northyorks.gov.uk
  url: www.northyorks.gov.uk/libraries/branches/harrogate.shtm
  Principal Officer Ms Jill Fellerman BA MCLIP (01423 720305)
- Library and Information Centre Scarborough, Vernon Road, Scarborough, North Yorks YO11 2NN
  ☎(01723) 383400 (Lending), 383407 (Reference)

Fax (01723) 353893
e-mail: scarborough.library@northyorks.gov.uk
url: www.northyorks.gov.uk/libraries/branches/scarborough.shtm
Principal Officer Ms Sandra Turner BA MCLIP (01723 383401; e-mail: sandra.turner@northyorks.gov.uk)

(Note: These do not represent the full list of Library and Information Centres. Please see website for more details: www.northyorks.gov.uk/libraries)

NORTHAMPTONSHIRE

ILL 01604 773936

Authority: Northamptonshire County Council
HQ Libraries HQ, Culture and Healthier Communities, PO Box 216, John Dryden House, 8-10 The Lakes, Northampton NN4 7DD
☎(01604) 236236
Fax (01604) 237937
e-mail: nlis@northamptonshire.gov.uk
url: www.northamptonshire.gov.uk
Libraries Service Manager Ms Grace Kempster OBE BA(Hons) MLib MCLIP FRSA (e-mail: gkempster@northamptonshire.gov.uk)

Central/largest library

Central Library, Abington Street, Northampton NN1 2BA
☎(01604) 462040
Fax (01604) 462055
Central Library Manager Miss Gill Howe BA(Hons) MCLIP (e-mail: gihowe@northamptonshire.gov.uk)

Area libraries

- Daventry Library, North Street, Daventry, Northants NN11 4GH
  ☎(01327) 703130
  Fax (01327) 300501
  Principal Librarian Mrs Anne Lovely BA(Hons) MCLIP (e-mail: alovely@northamptonshire.gov.uk)
- Kettering Library, Sheep Street, Kettering, Northants NN16 0AY
  ☎(01536) 512315
  Fax (01536) 411349
  Principal Librarian Ms Ingrid Mercer BLS MCLIP (e-mail: imercer@northamptonshire.gov.uk)
- Wellingborough Library, Pebble Lane, Wellingborough, Northants NN8 1AS
  ☎(01933) 225365
  Fax (01933) 442060
  Principal Librarian Mrs Hilary Ward BA(Hons) MCLIP (e-mail: rhward@northamptonshire.gov.uk)
- Weston Favell Library, Weston Favell Centre, Northampton NN3 8JZ
  ☎(01604) 403100
  Fax (01604) 403112
  Principal Librarian Vacant

NORTHUMBERLAND

Authority: Northumberland County Council
HQ County Library HQ, Beechfield, Morpeth, Northumberland NE61 1TA
☎(01670) 534528
Fax (01670) 533409 (administration)
e-mail: libraries@northumberland.gov.uk
url: www.northumberland.gov.uk
Acting Divisional Director, Customer Services, Libraries and Archives
Ms Marguerite Gracey BA(Hons) DMS MCLIP (e-mail: marguerite.gracey@northumberland.gov.uk)

Central/largest library

County Library, Gas House Lane, Morpeth, Northumberland NE61 1TA
☎(01670) 534518 (lending), (01670) 534514 (reference)
Fax (01670) 534513
e-mail: morpethlibrary@northumberland.gov.uk

NOTTINGHAM

ILL 0115 985 4207

Authority: City of Nottingham Council
HQ Department of Leisure and Community Services, Libraries and Communications Division, Isabella Street, Nottingham NG1 6AT
☎0115 915 5555
Fax 0115 915 8680
e-mail: community_libraries.admin@nottinghamcity.gov.uk
url: www.nottinghamcity.gov.uk
Head of Service, Libraries and Information Services Ms Christina Dyer BA MCLIP (0115 915 8673)
Library Strategy Manager Ms Natalie Sellears (0115 915 8720)

Central/largest library

Nottingham City Library, Angel Row, Nottingham NG1 6HP
☎0115 915 2828
Fax 0115 915 2850
e-mail: central_admin.library@nottinghamcity.gov.uk
url: www.nottinghamcity.gov.uk/libraries
Senior Library Manager Martin Willis

NOTTINGHAMSHIRE

ILL 0115 985 4242

Authority: Nottinghamshire County Council
HQ Culture and Community/Libraries, Archives and Information, 4th Floor, County Hall, West Bridgford, Nottingham NG2 7QP
☎0115 977 4401
Fax 0115 977 2807
url: www.nottinghamshire.gov.uk

Head of Libraries, Archives and Information Peter Gaw BA MCLIP (0115 977 4201; e-mail: peter.gaw@nottscc.gov.uk)
Principal Libraries Officer (Public Services, Operations and Quality) Tony Cook BA MCLIP ALCM (0115 977 4437; e-mail: tony.cook@nottscc.gov.uk)
Principal Libraries Officer (Resources and Commissioning) Philip Marshall BA MCLIP (0115 985 4201; e-mail: philip.marshall@nottscc.gov.uk) (based at Glaisdale Parkway)

Central/largest library

County Library, Four Seasons Centre, Westgate, Mansfield, Notts NG18 1NH
☎(01623) 627591 (enquiries), (01623) 653551 (administration)
Fax (01623) 629276
e-mail: mansfield.library@nottscc.gov.uk
Principal Librarian Mrs Kath Owen BA MCLIP (e-mail: kath.owen@nottscc.gov.uk)

Group libraries

- Central Nottinghamshire Group. County Library, Front Street, Arnold, Nottingham NG5 7EE
  ☎0115 920 2247
  Fax 0115 967 3378
  e-mail: arnold.library@nottscc.gov.uk
  Principal Librarian Roger Jones BA MCLIP (e-mail: roger.jones@nottscc.gov.uk)
- East Nottinghamshire Group. County Library, Beaumond Gardens, Baldertongate, Newark-on-Trent, Notts NG24 1UW
  ☎(01636) 703966
  Fax (01636) 610045
  e-mail: newark.library@nottscc.gov.uk
  Acting Principal Librarian Ms Kirsty Blyth BA MCLIP (e-mail: kirsty.blyth@nottscc.gov.uk)
- North Nottinghamshire Group. County Library, Churchgate, Retford, Notts DN22 6PE
  ☎(01777) 708724
  Fax (01777) 710020
  e-mail: retford.library@nottscc.gov.uk
  Principal Librarian Mrs Linda Turner BA MCLIP (e-mail: linda.turner@nottscc.gov.uk)
- South Nottinghamshire Group. County Library, Foster Avenue, Beeston, Nottingham NG9 1AE
  ☎0115 925 5168/925 5084
  Fax 0115 922 0841
  e-mail: beeston.library@nottscc.gov.uk
  Principal Librarian Ms Carol Newman BA MCLIP (e-mail: carol.newman@nottscc.gov.uk)
- West Nottinghamshire Group. County Library, Four Seasons Centre, Westgate, Mansfield, Notts NG18 1NH
  ☎(01623) 627591
  Fax (01623) 629276
  e-mail: mansfield.library@nottscc.gov.uk
  Principal Librarian Mrs Kath Owen BA MCLIP (e-mail: kath.owen@nottscc.gov.uk)

Other services

- Support Services, Units 4-6, Glaisdale Parkway, Bilborough, Nottingham NG8 4GP
  ☎0115 985 4242
  Fax 0115 928 6400
  Principal Bibliographical Officer, Support Services Ms Anne Corin BA MCLIP (0115 985 4208; e-mail: anne.corin@nottscc.gov.uk)
  Principal Systems Officer, Support Services Nick London MCLIP (0115 985 5172; e-mail: nick.london@nottscc.gov.uk)

OLDHAM

Authority: Oldham Metropolitan District Council
HQ Oldham Library, Cultural Quarter, Greaves Street, Oldham, Lancashire OL1 1AL
☎0161 770 8000 (general enquiries)
e-mail: oldham.library@oldham.gov.uk
url: www.oldham.gov.uk
Head of Heritage, Libraries and Arts Ms Sheena Macfarlane (0161 770 4664; fax: 0161 770 4782; e-mail: sheena.macfarlane@oldham.gov.uk)

OXFORDSHIRE ILL 01865 810216

Authority: Oxfordshire County Council
HQ Social and Community Services, Cultural and Adult Learning Services, Central Library, Westgate, Oxford OX1 1DJ
☎(01865) 810191
Fax (01865) 810187
url: www.oxfordshire.gov.uk
Head of Cultural Services Richard Munro BA DipLib MCLIP (e-mail: richard.munro@oxfordshire.gov.uk)
County Librarian Ms Caroline Taylor BA DipLib MCLIP (e-mail: carolinej.taylor@oxfordshire.gov.uk) (based at Social and Community Services, Cultural and Adult Learning Services, Holton, Oxford OX33 1QQ; 01865 810212; fax 01865 810205)

Central/largest library

Central Library, Westgate, Oxford OX1 1DJ
☎(01865) 815549
Fax (01865) 721694
e-mail: oxford.central.library@oxfordshire.gov.uk
Principal Librarian Mrs Liz Rooke BA DipLib MCLIP (e-mail: liz.rooke@oxfordshire.gov.uk)

Additional services

- Performance and Development, Social and Community Services, Cultural and Adult Learning Services, Holton, Oxford OX33 1QQ
  ☎(01865) 810234
  Fax (01865) 810205

Assistant County Librarian Rex Harris MA DipLib MCLIP (e-mail: rex.harris@oxfordshire.gov.uk)

- Operations, Social and Community Services, Cultural and Adult Learning Services, Banbury Library, Marlborough Road, Banbury, Oxon OX16 5DB
  ☎(01295) 268249
  Fax (01295) 264331
  Assistant County Librarian Mrs Yvonne McDonald BA DMS DipLib MCLIP (e-mail: yvonne.mcdonald@oxfordshire.gov.uk)
- Information Services and Lifelong Learning, Social and Community Services, Cultural and Adult Learning Services, Holton, Oxford OX33 1QQ
  ☎(01865) 810221
  Fax (01865) 810205
  Assistant County Librarian Charles Pettit MA MA(Lib) MCLIP (e-mail: charles.pettit@oxfordshire.gov.uk)

PETERBOROUGH

Authority: Peterborough City Council
HQ Community Services: Libraries, Central Library, Broadway, Peterborough PE1 1RX
☎(01733) 742700
Fax (01733) 319140
e-mail: libraries@peterborough.gov.uk
url: www.peterborough.gov.uk/libraries
Library and Customer Services Manager Ms Heather Walton BLS MCLIP (01733 742702; e-mail: heather.walton@peterborough.gov.uk)
Central Library and Archives Manager Mrs Jane Brown (01733 742720; e-mail: jane.brown@peterborough.gov.uk)
Senior Operations Manager Mrs Varsha Hindocha (01733 742713; e-mail: varsha.hindocha@peterborough.gov.uk)
Libraries Project Manager Mrs Helen Sherley BLib MCLIP (01733 742704; e-mail: helen.sherley@peterborough.gov.uk)
Reading and Outreach Services Manager Vacant

District libraries

- Bretton Library, Bretton Centre, Bretton, Peterborough PE3 8DS
  ☎(01733) 742700
  e-mail: brettonlibrary@peterborough.gov.uk
- Orton Library, Orton Centre, Orton, Peterborough PE2 0RQ
  ☎(01733) 742700
  e-mail: ortonlibrary@peterborough.gov.uk
- Werrington Library, Staniland Way, Werrington, Peterborough PE4 6JT
  ☎(01733) 742700
  e-mail: werringtonlibrary@peterborough.gov.uk

Community libraries

- Dogsthorpe Library, Central Avenue, Dogsthorpe, Peterborough PE1 4LH
  ☎(01733) 742700
  e-mail: dogsthorpelibrary@peterborough.gov.uk

- Eye Library, Crowland Road, Eye, Peterborough PE6 7TN
  ☎(01733) 742700
  e-mail: eyelibrary@peterborough.gov.uk
- Stanground Library, Southfields Avenue, Stanground, Peterborough PE2 8RZ
  ☎(01733) 742700
  e-mail: stangroundlibrary@peterborough.gov.uk
- Thorney Library, Church Street, Thorney, Peterborough PE6 0QB
  ☎(01733) 742700
  e-mail: thorneylibrary@peterborough.gov.uk
- Woodston Library, Orchard Street, Woodston, Peterborough PE2 9AL
  ☎(01733) 742700
  e-mail: woodstonlibrary@peterborough.gov.uk

PLYMOUTH

1-L 01752 305963

Authority: Plymouth City Council
HQ Library and Information Services, Central Library, Drake Circus, Plymouth PL4 8AL
☎(01752) 305923 (enquiries and administration)
Fax (01752) 305929
e-mail: library@plymouth.gov.uk
url: www.plymouthlibraries.info; www.cyberlibrary.org.uk
City Librarian Alasdair MacNaughtan BA MCLIP DMS MCMI (01752 305901; e-mail: alasdair.macnaughtan@plymouth.gov.uk)
Resources Manager (Personnel & Finance) Frank Lowry MCLIP (01752 305911; e-mail: frank.lowry@plymouth.gov.uk)
Resources Manager (Stock & Services) Chris Goddard BMus DipLib MCLIP (01752 305900; e-mail: chris.goddard@plymouth.gov.uk)
Central Library Manager Ms Tracey Tremlett (01752 306792; e-mail: tracey.tremlett@plymouth.gov.uk)
Young People's Services Manager Ms Julia Hale BEd MA (01752 306799; e-mail: julia.hale@plymouth.gov.uk)

POOLE

Authority: Borough of Poole
HQ Culture and Community Learning, Central Library, Dolphin Centre, Poole, Dorset BH15 1QE
☎(01202) 262400
Fax (01202) 262431
url: www.poole.gov.uk
Head of Culture and Community Learning Kevin McErlane BA(Hons) DipLib MBA (e-mail: k.mcerlane@poole.gov.uk)
Library Services Development Manager John Lane MCLIP (01202 262433; e-mail: john.lane@poole.gov.uk)
Library Services Operations Manager Chas Rowling (01202 262423; e-mail: c.rowling@poole.gov.uk)

Central/largest library

Central Library, Dolphin Centre, Poole, Dorset BH15 1QE
☎(01202) 262424
e-mail: centrallibrary@poole.gov.uk
Healthpoint (health information centre also serving Dorset)
e-mail: healthpoint@poole.gov.uk
Manager Mrs V Grier BA MCLIP (01202 262436)

PORTSMOUTH

Authority: Portsmouth City Council
HQ Library Service, Central Library, Guildhall Square, Portsmouth PO1 2DX
☎023 9281 9311
Fax 023 9283 9855
e-mail: library.admin@portsmouthcc.gov.uk
url: www.portsmouth.gov.uk/learning/
Library Service Manager Colin Brown MCLIP (e-mail: colin.brown@portsmouthcc.gov.uk)
Lifelong Learning and Children's Services Manager Mrs Lindy Elliott BA MCLIP (023 9268 8058; e-mail: lindy.elliott@portsmouthcc.gov.uk)

School Library Service, Saxon Shore Infants School, Jubilee Avenue, Paulsgrove, Portsmouth PO6 4QJ
☎023 9232 6612

Branch libraries

- Alderman Lacey Library, Tangier Road, Copnor, Portsmouth PO3 6HU
  ☎023 9282 3991 (tel/fax)
  e-mail: alderman.library@portsmouthcc.gov.uk
- Beddow Library, Milton Road, Milton, Portsmouth PO4 8PR
  ☎023 9273 1848 (tel/fax)
  e-mail: beddow.library@portsmouthcc.gov.uk
- Carnegie Library, Fratton Road, Fratton, Portsmouth PO1 5EZ
  ☎023 9282 2581
  Fax 023 9273 9244
  e-mail: carnegie.library@portsmouthcc.gov.uk
- Cosham Library, Spur Road, Cosham, Portsmouth PO6 3ED
  ☎023 9237 6023
  Fax 023 9237 1877
  e-mail: cosham.library@portsmouthcc.gov.uk
- Elm Grove Library, Elm Grove, Southsea, Portsmouth PO5 1LJ
  ☎023 9282 6058
  e-mail: elmgrove.library@portsmouthcc.gov.uk
- North End Library, Gladys Avenue, North End, Portsmouth PO2 9AX
  ☎023 9266 2651
  Fax 023 9266 8151
  e-mail: northend.library@portsmouthcc.gov.uk
- Paulsgrove Library, Marsden Road, Paulsgrove, Portsmouth PO6 4JB

☎023 9237 7818 (tel/fax)
e-mail: paulsgrove.library@portsmouthcc.gov.uk

- Portsea Library, St James Street, Portsea, Portsmouth PO1 3AP
  ☎023 9229 7072
  e-mail: johnpounds.library@portsmouthcc.gov.uk

Community library services

- Carnegie Library, Fratton Road, Fratton, Portsmouth PO1 5EZ
  ☎023 9275 1737
  Fax 023 9273 9244
  e-mail: community.library@portsmouthcc.gov.uk

READING

Authority: Reading Borough Council
HQ Reading Central Library, Abbey Square, Reading RG1 3BQ
☎0118 901 5950
Fax 0118 901 5954
e-mail: info@readinglibraries.org.uk
url: www.readinglibraries.org.uk
Libraries and Resources Manager Ms Alison England BA(Hons) DipLib MCLIP (0118 901 5962)
Resources Manager Ms Sara Walkinshaw
Support Staff Manager Ms Karen Eccles

Branch libraries

- Battle Library, 420 Oxford Road, Reading RG3 1EE
  ☎0118 901 5100
  Fax 0118 901 5101
  Branch Manager Mrs Marjorie McClure
- Caversham Library, Church Street, Caversham, Reading RG4 8AU
  ☎0118 901 5103
  Fax 0118 901 5104
  Branch Manager Ms Virginia Hobbs
- Mobile Services, c/o Tilehurst Library, School Road, Tilehurst, Reading RG3 5AS
  ☎0118 901 5118
  Manager Ms Dawn Littlefield
- Palmer Park Library, St Bartholomew's Road, Reading RG1 3QB
  ☎0118 901 5106
  Fax 0118 901 5107
  Branch Manager Miss Christine Gosling
- Southcote Library, Southcote Lane, Reading RG3 3BA
  ☎0118 901 5109
  Fax 0118 901 5110
  Branch Manager Mrs Liz Long
- Tilehurst Library, School Road, Tilehurst, Reading RG3 5AS
  ☎0118 901 5112
  Fax 0118 901 5113

Branch Manager Andrew Mitchell

- Whitley Library, Northumberland Avenue, Reading RG2 7PX
  ☎0118 901 5115
  Fax 0118 901 5116
  Branch Managers Mrs Caroline Kelly, Ms Jan Westall

REDBRIDGE

Authority: London Borough of Redbridge
HQ Central Library, Clements Road, Ilford, Essex IG1 1EA
☎020 8478 7145
Fax 020 8708 2431
url: www.redbridge.gov.uk/libraries
Head of Libraries Martin Timms BA MCLIP (020 8708 2436; e-mail: martin.timms@redbridge.gov.uk)
Central Library Manager Mrs Rosamund Willis-Fear BA(Hons) MCLIP
Development Manager Mark Lenihan BSc DipLib MCLIP
Customer Services Manager Vacant

Branch libraries

- Aldersbrook Library, 2a Park Road, London E12 5HQ
  ☎020 8496 0006
  Branch Librarian Ms Linda Hubbard BA DipLib MCLIP (e-mail: linda.hubbard@redbridge.gov.uk)
- Fullwell Cross Library, 140 High Street, Barkingside, Ilford, Essex IG6 2EA
  ☎020 8708 9281
  Branch Librarian Mrs Elaine Sahlke BA(Hons) DipLib MCLIP
- Gants Hill Library, 490 Cranbrook Road, Gants Hill, Ilford, Essex IG2 6LA
  ☎020 8708 9275
  Branch Librarian John Weeks MCLIP (e-mail: john.weeks@redbridge.gov.uk)
- Goodmayes Library, 76 Goodmayes Lane, Goodmayes, Ilford, Essex IG3 9QB
  ☎020 8708 7750
  Branch Librarian Ms Lesley Gould (e-mail: lesley.gould@redbridge.gov.uk), Ms Rhonda Brooks (e-mail: rhonda.brooks@redbridge.gov.uk) (job-share)
- Hainault Library, 100 Manford Way, Chigwell, Essex IG7 4DD
  ☎020 8708 9206
  Branch Librarian Nick Dobson (e-mail: nick.dobson@redbridge.gov.uk)
- Keith Axon Centre, 160–170 Grove Road, Chadwell Heath, Essex RM6 4XB
  ☎020 8708 0790
  Branch Librarian Ms Lesley Gould (e-mail: lesley.gould@redbridge.gov.uk), Ms Rhonda Brooks (e-mail: rhonda.brooks@redbridge.gov.uk) (job-share)
- South Woodford Library, 116 High Road, London E18 2QS
  ☎020 8708 9067
  Branch Librarian Mrs Evelyn Reid BA MCLIP (e-mail: evelyn.reid@redbridge.gov.uk)
- Wanstead Library, Spratt Hall Road, London E11 2RQ
  ☎020 8708 7400
  Branch Librarian Ms Linda Hubbard BA DipLib MCLIP (e-mail: linda.hubbard@redbridge.gov.uk)

- Woodford Green Library, Snakes Lane, Woodford Green, Essex IG8 0DX
  ☎020 8708 9055
  Branch Librarian Archie Black LLB DipLib MCLIP (e-mail: archie.black@redbridge.gov.uk)

REDCAR AND CLEVELAND

Authority: Redcar and Cleveland Borough Council
HQ Chief Executive's Department, Information and Communication Division, Redcar and Cleveland House, Kirkleatham Street, Redcar, Cleveland TS10 1RT
☎08456 126126
Fax (01642) 444341
url: www.redcar-cleveland.gov.uk
Chief Communication, Information and Engagement Officer Mrs Carol McIntosh BA DipLib (01642 444357; e-mail: carol_mcintosh@redcar-cleveland.gov.uk)
Support Services Officer Mrs Janet Richardson (01642 444319; e-mail: janet_richardson@redcar-cleveland.gov.uk)
Stock Management Officer Ms Carol Bruce (01642 492253; e-mail: carol_bruce@redcar-cleveland.gov.uk)

Central/largest library

Central Library, Coatham Road, Redcar, Cleveland TS10 1RP
☎(01642) 472162
Fax (01642) 492253
e-mail: redcar_library@redcar-cleveland.gov.uk
Libraries Officer I L Wilson BA MCLIP (01642 444263)

RICHMOND UPON THAMES

Authority: London Borough of Richmond upon Thames
HQ Education and Children's Services, First Floor, Regal House, London Road, Twickenham, Middlesex TW1 3QB
☎020 8831 6136
Fax 020 8891 7904
e-mail: libraries@richmond.gov.uk
url: www.richmond.gov.uk/libraries
Head of Libraries and Culture Ms Aileen T Cahill BSocSc DipLib MCLIP
Deputy Head of Library and Information Services Mrs Lynda Farnworth BA DMA MCLIP
Operations Manager Vacant

Central/largest library

Richmond Lending Library, Little Green, Richmond, Surrey TW9 1QL
☎020 8940 0981/6857
Fax 020 8940 7516
e-mail: richmond.library@richmond.gov.uk
Customer Services Manager Leslie Cranfield MCLIP (e-mail: l.cranfield@richmond.gov.uk)

Branch libraries

- Central Reference Library, Old Town Hall, Whitaker Avenue, Richmond, Surrey TW9 1TP
  ☎020 8940 5529/9125
  Fax 020 8940 6899
  e-mail: reference.services@richmond.gov.uk
  Central Reference Librarian Vacant
- East Sheen Library, Sheen Lane, London SW14 8LP
  ☎020 8876 8801
  e-mail: eastsheen.library@richmond.gov.uk
- Teddington Library, Waldegrave Road, Teddington, Middlesex TW11 8LG
  ☎020 8977 1284
  e-mail: teddington.library@richmond.gov.uk
- Twickenham Library, Garfield Road, Twickenham, Middlesex TW1 3JT
  ☎020 8892 8091
  e-mail: twickenham.library@richmond.gov.uk

ROCHDALE

Authority: Rochdale Metropolitan Borough Council
HQ Wheatsheaf Library, Wheatsheaf Shopping Centre, Baillie Street, Rochdale, Greater Manchester OL16 1JZ
☎(01706) 924900 (enquiries), (01706) 924911 (administration)
Fax (01706) 924992
url: www.rochdale.gov.uk/libraries
Principal Librarian Mrs Sheila Sfrijan MCLIP (01706 924929; e-mail: sheila.sfrijan@rochdale.gov.uk)
Community Services Manager Mrs Freda Fletcher MCLIP (01706 924964; e-mail: freda.fletcher@rochdale.gov.uk)
Area Librarian (Rochdale and Pennine) Mrs Janice Tod BSc(Hons) MCLIP (01706 924976; e-mail: janice.tod@rochdale.gov.uk) (based at Wheatsheaf Library)

Main libraries

- Heywood Library, Church Street, Heywood, Greater Manchester OL10 1LL
  ☎(01706) 360947
  Fax (01706) 368683
  Area Librarian Vacant
- Middleton Library, Long Street, Middleton, Greater Manchester M24 6DU
  ☎0161 643 5228
  Fax 0161 654 0745
  Area Librarian Vacant

ROTHERHAM

Authority: Rotherham Metropolitan Borough Council
HQ Central Library, Walker Place, Rotherham, South Yorks S65 1JH
☎(01709) 823611 (enquiries), (01709) 823623 (management)
Fax (01709) 823650 (enquiries), (01709) 837649 (management)
e-mail: central.library@rotherham.gov.uk

url: www.rotherham.gov.uk
Libraries, Museums and Arts Manager Ms Elenore Fisher BA(Hons) DipLib MCLIP (e-mail: elenore.fisher@rotherham.gov.uk)
Manager, Library and Information Service Vacant

RUTLAND

Authority: Rutland County Council
HQ Rutland County Library, Catmose Street, Oakham, Rutland LE15 6HW
☎(01572) 722918 (enquiries)
Fax (01572) 724906 (enquiries)
e-mail: libraries@rutland.gov.uk
url: www.rutland.gov.uk/libraries
County Librarian Robert Clayton BA MA MCLIP (e-mail: rclayton@rutland.gov.uk)

Community libraries

- Ketton Library, High Street, Ketton, Rutland PE9 3TE
  ☎(01780) 720580
- Ryhall Library, Coppice Road, Ryhall, Rutland PE9 4HY
  ☎(01780) 751726
- Uppingham Library, Queen Street, Uppingham, Rutland LE15 9QR
  ☎(01572) 823218

ST HELENS

Authority: Metropolitan Borough of St Helens
HQ Chief Executive's Department, Public Affairs Division, The Gamble Building, Victoria Square, St Helens, Merseyside WA10 1DY
☎(01744) 677448 (enquiries and administration)
Fax (01744) 677082
e-mail: keithpatterson@sthelens.gov.uk
url: www.sthelens.gov.uk
Head of Service Vacant

Central/largest library

Central Library, The Gamble Building, Victoria Square, St Helens, Merseyside WA10 1DY
☎(01744) 456950
Fax (01744) 20836
e-mail: criu@sthelens.gov.uk
Principal Libraries Development Manager, Social Inclusion Miss Kerry Corbett BD DipLib MCLIP (e-mail: kerrycorbett@sthelens.gov.uk)
Principal Libraries Development Manager, Reading and Learning Ms Sue Thomas BA DMS (e-mail: suethomas@sthelens.gov.uk)

SALFORD

ILL 0161 7079612

Authority: Salford City Council
HQ Community, Health and Social Care Directorate, Crompton House, 100 Chorley Road, Swinton, Salford, Manchester M27 4BD
☎0161 793 2300
Fax 0161 794 0197
e-mail: libraries@salford.gov.uk
url: www.salford.gov.uk/libraries
Libraries and Information Service Manager Ms Sarah Spence BA(Hons) MCLIP (0161 778 0840; fax: 0161 745 9490; e-mail: sarah.spence@salford.gov.uk)

Main libraries

- Broadwalk Library, Broadwalk, Salford, Manchester M6 5FX
  ☎0161 737 5802
  Fax 0161 745 9157
  Senior Librarian Mrs Julie Stonebanks BA(Hons) DMS (e-mail: julie.stonebanks@salford.gov.uk)
- Eccles Library, Church Street, Eccles, Salford, Manchester M30 0EP
  ☎0161 789 1430
  Fax 0161 787 8430
  Divisional Librarian Mrs Hannah Quinlan BA(Hons) MA MCLIP (e-mail: hannah.quinlan@salford.gov.uk)
- Swinton Library, Chorley Road, Swinton, Salford, Manchester M27 4AE
  ☎0161 793 3560
  Fax 0161 727 7071
  Divisional Librarian Ms Carol Behrens BA DBA (e-mail: carol.behrens@salford.gov.uk)
- Walkden Library, Memorial Road, Walkden, Salford, Manchester M28 3AQ
  ☎0161 790 4579
  Fax 0161 703 8971
  Senior Librarian Chris Carson BA DMS MCLIP (e-mail: chris.carson@salford.gov.uk)

SANDWELL

Authority: Sandwell Metropolitan Borough Council
HQ Sandwell Library and Information Service, Town Hall, West Bromwich, West Midlands B70 8DX
☎0121 569 4924
Fax 0121 569 4907
e-mail: information.service@sandwell.gov.uk
url: www.libraries.sandwell.gov.uk
Chief Librarian Ms Linda Saunders BA DipLib MCLIP (e-mail: linda.saunders@sandwell.gov.uk)

Central/largest library

Central Library, High Street, West Bromwich, West Midlands B70 8DZ
☎0121 569 4904

Fax 0121 525 9465
Principal Libraries Officer (Learning and Information) Ms Heather Vickerman (0121 569 4906; e-mail: heather.vickerman@sandwell.gov.uk)

Additional services

- Community History and Archives Service, Smethwick Library, High Street, Smethwick, West Midlands B66 1AB
  ☎0121 558 2561
  Fax 0121 555 6064
  e-mail: archives.service@sandwell.gov.uk
  Borough Archivist Ms Sarah Chubb UDIP RMSA (0121 558 2861; e-mail: sarah.chubb@sandwell.gov.uk)
- Community Libraries, c/o Central Library, High Street, West Bromwich, West Midlands B70 8DZ
  ☎0121 569 4922
  Fax 0121 525 9465
  Principal Libraries Officer (Community Libraries) Anthony Piorowski MCLIP (0121 569 4922; e-mail: tony.piorowski@sandwell.gov.uk)
- Library Support Services, Town Hall, High Street, West Bromwich, West Midlands B70 8DT
  ☎0121 569 4909
  Fax 0121 569 4907
  Principal Libraries Officer (Library Support Services) Barry Clark BLib MCLIP (e-mail: barry.clark@sandwell.gov.uk)

SEFTON

ILL 01704 560090

Authority: Sefton Council
HQ Leisure Services Department, 2nd Floor, Magdalen House, 30 Trinity Road, Bootle, Liverpool L20 3NJ
☎0151 934 2376
Fax 0151 934 2370
e-mail: library.service@leisure.sefton.gov.uk
url: www.sefton.gov.uk
Head of Library and Information Services Ms Christine Hall (e-mail: christine.hall@leisure.sefton.gov.uk)
Principal Development Manager – Library Operations Ms Vena Walker (e-mail: vena.walker@leisure.sefton.gov.uk)
Principal Development Manager – Stock and Reader Development David Eddy (e-mail: david.eddy@leisure.sefton.gov.uk)
Principal Development Manager – Community Cohesion Ms Zoë Clarke BA MA MCLIP (e-mail: zoe.clarke@leisure.sefton.gov.uk)

Central/largest libraries

- Crosby Library, Crosby Road North, Waterloo, Liverpool L22 0LQ
  ☎0151 257 6400
  Fax 0151 330 5770

- Southport Library, Lord Street, Southport PR8 1DJ
☎0151 934 2118
Fax 0151 934 2115

SHEFFIELD

Authority: Sheffield City Council
HQ Sheffield Libraries, Archives and Information Services, Central Library, Surrey Street, Sheffield S1 1XZ
☎0114 273 4712 (enquiries), 0114 273 5052/205 3124 (library management)
Fax 0114 273 5009
e-mail: libraries@sheffield.gov.uk
url: www.sheffield.gov.uk/libraries
City Librarian Ms Janice Maskort BA(Hons) MCLIP DMS (e-mail: janice.maskort@sheffield.gov.uk)
Lifelong Learning Manager David Isaac BA(Hons) DipLib DMS MCLIP (0114 273 6959; e-mail: david.isaac@sheffield.gov.uk)
Customer Services Manager Ms Sue Cook MCLIP (0114 273 6642; e-mail: sue.cook@sheffield.gov.uk)
Policy and Development Manager Martin Dutch BA(Hons) DipLib MCLIP (0114 273 6998; e-mail: martin.dutch@sheffield.gov.uk)
Archives and Local Studies Manager Peter Evans (0114 273 9395; e-mail: pete.evans@sheffield.gov.uk)
Collections and Reader Development Manager Ms Alison Jobey BA MCLIP (0114 273 6499; e-mail: alison.jobey@sheffield.gov.uk)
ICT Manager John Murphy BSc(Hons) MA (0114 273 6645; e-mail: john.murphy@sheffield.gov.uk)
Information Services Manager Ms Elizabeth Wright MA MCLIP (0114 273 6645; e-mail: elizabeth.wright@sheffield.gov.uk)
Lending Services Manager Andrew Milroy BA DipLib (0114 273 4403; e-mail: andrew.milroy@sheffield.gov.uk)
Performance Manager Ms Judith Adam MA(Hons) DipLib MCLIP (0114 273 4254; e-mail: judith.adam@sheffield.gov.uk)
Marketing Officer Gurjit Bhachoo (0114 273 6942; e-mail: gurjit.bhachoo@sheffield.gov.uk)

District libraries

- Broomhill Library, Taptonville Road, Sheffield S10 5BR
  ☎0114 273 4276
  e-mail: broomhill.library@sheffield.gov.uk
- Burngreave Library, 179 Spital Hill, Sheffield S4 7LF
  ☎0114 203 9002
  e-mail: burngreave.library@sheffield.gov.uk
- Chapeltown Library, Nether Ley Avenue, Sheffield S35 1AE
  ☎0114 203 7000/1
  e-mail: chapeltown.library@sheffield.gov.uk
- Crystal Peaks Library, 1-3 Peak Square, Crystal Peaks Complex, Waterthorpe, Sheffield S20 7PH

☎0114 293 0612/3
e-mail: crystalpeaks.library@sheffield.gov.uk

- Darnall Library, Britannia Road, Sheffield S9 5JG
  ☎0114 203 7429
  e-mail: darnall.library@sheffield.gov.uk
- Ecclesall Library, Weetwood Gardens, Ecclesall Road South, Sheffield S11 9PL
  ☎0114 203 7222
  Fax 0114 203 7227
  e-mail: ecclesall.library@sheffield.gov.uk
- Ecclesfield Library, High Street, Ecclesfield, Sheffield S35 9UA
  ☎0114 203 7013 (tel/fax)
  e-mail: ecclesfield.library@sheffield.gov.uk
- Firth Park Library, 443 Firth Park Road, Sheffield S5 6QQ
  ☎0114 203 7433
  e-mail: firthpark.library@sheffield.gov.uk
- Frecheville Library, Smalldale Road, Sheffield S12 4YD
  ☎0114 203 7817
  e-mail: frecheville.library@sheffield.gov.uk
- Gleadless Library, White Lane, Sheffield S12 3GH
  ☎0114 203 7804 (tel/fax)
  e-mail: gleadless.library@sheffield.gov.uk
- Greenhill Library, Hemper Lane, Sheffield S8 7FE
  ☎0114 203 7700
  Fax 0114 293 0012
  e-mail: greenhill.library@sheffield.gov.uk
- Highfield Library, London Road, Sheffield S2 4NF
  ☎0114 203 7204
  e-mail: highfield.library@sheffield.gov.uk
- Hillsborough Library, Middlewood Road, Sheffield S6 4HD
  ☎0114 203 9529
  e-mail: hillsborough.library@sheffield.gov.uk
- Jordanthorpe Library, 15 Jordanthorpe Centre, Sheffield S8 8DX
  ☎0114 203 7701
  Fax 0114 293 0388
  e-mail: jordanthorpe.library@sheffield.gov.uk
- Limpsfield Library, Limpsfield Middle School, Jenkin Avenue, Sheffield S9 1AN
  ☎0114 203 7430
  Fax 0114 242 3808
  e-mail: limpsfield.library@sheffield.gov.uk
- Manor Library, Ridgeway Road, Sheffield S12 2SS
  ☎0114 203 7805
  e-mail: manor.library@sheffield.gov.uk
- Mobile Services, 443 Handsworth Road, Sheffield S13 9DD
  ☎0114 273 4277
- Newfield Green Library, Gleadless Road, Sheffield S2 2BT
  ☎0114 203 7818 (tel/fax)
  e-mail: newfieldgreen.library@sheffield.gov.uk

- Park Library, Duke Street, Sheffield S2 5QP
  ☎0114 203 9000 (tel/fax)
  e-mail: park.library@sheffield.gov.uk
- Parson Cross Library, Margetson Crescent, Sheffield S5 9ND
  ☎0114 203 9533
  Fax 0114 203 9656
  e-mail: parsoncross.library@sheffield.gov.uk
- Southey Library, Moonshine Lane, Sheffield S5 8RB
  ☎0114 203 9531
  Fax 0114 293 0024
  e-mail: southey.library@sheffield.gov.uk
- Stannington Library, Uppergate Road, Sheffield S6 8RB
  ☎0114 293 0489
  Fax 0114 293 0488
  e-mail: stannington.library@sheffield.gov.uk
- Stocksbridge Library, Manchester Road, Stocksbridge, Sheffield S36 1DH
  ☎0114 273 4205
  e-mail: stocksbridge.library@sheffield.gov.uk
- Tinsley Library, Tinsley Shopping Centre, Bawtry Road, Sheffield S9 1UY
  ☎0114 203 7432
  Fax 0114 293 0029
  e-mail: tinsley.library@sheffield.gov.uk
- Totley Library, 205 Baslow Road, Sheffield S17 4DT
  ☎0114 293 0406
  e-mail: totley.library@sheffield.gov.uk
- Upperthorpe Library, Upperthorpe Healthy Living Centre, 18 Upperthorpe, Sheffield S6 3NA
  ☎0114 270 2048
  Fax 0114 276 2189
  e-mail: upperthorpe.library@sheffield.gov.uk
- Walkley Library, South Road, Sheffield S6 3TD
  ☎0114 203 9532 (tel/fax)
  e-mail: walkley.library@sheffield.gov.uk
- Woodhouse Library, Tannery Street, Sheffield S13 7JU
  ☎0114 269 2607 (tel/fax)
  e-mail: woodhouse.library@sheffield.gov.uk
- Woodseats Library, Chesterfield Road, Sheffield S8 0SH
  ☎0114 293 0411
  e-mail: woodseats.library@sheffield.gov.uk

SHROPSHIRE

Authority: Shropshire County Council
HQ Library and Information Services, Community Services Directorate, The Shirehall, Abbey Foregate, Shrewsbury, Shropshire SY2 6ND
☎(01743) 255019
Fax (01743) 255001
e-mail: libraries@shropshire-cc.gov.uk

url: www.shropshire-cc.gov.uk/library.nsf
Head of Library and Information Services Jim Roads BA MCLIP (e-mail: jim.roads@shropshire-cc.gov.uk)
Principal Librarian – Development and Support Don Yuile BA MCLIP (e-mail: don.yuile@shropshire-cc.gov.uk)
Principal Librarian – Young People and Access Gordon Dickins BA MCLIP (e-mail: gordon.dickins@shropshire-cc.gov.uk)

Central/largest libraries

- Castle Gates Library, Shrewsbury, Shropshire SY1 2AS
  ☎(01743) 255300
  Fax (01743) 255309
  Principal Librarian – Shrewsbury Ms Elaine Moss MCLIP (e-mail: elaine.moss@shropshire-cc.gov.uk)
- Reference and Information Service, 1a Castle Gates, Shrewsbury, Shropshire SY1 2AQ
  ☎(01743) 255380
  Fax (01743) 255383
  Principal Librarian – Shrewsbury Ms Elaine Moss MCLIP (e-mail: elaine.moss@shropshire-cc.gov.uk)

Area libraries

- North Area. Oswestry Library, Arthur Street, Oswestry, Shropshire SY11 1JN
  ☎(01691) 653211
  Fax (01691) 656994
  Principal Librarian – North Ms Claire Cartlidge MCLIP (e-mail: claire.cartlidge@shropshire-cc.gov.uk)
- South Area. Bridgnorth Library, Listley Street, Bridgnorth, Shropshire WV16 4AW
  ☎(01746) 763257
  Fax (01746) 766625
  Principal Librarian – South Adrian Williams BA MCLIP (e-mail: adrian.williams@shropshire-cc.gov.uk)

SLOUGH

Authority: Slough Borough Council
HQ Libraries, Heritage and Information, Community and Cultural Services, 1st Floor Annexe, Wellington House, Slough SL1 1DB
☎(01753) 875578
Fax (01753) 875419
url: www.sloughlibrary.org.uk
Head of Library Services Ms Jackie Menniss BA(Hons) DipIM MCLIP (e-mail: jackie menniss@slough.gov.uk)

Central/largest library

Slough Library, High Street, Slough SL1 1EA
☎(01753) 535166
Fax (01753) 825050

Assistant Head of Library Services Vacant
Library IT Manager Damon Guy (e-mail: damon.guy@slough.gov.uk)
Resource Manager Mrs Gail Stuckey

SOLIHULL

Authority: Solihull Metropolitan Borough Council
HQ Central Library, Homer Road, Solihull, West Midlands B91 3RG
☎0121 704 6965 (public enquiries), 0121 704 6941 (administration)
Fax 0121 704 6991
e-mail: libraryarts@solihull.gov.uk
url: www.solihull.gov.uk
Interim Head for Community Services (Libraries, Arts and Lifelong Learning) Ms Tracey Juric BLS(Hons) MCLIP (0121 704 6963; e-mail: tjuric@solihull.gov.uk)
Support Services Manager Ms Hilary Halliday BA MCLIP (0121 704 8227; e-mail: hhalliday@solihull.gov.uk)
Children's, Family Learning and Schools Manager Vacant

Main area libraries

- Central Library, Homer Road, Solihull, West Midlands B91 3RG
  ☎0121 704 6965
  Fax 0121 704 6991
  Central Area Manager Ms Tracey Juric BLS(Hons) MCLIP (e-mail: tjuric@solihull.gov.uk)
- Chelmsley Wood Library, Stephenson Drive, Chelmsley Wood, Solihull, West Midlands B37 5TA
  ☎0121 788 4385
  Fax 0121 788 4381
  Community Libraries Manager Ms Yvonne Negus BA MCLIP MISM (01564 776331; e-mail: ynegus@solihull.org.uk)

SOMERSET

Glastonbury ILL 01458 832148

Authority: Somerset County Council – ILL 01273 451201
HQ Cultural Service, Administration Centre, Mount Street, Bridgwater, Somerset TA6 3ES
☎(01278) 451201
Fax (01278) 452787
e-mail: librec@somerset.gov.uk
url: www.somerset.gov.uk/libraries; www.librarieswest.org.uk
Helpline, Somerset Direct: 0845 345 9177
Group Manager – Cultural Services Robert N Froud BLib DMS MIMgt FCLIP (e-mail: rnfroud@somerset.gov.uk)
Senior Manager – Library Operations Philip Nichols BA MCLIP (01935 429614; e-mail: penichols@somerset.gov.uk) (located at Yeovil Library)
Senior Manager – Policy and Development (including Children and Youth) Miss Rachel Boyd BA MCLIP (e-mail: rboyd@somerset.gov.uk)

Business and Performance Manager Stephen G May (e-mail: sgmay@somerset.gov.uk)
Senior Librarian – Operations Mrs Sue Crowley BLib MCLIP (e-mail: sacrowley@somerset.gov.uk)
Senior Librarian – Stock and Community Ms Deborah Stevens
Ms Mary Yardley MA MCLIP
Senior Librarian – Service Development Julian Luke BA DipLib MCLIP
Consortium and Performance Manager Nigel J Humphrey BLib MA MCLIP (e-mail: nhumphrey@somerset.gov.uk)
Bibliographic Services Manager Miss Carol Gold (e-mail: cgold2@somerset.gov.uk)
Enquiry Centre Manager Mrs Jane Gill BA MCLIP (e-mail: jgill@somerset.gov.uk)
Projects, Research and Marketing Officer Paul Smith BA(Hons) DipLib DMS MCLIP (e-mail: psmith@somerset.gov.uk)

Group libraries

- Mendip & Sedgemoor Group, Bridgwater Library, Binford Place, Bridgwater, Somerset TA6 3LF
  ☎(01278) 458373
  Fax (01278) 451027
- South Somerset Group, Yeovil Library, King George Street, Yeovil, Somerset BA20 1PY
  ☎(01935) 423144
  Fax (01935) 431847
- Taunton Deane & West Somerset Group, Taunton Library, Paul Street, Taunton, Somerset TA1 3XZ
  ☎(01823) 336334
  Fax (01823) 340302

SOUTH GLOUCESTERSHIRE

Authority: South Gloucestershire Council
HQ Library Service, Civic Centre, High Street, Kingswood, South Glos BS15 9TR
☎(01454) 865782
Fax (01454) 868535
e-mail: libraries@southglos.gov.uk
url: www.southglos.gov.uk/libraries
Head of Library and Information Service Martin Burton BA MCLIP
Team Manager (North) Ms Anne Hartridge MCLIP (01454 865664)
Team Manager (South) Michael Duffy MCLIP (01454 868450)

Central/largest library

Yate Library, 44 West Walk, Yate, South Glos BS37 4AX
☎(01454) 868006
Fax (01454) 865665
Group Librarian Neil Weston BA MCLIP

Group libraries

- Bradley Stoke Library, Fiddlers Wood Lane, Bradley Stoke, South Glos BS32 9BS
  ☎(01454) 868006
  Librarian Ms Catherine Whiteman MCLIP

- Downend Library, Buckingham Gardens, Downend, South Glos BS16 5TW
  ☎(01454) 868006
  Librarian Mrs Helen Egarr MCLIP
- Kingswood Library, High Street, Kingswood, South Glos BS15 4AR
  ☎(01454) 868006
  Librarian Ms Julie Barker
- Thornbury Library, St Mary Street, Thornbury, South Glos BS35 2AA
  ☎(01454) 868006
  Librarian Bob Filer BA MCLIP

SOUTH TYNESIDE

Authority: South Tyneside Metropolitan Borough Council
HQ South Tyneside Libraries, Central Library, Prince Georg Square, South Shields, Tyne and Wear NE33 2PE
☎0191 427 1818
Fax 0191 455 8085
e-mail: reference.library@southtyneside.gov.uk
url: www.southtyneside.info
Libraries Manager Mark C E Freeman BA(Hons) MCLIP (e-mail: mark.freeman@southtyneside.gov.uk)
Development and Planning Co-ordinator David Whale MCLIP
Young People's Services Co-ordinator Ms Kathryn Armstrong MA MCLIP (e-mail: kathryn.armstrong@southtyneside.gov.uk)
Information and Education Co-ordinator Ms Hildred Whale MCLIP
Community Development Co-ordinator Ms Lindsay Casselden BA(Hons) MA MCLIP
Resources and Electronic Services Co-ordinator Ms Yvonne Gordon BA(Hons) MCLIP

SOUTHAMPTON

023 8083 2596 ILL

Authority: Southampton City Council
HQ City Library, Archives and Information Service, Central Library, Civic Centre, Southampton SO14 7LW
☎023 8083 2459
Fax 023 8033 6305
url: www.southampton.gov.uk/leisure/libraries
Libraries Manager David Baldwin (e-mail: david.baldwin@southampton.gov.uk)
Resources and Development Manager Mrs Elizabeth Whale (023 8083 2595; e-mail: elizabeth.whale@southampton.gov.uk)
Neighbourhood Services Manager Ms Siobhan McGarrigle (e-mail: siobhan.mcgarrigle@southampton.gov.uk)

Central/largest library

Central Library, Civic Centre, Southampton SO14 7LW
☎023 8083 2597 (Lending Library renewals), 023 8083 2664 (enquiry desk), 023 8083 2462/3 (Reference Library)
e-mail: lending.library@southampton.gov.uk

Central Library Manager Richard Ashman (e-mail: richard.ashman@southampton.gov.uk)

Branch libraries

- Bitterne Library, Bitterne Road East, Southampton SO18 5EG
  ☎023 8044 9909
  e-mail: bitterne.library@southampton.gov.uk
  Supervisor Ms Barbara McCaffrey (e-mail: barbara.mccaffrey@southampton.gov.uk)
- Burgess Road Library, Burgess Road, Southampton SO16 3HF
  ☎023 8067 8873
  e-mail: burgess.road.library@southampton.gov.uk
  Supervisor Ms Jackie Sutton (e-mail: jackie.sutton@southampton.gov.uk)
- Cobbett Road Library, Cobbett Road, Southampton SO18 1HL
  ☎023 8022 5555
  e-mail: cobbett.road.library@southampton.gov.uk
  Supervisor Ms Norma Belbin (e-mail: norma.belbin@southampton.gov.uk)
- Lord's Hill Library, Lord's Hill District Centre, Southampton SO16 8HY
  ☎023 8073 2845
  e-mail: lordshill.library@southampton.gov.uk
  Acting Supervisor Ms Linda Gregory (e-mail: linda.gregory@southampton.gov.uk)
- Millbrook Library, 67 Cumbrian Way, Southampton SO16 4AT
  ☎023 8078 1819
  e-mail: millbrook.library@southampton.gov.uk
  Supervisor Mrs Angela Zabiela (e-mail: angela.zabiela@southampton.gov.uk)
- Portswood Library, Portswood Road, Southampton SO17 2NG
  ☎023 8055 4634
  e-mail: portswood.library@southampton.gov.uk
  Supervisor Ms Sara Goddard (e-mail: sara.goddard@southampton.gov.uk)
- Shirley Library, Redcar Street, Southampton SO15 5LL
  ☎023 8077 2136
  e-mail: shirley.library@southampton.gov.uk
  Supervisor Ms Judith O'Callaghan (e-mail: judith.o'callaghan@southampton.gov.uk)
- Thornhill Library, 380 Hinkler Road, Southampton SO19 6DF
  ☎023 8044 7245
  e-mail: thornhill.library@southampton.gov.uk
- Weston Library, 6 Wallace Road, Weston, Southampton SO19 9GX
  ☎023 8044 4363
  e-mail: weston.library@southampton.gov.uk
  Supervisor Mrs Carolyn Taplin (e-mail: carolyn.taplin@southampton.gov.uk)
- Woolston Library, Portsmouth Road, Southampton SO19 9AF
  ☎023 8044 8481
  e-mail: woolston.library@southampton.gov.uk
  Supervisor Ms Jo Harley (e-mail: jo.harley@southampton.gov.uk)

Community Services: Mobile Library, BookBus, services to your home
☎023 8083 2216
e-mail: community.service@southampton.gov.uk

SOUTHEND-ON-SEA

Authority: Southend-on-Sea Borough Council
HQ Southend Library, Victoria Avenue, Southend-on-Sea, Essex SS2 6EX
☎(01702) 534100
Fax (01702) 469241
e-mail: library@southend.gov.uk
url: www.southend.gov.uk
Library Services Manager Simon May BSc MSc
Head of Information and Resources Chris Hayes BA DipLib

SOUTHWARK

Authority: London Borough of Southwark
HQ Southwark Environment and Leisure, 15 Spa Road, London SE16 3QW
☎020 7525 3719
Fax 020 7525 1568
e-mail: southwark.libraries@southwark.gov.uk
url: www.southwark.gov.uk
Head of Culture, Libraries and Learning Adrian Whittle BA (020 7525 1577; e-mail: adrian.whittle@southwark.gov.uk)
Library Services Manager Ms Pam Usher BA(Hons) DMS MCLIP (020 7525 3918; e-mail: pam.usher@southwark.gov.uk)

Branch libraries

- Blue Anchor Library, Market Place, Southwark Park Road, London SE16 3UQ
  ☎020 7525 6300
  Fax 020 7525 6302
- Brandon Library, Maddock Way, Cooks Road, London SE17 3NH
  ☎020 7735 3430
  Fax 020 7735 1664
- Camberwell Library, 17-21 Camberwell Church Street, London SE5 8TR
  ☎020 7525 6320
  Fax 020 7525 6326
- Dulwich Library, 368 Lordship Lane, London SE22 8NB
  ☎020 7525 6220
  Fax 020 7525 6221
- East Street/Old Kent Road Library, 168-170 Old Kent Road, London SE1 5TY
  ☎020 7703 0395
  Fax 020 7703 2224
- Education Library Service, Southwark Education Resource Centre, Cator Street, London SE15 6AA
  ☎020 7525 2830
  Fax 020 7525 2837
- Grove Vale Library, 25-27 Grove Vale, London SE22 8EQ
  ☎020 8693 5734
  Fax 020 8693 0755
- John Harvard Library, 211 Borough High Street, London SE1 1JA

☎020 7407 0807
Fax 020 7378 9917

- Kingswood Library, Seeley Drive, London SE21 8QR
  ☎020 8670 4803
  Fax 020 8671 5125
- Local History Library, 211 Borough High Street, London SE1 1JA
  ☎020 7403 3507
  Fax 020 7403 8633
- Newington Library, 155-7 Walworth Road, London SE17 1RS
  ☎020 7525 2176
  Fax 020 7525 2175
- Newington Reference Library, 155-7 Walworth Road, London SE17 1RS
  ☎020 7525 2181
  Fax 020 7525 2175
- Nunhead Library, Gordon Road, London SE15 3RW
  ☎020 7639 0264
  Fax 020 7277 5721
- Peckham Library, 122 Peckham Hill Street, London SE15 5JR
  ☎020 7525 0200
  Fax 020 7525 0202
- Rotherhithe Library, Albion Street, London SE16 1JA
  ☎020 7237 2010
  Fax 020 7394 0672
- Special Library Services, Rotherhithe Library, Albion Street, London SE16 1JA
  ☎020 7237 1487
  Fax 020 7237 8417

STAFFORDSHIRE

Authority: Staffordshire County Council
HQ Library and Information Services, Children and Lifelong Learning, Tipping Street, Stafford ST16 2DH
☎(01785) 278311
Fax (01785) 278319
url: www.staffordshire.gov.uk
Head of Culture and Libraries Ms Janene Cox BLib MCLIP (01785 278368; e-mail: janene.cox@staffordshire.gov.uk)
Principal Librarian: Policy Development, Books, Reading and Learning Mrs Judy Goodson MCLIP (01785 278320; e-mail: judy.goodson@staffordshire.gov.uk)
Service Delivery Manager Mrs Elizabeth Rees-Jones BA(Hons) MCLIP (01785 278344; e-mail: elizabeth.rees-jones@staffordshire.gov.uk)
Principal Librarian: Policy Development, Community Engagement and Local Delivery Mrs Hilary Jackson BLib MCLIP (01785 278591; e-mail: hilary.jackson@staffordshire.gov.uk)
Group Manager: North Alan Medway BLib MCLIP (01785 278388; e-mail: alan.medway@staffordshire.gov.uk)
Group Manager: South Mrs Alison Reynolds BA(Hons) MA MCLIP (e-mail: alison.reynolds@staffordshire.gov.uk)

Senior Librarian – Prison Library Service Ms Lindsay Alcock MCLIP (01785 278412; e-mail: lindsay.alcock@staffordshire.gov.uk)
Service Development Officer – Children and Young People Ms Sue Ball BA MCLIP (01785 854170; e-mail: sue.ball@staffordshire.gov.uk)

Districts – North Group

East Staffs

- Burton Library, Riverside, High Street, Burton-on-Trent, Staffs DE14 1AH
  ☎(01283) 239556
  Fax (01283) 239571
  e-mail: burton.library@staffordshire.gov.uk
  District Librarian Kevin Reynolds MCLIP (01283 239559; e-mail: kevin.reynolds@staffordshire.gov.uk)

Newcastle

- Newcastle Library, Ironmarket, Newcastle, Staffs ST5 1AT
  ☎(01782) 297300
  Fax (01782) 297323
  e-mail: newcastle.library@staffordshire.gov.uk
  District Librarian Mrs Sam Mellenchip BA(Hons) PGDipLIS (01782 297305; e-mail: samantha.mellenchip@staffordshire.gov.uk)

Stafford

- Shire Hall Library, Market Street, Stafford ST16 2LQ
  ☎(01785) 278585
  Fax (01785) 278599
  e-mail: stafford.library@staffordshire.gov.uk
  District Librarian Andrew Baker BA(Hons) MCLIP TSSF (01785 278335; e-mail: andrew.baker@staffordshire.gov.uk)

Staffs Moorlands

- Leek Library, Nicholson Institute, Stockwell Street, Leek, Staffs ST13 6DW
  ☎(01538) 483209
  Fax (01538) 483216
  e-mail: leek.library@staffordshire.gov.uk
  District Librarian Ms Cathy Braddock BLib(Hons) MCLIP (01538 483206; e-mail: cathy.braddock@staffordshire.gov.uk)

Community Library Service

- Library and Information Service, Children and Lifelong Learning, Tipping Street, Stafford ST16 2DH
  ☎(01785) 278369
  Fax (01785) 278309
  Senior Librarian Mrs Olwen Johnson MCLIP (01785 278317; e-mail: olwen.johnson@staffordshire.gov.uk)

Districts – South Group

Cannock

- Cannock Library, Manor Avenue, Cannock, Staffs WS11 1AA
  ☎(01543) 510366
  Fax (01543) 510373
  e-mail: cannock.library@staffordshire.gov.uk
  District Librarian Ms Karen Yeomans BA(Hons) (01543 510366; e-mail: karen.yeomans@staffordshire.gov.uk)

Lichfield

- Lichfield Library, The Friary, Lichfield, Staffs WS13 6QG
  ☎(01543) 510700
  Fax (01543) 510706
  e-mail: lichfield.library@staffordshire.gov.uk
  District Librarian Ms Jane Sanderson BA(Hons) MCLIP (01543 510702; e-mail: jane.sanderson@staffordshire.gov.uk), Ms Lorraine Riley BA(Hons) DipEd MA CBA MCLIP (e-mail: lorraine.riley@staffordshire.gov.uk) (job-share)

South Staffs

- Perton Library, Severn Drive, Perton, Staffs WV6 7QU
  ☎(01902) 755794
  Fax (01902) 756123
  e-mail: perton.library@staffordshire.gov.uk
  District Manager Graham Riley MCLIP (01902 755794; e-mail: graham.riley@staffordshire.gov.uk)

Tamworth

- Tamworth Library, Corporation Street, Tamworth, Staffs B79 7DN
  ☎(01827) 475645
  Fax (01827) 475658
  e-mail: tamworth.library@staffordshire.gov.uk
  District Librarian Ms Cathy Attwood (01827 475651; e-mail: cathy.attwood@staffordshire.gov.uk)

Schools Library Service

- Kingsway Centre, Fairway, Stafford ST16 3TW
  ☎(01785) 278346/278440
  e-mail: sls@staffordshire.gov.uk
  Development Manager Ms Lisa Westmorland BA(Hons) MA MCLIP (e-mail: lisa.westmorland@staffordshire.gov.uk)

STOCKPORT ILL 0161 4744410

Authority: Stockport Metropolitan Borough Council
HQ Adults and Communities Directorate, Ponsonby House, Edward Street, Stockport SK1 3UR
☎0161 474 4445 (enquiries and administration)

Fax 0161 474 7895
url: www.stockport.gov.uk
Head of Library and Information Services John Condon (e-mail: john.condon@stockport.gov.uk)

Central/largest library

Central Library, Wellington Road South, Stockport SK1 3RS
☎0161 474 4530 (Local Heritage Library), 0845 644 4307 (all other library enquiries)
Fax 0161 474 7750
e-mail: lending.library@stockport.gov.uk; information.library@stockport.gov.uk; localheritage.library@stockport.gov.uk

Bibliographical Services Unit, Phoenix House, Bird Hall Lane, Stockport SK3 0RA
☎0161 474 5605
Fax 0161 491 6516

STOCKTON-ON-TEES

Authority: Stockton-on-Tees Borough Council
HQ Children, Education and Social Care, Stockton Borough Libraries, Church Road, Stockton-on-Tees TS18 1TU
☎(01642) 526522
Fax (01642) 528078
url: www.stockton.gov.uk
Head of Arts and Culture Reuben Kench (01642 527039; e-mail: reuben.kench@stockton.gov.uk) (located at Municipal Buildings, Church Road, Stockton-on-Tees TS18 1XE)
Community Engagement Officer Ms Emma Shields MSc (01642 526520; e-mail: emma.shields@stockton.gov.uk) (also responsible for children's services)
Priority Services Officer Mrs Pam Wilson (01642 526519; e-mail: pamela.wilson@stockton.gov.uk)
Lending Services Officer Mrs Penny Slee (01642 526521; e-mail: penny.slee@stockton.gov.uk)
Information Services Officer Ms Carole Wood (01642 528079; e-mail: carole.wood@stockton.gov.uk)
Community Libraries Officer Ms Deb McDonagh (01642 526520; e-mail: debbie.mcdonagh@stockton.gov.uk)
Libraries and Information Manager Ms Laurayne Featherstone (01642 526463; e-mail: laurayne.featherstone@stockton.gov.uk)
Improvement Co-ordinator Mrs Sue Sneyd (01642 526472; e-mail: sue.sneyd@stockton.gov.uk)
Reader Development Officer Mrs Claire Pratt BA MCLIP (01642 528044; e-mail: claire.pratt@stockton.gov.uk)
Access to Digital Services Co-ordinator Steve Wild (01642 526501; e-mail: steve.wild@stockton.gov.uk)
Stock Performance Officer Richard Lacey MCLIP (01642 526998; e-mail: richard.lacey@stockton.gov.uk)

Branch libraries

- Billingham Branch Library, Bedale Avenue, Billingham, Stockton-on-Tees TS23 1AJ
  ☎(01642) 527895
  e-mail: billingham.library@stockton.gov.uk
  Branch Librarian Mrs Glynis Thirlaway
- Egglescliffe Branch Library, Butterfield Drive, Orchard Estate, Egglescliffe, Stockton-on-Tees TS16 0EL
  ☎(01642) 527958
  e-mail: egglescliffe.library@stockton.gov.uk
  Branch Librarian Miss Margaret Chapman MA(Lib)
- Fairfield Branch Library, Fairfield Road, Stockton-on-Tees TS19 7AJ
  ☎(01642) 577962
  e-mail: fairfield.library@stockton.gov.uk
  Branch Librarian Richard Lacey MCLIP (e-mail: richard.lacey@stockton.gov.uk)
- Ingleby Barwick Library, Ingleby Barwick Community Campus, Blair Avenue, Ingleby Barwick, Stockton-on-Tees TS17 5BL
  ☎(01642) 750767
  e-mail: inglebybarwick.library@stockton.gov.uk
  Branch Librarian Mrs Cath Watkins
- Norton Branch Library, 87 High Street, Norton, Stockton-on-Tees TS20 1AE
  ☎(01642) 528019
  e-mail: norton.library@stockton.gov.uk
  Branch Librarian Mrs Cath Maddison BSc DipLib
- Roseberry Billingham Branch Library, The Causeway, Billingham, Stockton-on-Tees TS23 2LB
  ☎(01642) 528084
  e-mail: roseberry.library@stockton.gov.uk
  Branch Librarian Miss Beryl Sandles MCLIP
- Roseworth Branch Library, Redhill Road, Stockton-on-Tees TS19 9BX
  ☎(01642) 528098
  Branch Librarian Mrs Jackie Fraser
- Thornaby Central Branch Library, The Pavillion, New Town Centre, Thornaby, Stockton-on-Tees TS17 9EW
  ☎(01642) 528117
  e-mail: thornaby.central.library@stockton.gov.uk
  Branch Librarian Mrs Shelagh Freeman MCLIP
- Thornaby Westbury Street Branch Library, Westbury Street, Thornaby, Stockton-on-Tees TS17 6PG
  ☎(01642) 528150
  e-mail: thornaby.library@stockton.gov.uk
  Branch Librarian Ms Lucie Kirton
- Yarm Branch Library, 41 High Street, Yarm, Stockton-on-Tees TS15 9BH
  ☎(01642) 528152
  e-mail: yarm.library@stockton.gov.uk
  Branch Librarian Mrs Wanda Sandham BA MCLIP

STOKE-ON-TRENT

Authority: Stoke-on-Trent City Council
HQ Libraries, Information and Archives, City Central Library, Bethesda Street, Hanley, Stoke-on-Trent ST1 3RS
☎(01782) 238455 (enquiries); (01782) 238405 (administration)
Fax (01782) 238499
e-mail: stoke.libraries@stoke.gov.uk
url: www.stoke.gov.uk/council/libraries
Head of Libraries, Learning and Archives Ian Van Arkadie BA DipLib DipMgt MCLIP (e-mail: ian.vanarkadie@stoke.gov.uk)
Customer and Support Services Manager Mrs Janet Simpson BA MCLIP (e-mail: janet.simpson@stoke.gov.uk)
City Archivist Chris Latimer MA DAA (e-mail: chris.latimer@stoke.gov.uk)

SUFFOLK 01473 260622

Authority: Suffolk County Council
HQ Adult and Community Services, Endeavour House, Russell Road, Ipswich IP1 2BX
☎(01473) 264285 (enquiries and administration)
Fax (01473) 216847
url: www.suffolkcc.gov.uk/libraries_and_heritage
Service Director for Culture, Information, Inclusion and Learning Ms Guenever J Pachent BA DLIS MCLIP MILAM (01473 264385; e-mail: guenever.pachent@libher.suffolkcc.gov.uk)
Head of Service Development for Libraries, Archives and Information Roger McMaster BA MA MCLIP (e-mail: roger.mcmaster@libher.suffolkcc.gov.uk)
Head of Children and Young People's Service Ms Helen Boothroyd BA MCLIP (01473 264623; e-mail: helen.boothroyd@libher.suffolkcc.gov.uk)

Central/largest library

County Library, Northgate Street, Ipswich IP1 3DE
☎(01473) 583705/10 (enquiries and administration)
Fax (01473) 583700
Area Manager (South) Ms Amanda Hewitt (e-mail: amanda.hewitt@libher.suffolkcc.gov.uk)

Area libraries

- Central Library, Sergeant's Walk, Off St Andrew's Street North, Bury St Edmunds, Suffolk IP33 1TZ
  ☎(01284) 352542
  Fax (01284) 352566
  Area Manager (West) Stephen Taylor (e-mail: stephen.taylor@libher.suffolkcc.gov.uk)
- Central Library, Clapham Road South, Lowestoft, Suffolk NR32 1DR
  ☎(01502) 405342
  Fax (01502) 405350
  Area Manager (North) Ms Gill Jenkins (e-mail: gill.jenkins@libher.suffolkcc.gov.uk)

Selected branch libraries

- Beccles Library, Blyburgate, Beccles, Suffolk NR34 9TB
  ☎(01502) 714073/716471
  Fax (01502) 714073
  Library Manager Ms Mary Storey
- Felixstowe Library, Crescent Road, Felixstowe, Suffolk IP11 7BY
  ☎(01394) 625766
  Fax (01394) 625770
  Library Manager Mrs Lynne Gibbs
- Hadleigh Library, 29 High Street, Hadleigh, Ipswich IP7 5AG
  ☎(01473) 823778
  Fax (01473) 822557
  Library Manager Geoff Ross BA
- Haverhill Library, Camps Road, Haverhill, Suffolk CB9 8HB
  ☎(01440) 702638
  Library Manager Ms Madeline Tuck
- Mildenhall Library, Chestnut Close, Mildenhall, Bury St Edmunds, Suffolk IP28 7HL
  ☎(01638) 713558
  Fax (01638) 510108
  Library Manager Ms Denise Gray
- Newmarket Library, 1a The Rookery, Newmarket, Suffolk CB8 8EQ
  ☎(01638) 661216
  Library Manager Mrs Grace Myers-Crump
- Stowmarket Library, Milton Road North, Stowmarket, Suffolk IP14 1EX
  ☎(01449) 613143
  Fax (01449) 672629
  Library Manager Ms Frances Law
- Sudbury Library, Market Hill, Sudbury, Suffolk CO10 2EN
  ☎(01787) 296000
  Fax (01787) 296004
  Acting Library Manager Gavin Talbot
- Woodbridge Library, New Street, Woodbridge, Suffolk IP12 1DT
  ☎(01394) 625095
  Fax (01394) 625091
  Library Manager Vacant

SUNDERLAND 0191 5148480

Authority: Sunderland City Council
HQ City Library and Arts Centre, Fawcett Street, Sunderland SR1 1RE
☎0191 514 1235 (enquiries and administration)
Fax 0191 514 8444
e-mail: libraries@sunderland.gov.uk
url: www.sunderland.gov.uk
Assistant Head of Culture and Tourism (Libraries, Heritage and Events) Ms Jane F Hall BA(Hons) MCLIP (e-mail: Jane.Hall@sunderland.gov.uk)
City Librarian and Events Co-ordinator Mrs Valerie Craggs MCLIP (e-mail: val.craggs@sunderland.gov.uk)

Principal Librarian (Development and Projects) Mrs Ann Scott MCLIP (e-mail: ann.scott@sunderland.gov.uk)
Principal Librarian (Resources and Performance) Ms Julie McCann BA(Hons) MCLIP (e-mail: julie.mccann@sunderland.gov.uk)
Principal Librarian (Reader Development) Mrs Joanne Parkinson BA(Hons) (e-mail: joanne.parkinson@sunderland.gov.uk)
Principal Librarian (Library Development) Ms Vivienne Foster BA (e-mail: vivienne.foster@sunderland.gov.uk)
Principal Librarian (Library Operations) Mrs Allison Clarke BA (e-mail: allison.clarke@sunderland.gov.uk)

Area library

- Washington Town Centre Library, Independence Square, Washington, Tyne and Wear NE38 7RZ
  ☎0191 219 3440

SURREY 01737 768983

Authority: Surrey County Council
HQ Libraries and Culture, Room 356, County Hall, Kingston upon Thames, Surrey KT1 2DN
☎020 8541 7771
Fax 020 8541 9447
url: www.surreycc.gov.uk/libraries
Head of Libraries and Culture Ms Yvonne Rees (e-mail: yvonne.rees@surreycc.gov.uk)

Information Service

Enquiries Direct, c/o Guildford Library, 77 North Street, Guildford, Surrey GU1 4AL
☎(01483) 543599
Fax (01483) 543597

Area management teams and largest libraries

- East Area Office, Omnibus, Lesbourne Road, Reigate, Surrey RH2 7JA
  ☎(01737) 737692
  Fax (01737) 737649
  Library Area Manager Mrs Hilary Ely MA MCLIP (020 8541 7060; e-mail: h.ely@surreycc.gov.uk)
  Library Service Development Manager (Information Services) Ms Janet Thomas BA(Hons) MCLIP (01483 543598; e-mail: janet.thomas@surreycc.gov.uk)
- Redhill Library, Warwick Quadrant, Redhill, Surrey RH1 1NN
  ☎(01737) 763332
  Senior Library Manager Mrs Marion Saberi
- Mid-Surrey Area Office, Opus 2, Bay Tree Avenue, Kingston Road, Leatherhead, Surrey KT22 7SY
  ☎(01372) 363920
  Fax (01372) 360169
  Library Area Manager Ms Sally Parker BA MCLIP (01372 363920; e-mail: sally.p@surreycc.gov.uk)

Library Service Development Manager (Lifelong Learning, Children & Social Inclusion) Mrs Sue Gent BSc(Hons) MCLIP (020 8786 7361; e-mail: sue.gent@surreycc.gov.uk)

- Epsom Library, 6 The Derby Square, Epsom, Surrey KT19 8AG
  ☎(01372) 721707
  Fax (01372) 744441
  Senior Library Manager Mrs Pauline Fella
- North West Area Office, Runnymede Centre, Chertsey Road, Addlestone, Surrey KT15 2EP
  ☎(01932) 794179
  Fax (01932) 794189
  Library Area Manager Mrs Rose Wilson BA(Hons) (01932 794178; e-mail: r.wilson@surreycc.gov.uk)
- Woking Library, Gloucester Walk, Woking, Surrey GU21 6EP
  ☎(01483) 770591/2
  Fax (01483) 756073
  Library Manager Ms Crishna Simmons
- South West Area Office, AO3 London Square, Cross Lanes, Guildford, Surrey GU1 1FA
  ☎(01483) 517402
  Fax (01483) 517401
  Library Area Manager Chris Phillips (01483 517337)
  Library Services Development Manager (Resources and Reader Development) Mrs Wendy Barrow MCLIP (01483 543584; e-mail: wendy.barrow@surreycc.gov.uk)
- Guildford Library, 77 North Street, Guildford, Surrey GU1 4AL
  ☎(01483) 568496
  Fax (01483) 579177
  Library Manager Mrs Susanne Bray

Selected branch libraries

- Ashford Library, Church Road, Ashford, Middlesex TW15 2XB
  ☎(01784) 253651
  Fax (01784) 257603
  Library Manager Chris Ganderton
- Banstead Library, The Horseshoe, Bolters Lane, Banstead, Surrey SM7 2AN
  ☎(01737) 531271
  Fax (01737) 373693
  Library Manager Ms Gill McCormick
- Camberley Library, Knoll Road, Camberley, Surrey GU15 3SY
  ☎(01276) 63184; 01276 27718 (administration)
  Fax (01276) 65701
  Library Manager Geoff Cox
- Dorking Library, Pippbrook House, Regiate Road, Dorking, Surrey RH4 1SL
  ☎(01306) 882948
  Fax (01306) 875006
  Library Manager Mrs L Wyatt
- Ewell Library, Bourne Hall, Spring Street, Ewell, Epsom, Surrey KT17 1UF
  ☎020 8394 0951

Fax 020 8873 1603
Library Manager Ms Brenda Kebbell

- Farnham Library, Vernon House, 28 West Street, Farnham, Surrey GU9 7DR
  ☎(01252) 716021
  Fax (01252) 717377
  Library Manager Steve Sansom (e-mail: steve.sansom@surreycc.gov.uk)
- Godalming Library, Bridge Street, Godalming, Surrey GU7 1HT
  ☎(01483) 422743
  Fax (01483) 425480
  Library Manager Mrs Maria Collings
- Horley Library, Victoria Road, Horley, Surrey RH6 7AG
  ☎(01293) 884141
  Fax (01293) 820084
  Library Manager Ms Terry Cox
- Oxted Library, 12 Gresham Road, Oxted, Surrey RH8 0BQ
  ☎(01883) 714225
  Fax (01883) 722742
  Library Manager Ms Lyn Ives
- Staines Library, Friends Walk, Staines, Middlesex TW18 4PG
  ☎(01784) 454430; (01784) 463279 (administration)
  Fax (01784) 461780
  Library Manager Miss Wendy Broadfoot
- Weybridge Library, Church Street, Weybridge, Surrey KT13 8DE
  ☎(01932) 843812
  Fax (01932) 850878
  Library Manager Mrs Judith White

SUTTON

Authority: London Borough of Sutton
HQ Sutton Central Library, St Nicholas Way, Sutton, Surrey SM1 1EA
☎020 8770 4700 (enquiries), 020 8770 4602 (administration)
Fax 020 8770 4777
e-mail: sutton.library@sutton.gov.uk
url: www.sutton.gov.uk
Executive Head of Leisure and Libraries Colin Beech (020 8770 4642; e-mail: colin.beech@sutton.gov.uk)
Head of Libraries and Heritage Service Mrs Cathy McDonough BSc MCLIP (020 8770 4755; e-mail: cathy.mcdonough@sutton.gov.uk), Mrs Angela Fletcher BA(Hons) PGCE (020 8770 4755; e-mail: angela.fletcher@sutton.gov.uk) (job-share)
Assistant Head of Libraries David Bundy BA MCLIP (020 8770 4761; e-mail: david.bundy@sutton.gov.uk)
Library Projects Manager Ms Tola Dabiri BA(Hons) (020 8770 4772; e-mail: tola.dabiri@sutton.gov.uk), Mrs Pauline Deakin BA MCLIP (020 8770 4772; e-mail: pauline.deakin@sutton.gov.uk) (job-share)
Facilities Manager (Libraries and Heritage) Jon Ward (020 8770 4708; e-mail: jon.ward@sutton.gov.uk)

Principal Librarian (Children's and AV) Mrs Jane Allen BA(Hons) MCLIP (020 8770 4622; e-mail: jane.allen@sutton.gov.uk)

Main libraries

- Carshalton Library, The Square, Carshalton, Surrey SM5 3BN
  ☎020 8647 1151
  Library Manager Mrs Helen Viola
- Cheam Library, Church Road, Cheam, Surrey SM3 8QH
  ☎020 8644 9377
  Library Manager Ms Christine McCarthy
- Wallington Library, Shotfield, Wallington, Surrey SM6 0HY
  ☎020 8770 4900
  Library Manager Steve Winser
- Worcester Park Library, Windsor Road, Worcester Park, Surrey KT4 8ES
  ☎020 8337 1609
  Library Manager Ms Tracey Parker

SWINDON

~~0161 342 2039~~ 01793 463511

Authority: Swindon Borough Council
HQ Environment and Leisure, Premier House, Station Road, Swindon SN1 1TZ
☎(01793) 466035
Fax (01793) 466484
url: www.swindon.gov.uk
Library Services Manager Ms Allyson Jordan MCLIP (e-mail: ajordan@swindon.gov.uk)

Central/largest library

Swindon Central Library, Paramount, Princes Street, Swindon SN1 2SD
☎(01793) 463238
Fax (01793) 529572
e-mail: central.library@swindon.gov.uk

Group libraries

- Acquisitions Group. Library Support Unit, Liden Library, Barrington Close, Liden, Swindon SN3 6HF
  ☎(01793) 463510
  Fax (01793) 463508
  Acquisitions and Lending Manager Adrian Peace (e-mail: apeace@swindon.gov.uk)
- Coate Group. Central Library, Regent Circus, Swindon SN1 1QG
  ☎(01793) 463795
  Fax (01793) 529572
  Group Library Manager Mark Jones MCLIP (e-mail: markjones@swindon.gov.uk)
- Lydiard Group. North Swindon Library, Orbital Shopping Park, Thamesdown Drive, Swindon SN25 4AN
  ☎(01793) 707122
  Group Library Manager Shaun Smith MCLIP (01793 707122; e-mail: ssmith@swindon.gov.uk)

TAMESIDE 0161 342 2039.

Authority: Tameside Metropolitan Borough Council
HQ Sustainable Communities Directorate, Council Offices, Wellington Road, Ashton-under-Lyne, Tameside OL6 6DL
☎0161 342 3673
url: www.tameside.gov.uk/libraries
Service Unit Manager Mrs Mandy Kinder (0161 342 2061; e-mail: mandy.kinder@tameside.gov.uk)
Service Delivery and Inclusion Manager Ms Judith Hall BLib MCLIP (e-mail: judith.hall@tameside.gov.uk)
Operations Manager Ms Denise Lockyer (0161 336 8234; e-mail: denise.lockyer@tameside.gov.uk)
Service Development Manager Philip Jones BA MCLIP (0161 342 2035; e-mail: philip.jones@tameside.gov.uk)

Central/largest library

Tameside Central Library, Old Street, Ashton-under-Lyne, Tameside OL6 7SG
☎0161 342 2029 (lending/enquiries), 0161 342 2037 (bibliographical enquiries), 0161 342 2031 (information)
Fax 0161 330 4762
e-mail: information.direct@tameside.gov.uk; central.library@tameside.gov.uk
Information Services Librarian Ms Karen Heathcote BA DipLIS MCLIP
Young People's Services Co-ordinator Mrs Ruth Lomas (0161 342 2664; e-mail: ruth.lomas@tameside.gov.uk)

Other large library

- Hyde Library, Union Street, Hyde, Cheshire SK14 1ND
  ☎0161 342 4450
  Fax 0161 368 0909
  e-mail: hyde.library@tameside.gov.uk

TELFORD AND WREKIN

Authority: Borough of Telford and Wrekin
HQ Lifelong Learning and Libraries, Telford Library, St Quentin Gate, Telford, Shropshire TF3 4JG
☎(01952) 382915 (general enquiries), (01952) 382918 (information desk)
Fax (01952) 382937
e-mail: telford.library@telford.gov.uk
url: www.telford.gov.uk
Borough Librarian Ms Sharon Smith BA MCLIP
Lifelong Learning and Libraries Manager Ian Yarroll
Acquisitions Manager Mrs Pat Narey
Senior Librarian, Information Services Mrs Helen Nahal BLib MCLIP

THURROCK

Authority: Thurrock Council
HQ Communities, Libraries and Cultural Services Department, Thameside Complex, Orsett Road, Grays, Essex RM17 5DX
☎(01375) 413973 (enquiries), (01375) 413963 (administration)
Fax (01375) 385504
e-mail: grays.library@thurrock.gov.uk
url: www.thurrock.gov.uk
Head of Communities, Libraries and Cultural Services Simon Black (01375 413962)
Chief Librarian Mrs Ann Halliday BA(Hons) DipLIS MCLIP (01375 413972)
Children's Services Manager Miss Rosalyn Jones BA(Hons) DipLib (e-mail: rjones@thurrock.gov.uk)

Central/largest library

Grays Library, Thameside Complex, Orsett Road, Grays, Essex RM17 5DX
☎(01375) 413973 (enquiries), (01375) 413963 (administration)
e-mail: grays.library@thurrock.gov.uk

TORBAY

Authority: Torbay Council
HQ Torquay Library, Lymington Road, Torquay, Devon TQ1 3DT
☎(01803) 208300 (enquiries), (01803) 208310 (administration)
Fax (01803) 208311
url: www.torbay.gov.uk/libraries
Head of Library Services Peter Bottrill BA MCLIP (01803 208310; e-mail: peter.bottrill@torbay.gov.uk)
Professional Services Librarian Miss Katie Lusty BA MCLIP (01803 208286; e-mail: katie.lusty@torbay.gov.uk)
Resources and Technical Services Librarian Miss Elizabeth Kent BSc MCLIP (01803 208287; e-mail: liz.kent@torbay.gov.uk)
Operational Services Librarian Nick Niles BA DipLib (01803 208288; e-mail: nick.niles@torbay.gov.uk)

Branch libraries

- Brixham Library, Market Street, Brixham, Devon TQ5 8EU
  ☎(01803) 853870
  Branch Librarian Mrs Angie Weatherhead
- Churston Library, Broadsands Road, Paignton, Devon TQ4 6LL
  ☎(01803) 843757
  Branch Librarian Mrs Susie Murr MCLIP
- Paignton Library, Courtland Road, Paignton, Devon TQ3 2AB
  ☎(01803) 208321
  Branch Librarian Mrs Rosie Corby BA MCLIP

TOWER HAMLETS

Authority: London Borough of Tower Hamlets
HQ Shadwell Centre, 455 The Highway, London E1W 3HP
☎020 7364 5684
url: www.ideastore.co.uk
Interim Head of Idea Stores Ian McNicholl (020 7364 5694)
Strategy & Project Development Manager Ms Judith St John (020 7364 5630; e-mail: judith.st.john@towerhamlets.gov.uk)
Access and Inclusion Manager Graham Pollard (020 7364 5091; e-mail: graham.pollard@towerhamlets.gov.uk)
Library Development Adviser Ms Kate Pitman BA MCLIP (020 7364 5740; e-mail: kate.pitman@towerhamlets.gov.uk)
Information Manager John Jasinski MCLIP (020 7364 5026; e-mail: john.jasinski@towerhamlets.gov.uk)
Stock Development Manager Ms Sue Bridgwater BA MPhil MCLIP (020 7364 5794; e-mail: sue.bridgwater@towerhamlets.gov.uk)
Principal Idea Store Manager Sergio Dogliani (020 7364 2649; e-mail: sergio.dogliani@towerhamlets.gov.uk)

Largest idea store/library

Idea Store Whitechapel, 321 Whitechapel Road, London E1 1BU
☎020 7364 4332
e-mail: ideastore@towerhamlets.gov.uk
Idea Store Manager Zoinul Abidin (020 7364 1742; e-mail: zoinul.abidin@towerhamlets.gov.uk)

Full-time idea stores/libraries

- Bethnal Green Library, Cambridge Heath Road, London E2 0HL
  ☎020 8980 3902
  e-mail: ideastore@towerhamlets.gov.uk
  Idea Store Manager Mrs Lesley Harris MCLIP (e-mail: lesley.harris@towerhamlets.gov.uk), Ms Sarah Paxton (e-mail: sarah.paxton@towerhamlets.gov.uk) (job-share)
- Cubitt Town Library, Strattondale Street, London E14 3HG
  ☎020 7987 3152
  e-mail: ideastore@towerhamlets.gov.uk
  Idea Store Manager Stephen Clarke BA MCLIP (e-mail: steve.j.clarke@towerhamlets.gov.uk)
- Idea Store Bow, 1 Gladstone Place, Roman Road, London E3 5ES
  ☎020 7364 4332
  e-mail: ideastore@towerhamlets.gov.uk
  Idea Store Manager Ms Barbara Stretch (020 7364 5775; e-mail: barbara.stretch@towerhamlets.gov.uk)
- Idea Store Canary Wharf, Churchill Place, Canary Wharf, London E14 5RB
  ☎020 7364 4332
  e-mail: ideastore@towerhamlets.gov.uk

Idea Store Manager Stephen Clarke BA MCLIP (020 7364 1742; e-mail: steve.j.clarke@towerhamlets.gov.uk)

- Idea Store Chrisp Street, 1 Vesey Path, East India Dock Road, London E14 6BT
  ☎020 8364 4332
  e-mail: ideastore@towerhamlets.gov.uk
  Idea Store Manager Shaw Rahman (020 7364 1502; e-mail: shaw.rahman@towerhamlets.gov.uk)
- Watney Market Library, 30-32 Watney Market, London E1 2PR
  ☎020 7790 4039
  e-mail: ideastore@towerhamlets.gov.uk
  Idea Store Manager Ms Sheila Brown BA (e-mail: sheila.brown@towerhamlets.gov.uk)

Local Studies and Archives

- Bancroft Library, 277 Bancroft Road, London E1 4DQ
  e-mail: localhistorylibrary@towerhamlets.gov.uk
  Local History Librarian Christopher Lloyd BLib MCLIP (020 7364 1290)
  Borough Archivist Malcolm Barr-Hamilton BA DAS (020 7364 1289)

: (by appointment only)

Part-time libraries

- Dorset Library, Ravenscroft Street, London E2 7QX
  ☎020 7739 9489
- Wapping Library, St Peter's Centre, Reardon Street, London E1W 2QH
  ☎020 7488 3535

TRAFFORD

Authority: Trafford Metropolitan Borough Council
HQ Culture and Sport, Stretford Library, Kingsway, Stretford, Manchester M32 8AP
☎0161 912 5175 (enquiries and administration)
Fax 0161 865 3835
e-mail: libraries@trafford.gov.uk
url: www.trafford.gov.uk/libraries
Principal Librarian (Culture and Sport) Mrs Gillian Fitzpatrick BA

Regional/district libraries

- Altrincham Library, 20 Stamford New Road, Altrincham, Cheshire WA14 1EJ
  ☎0161 912 5920
  Fax 0161 941 6452
- Bibliographical Services, Davyhulme Library Site, Hayeswater Road, Davyhulme, Manchester M41 7BL
  ☎0161 912 2882
  Fax 0161 912 2895
- Sale Library, Sale Waterside, Sale, Cheshire M33 7ZF
  ☎0161 912 3008
  Fax 0161 912 3019
- Stretford Library, Kingsway, Stretford, Manchester M32 8AP

☎0161 912 5150
Fax 0161 865 3835

- Urmston Library, Crofts Bank Road, Urmston, Manchester M41 0TZ
  ☎0161 912 2727
  Fax 0161 912 2947

UPPER NORWOOD JOINT LIBRARY

Authority: Upper Norwood Joint Library
HQ Upper Norwood Joint Library, Westow Hill, Upper Norwood, London SE19 1TJ
☎020 8670 2551
Fax 020 8670 5468
e-mail: unjl@unisonfree.net
Chief Librarian Bradley Millington MCLIP (e-mail: bmillington@uppernorwood.akhter.com)
Assistant Librarian, Reading and Development (including Children's Services) Ms Fiona Byers (e-mail: fbyers@uppernorwood.akhter.com)

WAKEFIELD

Music & Drama Renewals 01924 302229

Authority: Wakefield Metropolitan District Council
HQ Library Headquarters, Balne Lane, Wakefield, West Yorks WF2 0DQ
☎(01924) 302210 (enquiries and administration)
Fax (01924) 302245
e-mail: lib.admin@wakefield.gov.uk
url: www.wakefield.gov.uk/libraries
Head of Cultural Services Colin J MacDonald BA MBA DipLib MCLIP
Principal Cultural Officer: Children and Social Cohesion Ms Catherine Threapleton MCLIP DMS
Principal Cultural Officer: Information and Lifelong Learning Ms Anne Farrington BA(Hons) MCLIP
Principal Cultural Officer: Resources and Performance Neil Scarlett DMA
Stock and Reader Development Manager Ms Rachael Baxter BA(Hons)
Senior Cultural Officer: Information Mrs Jayne Britton BA(Hons) DipLib MCLIP, Ms Pam Yates BA MCLIP
Senior Cultural Officer: Children Ms Mary Young (e-mail: maryyoung@wakefield.gov.uk)

WALSALL

Authority: Walsall Council
HQ Leisure, Culture and Lifelong Learning, Tameway Tower, 12 Floor, 48 Bridge Street, Walsall, West Midlands WS1 1JZ
☎(01922) 650000
Fax (01922) 634093
e-mail: thelibrarian@walsall.gov.uk
url: www.walsall.gov.uk/libraries

Head of Libraries and Heritage Mrs Sue Grainger MCLIP (e-mail: graingers@walsall.gov.uk)

Central/largest library

Central Library, Lichfield Street, Walsall, West Midlands WS1 1TR
☎(01922) 653121 (lending), (01922) 653110 (reference); (01922) 653109 (computer booking)
Fax (01922) 722687 (lending), (01922) 654013 (reference)
e-mail: reference@walsall.gov.uk
Central Library Manager Ms Barbara Wallace
Information Services Manager Ms Rita Kennedy
Children's Services Manager Paul Thompson BA MCLIP (01922 724995; e-mail: thompsonp@walsall.gov.uk)

Area libraries

- Aldridge Library, Rookery Lane, Aldridge, Walsall, West Midlands WS9 8NN
  ☎(01922) 743601
  e-mail: aldridgelibrary@walsall.gov.uk
- Beechdale Library, Beechdale Centre, Stephenson Square, Walsall, West Midlands WS2 7DX
  ☎(01922) 721431
  e-mail: beechdalelibrary@walsall.gov.uk
- Blakenall Library, Blakenall Village Centre, Thames Road, Blakenall, Walsall, West Midlands WS3 1LZ
  ☎(01922) 714967
  e-mail: blakenalllibrary@walsall.gov.uk
- Bloxwich Library, Elmore Row, Bloxwich, Walsall, West Midlands WS3 2HR
  ☎(01922) 710059
  e-mail: bloxwichlibrary@walsall.gov.uk
- Brownhills Library, Park View Centre, Chester Road North, Walsall, West Midlands WS8 7JB
  ☎(01922) 650730
  e-mail: brownhillslibrary@walsall.gov.uk
- Darlaston Library, 1 King Street, Darlaston, Walsall, West Midlands WS10 8DD
  ☎0121 526 4530
  Fax 0121 526 2298
  e-mail: darlastonlibrary@walsall.gov.uk
- Forest Gate Library, New Invention, Willenhall, Walsall, West Midlands WV12 5LF
  ☎(01922) 710208
  e-mail: forestgatelibrary@walsall.gov.uk
- Home Library Service and Public Mobile Library, Mobile Library Depot, Willenhall Lane, Bloxwich, Walsall, West Midlands WS3 2XN
  ☎(01922) 710625
  e-mail: mobilelibrary@walsall.gov.uk
- Local History Centre, Essex Street, Walsall, West Midlands WS2 7AS
  ☎(01922) 721305
  Fax (01922) 634954

e-mail: localhistorycentre@walsall.gov.uk

- Pelsall Library, High Street, Pelsall, Walsall, West Midlands WS3 4LX
  ☎(01922) 682212
  e-mail: pelsalllibrary@walsall.gov.uk
- Pheasey Library, Collingwood Centre, Collingwood Drive, Great Barr, Pheasey, Birmingham B43 7NE
  ☎(01922) 654865
  e-mail: pheaseylibrary@walsall.gov.uk
- Pleck Library, Darlaston Road, Pleck, Walsall, West Midlands WS2 9RE
  ☎(01922) 721307
  e-mail: plecklibrary@walsall.gov.uk
- Rushall Library, Pelsall Lane, Walsall, West Midlands WS4 1NL
  ☎(01922) 721310
  e-mail: rushalllibrary@walsall.gov.uk
- South Walsall Library, West Bromwich Road, Walsall, West Midlands WS5 4NW
  ☎(01922) 721347
  e-mail: southwalsalllibrary@walsall.gov.uk
- Streetly Library, Blackwood Road, Streetly, Birmingham B74 3PL
  ☎0121 353 4230
  e-mail: streetlylibrary@walsall.gov.uk
- Walsall Wood Library, Lichfield Road, Walsall Wood, Walsall, West Midlands WS9 9NT
  ☎(01543) 452517 (tel/fax)
  e-mail: walsallwoodlibrary@walsall.gov.uk
- Willenhall Library, Walsall Street, Willenhall, Walsall, West Midlands WV13 2EX
  ☎(01902) 366513
  e-mail: willenhalllibrary@walsall.gov.uk

WALTHAM FOREST

Authority: London Borough of Waltham Forest
HQ Administrative Office, Silver Birch House, Uplands Business Park, Blackhorse Lane, Walthamstow, London E17 5SD
☎020 8496 3644 (enquiries and administration)
Fax 020 8496 3508
url: www.walthamforest.gov.uk
Head of Libraries, Museum and Gallery Ms Lorna Lee BA(Hons) MA MSc (e-mail: lorna.lee@walthamforest.gov.uk)
Support & Development Manager Manny Manoharan BSc(Hons) PGDip (e-mail: manny.manoharan@walthamforest.gov.uk)

Group libraries

Group Manager Paul Drumm BA(Hons) MA MSc (e-mail: paul.drumm@walthamforest.gov.uk)

- Higham Hill Library, North Countess Road, Walthamstow, London E17 5HF
  ☎020 8496 1173
  Fax 020 8496 1172
- Lea Bridge Library, Lea Bridge Road, Leyton, London E10 7HU

☎020 8496 1152
Fax 020 8496 1151

- South Chingford Library, Hall Lane, Chingford, London E4 8EU
☎020 8496 1079
Fax 020 8496 1080
- Walthamstow Library, High Street, Walthamstow, London E17 7JN
☎020 8496 1100
- Wood Street Library, Forest Road, Walthamstow, London E17 4AA
☎020 8496 1156
Fax 020 8496 1155

Group Manager Daniel Waller BA(Hons) (e-mail: daniel.waller@walthamforest.gov.uk)

- Hale End Library, Castle Avenue, Chingford, London E4 9QD
☎020 8496 1050
Fax 020 8496 1055
- Harrow Green Library, Cathall Road, Leytonstone, London E11 4LF
☎020 8496 1063
Fax 020 8496 1064
- Leyton Library, High Road, Leyton, London E10 5QH
☎020 8496 1090
Fax 020 8496 1094
- Leytonstone Library, Church Lane, Leytonstone, London E11 1HG
☎020 8496 1190
Fax 020 8496 1191
- North Chingford Library, The Green, Chingford, London E4 7EN
☎020 8496 1070
Fax 020 8496 1069

WANDSWORTH

Authority: London Borough of Wandsworth
HQ Leisure and Amenity Services Department, Wandsworth High Street, London SW18 2PU
☎020 8871 6369 (enquiries and administration)
Fax 020 8871 7630
e-mail: libraries@wandsworth.gov.uk
url: www.wandsworth.gov.uk/libraries
Head of Libraries, Museum and Arts Ms Jane Allen BA(Hons) DMS DipLib MCLIP
Assistant Head of Libraries Ms Meryl Jones MCLIP

Largest libraries

- Balham Library, Ramsden Road, London SW12 8QY
☎020 8871 7195
Fax 020 8675 4015
- Battersea Library, Lavender Hill, London SW11 1JB
☎020 8871 7466
Fax 020 7978 4376

- Putney Library, Disraeli Road, London SW15 2DR
  ☎020 8871 7090
  Fax 020 8789 6175
- Tooting Library, Mitcham Road, London SW17 9PD
  ☎020 8871 7175
  Fax 020 8672 3099

WARRINGTON

01925 416797

Authority: Warrington Borough Council
HQ Central Library, Museum and Art Gallery, Museum Street, Cultural Quarter, Warrington, Cheshire WA1 1JB
☎(01925) 442889 (enquiries), (01925) 442733 (Divisional Support Team)
Fax (01925) 411395
e-mail: library@warrington.gov.uk
url: www.warrington.gov.uk
Head of Libraries, Heritage and Learning Martin Gaw BA DipLib MCLIP (01925 442733)
Principal Libraries Manager Ms Fiona Barry BA MCLIP (01925 442892)

Branch libraries

- Birchwood Library, Brock Road, Warrington, Cheshire WA3 7PT
  ☎(01925) 827491 (tel/fax)
- Burtonwood Library, Chapel Lane, Burtonwood, Warrington, Cheshire WA5 4PS
  ☎(01925) 226563 (tel/fax)
- Culcheth Library, Warrington Road, Culcheth, Warrington, Cheshire WA3 5SL
  ☎(01925) 763293 (tel/fax)
- Grappenhall Library, Victoria Avenue, Grappenhall, Warrington, Cheshire WA4 2PE
  ☎(01925) 262861 (tel/fax)
- Great Sankey Library, Marina Avenue, Great Sankey, Warrington, Cheshire WA5 1JH
  ☎(01925) 231451 (tel/fax)
- Lymm Library, Davies Way, Off Brookfield Road, Lymm, Warrington, Cheshire WA13 0QW
  ☎(01925) 754367 (tel/fax)
- Orford Library, Poplars Avenue, Orford, Warrington, Cheshire WA2 9LW
  ☎(01925) 812821 (tel/fax)
- Padgate Library, Insall Road, Padgate, Warrington, Cheshire WA2 0HD
  ☎(01925) 818096 (tel/fax)
- Penketh Library, Honiton Way, Penketh, Warrington, Cheshire WA5 2EY
  ☎(01925) 723730
  Fax (01925) 791264
- Stockton Heath Library, Alexandra Park, Stockton Heath, Warrington, Cheshire WA4 2AN
  ☎(01925) 261148
  Fax (01925) 267787
- Westbrook Library, Westbrook Centre, Westbrook Crescent, Warrington, Cheshire WA5 5UG
  ☎(01925) 416561

Fax (01925) 230462

- Woolston Library, Holes Lane, Woolston, Warrington, Cheshire WA1 3UJ
  ☎(01925) 816146 (tel/fax)

WARWICKSHIRE

Authority: Warwickshire County Council

HQ Libraries, Learning and Culture, Adult, Health and Community Services, Barrack Street, Warwick CV34 4TH

☎(01926) 418154 (enquiries and administration)

Fax (01926) 412471/412165

e-mail: librariesandheritage@warwickshire.gov.uk

url: www.warwickshire.gov.uk

Head of Libraries, Learning and Culture Ms Edwina Cordwell

Head of Library and Information Services - Strategy Ayub Khan BA(Hons) FCLIP (01926 412657; e-mail: ayubkhan@warwickshire.gov.uk)

Head of Library and Information Services - Operations Ms Linda Smith MCLIP (e-mail: lindasmith@warwickshire.gov.uk)

Principal Librarian, Children and Young People Ms Liz Wood (01926 736 360; e-mail: lizwood@warwickshire.gov.uk)

Divisional libraries

- Central Warwickshire Division. Leamington Library (Central Divisional Library), Royal Pump Rooms, The Parade, Leamington Spa, Warwicks CV32 4AA
  ☎(01926) 742721/742722
  Fax (01926) 742749
  e-mail: leamingtonlibrary@warwickshire.gov.uk
  Divisional Librarian Paul MacDermott BA DipLib MCLIP (e-mail: paulmacdermott@warwickshire.gov.uk)
- North Warwickshire Division. Atherstone Library (North Divisional Library), Long Street, Atherstone, Warwicks CV9 1AX
  ☎(01827) 712395/712034
  Fax (01827) 720285
  e-mail: atherstonelibrary@warwickshire.gov.uk
  Divisional Librarian Andrew Button BA MCLIP (e-mail: andrewbutton@warwickshire.gov.uk)
- Nuneaton and Bedworth Division. Nuneaton Library, Church Street, Nuneaton, Warwicks CV11 4DR
  ☎024 7638 4027/024 7634 7006
  Fax 024 7635 0125
  e-mail: nuneatonlibrary@warwickshire.gov.uk
  Divisional Librarian David Reed BA(Hons) MCLIP (e-mail: davidreed@warwickshire.gov.uk)
- South/East Division. Rugby Library (South Divisional Library), Little Elborow Street, Rugby, Warwicks CV21 3BZ
  ☎(01788) 533250
  Fax (01788) 533252
  e-mail: rugbylibrary@warwickshire.gov.uk

Divisional Librarian Ms Corinne Harvey (e-mail: corinneharvey@warwickshire.gov.uk)

- Stratford Library, Henley Street, Stratford-upon-Avon, Warwicks CV37 6PZ
  ☎(01789) 292209/296904
  Fax (01789) 268554
  e-mail: stratfordlibrary@warwickshire.gov.uk
  Divisional Librarian Ms Tanya Butchers BA(Hons) MA MCLIP (e-mail: tanyabutchers@warwickshire.gov.uk)

WEST BERKSHIRE

Authority: West Berkshire District Council
HQ Cultural Services, Council Offices, Market Street, Newbury, Berks RG14 5LD
☎(01635) 519904
Fax (01635) 519392
e-mail: library@westberks.gov.uk
url: www.westberks.gov.uk
Strategic Development Manager Mrs Christine Owen BA(Hons) MCLIP (01635 519904; e-mail: cowen@westberks.gov.uk)

Central/largest library

Newbury Central Library, The Wharf, Newbury, Berks RG14 5AU
☎(01635) 519900

WEST SUSSEX

01243 816749.

Authority: West Sussex County Council
HQ Library Service Administration Centre, Tower Street, Chichester, West Sussex PO19 1QJ
☎(01243) 382540
Fax (01243) 382554
url: www.westsussex.gov.uk
BT Gold 74: SKK125
County Librarian Mrs Susan Hawker BA(Hons) MCLIP (e-mail: susan.hawker@westsussex.gov.uk)
(For management enquiries contact headquarters; for services contact one of the principal libraries)

Principal libraries

- Crawley Library, Northgate Avenue, Crawley, West Sussex RH10 1XG
  ☎(01293) 895130
  Fax (01293) 895141
  Area Librarian: Crawley Mrs Rita Lucas MCLIP (e-mail: rlucas@westsussex.gov.uk)
- Worthing Library, Richmond Road, Worthing, West Sussex BN11 1HD
  ☎(01903) 704824
  Fax (01903) 821902
  Area Librarian: Worthing David Nye BA MCLIP (e-mail: david.nye@westsussex.gov.uk)

WESTMINSTER

Authority: Westminster City Council
HQ Westminster Libraries, 2nd Floor, Westminster City Hall, 64 Victoria Street, London SW1E 6QP
☎020 7641 2496 (administration); **All libraries**: 020 7641 1300 (library enquiries), 020 7641 1400 (renewals)
Fax 020 7641 2764
url: www.westminster.gov.uk/libraries
Minicom: 020 7641 4879 (**all libraries**)
Director of Library Services David Ruse MCLIP MILAM (020 7641 2496; e-mail: druse@westminster.gov.uk)
Head of Library Operations Ms Iona Cairns MCLIP (020 7641 8969; e-mail: icairns@westminster.gov.uk)
Development Manager ICT/Staff Vacant
Group Manager – Performance Tony Rice (020 7641 8970; e-mail: trice@westminster.gov.uk)
Group Manager – Learning Ms Mary Enright BA DLIS MSc (020 7641 1782; e-mail: menright@westminster.gov.uk)
Development Manager – Information Ms Susanna Barnes (e-mail: sbarnes2@westminster.gov.uk)
Development Manager – Stock Ms Pat Chamberlain (020 7641 4280; e-mail: pchamberlain@westminster.gov.uk)

Largest libraries

- Charing Cross Library, 6 Charing Cross Road, London WC2H 0HF
  ☎020 7641 1300 (Chinese Community Librarian)
  e-mail: charingcrosslibrary@westminster.gov.uk
  Site Manager Tommy Hanover
- Marylebone Library, 109 Marylebone Road, London NW1 5PS
  e-mail: marylebonelibrary@westminster.gov.uk; (Marylebone Information Service): referencelibrarynw1@westminster.gov.uk
  Site Manager Ms Ann Farrell
- Paddington Library, Porchester Road, London W2 5DU
  e-mail: paddingtonlibrary@westminster.gov.uk
  Site Manager Miss Elizabeth Williams BA MCLIP
- Victoria Library, 160 Buckingham Palace Road, London SW1W 9UD
  ☎020 7641 1300 (Westminster Music Library)
  e-mail: victorialibrary@westminster.gov.uk
  Site Manager Ms Helen Rogers
- Westminster Reference Library, 35 St Martin's Street, London WC2H 7HP
  e-mail: referencelibrarywc2@westminster.gov.uk
  Site Manager Ms Susanna Barnes

Community libraries

- Church Street Library, Church Street, London NW8 8EU
  e-mail: churchstreetlibrary@westminster.gov.uk
  Site Manager Ms Lina Van Velzen

- Maida Vale Library, Sutherland Avenue, London W9 2QT
  e-mail: maidavalelibrary@westminster.gov.uk
  Site Manager Vic Stewart
- Mayfair Library, 25 South Audley Street, London W1K 2PB
  e-mail: mayfairlibrary@westminster.gov.uk
  Site Managers Frederic Jardin, Ms Mary Houlihan
- Pimlico Library, Rampayne Street, London SW1V 2PU
  e-mail: pimlicolibrary@westminster.gov.uk
  Site Manager Hugh Thomas
- Queen's Park Library, 666 Harrow Road, London W10 4NE
  e-mail: queensparklibrary@westminster.gov.uk
  Site Manager Mark Tiller
- St James's Library, 62 Victoria Street, London SW1E 6QP
  e-mail: stjameslibrary@westminster.gov.uk
  Site Manager Ms Sarah Goward-Jones
- St John's Wood Library, 20 Circus Road, London NW8 6PD
  e-mail: stjohnswoodlibrary@westminster.gov.uk
  Site Manager Ms Anabel Lopez

Other services

- City of Westminster Archives Centre, 10 St Ann's Street, London SW1P 2DE
  ☎020 7641 5180
  e-mail: archives@westminster.gov.uk
  Archives and Local Studies Manager John Sargent (020 7641 5160; e-mail: jsargent@westminster.gov.uk)

WIGAN

Authority: Wigan Council
HQ Wigan Leisure and Culture Trust, Robin Park Headquarters, The Indoor Sports Complex, Loire Drive, Robin Park, Wigan WN5 0UL
☎(01942) 828508
Fax (01942) 828542
e-mail: wiglib@wlct.org
url: www.wlct.gov.uk
Libraries Management Team:
Libraries Operations Manager Ms Wendy Heaton MCLIP
Service Development Manager Stephen Ruffley BA(Hons) MCLIP DMS
Information and Children's Services Manager Ms Jean Lamb

Central/largest libraries

- Leigh Library, Turnpike Centre, Civic Square, Leigh, Lancs WN7 1EB
  ☎(01942) 404556 (lending), (01942) 404557 (information)
  Fax (01942) 404567
- Wigan Library, College Avenue, Wigan WN1 1NN
  ☎(01942) 827621 (lending), (01942) 827619 (information)
  Fax (01942) 827640

WILTSHIRE

01225 713721

Authority: Wiltshire County Council
HQ Libraries and Heritage, Bythesea Road, Trowbridge, Wilts BA14 8BS
☎(01225) 713700 (enquiries), (01225) 713727 (information)
Fax (01225) 713993
e-mail: libraryenquiries@wiltshire.gov.uk
url: www.wiltshire.gov.uk/libraries/
Assistant Director, Department of Community Services, Libraries and Heritage Mrs Pauline Palmer MSc MCLIP DMS MIMgt (e-mail: paulinepalmer@wiltshire.gov.uk)
Library Services Manager Geoff Langridge MA MLS MCLIP (e-mail: geofflangridge@wiltshire.gov.uk)
Head of Customer Services Ms Joan Davis BALib MCLIP (e-mail: joandavis@wiltshire.gov.uk)
Head of Learning Services Vacant
Heritage Services Manager Tom Craig MA BA (e-mail: tomcraig@wiltshire.gov.uk)
Stock Manager David Green BA MCLIP (e-mail: davidgreen@wiltshire.gov.uk)

District libraries

- North Wilts and Kennet Area. Chippenham Library, Timber Street, Chippenham, Wilts SN15 3EJ
  ☎(01249) 650536
  Fax (01249) 553793
  Area Manager Vacant
- South and West Area. Salisbury Library, Market Place, Salisbury, Wiltshire SP1 1BL
  ☎(01722) 324145
  Fax (01722) 413214
  Area Manager Chris S Harling BA(Hons) MCLIP (01722 330606; e-mail: chrisharling@wiltshire.gov.uk)

WINDSOR AND MAIDENHEAD

Authority: Royal Borough of Windsor and Maidenhead
HQ Library, Information, Heritage and Arts Services, Maidenhead Library, St Ives Road, Maidenhead, Berks SL6 1QU
☎(01628) 796969
Fax (01628) 796971
e-mail: maidenhead.library@rbwm.gov.uk
url: www.rbwm.gov.uk/web/onlinelibrary.htm
Head of Library, Information, Heritage and Arts Services Mark Taylor BA MCLIP (01628 796989; fax: 01628 796986; e-mail: mark.taylor@rbwm.gov.uk)
Information and Electronic Delivery Manager Ms Sara Hudson BA DipLib MCLIP (01628 796742)

Central/largest library

Maidenhead Library, St Ives Road, Maidenhead, Berks SL6 1QU
☎(01628) 796968 (1st floor), 796969 (issue desk), 796985 (administration)
Fax (01628) 796971

e-mail: maidenhead.library@rbwm.gov.uk
Business Performance Manager Mrs Angela Gallacher BA(Hons) AUDIS (01628 796999; e-mail: angela.gallacher@rbwm.gov.uk), Richard Palfrey BSc MA (e-mail: richard.palfrey@rbwm.gov.uk) (job-share)
Reading & Learning Manager Mrs Victoria Law BA (01628 796999) (responsible for children's library services)
Community & Development Manager Mrs Margaret Kirby (01628 685811)
Library Manager: Maidenhead Mrs Avril Heaney (01628 796982)
Library Manager: Windsor & Community Libraries Paul Noakes (01753 743940)
Administration Officer Mrs Deepali Soni (01628 796985)

Other libraries

- Ascot Durning Library, Ascot Racecourse, High Street, Ascot, Berks SL5 7JF
  ☎(01344) 630140
- Cookham Library, High Road, Cookham Rise, Maidenhead, Berks SL6 9JF
  ☎(01626) 526147
- Cox Green Library, Highfield Lane, Cox Green, Maidenhead, Berks SL6 3AX
  ☎(01628) 673942
- Datchet Library, Village Hall, Horton Road, Datchet, Berks SL3 9HR
  ☎(01753) 545310
- Dedworth Library, Dedworth County School, Smith's Lane, Windsor, Berks SL4 5PE
  ☎(01753) 868733
- Eton Library, 136 High Street, Eton, Berks SL4 6LT
  ☎(01753) 860506
- Eton Wick Library, Village Hall, Eton Wick, Berks SL4 6LT
  ☎(01753) 857933
- Old Windsor Library, Memorial Hall, Straight Road, Windsor, Berks SL4 2JL
  ☎(01753) 852098
- Sunninghill Library, Reading Room, School Road, Sunninghill, Berks SL5 7AD
  ☎(01344) 621493
- Windsor Library, Bachelors Acre, Windsor, Berks SL4 1ER
  ☎(01753) 743940

Container Library operating at three sites:
Holyport (01628 673931)
Sunningdale (01344 626720)
Wraysbury (01784 482431)

Mobile and Home Library Service operating through two vehicles (01628 796314)

WIRRAL

0151 6538932

Authority: Metropolitan Borough of Wirral
HQ Regeneration and Culture, Westminster House, Hamilton Street, Birkenhead, Wirral, Cheshire CH41 5FN
☎0151 666 4717
url: www.wirral-libraries.net

Head of Libraries and Halls Ms Sue Powell BA MCLIP (e-mail: suepowell@wirral.gov.uk)

Central/largest library

Birkenhead Central Library, Borough Road, Birkenhead, Wirral, Cheshire CH41 2XB
☎0151 652 6106 (enquiries), 0151 653 4700 (administration)
Fax 0151 653 7320
e-mail: co-ord@wirral.libraries.net
Principal Librarian, Operational Services John Baxter BA DipLib MCLIP (e-mail: johnbaxter@wirral-libraries.net)

Regional/district libraries

- Bebington Central Library, Civic Way, Bebington, Wirral, Cheshire CH63 7PN
  ☎0151 643 7219
  Fax 0151 643 7231
  e-mail: bebington@wirral-library.net
  Senior Library Manager Ms Clare Oxley (e-mail: clareoxley@wirral-libraries.net)
- Wallasey Central Library, Earlston Road, Wallasey, Wirral, Cheshire CH45 5DY
  ☎0151 639 2334
  Fax 0151 691 2040
  e-mail: wallasey@wirral-library.net
  Principal Librarian, Community Services Paul Irons BA MCLIP (e-mail: paulirons@wirral-libraries.net)
- West Kirby Library, The Concourse, West Kirby, Wirral, Cheshire CH48 4HX
  ☎0151 929 7808
  Fax 0151 625 2558
  e-mail: west.kirby@wirral-library.net
  Team Librarians Mrs Julie Mann BA MCLIPMrs Julie Barkway BA DipLib MCLIP

WOKINGHAM

Authority: Wokingham Borough Council
HQ Libraries and Information Service, Cultural Services and Development, Shute End, Wokingham, Berks RG40 1WN
☎0118 974 6261
e-mail: libraries@wokingham.gov.uk
url: www.wokingham.gov.uk/libraries
Corporate Head of Knowledge Development Chris Hamilton MCLIP (0118 974 6261; e-mail: chris.hamilton@wokingham.gov.uk)

Central/largest library

Wokingham Library, Denmark Street, Wokingham, Berks RG40 2BB
☎0118 978 1368
Fax 0118 989 1214

WOLVERHAMPTON

Authority: Wolverhampton City Council
HQ Adult and Communities Department, Cultural Services Division, Libraries and Information Services, Central Library, Snow Hill, Wolverhampton WV1 3AX
☎(01902) 552025 (enquiries and administration)
Fax (01902) 552024
e-mail: libraries@wolverhampton.gov.uk
url: www.wolverhampton.gov.uk/libraries
City Librarian Mrs Karen Lees BA MCLIP (01902 552010; e-mail: karen.lees@dial.pipex.com)
Assistant City Librarians Graeme Kent BA DipLib (01902 552011; e-mail: gkent@dial.pipex.com), Andrew Scragg MA LLB DipHE MCLIP (01902 552012; e-mail: a.scragg@dial.pipex.com), Robert Johnson BA(Hons) (01902 552186; e-mail: robert.johnson@wolverhampton.gov.uk), Mrs Marion Cockin MCLIP (01902 552013; e-mail: marion.cockin@dial.pipex.com)

Branch Libraries (Group One)

- Ashmore Park Library, Griffiths Drive, Wednesfield, Wolverhampton WV11 2JW
  ☎(01902) 556296
  e-mail: libraries@wolverhampton.gov.uk
  Branch Group Librarian Mrs Kath Fletcher MCLIP (01902 556293)
- Collingwood Community Library, 24 The Broadway, Bushbury, Wolverhampton WV10 8EB
  ☎(01902) 556302
  e-mail: libraries@wolverhampton.gov.uk
- Low Hill Library, Showell Circus, Low Hill, Wolverhampton WV10 9JJ
  ☎(01902) 556293
  e-mail: libraries@wolverhampton.gov.uk
- Mary Pointon Community Library, Ettingshall Road, Wood Cross, Wolverhampton WV14 9UG
  ☎(01902) 556263
  e-mail: libraries@wolverhampton.gov.uk
- Pendeford Library, Whitburn Close, Pendeford, Wolverhampton WV9 5NJ
  ☎(01902) 556250
  e-mail: libraries@wolverhampton.gov.uk
- Penn Library, Coalway Avenue, Penn, Wolverhampton WV3 7LT
  ☎(01902) 556281
  e-mail: libraries@wolverhampton.gov.uk
- Whitmore Reans Library, Bargate Drive, Whitmore Reans, Wolverhampton WV6 0QW
  ☎(01902) 556269
  e-mail: libraries@wolverhampton.gov.uk

Branch Libraries (Group Two)

- Bilston Library, Mount Pleasant, Bilston, Wolverhampton WV14 7LU
  ☎(01902) 556253
  e-mail: libraries@wolverhampton.gov.uk
  Branch Group Librarian Kevin Hudson BA (01902 556257)

- Daisy Bank Community Library, Ash Street, Bradley, Bilston, Wolverhampton WV14 8UP
  ☎(01902) 556305
  e-mail: libraries@wolverhampton.gov.uk
- East Park Library, Hurstbourne Crescent, Eastfield, Wolverhampton WV1 2EE
  ☎(01902) 556257
  e-mail: libraries@wolverhampton.gov.uk
- Finchfield Library, White Oak Drive, Finchfield, Wolverhampton WV3 9AF
  ☎(01902) 556260
  e-mail: libraries@wolverhampton.gov.uk
- Oxley Library, Probert Road, Oxley, Wolverhampton WV10 6UF
  ☎(01902) 556287
  e-mail: libraries@wolverhampton.gov.uk
- Tettenhall Library, Upper Street, Tettenhall, Wolverhampton WV6 8QF
  ☎(01902) 556308
  e-mail: libraries@wolverhampton.gov.uk

Branch libraries (Group Three)

- Bradmore Community Library, Bantock House, Bradmore Road, Wolverhampton WV3 9BH
  ☎(01902) 556299
  e-mail: libraries@wolverhampton.gov.uk
  Branch Group Librarian Mrs Denise Jones BA (01902 556284)
- Long Knowle Library, Wood End Road, Wednesfield, Wolverhampton WV11 1YG
  ☎(01902) 556290
  e-mail: libraries@wolverhampton.gov.uk
- Scotlands and Underhill Community Library, Masefield Road, Wolverhampton WV10 8SA
  ☎(01902) 552199
  e-mail: libraries@wolverhampton.gov.uk
- Spring Vale Library, Bevan Avenue, Wolverhampton WV4 6SG
  ☎(01902) 556284
  e-mail: libraries@wolverhampton.gov.uk
- Warstones Library, Pinfold Grove, Penn, Wolverhampton WV4 9PT
  ☎(01902) 556275
  e-mail: libraries@wolverhampton.gov.uk
- Wednesfield Library, Church Street, Wednesfield, Wolverhampton WV11 1SR
  ☎(01902) 556278
  e-mail: libraries@wolverhampton.gov.uk

WORCESTERSHIRE

Authority: Worcestershire County Council
HQ Libraries and Information Service, Cultural Services, County Hall, Spetchley Road, Worcester WR5 2NP
☎(01905) 766231
Fax (01905) 766244
e-mail: librarieshq@worcestershire.gov.uk
url: www.worcestershire.gov.uk/libraries

Library Services Manager Mrs Cathy Evans MCLIP FISCT (01905 766232; e-mail: cevans@worcestershire.gov.uk)
Strategic Library Manager (North + Young People, Lifelong Learning, Performance, Quality) Mrs Carmel Reed BA DMS MCLIP (01905 766233; e-mail: creed@worcestershire.gov.uk)
Strategic Library Manager (South + Stock, Social Inclusion, Special Services, Information, ICT) Nigel Preedy BSc MCLIP (01905 766239; e-mail: npreedy@worcestershire.gov.uk)

Libraries Development Team, Libraries Service, Sherwood Lane, Lower Wick, Worcester WR2 4NU
☎(01905) 428945
Fax (01905) 748619
Area Co-ordinator: North Mrs Jane McCallum MCLIP (e-mail: jmccallum@worcestershire.gov.uk)
Area Co-ordinator: South Mrs Ruth Foster BA MCLIP MCMI (e-mail: refoster@worcestershire.gov.uk)
Service Development Manager: Stock, Social Inclusion, Special Services David Pearson BA MCLIP (e-mail: dpearson@worcestershire.gov.uk)
Service Development Manager: Young People, Lifelong Learning, Performance/Quality Vacant
Service Development Manager: Information, ICT, E-gov Mrs Carol Woolley BA MCLIP MCMI (e-mail: cwoolley@worcestershire.gov.uk)
Service Development Manager: Marketing and Reader Development Dr Christine Tootill MCLIP MCMI (e-mail: ctootill@worcestershire.gov.uk)

Main libraries

- Bromsgrove Library, Stratford Road, Bromsgrove, Worcs B60 1AP
  ☎(01527) 575855 575856 (outside office hours)
  Fax (01905) 575855
  e-mail: bromsgrovelib@worcestershire.gov.uk
  Bromsgrove Librarian Vacant
- Countywide Information Service (Intranet and Website), Information and Business Systems Division, County Hall, Spetchley Road, Worcester WR5 2NP
  ☎(01905) 766927
  url: www.worcestershire.gov.uk
  Web Manager Paul Taylor (e-mail: ptaylor@worcestershire.gov.uk)
- Droitwich Library, Victoria Square, Droitwich, Worcs WR9 8DQ
  ☎(01905) 773292
  Fax (01905) 797401
  e-mail: droitwichlib@worcestershire.gov.uk
  Droitwich Librarian Vacant
- Evesham Library, Oat Street, Evesham, Worcs WR11 4JP
  ☎(01386) 442291/41348
  Fax (01386) 765855
  e-mail: eveshamlib@worcestershire.gov.uk
  Evesham Librarian Vacant

- Kidderminster Library, Market Street, Kidderminster, Worcs DY10 1PE
  ☎(01562) 824500
  Fax (01562) 512907
  e-mail: kidderminsterlib@worcestershire.gov.uk
  Kidderminster Librarian Kurt Sidaway BA(Hons) MCLIP
- Malvern Library, Graham Road, Malvern, Worcs WR14 2HU
  ☎(01902) 552199
  Fax (01684) 892999
  e-mail: malvernlib@worcestershire.gov.uk
  Malvern Librarian Ms Carol Brown
- Redditch Library, 15 Market Place, Redditch, Worcs B98 8AR
  ☎(01527) 63291
  Fax (01527) 68571
  e-mail: redditchlib@worcestershire.gov.uk
  Redditch Librarian Vacant
- Worcester Library, Foregate Street, Worcester WR1 1DT
  ☎(01905) 765314
  Fax (01905) 726664
  e-mail: worcesterlib@worcestershire.gov.uk
  Worcester Librarian Ms Nicki Hitchcock BA DipILS MCLIP

YORK

Authority: City of York Council
HQ Lifelong Learning and Culture, 18 Back Swinegate, York YO1 8ZD
☎(01904) 553440
Fax (01904) 553378
Head of Libraries and Heritage Ms Fiona Williams BA(Hons) DipLib MCLIP
Business Support Manager Ms Diana Storey (e-mail: diana.storey@york.gov.uk)
Strategic Manager, Children, Young People and Families Ms Alison Jones BA(Hons) DipInf

Central/largest library

York Library, Museum Street, York YO1 7DS
☎(01904) 552815 (Lending), 552824 (Reference)
Fax (01904) 552835
e-mail: lending@york.gov.uk
url: www.york.gov.uk/libraries

NORTHERN IRELAND

BELFAST EDUCATION AND LIBRARY BOARD

Authority: Belfast Education and Library Board
HQ Belfast Public Libraries, Central Library, Royal Avenue, Belfast BT1 1EA
☎028 9050 9150
Fax 028 9033 2819
e-mail: info.belfast@ni-libraries.net
url: www.ni-libraries.net
Chief Librarian Ms Katherine McCloskey (e-mail: katherine.mccloskey@ni-libraries.net)

NORTH EASTERN EDUCATION AND LIBRARY BOARD

Authority: North Eastern Education and Library Board
HQ Area Library HQ, Demesne Avenue, Ballymena, Co Antrim BT43 7BG
☎028 2566 4100
Fax 028 2563 2038
e-mail: info.neelb@ni-libraries.net
url: www.ni-libraries.net
Director of Libraries and Corporate Services Mrs Anne Connolly BA(Hons) MA MBA (e-mail: anne.connolly@ni-libraries.net)
Assistant Chief Librarian (Head of Library Services) Mrs Mandy Bryson BA MCLIP (028 2566 4104; e-mail: mandy.bryson@ni-libraries.net)
Assistant Chief Librarian (Head of Library Systems) Michael McFaul MBA(Hons) DipM MCLIP (028 2566 4103; e-mail: michael.mcfaul@ni-libraries.net)

SOUTH EASTERN EDUCATION AND LIBRARY BOARD

Authority: South Eastern Education and Library Board
HQ Library Headquarters, Windmill Hill, Ballynahinch, Co Down BT24 8DH
☎028 9756 6400
Fax 028 9756 5072
e-mail: info.seelb@ni-libraries.net
url: www.seelb.org.uk; www.ni-libraries.net
Chief Librarian Mrs Beth Porter BA(Hons) DipLibStud MCLIP (028 9756 6400)
Assistant Chief Librarian Ms Adrienne Adair BA(Hons) MPhil DipLibStud MCLIP (028 9756 6400)
Front Line Services Manager Mrs Norma Millar BA(Hons) DipLibStud MCLIP (028 9042 5708)

Area libraries

- Downpatrick Library, Market Street, Downpatrick, Co Down BT30 6LZ

☎028 4461 2895
Fax 028 4461 1444
e-mail: downpatricklibrary@ni-libraries.net
Group Library Manager Mrs Pamela Cooper BLS PGDipA&LS MCLIP

- Holywood Library, Sullivan Building, 86-88 High Street, Holywood, Co Down BT18 9AE
☎028 9042 4232
Fax 028 9042 4194
e-mail: holywoodlibrary@ni-libraries.net
Group Library Manager Vacant
- Lisburn City Library, Colin Centre, 30 Linenhall Street, Lisburn BT28 1FJ
☎028 9266 9345
e-mail: lisburncitylibrary@ni-libraries.net
Group Library Manager Mrs Margaret Bell BLS MCLIP
- Tullycarnet Library, Kinross Avenue, Kings Road, Belfast BT5 7GF
☎028 9048 5079
Fax 028 9048 2342
e-mail: tullycarnetlibrary@ni-libraries.net
Group Library Manager Mrs Rosemary Wright BLS MCLIP

SOUTHERN EDUCATION AND LIBRARY BOARD

Authority: Southern Education and Library Board
HQ Library Headquarters, 1 Markethill Road, Armagh, Co Armagh BT60 1NR
☎028 3752 5353
Fax 028 3752 6879
url: www.selb.org
Head of Libraries Mrs Kathleen Ryan BA MBA FCLIP
Assistant Chief Librarian Miss Janet Blair MCLIP (028 3752 0715)
Education Services Manager Gerry Burns BA (028 3752 0754)
Communities, Learning & Access Manager Ms Anne McCart BA MCLIP (028 3752 0760)
Operations Manager Ms Christina Sloan MBE BA DipLib St MCLIP (028 3752 0740)
Resources and Support Services Manager Sean Beattie (028 3752 0707)

Specialist Library

- Irish and Local Studies Service, 39c Abbey Street, Armagh, Co Armagh BT61 7EB
☎028 3752 7851
Fax 028 3752 7127
Irish and Local Studies Librarian Ms Mary McVeigh BA MSSc(Irish Studies) DipLib

WESTERN EDUCATION AND LIBRARY BOARD

Authority: Western Education and Library Board
HQ Library Headquarters, 1 Spillars Place, Omagh, Co Tyrone BT78 1HL
☎028 8224 4821
Fax 028 8224 6772
e-mail: info.welb@ni-libraries.net
url: www.welbni.org
Omagh District Librarian Mrs M Cummings MBE DLibStud

Assistant Chief Librarians Ms A Peoples BA MCLIP DMS, Ms T Ward BLS MCLIP MBA
Head of Libraries and Corporate Services Ms H Osborn MLib MCLIP
Executive Officer Ms Geraldine McNabb
Children's Services Librarian Ms Gerry McSourley BA DipLibStud

Central/largest library

Central Library, Foyle Street, Londonderry BT48 1AL
☎028 7127 2310
Fax 028 7126 9084
Librarian Mrs M Craig

District libraries

- Enniskillen Library, Halls Lane, Enniskillen, Co Fermanagh BT74 7DR
  ☎028 6632 2886
  Fax 028 6632 4685
  Librarian S Bleakley BA(Hons) DLS
- Limavady Library, 5 Connell Street, Limavady, Londonderry BT47 0EA
  ☎028 7776 2540
  Fax 028 7772 2006
  Librarian Mrs L Brown BA MCLIP
- Omagh Library, 1 Spillars Place, Omagh, Co Tyrone BT78 1HL
  ☎028 8224 4821
  Fax 028 8224 6772
  Librarian Mrs M Cummings MBE DLibStud
- Strabane Library, 1 Railway Road, Strabane, Co Tyrone BT82 8AW
  ☎028 7138 3686
  Fax 028 7138 2745
  Librarian Mrs M Coyle

ABERDEEN

Authority: Aberdeen City Council
HQ Aberdeen City Library and Information Services, Central Library, Rosemount Viaduct, Aberdeen AB25 1GW
☎(01224) 652500 (enquiries and administration)
Fax (01224) 641985
e-mail: CentralLibrary@aberdeencity.gov.uk
url: www.aberdeencity.gov.uk
Library and Information Services Manager Ms Fiona Clark BA MCLIP (e-mail: fclark@aberdeencity.gov.uk)
Public Services Librarian (Lending) John Grant BA MCLIP (01224 652549; e-mail: Jogrant@aberdeencity.gov.uk)
Public Services Librarian (Information) Ms Susan Bell BA MCLIP (01224 652552; e-mail: sbell@aberdeencity.gov.uk)

ABERDEENSHIRE

Authority: Aberdeenshire Council
HQ Library and Information Service, Meldrum Meg Way, Oldmeldrum, Aberdeenshire AB51 0GN
☎(01651) 872707 (enquiries and administration)
Fax (01651) 872142
e-mail: alis@aberdeenshire.gov.uk
url: www.aberdeenshire.gov.uk/alis
Libraries and Heritage Manager Gerald Moore BA MCLIP (01651 871202; e-mail: gerald.moore@aberdeeenshire.gov.uk)
Media Resources Manager Vacant
Central Support Services Manager Mrs Anne A M Harrison MCLIP (01651 871210; fax: 01651 872142; e-mail: anne.harrison@aberdeenshire.gov.uk)
Client Services Librarians Mrs Helen W Dewar MA MCLIP (01358 729208; fax: 01358 722864; e-mail: helen.dewar@aberdeenshire.gov.uk), Rufus A de Silva BA MEd MBA MCLIP (01330 823784; fax: 01330 824516; e-mail: rufus.de.silva@aberdeenshire.gov.uk)

ANGUS

Authority: Angus Council
HQ Cultural Services Department, County Buildings, Market Street, Forfar, Angus DD8 3WF
☎(01307) 461460
Fax (01307) 462590
e-mail: cultural.services@angus.gov.uk
url: www.angus.gov.uk
Senior Services Manager Cultural Services Norman K Atkinson DipEd AMA FMA
Libraries Manager John Doherty BSc MCLIP
Arts and Resources Manager Colin Dakers BA MCLIP

Central/largest library

Library Support Services, 50 West High Street, Forfar, Angus DD8 1BA
☎(01307) 466966
Fax (01307) 468451
e-mail: librarysupport.services@angus.gov.uk
Support Services Librarian Jim Fraser BA DipLib MCLIP

Area libraries

- Arbroath Library, Hill Terrace, Arbroath, Angus DD11 1AH
  ☎(01241) 872248
  Fax (01241) 434396
  e-mail: arbroath.library@angus.gov.uk
  Librarian Henry Logan BA DipLib MCLIP
- Brechin Library, 10 St Ninian's Square, Brechin, Angus DD9 7AA
  ☎(01356) 622687
  e-mail: brechin.library@angus.gov.uk
  Librarian Gavin Hunter MA MCLIP
- Carnoustie Library, 21 High Street, Carnoustie, Angus DD7 6AN
  ☎(01241) 859620
  e-mail: carnoustie.library@angus.gov.uk
  Librarian Alasdair Sutherland BA MCLIP
- Forfar Library, 50-56 West High Street, Forfar, Angus DD8 1BA
  ☎(01307) 466071
  Fax (01307) 468451
  e-mail: forfar.library@angus.gov.uk
  Librarian Ms Fiona J. G. Dakers BA DipIM MCLIP
- Kirriemuir Library, Town Hall, 28/30 Reform Street, Kirriemuir, Angus DD8 4BS
  ☎(01575) 572357
  Librarian Ms Christine Sharp BA MCLIP
- Monifieth Library, High Street, Monifieth, Angus DD5 4AE
  ☎(01382) 533819
  e-mail: monifieth.library@angus.gov.uk
  Librarian Ms Hazel Cook BA MCLIP
- Montrose Library, 214 High Street, Montrose, Angus DD10 8PH
  ☎(01674) 673256
  e-mail: montrose.library@angus.gov.uk
  Librarian Ms Victoria Fraser BA MCLIP

ARGYLL AND BUTE

Authority: Argyll and Bute Council
HQ Library and Information Service HQ, Highland Avenue, Sandbank, Dunoon, Argyll PA23 8PB
☎(01369) 703214
Fax (01369) 705797
url: www.argyll-bute.gov.uk
Culture and Libraries Manager Andy I Ewan MCLIP (e-mail: andy.ewan@argyll-bute.gov.uk)

Youth Services Librarian Mrs Dorothy A McLennan MA(Hons) MCLIP (e-mail: Dorothy.McLennan@argyll-bute.gov.uk)

Area libraries

- Campbeltown Library, Aqualibrium, Kinloch Road, Campbeltown, Argyll PA28 6EG
  ☎(01586) 555435
  Fax (01586) 555438
  Area Librarian Ms Sue Fortune MCLIP
- Dunoon Library, 248 Argyll Street, Dunoon, Argyll PA23 7LT
  ☎(01369) 708682
  Fax (01369) 701323
  Area Librarian Ms Pauline Flynn BA MCLIP
- Helensburgh Library, West King Street, Helensburgh, Dunbartonshire G84 8EB
  ☎(01436) 674626
  Fax (01436) 679567
  Area Librarian/IT Systems Development Manager Pat McCann BA MCLIP
- Oban Library, 77 Albany Street, Oban, Argyll PA34 4AW
  ☎(01631) 571444
  Fax (01631) 571372
  Area Librarian Kevin Baker BA DipLib MCLIP
- Rothesay Library, Moat Centre, Stuart Street, Rothesay, Bute PA20 0BX
  ☎(01700) 503266
  Fax (01700) 500511
  Branch Librarian Eddie Monaghan MCLIP

CLACKMANNANSHIRE

Authority: Clackmannanshire Council
HQ Clackmannanshire Libraries, Alloa Library, 26-28 Drysdale Street, Alloa, Clackmannanshire FK10 1JL
☎(01259) 722262
Fax (01259) 219469
e-mail: libraries@clacks.gov.uk
url: www.clacksweb.org.uk/dyna/library
Team Leader, Community Library Service John A Blake BSc DipLib MCLIP DipEdTech (ext 220)
Training and Stock Circulation Librarian Ms Helen Finlayson MA DipLib MCLIP
Information Librarian and Archivist Ian D Murray MA DipLib MCLIP DAA
Mobile Librarian Alex Pollock

Branches within community access points

- Alva Community Access Point, 153 West Stirling Street, Alva, Clackmannanshire FK12 2EL
  ☎(01259) 760652
  Fax (01259) 760354
  Senior Community Access Officer Ms N Foster (e-mail: nfoster@clacks.gov.uk)
- Clackmannan Community Access Point, Main Street, Clackmannan FK10 4JA
  ☎(01259) 721579

Fax (01259) 212493
Senior Community Access Officer Ms J Laird (e-mail: jlaird@clacks.gov.uk)

- Dollar Community Access Point, Dollar Civic Centre, Park Place, Dollar, Clackmannanshire FK14 7AA
☎(01259) 743253
Fax (01259) 743328
Senior Community Access Officer Mrs K Waddell (e-mail: kwaddell@clacks.gov.uk)
- Menstrie Community Access Point, The Dumyat Leisure Centre, Main Street East, Menstrie, Clackmannanshire FK11 7BJ
☎(01259) 769439
Fax (01259) 762941
Senior Community Access Officer Mrs K Waddell (e-mail: kwaddell@clacks.gov.uk)
- Sauchie Community Access Point, 42-48 Main Street, Sauchie, Clackmannanshire FL10 3JY
☎(01259) 721679
Fax (01259) 218750
Senior Community Access Officer Ms M Hunter (e-mail: mhunter@clacks.gov.uk)
- Tillicoultry Branch Library, 99 High Street, Tillicoultry, Clackmannanshire FK13 6DL
☎(01259) 751685 (tel/fax)
Branch Library Co-ordinator Ms L Paterson (e-mail: lpaterson@clacks.gov.uk)
- Tullibody Library, Leisure Centre, Abercromby Place, Tullibody, Clackmannanshire FK10 2RS
☎(01259) 218725
Branch Library Co-ordinator Ms I Dykes (e-mail: idykes@clacks.gov.uk)

COMHAIRLE NAN EILEAN SIAR

Authority: Comhairle nan Eilean Siar
HQ Public Library, 19 Cromwell Street, Stornoway, Isle of Lewis, Hebrides HS1 2DA
☎(01851) 708631
Fax (01851) 708677
url: www.cne-siar.gov.uk
Chief Librarian R M Eaves BA DipEd MCLIP (e-mail: bobeaves@cne-siar.gov.uk)
Youth Services Librarian Mrs Mary Ferguson MA MCLIP (01851 708650; e-mail: mary-ferguson@cne-siar.gov.uk)

Area libraries

- Community Library, Castlebay Community School, Castlebay, Isle of Barra, Hebrides HS9 5XD
☎(01871) 810124
Fax (01871) 810125
e-mail: castlebaylibrary@fnes.net
Senior Library Assistant Mrs L Mackinnon
- Community Library, Daliburgh School, Daliburgh, Isle of South Uist, Hebrides HS8 5SS
☎(01878) 700882
Library Assistant Mrs J Macinnes (e-mail: jmacinnes2e@fnes.net)
- Community Library, Sgoil Lionacleit, Liniclate, Isle of Benbecula, Hebrides HS7 5PJ
☎(01870) 603532

Fax (01870) 602817
e-mail: lionacleitlibrary@fnes.net
Community Librarian Mrs J F Bramwell BA DipLib MCLIP (e-mail: fbramwell1a@fnes.net)

- Community Library, Sgoil Shiaboist, Shawbost, Isle of Lewis, Hebrides HS2 9PQ
☎(01851) 710213
e-mail: shawlib@fnes.net
Library Assistant Mrs C A Campbell
- Community Library, Sir E Scott School, Tarbert, Isle of Harris, Hebrides HS3 3BG
☎(01859) 502926
Library Assistant Mrs F M Morrison MA MCLIP (e-mail: fmmorrison1b@fnes.net)

DUMFRIES AND GALLOWAY

Authority: Dumfries and Galloway Council
HQ Libraries, Information and Archives, Central Support Unit, Catherine Street, Dumfries DG1 1JB
☎(01387) 253820 (enquiries), 01387 252070 (administration)
Fax (01387) 260294
e-mail: libs&i@dumgal.gov.uk
url: www.dumgal.gov.uk
Cultural Services Manager: Libraries, Information and Archives J H Goldie BA DipLib MCLIP

District libraries

- Annan Library, Charles Street, Annan, Dumfries and Galloway DG12 5AG
☎(01461) 202809 (tel/fax)
- Archive Centre, 33 Burns Street, Dumfries DG1 2PS
☎(01387) 269254
Fax (01387) 264126
- Castle Douglas Library, Market Hill, King Street, Castle Douglas, Dumfries and Galloway DG7 1AE
☎(01556) 502643 (tel/fax)
- Dalbeattie Library, 23 High Street, Dalbeattie, Dumfries and Galloway DG5 4AD
☎(01556) 610898 (tel/fax)
- Dalry Library, Main Street, Dalry, Castle Douglas, Dumfries and Galloway DG7 3UP
☎(01644) 430234 (tel/fax)
- Eastriggs Library, Eastriggs Community School, Eastriggs, Annan, Dumfries and Galloway DG12 6PZ
☎(01461) 40844 (tel/fax)
- Ewart Library, Catherine Street, Dumfries DG1 1JB
☎(01387) 253820/252070/260000
Fax (01387) 260294
- Gatehouse Library, 63 High Street, Gatehouse of Fleet, Dumfries and Galloway DG7 2HS
☎(01557) 814646 (tel/fax)
- Georgetown Library, Gillbrae Road, Georgetown, Dumfries DG1 4EJ
☎(01387) 256059 (tel/fax)

- Gretna Library, The Richard Greenhow Centre, Central Avenue, Gretna, Dumfries and Galloway DG16 5AQ
  ☎(01461) 338000 (tel/fax)
- Kirkconnel Library, Greystone Avenue, Kelloholm, Dumfries and Galloway DG4 6RA
  ☎(01659) 67191 (tel/fax)
- Kirkcudbright Library, Sheriff Court House, High Street, Kirkcudbright, Dumfries and Galloway DG6 4JW
  ☎(01557) 331240 (tel/fax)
- Langholm Library, Charles Street, Old Langholm, Dumfries and Galloway DG13 0AA
  ☎(01387) 380040 (tel/fax)
- Lochmaben Library, Masonic Hall, High Street, Lochmaben, Lockerbie, Dumfries and Galloway DG11 1NQ
  ☎(01387) 811865 (tel/fax)
- Lochside Library, Lochside Road, Dumfries DG2 0LW
  ☎(01387) 268751 (tel/fax)
- Lochthorn Library, Lochthorn, Dumfries DG1 1UF
  ☎(01387) 265780
  Fax (01387) 266424
- Lockerbie Library, 31–33 High Street, Lockerbie, Dumfries and Galloway DG11 2JL
  ☎(01576) 203380 (tel/fax)
- Moffat Library, Town Hall, High Street, Moffat, Dumfries and Galloway DG10 9HF
  ☎(01683) 220952 (tel/fax)
- Newton Stewart Library, Chuch Street, Newton Stewart, Dumfries and Galloway DG8 6ER
  ☎(01671) 403450 (tel/fax)
- Port William Library, Church Street, Port William, Newton Stewart, Dumfries and Galloway DG8 9QJ
  ☎(01988) 700406 (tel/fax)
- Sanquhar Library, 106 High Street, Sanquhar, Dumfries and Galloway DG4 6DZ
  ☎(01659) 50626 (tel/fax)
- Stranraer Library, North Strand Street, Stranraer, Dumfries and Galloway DG9 7LD
  ☎(01776) 707400/707440
  Fax (01776) 703565
- Thornhill Library, Townhead Street, Thornhill, Dumfries and Galloway DG3 5NW
  ☎(01848) 330654 (tel/fax)
- Whithorn Library, St John's Street, Whithorn, Dumfries and Galloway DG8 8PF
  ☎(01988) 500406 (tel/fax)
- Wigtown Library, County Buildings, Wigtown, Dumfries and Galloway DG8 9JH
  ☎(01988) 403329 (tel/fax)

DUNDEE

Authority: Dundee City Council
HQ Leisure and Communities Department Head Office, Central Library Level 3, The Wellgate, Dundee DD1 1DB
☎(01382) 307462
Fax (01382) 307487
url: www.dundeecity.gov.uk/communities

Director of Leisure and Communities Department Stewart Murdoch MSc DPSE DipYCW (e-mail: stewart.murdoch@dundeecity.gov.uk)
Head of Libraries, Information and Cultural Services Mrs Moira Methven MCLIP (e-mail: moira.methven@dundeecity.gov.uk)

Central/largest library

Central Library, The Wellgate, Dundee DD1 1DB
☎(01382) 431500 (enquiries), (01382) 431501 (administration)
Fax (01382) 434642
url: www.dundeecity.gov.uk/library
Central Library Manager Mrs Judy Dobbie MA MCLIP (01382 431526; e-mail: judy.dobbie@dundeecity.gov.uk)
Section Leader (Reader Services) Ms Christine Ferguson MA MCLIP (01382 431549; e-mail: christine.ferguson@dundeecity.gov.uk)
Community Information Team Leader Mrs Frances Robertson MA MCLIP (01382 431533; e-mail: frances.robertson@dundeecity.gov.uk)
Reference Services Team Leader David Kett MCLIP (01382 431552; e-mail: david.kett@dundeecity.gov.uk)
Senior Library and Information Worker (Central Library) Ms Amina Shah MCLIP (01382 431523; e-mail: amina.shah@dundeecity.gov.uk)
Community Libraries and Learning Centres Manager Ms Frances Foster MCLIP (01382 436360; e-mail: frances.foster@dundeecity.gov.uk)
Community Outreach Team Ms Jayne Gair BA MCLIP (01382 438894; e-mail: jayne.gair@dundeecity.gov.uk)
Community Learning Team Ms Fiona Macpherson MA MCLIP (01382 438833; e-mail: fiona.macpherson@dundeecity.gov.uk)
Marketing and Promotion Team Ms Lynn Moy BA MCLIP (01382 438889; e-mail: lynn.moy@dundeecity.gov.uk)
Stock Management Team Ms Janis Milne BA MCLIP (01382 431535; e-mail: janis.milne@dundeecity.gov.uk)
Staff Development Worker Mrs Frances Scott MCLIP (01382 438891; e-mail: frances.scott@dundeecity.gov.uk)
Senior Library and Information Worker (Schools Service) Stuart Syme BA MCLIP (01382 431546; e-mail: stuart.syme@dundeecity.gov.uk)

Community libraries

- Ardler Community Library, Ardler Complex, Turnberry Avenue, Ardler, Dundee DD2 3TP
  ☎(01382) 432863
  Fax (01382) 436446
  e-mail: ardler.library@dundeecity.gov.uk
  Library and Information Worker Ms Susan Ferguson
- Arthurstone Community Library, Arthurstone Terrace, Dundee DD4 6RT
  ☎(01382) 438881
  Fax (01382) 438886
  e-mail: arthurstone.library@dundeecity.gov.uk
  Library and Information Worker Mrs Shona Wood

- Blackness Community Library, 225 Perth Road, Dundee DD2 1EJ
  ☎(01382) 435936
  Fax (01382) 435942
  e-mail: blackness.library@dundeecity.gov.uk
  Library and Information Worker Ms Karen Duffy
- Broughty Ferry Community Library, Queen Street, Broughty Ferry, Dundee DD5 2HN
  ☎(01382) 436919
  Fax (01382) 436913
  e-mail: broughty.library@dundeecity.gov.uk
  Library and Information Worker Mrs Sandra Westgate
- Charleston Community Library, 60 Craigowan Road, Dundee DD2 4NL
  ☎(01382) 436639
  Fax (01382) 436640
  e-mail: charleston.library@dundeecity.gov.uk
  Library and Information Worker Ian Cranmer MCLIP
- Coldside Neighbourhood Library, 150 Strathmartine Road, Dundee DD3 7SE
  ☎(01382) 432849
  Fax (01382) 432850
  e-mail: coldside.library@dundeecity.gov.uk
  Library and Information Worker Ms Barbara Cook
- Douglas Community Library, Balmoral Place, Douglas, Dundee DD4 8SH
  ☎(01382) 436915
  Fax (01382) 436922
  e-mail: douglas.library@dundeecity.gov.uk
  Library and Information Worker Mrs Lorraine Kell
- Fintry Community Library, Finmill Centre, Findcastle Street, Dundee DD4 9EW
  ☎(01382) 432560
  Fax (01382) 432559
  e-mail: fintry.library@dundeecity.gov.uk
  Library and Information Worker Ms Ailsa Caldwell
- Hub Community Library and Learning Centre, Pitkerro Road, Dundee DD4 8ES
  ☎(01382) 438648
  Fax (01382) 438627
  e-mail: hub.library@dundeecity.gov.uk
  Library and Information Worker Ms Liz Young
- Kirkton Community Library, Derwent Avenue, Dundee DD3 0BW
  ☎(01382) 432851
  Fax (01382) 432852
  e-mail: kirkton.library@dundeecity.gov.uk
  Library and Information Worker Mrs Ann Smith
- Lochee Community Library, High Street, Lochee, Dundee DD2 3AU
  ☎(01382) 431835
  Fax (01382) 431837
  e-mail: lochee.library@dundeecity.gov.uk
  Library and Information Worker Mrs Joan Rodger
- Menzieshill Community Library, Orleans Place, Menzieshill, Dundee DD2 4BH
  ☎(01382) 432945

Fax (01382) 432948
e-mail: menzieshill.library@dundeecity.gov.uk
Library and Information Worker Ms Lorraine Andrews

- Whitfield Community Library and Learning Centre, Whitfield Drive, Dundee DD4 0DX
☎(01382) 432561
Fax (01382) 432562
e-mail: whitfield.library@dundeecity.gov.uk
Library and Information Worker Mrs Ruth McDowall

EAST AYRSHIRE

Authority: East Ayrshire Council
HQ Library, Registration and Information Services, Dick Institute, 14 Elmbank Avenue, Kilmarnock, Ayrshire KA1 3BU
☎(01563) 554300 (general enquiries)
Fax (01563) 554311
e-mail: libraries@east-ayrshire.gov.uk
url: www.east-ayrshire.gov.uk/thelibrary
Library, Registration and Information Services Manager Gerard Cairns BA DipLib MCLIP DMS (e-mail: gerard.cairns@east-ayrshire.gov.uk)
Senior Librarian Mrs Elaine Gray MA DipLib MCLIP (e-mail: elaine.gray@east-ayrshire.gov.uk)
Senior Librarian John Laurenson BSc DipLib EMBA MCLIP (e-mail: john.laurenson@east-ayrshire.gov.uk)
Support Services Librarian Mrs Julia A Harvey MA(Hons) DipLib MCLIP (e-mail: julia.harvey@east-ayrshire.gov.uk)
Information Officer Ms Dawn Vallance BA(Hons) DipLib MCLIP (e-mail: dawn.vallance@east-ayrshire.gov.uk)
Community Librarian (Staff Development) Mrs Lynn Mee BA(Hons) MCLIP (e-mail: lynn.mee@east-ayrshire.gov.uk)
Marketing and Development Officer Ms Dianne McGregor BA(Hons) (e-mail: dianne.mcgregor@east-ayrshire.gov.uk)
Community Librarian (Heritage Services) Mrs Anne Geddes MCLIP (e-mail: baird.institute@east-ayrshire.gov.uk)
Community Librarian (Operations) Hugh MacLean MA(Hons) DipLib MCLIP (e-mail: hugh.maclean@east-ayrshire.gov.uk)
Education Liaison Officer Miss Pat Standen BA MCLIP (e-mail: pat.standen@east-ayrshire.gov.uk)

EAST DUNBARTONSHIRE

Authority: East Dunbartonshire Council
HQ Corporate Directorate: Community Department: Community Services Section: Libraries and Cultural Services, Library HQ, William Patrick Library, 2–4 West High Street, Kirkintilloch, East Dunbartonshire G66 1AD
☎0141 775 4501
Fax 0141 776 0408
e-mail: libraries@eastdunbarton.gov.uk

url: www.eastdunbarton.gov.uk
Libraries and Cultural Services Manager Ms Elizabeth Brown MA MCLIP (0141 775 4501; e-mail: elizabeth.brown@eastdunbarton.gov.uk)
Assistant Manager, Community Libraries David Kenvyn BA MCLIP (0141 775 4519; e-mail: david.kenvyn@eastdunbarton.gov.uk)
Support Services Librarian Ms Anne Murray BA MCLIP (0141 775 4511; e-mail: anne.murray@eastdunbarton.gov.uk)
Assistant Manager, Information and Archives Don Martin FCLIP (0141 775 4529; e-mail: don.martin@eastdunbarton.gov.uk)
Assistant Manager, Children and Young People's Library Services Ms Frances MacArthur MA MCLIP (0141 775 4526; e-mail: frances.macarthur@eastdunbarton.gov.uk)
Outreach Officer Jim Fergusson MCLIP (0141 775 4509; e-mail: jim.fergusson@eastdunbarton.gov.uk)

Central/largest library

William Patrick Library, 2-4 West High Street, Kirkintilloch, East Dunbartonshire G66 1AD
☎0141 775 4524 (Lending Library)
Community Librarians Mrs Doreen Fergusson MA MCLIP (e-mail: doreen.fergusson@eastdunbarton.gov.uk), Mrs Eryl Morris BA DipLib MCLIP (e-mail: eryl.morris@eastdunbarton.gov.uk) (job-share)
Information and Local Studies Librarian Mrs Christine Miller BA DipLib MCLIP (0141 775 4537; e-mail: christine.miller@eastdunbarton.gov.uk)
Assistant Information and Local Studies Librarian David Smith DipLib MCLIP (0141 776 8090; e-mail: david.smith@eastdunbarton.gov.uk)
Archivist Ms Jane Jamieson (0141 775 4573; e-mail: jane.jamieson@eastdunbarton.gov.uk)
Freedom of Information Officer Ms Janice Miller (e-mail: janice.miller@eastdunbarton.gov.uk)

Branch libraries

- Bishopbriggs Library, 170 Kirkintilloch Road, Bishopbriggs, East Dunbartonshire G64 2LX
  ☎0141 772 4513
  Fax 0141 762 5363
  Community Librarian Mrs Fiona Warner BA MCLIP (e-mail: fiona.warner@eastdunbarton.gov.uk)
- Brookwood Library, 166 Drymen Road, Bearsden, Glasgow G61 3RJ
  ☎0141 942 6811
  Fax 0141 943 1119
  Community Librarian Ms Sandra Busby BA MCLIP (e-mail: sandra.busby@eastdunbarton.gov.uk)
- Lennoxtown Library, Main Street, Lennoxtown, East Dunbartonshire G65 7DG
  ☎(01360) 311436 (tel/fax)
  Library Supervisor Ms Lesley Finlayson (e-mail: lesley.finlayson@eastdunbarton.gov.uk)
- Lenzie Library, 13 Alexandra Avenue, Lenzie, East Dunbartonshire G66 5BG
  ☎0141 776 3021
  Library Supervisor Ms Maureen Fraser (e-mail: maureen.fraser@eastdunbarton.gov.uk), Ms Naomi Niven (e-mail: naomi.niven@eastdunbarton.gov.uk) (job-share)

- Milngavie Library, Community Centre, Allander Way, Milngavie, Glasgow G62 8PN
  ☎0141 956 2776
  Fax 0141 570 0052
  Community Librarian John Murray MCLIP (e-mail: john.murray@eastdunbarton.gov.uk)
- Milton of Campsie Library, Craighead Road, Milton of Campsie, East Dunbartonshire G65 8DL
  ☎(01360) 311925
  Assistant in Charge Ms May Newton (e-mail: may.newton@eastdunbarton.gov.uk), Ms Sandra Vernon (e-mail: sandra.vernon@eastdunbarton.gov.uk) (job-share)
- Westerton Library, 82 Maxwell Avenue, Bearsden, Glasgow G61 1NZ
  ☎0141 943 0780
  Library Supervisor Ms Elizabeth Bushfield (e-mail: elizabeth.bushfield@eastdunbarton.gov.uk), Neil Davidson (e-mail: neil.davidson@eastdunbarton.gov.uk) (job-share)
  Mobile Library Supervisor Ms Paula McGonigal (e-mail: paula.mcgonigal@eastdunbarton.gov.uk)
  Area and Mobile Librarian (responsible for Lennoxtown, Lenzie, Milton of Campsie, Mobile and Westerton Libraries): Gerard Robertson (e-mail: gerard.robertson@eastdunbarton.gov.uk)

EAST LOTHIAN

Authority: East Lothian Council
HQ Library and Museum Headquarters, Dunbar Road, Haddington, East Lothian EH41 3PJ
☎(01620) 828205 (enquiries), (01620) 828200 (administration)
Fax (01620) 828201
e-mail: libraries@eastlothian.gov.uk (for general enquiries)
url: www.eastlothian.gov.uk
Principal Libraries Officer Ms Alison Hunter BA MCLIP

Largest library

Musselburgh Library, 10 Bridge Street, Musselburgh, East Lothian EH21 6AG
☎0131 665 2183
e-mail: musselburgh.library@eastlothian.gov.uk
Area Librarian Mrs Dorothy Elliott MA DipLib

Branch libraries

- Dunbar Library, Castellau, Belhaven Road, Dunbar, East Lothian EH42 1DA
  ☎(01368) 863521
  e-mail: dunbar.library@eastlothian.gov.uk
  Assistant i/c Mrs Anne Hampshire
- East Linton Library, 60A High Street, East Linton, East Lothian EH40 3BX
  ☎(01620) 860015
  e-mail: eastlinton.library@eastlothian.gov.uk
  Assistant i/c Ms Barbel Burns
- Gullane Library, East Links Road, Gullane, East Lothian EH31 2AF
  ☎(01620) 842073

e-mail: gullane.library@eastlothian.gov.uk
Assistant i/c Ms Avril Stevens

- Haddington Library, Newton Port, Haddington, East Lothian EH41 3NA
☎(01620) 822531
e-mail: haddington.library@eastlothian.gov.uk
Area Librarian Ms Trina Gavan MCLIP
- Longniddry Library, Church Way, Longniddry, East Lothian EH32 0LW
☎(01875) 852735
e-mail: longniddry.library@eastlothian.gov.uk
Assistant i/c Ms Anne Sturgeon
- North Berwick Library, The Old School, School Road, North Berwick, East Lothian EH39 4JU
☎(01620) 893470
e-mail: northberwick.library@eastlothian.gov.uk
Branch Librarian Ms Jane Paterson BA DipLib
- Ormiston Library, 5A Meadowbank, Ormiston, East Lothian EH35 5LQ
☎(01875) 616675
e-mail: ormiston.library@eastlothian.gov.uk
Assistant i/c Bill Wilson
- Port Seton Library, Community Centre, South Seton Park, Port Seton, East Lothian EH32 0BG
☎(01875) 811709
Fax (01875) 815177
e-mail: portseton.library@eastlothian.gov.uk
Assistant i/c Mrs Irene Muir
- Prestonpans Library, West Loan, Prestonpans, East Lothian EH32 9NX
☎(01875) 810788
e-mail: prestonpans.library@eastlothian.gov.uk
Branch Librarian Ms Erica Thomson BA MCLIP
- Tranent Library, 3 Civic Square, Tranent, East Lothian EH33 1LH
☎(01875) 610254
e-mail: tranent.library@eastlothian.gov.uk
Branch Librarian Ms Marjory Daly MCLIP
- Wallyford Library, 3 Fa'side Buildings, Wallyford, East Lothian EH21 8BA
☎0131 653 2035
e-mail: wallyford.library@eastlothian.gov.uk
Assistant i/c Ms Kate Shilton

Specialist library

- Local History Centre, Newton Port, Haddington, East Lothian EH41 3NA
☎(01620) 823307
e-mail: localhistory@eastlothian.gov.uk
Local History Librarian Ms Sheila Millar BA(Hons) MSc MCLIP

EAST RENFREWSHIRE

Authority: East Renfrewshire Council
HQ Library and Information Services, Glen Street, Barrhead, East Renfrewshire G78 1QA

☎0141 577 3500 (enquiries)
Fax 0141 577 3501
url: www.eastrenfrewshire.gov.uk/libraries
Head of Culture and Sport Ken McKinlay MA(Hons) PGDipLib MCLIP (0141 577 3103; e-mail: ken.mckinlay@eastrenfrewshire.gov.uk)
Libraries and Information Services Manager Mrs Liz McGettigan BA MCLIP (0141 577 3503; e-mail: liz.mcgettigan@eastrenfrewshire.gov.uk)
Community Information Access Manager Graeme McWilliams (0141 577 3530; e-mail: graeme.mcwilliams@eastrenfrewshire.gov.uk)
Learning Services Manager Ms Janice Weir BA MCLIP (0141 577 3516; e-mail: janice.weir@eastrenfrewshire.gov.uk)
Systems Manager Scott Simpson BA PGDipIT MCLIP (0141 577 3509; e-mail: scott.simpson@eastrenfrewshire.gov.uk)
Customer Services Manager Ms Claire Scott (0141 577 3531; e-mail: claire.scott@eastrenfrewshire.gov.uk)

Community libraries

- Barrhead Community Library, Glen Street, Barrhead, East Renfrewshire G78 1QA
  ☎0141 577 3518
  e-mail: barrhead.library@eastrenfrewshire.gov.uk
- Busby Community Library, Duff Memorial Hall, Main Street, Busby, East Renfrewshire G76 8DX
  ☎0141 577 4971
  e-mail: busby.library@eastrenfrewshire.gov.uk
- Clarkston Community Library, Clarkston Road, Clarkston, East Renfrewshire G76 8NE
  ☎0141 577 4972
  Fax 0141 577 4973
  e-mail: clarkston.library@eastrenfrewshire.gov.uk
- Eaglesham Community Library, Montgomerie Hall, Eaglesham, Eaglesham, East Renfrewshire G76 0LH
  ☎(01355) 302649 (tel/fax)
  e-mail: eaglesham.library@eastrenfrewshire.gov.uk
- Giffnock Community Library, Station Road, Giffnock, East Renfrewshire G46 6JF
  ☎0141 577 4976
  Fax 0141 577 4978
  e-mail: giffnock.library@eastrenfrewshire.gov.uk
- Mearns Community Library, McKinley Place, Newton Mearns, East Renfrewshire G77 6EZ
  ☎0141 577 4979
  Fax 0141 577 4980
  e-mail: mearns.library@eastrenfrewshire.gov.uk
- Neilston Community Library, Main Street, Neilston, East Renfrewshire G78 3NN
  ☎0141 577 4981
  Fax 0141 577 4982
  e-mail: neilston.library@eastrenfrewshire.gov.uk
- Netherlee Community Library, Netherlee Pavilion, Linn Park Avenue, East Renfrewshire G44 3PH

☎0141 637 5102
e-mail: netherlee.library@eastrenfrewshire.gov.uk

- Thornliebank Community Library, 1 Spiersbridge Road, Thornliebank, East Renfrewshire G46 7SJ
  ☎0141 577 4983
  Fax 0141 577 4816
  e-mail: thornliebank.library@eastrenfrewshire.gov.uk
- Uplawmoor Community Library, Mure Hall, Tannoch Road, Uplawmoor, East Renfrewshire G78 4AF
  ☎(01505) 850564

EDINBURGH

Authority: City of Edinburgh Council
HQ Central Library, George IV Bridge, Edinburgh EH1 1EG
☎0131 242 8000
Fax 0131 242 8009
e-mail: eclis@edinburgh.gov.uk
url: www.edinburgh.gov.uk
Head of Libraries and Information Services W Wallace MA MCLIP
Central Library and Information Services Manager Ms M Corr BA DipLib MCLIP
Service Development Manager M Hinds BA DipLib MCLIP
Community and Library Services Manager Ms G McCaig DipLib MCLIP

Community libraries

- Balerno Library, 1 Main Street, Balerno, Edinburgh EH14 7EQ
  ☎0131 529 5500
  Fax 0131 529 5502
- Balgreen Library, 173 Balgreen Road, Edinburgh EH11 3AT
  ☎0131 529 5585
  Fax 0131 529 5583
- Blackhall Library, 56 Hillhouse Road, Edinburgh EH4 5EG
  ☎0131 529 5595
  Fax 0131 336 5419
  Principal Library Officer Ms E Kilmurry BA MCLIP
- Colinton Library, 14 Thorburn Road, Edinburgh EH13 0BQ
  ☎0131 529 5603
  Fax 0131 529 5607
- Corstophine Library, 12 Kirk Loan, Edinburgh EH12 7HD
  ☎0131 529 5506
  Fax 0131 529 5508
- Craigmillar Library, 7 Niddrie Marischal Gardens, Edinburgh EH16 4LX
  ☎0131 529 5597
  Fax 0131 529 5601
- Currie Library, 210 Lanark Road, Edinburgh EH14 5NN
  ☎0131 529 5609
  Fax 0131 529 5613
- Fountainbridge Library, 137 Dundee Street, Edinburgh EH11 1BG

☎0131 529 5616
Fax 0131 529 5621

- Gilmerton Library, 13 Newtoft Street, Edinburgh EH17 8RG
☎0131 529 5628
Fax 0131 529 5627
- Granton Library, Wardieburn Terrace, Edinburgh EH5 1DD
☎0131 529 5630
Fax 0131 529 5634
- Kirkliston Library, 16 Station Road, Edinburgh EH29 9BE
☎0131 529 5510
Fax 0131 529 5514
- Leith Library, 28–30 Ferry Road, Edinburgh EH6 5AE
☎0131 529 5517
Fax 0131 554 2720
e-mail: leith.library@edinburgh.gov.uk
Principal Library Officer Ms M McChrystal BLib MCLIP
- McDonald Road Library, 2 McDonald Road, Edinburgh EH7 4LU
☎0131 529 5652
Fax 0131 529 5646
- Moredun Library, 92 Moredun Park Road, Edinburgh EH17 7HL
☎0131 529 5652
Fax 0131 529 5651
- Morningside Library, 184 Morningside Road, Edinburgh EH10 4PU
☎0131 529 5654
Fax 0131 447 4685
- Muirhouse Library, 15 Pennywell Court, Edinburgh EH4 4TZ
☎0131 529 5528
Fax 0131 529 5532
- Newington Library, 17–21 Fountainhall Road, Edinburgh EH9 2LN
☎0131 529 5536
Fax 0131 667 5491
Principal Library Officer M Spells
- Oxgangs Library, 343 Oxgangs Road, Edinburgh EH13 9LY
☎0131 529 5549
Fax 0131 529 5554
- Piershill Library, 30 Piersfield Terrace, Edinburgh EH8 7BQ
☎0131 529 5685
Fax 0131 529 5691
- Portobello Library, 14 Rosefield Avenue, Edinburgh EH15 1AU
☎0131 529 5558
Fax 0131 669 2344
- Ratho Library, 6 School Wynd, Ratho, Edinburgh EH28 8TT
☎0131 333 5297 (tel/fax)
- Sighthill Library, 6 Sighthill Wynd, Edinburgh EH11 4BL
☎0131 529 5569
Fax 0131 529 5572
- South Queensferry Library, 9 Shore Road, South Queensferry, Edinburgh EH30 9RD

☎0131 529 5576
Fax 0131 529 5578

- Stockbridge Library, 11 Hamilton Place, Edinburgh EH3 5BA
☎0131 529 5665
Fax 0131 529 5681
- Wester Hailes Library, 1 Westside Plaza, Wester Hailes, Edinburgh EH14 2FT
☎0131 529 5667
Fax 0131 529 5671
Principal Library Officer Ms L Spells BSc DipLib MCLIP

Access Services/Mobiles

- Access Services, 343 Oxgangs Road North, Edinburgh EH13 9LY
☎0131 529 5683

Ethnic Services

- c/o McDonald Road Library, 2 McDonald Road, Edinburgh EH7 4LU
☎0131 529 5636

FALKIRK

Authority: Falkirk Council
HQ Library, Victoria Buildings, Queen Street, Falkirk FK2 7AF
☎(01324) 506800
Fax (01324) 506801
url: www.falkirk.gov.uk
Libraries Manager Mrs Irene McIntyre MCLIP (e-mail: irene.mcintyre@falkirk.gov.uk)

Central/largest library

Falkirk Library, Hope Street, Falkirk FK1 5AU
☎(01324) 503605
Fax (01324) 503606
e-mail: falkirk.library@falkirk.gov.uk
Principal Librarian Ms Anna Herron MA DipLib MCLIP

Other libraries

- Bo'ness Library, Scotland's Close, Bo'ness, Falkirk EH51 0AH
☎(01506) 778520
Fax (01506) 778521
e-mail: bo'ness.library@falkirk.gov.uk
Librarians Ruaraidh Murray MCLIP, Miss Christine Simm BA MCLIP
- Bonnybridge Library, Bridge Street, Bonnybridge, Falkirk FK4 1AA
☎(01324) 503295
Fax (01324) 503296
e-mail: bonnybridge.library@falkirk.gov.uk
Librarian Ms Vikki Ring BA MCLIP
- Denny Library, 49 Church Walk, Denny, Falkirk FK6 6DF
☎(01324) 504242
Fax (01324) 504240

e-mail: denny.library@falkirk.gov.uk
Librarians Mrs Lorraine Alexander BA MCLIP, Mrs Shona Hill BA MCLIP

- Grangemouth Library, Bo'ness Road, Grangemouth, Falkirk FK3 8AG
☎(01324) 504690
Fax (01324) 504691
e-mail: grangemouth.library@falkirk.gov.uk
Senior Librarians Mrs Sharon Woodforde MCLIP, Mrs Rachel Williams BSc(Hons) DipLib
- Larbert Library, Main Street, Stenhousemuir, Larbert, Falkirk FK5 3JX
☎(01324) 503590
Fax (01324) 503592
e-mail: larbert.library@falkirk.gov.uk
Senior Librarians Mrs Karyn Jaffray BA MCLIP, Miss Tanya Milligan MA MCLIP, Ms Fiona Fraser BA MCLIP
- Slamannan Library, The Cross, Slamannan, Falkirk FK1 3EX
☎(01324) 851373
Fax (01324) 851862
e-mail: slamannan.library@falkirk.gov.uk
Librarian Mrs Gil Vick BA MCLIP

FIFE

Authority: Fife Council
HQ Libraries and Museums, Library Headquarters, East Fergus Place, Kirkcaldy, Fife KY1 1XT
☎(01592) 412930
Fax (01592) 412941
e-mail: fife.libraries@fife.gov.uk
url: www.fifedirect.org.uk
Service Manager, Libraries & Museums Ms Dorothy Browse MBA MA MCLIP (e-mail: dorothy.browse@fife.gov.uk)

Area libraries

- Dunfermline Carnegie Library, Abbot Street, Dunfermline, Fife KY12 7NL
☎(01383) 312605
Fax (01383) 314314
Operations Co-ordinator Robert Izatt BA MCLIP (e-mail: bob.izatt@fife.gov.uk)
- East Fife Library HQ, County Buildings, St Catherine Street, Cupar, Fife KY15 4TA
☎(01334) 412737
Fax (01334) 412941
Libraries Systems and Support Co-ordinator David Burns (e-mail: david.burns@fife.gov.uk)

Group libraries

- Cupar Library, 33-35 Crossgate, Cupar, Fife KY15 5AS
☎(01334) 412285
Fax (01334) 412467
Community Librarian David Castle-Smith BA(Hons) MCLIP

- Glenwood Library, Glenwood Shopping Centre, Glenrothes, Fife KY6 1PA
  ☎(01592) 416840
  Fax (01592) 416843
  Community Librarian Ms Isabel McNab BScEcon) MCLIP
- Kirkcaldy Central Library, War Memorial Gardens, Kirkcaldy, Fife KY1 1YG
  ☎(01592) 412878
  Fax (01592) 412750
  Customer Services Librarian Ms Tracey Steedman MA DipILS MCLIP
- Leven Library, Durie Street, Leven, Fife KY8 4HE
  ☎(01333) 592650
  Fax (01333) 592655
  Learning Services Co-ordinator Ms Yvonne Melville
- St Andrews Library, Church Square, St Andrews, Fife KY16 9NN
  ☎(01334) 412657
  Fax (01334) 413029
  Community Librarian Ms Lindsay Cordiner

GLASGOW

Authority: Glasgow City Council
HQ Cultural and Leisure Services, Libraries, Information and Learning, The Mitchell Library, North Street, Glasgow G3 7DN
☎0141 287 2999 (enquiries), 0141 287 2870 (service development)
Fax 0141 287 2815
e-mail: lil@cls.glasgow.gov.uk
url: www.glasgowlibraries.org
Head of Libraries, Information and Learning Ms Karen Cunningham MA DipLib MCLIP (0141 287 5114; fax: 0141 287 5151; e-mail: karen.cunningham@cls.glasgow.gov.uk) (located at 20 Trongate, Glasgow G1 1LX)
Service Development Manager Gordon Anderson BA MCLIP (0141 287 2949; e-mail: gordon.anderson@cls.glasgow.gov.uk)
Information Services Manager Ms Pamela Tulloch MA MBA DipLib MCLIP (0141 287 2862; e-mail: pamela.tulloch@cls.glasgow.gov.uk)
Community Libraries Network Manager Ms Wilma Moore MCLIP (0141 287 2806; e-mail: wilma.moore@cls.glasgow.gov.uk)
Community Learning Manager Ms Jane Edgar DipYCW (0141 287 2881; e-mail: jane.edgar@cls.glasgow.gov.uk)

Community libraries

- Anniesland Library, 833 Crow Road, Glasgow G13 1LE
  ☎0141 954 5687
  Fax 0141 954 5548
- Baillieston Library, 141 Main Street, Glasgow G69 6AA
  ☎0141 771 2433 (tel/fax)
- Barmulloch Library, Wallacewell Quadrant, Glasgow G21 3DY
  ☎0141 558 1772
  Fax 0141 558 8294
- Bridgeton Library, 23 Landressy Street, Glasgow G40 1BP

☎0141 554 0217 (tel/fax)

- Cardonald Library, 1113 Mosspark Drive, Glasgow G52 3BU
  ☎0141 882 1381
  Fax 0141 810 5490
- Castlemilk Library, 100 Castlemilk Drive, Glasgow G45 9TN
  ☎0141 634 2066 (tel/fax)
- Couper Institute Library, 84 Clarkston Road, Glasgow G44 3DA
  ☎0141 637 1544 (tel/fax)
- Dennistoun Library, 2a Craigpark, Glasgow G31 2NA
  ☎0141 554 0055
  Fax 0141 551 9971
- Drumchapel Library, 65 Hecla Avenue, Glasgow G15 8LX
  ☎0141 944 5698 (tel/fax)
- Elder Park Library, 228a Langlands Road, Glasgow G51 3TZ
  ☎0141 445 1047 (tel/fax)
- Gorbals Library and Cybercafé, 180 Crown Street, Glasgow G5 4XD
  ☎0141 429 0949
  Fax 0141 429 0167
- Govanhill Library, 170 Langside Road, Glasgow G42 7JU
  ☎0141 423 0335 (tel/fax)
- Hillhead Library, 348 Byres Road, Glasgow G12 8AP
  ☎0141 339 7223
  Fax 0141 337 2783
- Ibrox Library, 1 Midlock Street, Glasgow G51 1SL
  ☎0141 427 5831
  Fax 0141 427 1139
- Knightswood Library, 27 Dunterlie Avenue, Glasgow G13 3BB
  ☎0141 959 2041 (tel/fax)
- Langside Library, 2 Sinclair Drive, Glasgow G42 9QE
  ☎0141 632 0810
  Fax 0141 632 8982
- Leisure and Lifestyle at the Mitchell, Granville Street, Glasgow G3 7DN
- Library at the Bridge, 1000 Westhouse Road, Glasgow G34 9JW
  ☎0141 276 9712
  Fax 0141 276 9711
- Library@Goma, Queen Street, Glasgow G1 3AZ
  ☎0141 248 0143
  Fax 0141 249 9943
- Maryhill Library, 1508 Maryhill Road, Glasgow G20 9AD
  ☎0141 946 2348 (tel/fax)
- Milton Library, 163 Ronaldsay Street, Glasgow G22 7AP
  ☎0141 772 1410 (tel/fax)
- Parkhead Library, 64 Tollcross Road, Glasgow G31 4XA
  ☎0141 554 0198 (tel/fax)
- Partick Library, 305 Dumbarton Road, Glasgow G11 6AB
  ☎0141 339 1303 (tel/fax)
- Pollok Library and Leisure Centre, The Wedge, 1066 Barrhead Road, Glasgow G53 5AB

☎0141 270 1826
e-mail: lil@csglasgow.org

- Pollokshaws Library, 50-60 Shawbridge Street, Glasgow G43 1RW
  ☎0141 632 3544 (tel/fax)
- Pollokshields Library, 30 Leslie Street, Glasgow G41 2LF
  ☎0141 423 1460 (tel/fax)
- Possilpark Library, 127 Allander Street, Glasgow G22 5JJ
  ☎0141 336 8110 (tel/fax)
- Riddrie Library, 1020 Cumbernauld Road, Glasgow G33 2QS
  ☎0141 770 4043 (tel/fax)
- Royston Library, 67 Royston Road, Glasgow G21 2QW
  ☎0141 552 1657 (tel/fax)
- Service Development, The Mitchell Library, North Street, Glasgow G3 7DN
  ☎0141 287 2870
  Fax 0141 287 2815
- Shettleston Library, 154 Wellshot Road, Glasgow G32 7AX
  ☎0141 778 1221
  Fax 0141 778 9004
- Sighthill Drop-in Centre, Sighthill Library, 27 Fountainwell Drive, Glasgow G21 1RR
  ☎0141 558 6910 (tel/fax)
- Springburn Library, Kay Street, Glasgow G21 1JY
  ☎0141 577 5878
  Fax 0141 557 5893
- Whiteinch Library, 14 Victoria Park Drive South, Glasgow G14 9RL
  ☎0141 959 1376 (tel/fax)
- Woodside Library, 343 St George's Road, Glasgow G3 6JQ
  ☎0141 832 1808 (tel/fax)

HIGHLAND

Authority: The Highland Council
HQ Education, Culture and Sport Service, Glenurquhart Road, Inverness IV3 5NX
☎(01463) 702046
Fax (01463) 711177
Lifelong Learning Manager Christopher Phillips BA DipLib MCLIP (e-mail: christopher.phillips@highland.gov.uk)

Library Service HQ

Library Support Unit, 31A Harbour Road, Inverness IV1 1UA
☎(01463) 235713
Fax (01463) 236986
e-mail: libraries@highland.gov.uk
Library and Information Services Co-ordinator Ms Joyce Watson BA MCLIP (e-mail: joyce.watson@highland.gov.uk)

Ross, Skye and Lochaber

Library Area Base

Library Area Base, Council Offices, High Street, Dingwall, Ross-shire IV15 9QN
☎(01349) 868460
Fax (01349) 863107
Area Libraries Officer Mrs Charlotte E MacArthur BA(Hons) DipLib MCLIP (e-mail: charlotte.macarthur@highland.gov.uk)

Area libraries

- Dingwall Library, Old Academy Buildings, Tulloch Street, Dingwall, Ross-shire IV15 9JZ
  ☎(01349) 863163
  Fax (01349) 865239
  e-mail: dingwall.library@highland.gov.uk
  Dingwall and Wester Ross Librarian Ms Pauline Chapman MCLIP (e-mail: pauline.chapman@highland.gov.uk)
- Fort William Library, Education Culture and Sport Service, Airds Crossing, Fort William, Inverness-shire PH33 6EU
  ☎(01397) 703552
  Fax (01397) 703528
  e-mail: fortwilliam.library@highland.gov.uk
- Fortrose Library, Fortrose Academy, Fortrose, Highland IV10 8TW
  ☎(01381) 622235 (tel/fax)
  e-mail: fortrose.library@highland.gov.uk
  Librarian Ms Sheena Paterson MCLIP (e-mail: sheena.paterson@highland.gov.uk)
- Gairloch Library, Gairloch Community Library, Auchtercairn, Gairloch, Highland IV21 2BP
  ☎(01445) 712469
  Fax (01445) 712438
  e-mail: gairloch.library@highland.gov.uk
- Portree Library, Bayfield Road, Portree, Isle of Skye, Inverness-shire IV51 9EL
  ☎(01478) 612697
  Fax (01478) 613314
  e-mail: portree.library@highland.gov.uk
  Assistant Area Libraries Officer David Linton MCLIP (01478 613861; fax: 01478 613751; e-mail: david.linton@highland.gov.uk)
- Ullapool Library, Community High School, Ullapool, Highland IV26 2UN
  ☎(01854) 612543 (tel/fax)
  e-mail: ullapool.library@highland.gov.uk
  (Joint school/community library)

Caithness, Sutherland and East Ross

Library Area Base

Dornoch Library, Carnegie Building, High Street, Dornoch, Sutherland IV25 3SH
☎(01862) 811585
Fax (01862) 811079
Area Libraries Officer Mrs Alison Forrest BA MCLIP (e-mail: alison.forrest@highland.gov.uk)

Area libraries

- Alness Library, Averon Centre, High Street, Alness, Highland IV17 0QB
  ☎(01349) 882674
  Fax (01349) 883587
  e-mail: alness.library@highland.gov.uk
- Brora Library, Gower Street, Brora, Highland KW9 6PD
  ☎(01408) 621128
  Fax (01408) 622064
  e-mail: brora.library@highland.gov.uk
- Dornoch Library, Carnegie Building, High Street, Dornoch, Sutherland IV25 3SH
  ☎(01862) 811079 (tel/fax)
  e-mail: dornoch.library@highland.gov.uk
- Invergordon Library, High Street, Invergordon, Ross-shire IV18 0DG
  ☎(01349) 852698 (tel/fax)
  e-mail: invergordon.library@highland.gov.uk
  East Ross Librarian Ms Patricia Hannah MCLIP (e-mail: patricia.hannah@highland.gov.uk)
- Tain Library, Stafford Street, Tain, Highland IV19 1AZ
  ☎(01862) 892391 (tel/fax)
  e-mail: tain.library@highland.gov.uk
- Thurso Library, Davidson's Lane, Thurso, Caithness KW14 7AF
  ☎(01847) 893237
  Fax (01847) 896114
  e-mail: thurso.library@highland.gov.uk
- Wick Library, Carmegie Public Library, Sinclair Terrace, Wick, Caithness KW1 5AB
  ☎(01955) 602864
  Fax (01955) 603000
  e-mail: wick.library@highland.gov.uk

Inverness, Nairn, Badenoch and Strathspey

Badenoch Library & Learning Centre, Spey Street, Kingussie, Highland PH21 1EH
☎(01540) 661596 (tel/fax)
e-mail: badenoch.library@highland.gov.uk

Area libraries

- Culloden Library, Keppoch Road, Culloden, Inverness IV1 2LL
  ☎(01463) 792531
  Fax (01463) 793162
  e-mail: culloden.library@highland.gov.uk
  Librarian Mrs Angela Donald MCLIP (e-mail: angela.donald@highland.gov.uk)
- Glenurquhart Library, Pitkerrald Road, Drumnadrochit, Inverness IV63 6TX
  ☎(01456) 459223 (tel/fax)
  e-mail: glenurquhart.library@highland.gov.uk
- Grantown Library, YMCA Building, 80 High Street, Grantown-on-Spey, Perthshire PH26 3HB
  ☎(01479) 873175 (tel/fax)
  e-mail: grantown.library@highland.gov.uk
- Inshes Community Library, Inshes Primary School, Inshes Road, Inverness IV2 3RP

☎(01463) 725928 (tel/fax)
e-mail: inshes.library@highland.gov.uk

- Inverness Library, Farraline Park, Inverness IV1 1NH
  ☎(01463) 236463
  Fax (01463) 237001
  e-mail: inverness.library@highland.gov.uk
  Area Libraries Officer Ms Carol Goodfellow MA MCLIP (e-mail: carol.goodfellow@highland.gov.uk)
- Nairn Library, 68 High Street, Nairn, Nairnshire IV12 4AU
  ☎(01667) 458506
  Fax (01667) 458548
  e-mail: nairn.library@highland.gov.uk
  Assistant Area Libraries Officer Ms Eleanor Somerville BEd DipLib MCLIP (e-mail: eleanor.somerville@highland.gov.uk)

INVERCLYDE

Authority: Inverclyde Council
HQ Central Library, Clyde Square, Greenock, Renfrewshire PA15 1NA
☎(01475) 712323
Fax (01475) 712339
e-mail: library.central@inverclyde.gov.uk
url: www.inverclyde.gov.uk
Libraries Manager Miss Sandra MacDougall MA(Hons) MCLIP (e-mail: sandra.macdougall@inverclyde.gov.uk)

MIDLOTHIAN

Authority: Midlothian Council
HQ Library HQ, 2 Clerk Street, Loanhead, Midlothian EH20 9DR
☎0131 271 3980
Fax 0131 440 4635
e-mail: library.hq@midlothian.gov.uk
url: www.midlothian.gov.uk/library/
Library Services Manager Alan Reid MA MCLIP

Central/largest library

Dalkeith Library, White Hart Street, Dalkeith, Midlothian EH22 1AE
☎0131 663 2083
Fax 0131 654 9029
e-mail: dalkeith.library@midlothian.gov.uk
Senior Librarian Thomas Regan BA MCLIP

Branch libraries

- Bonnyrigg Library, Polton Street, Bonnyrigg, Midlothian EH19 3HB
  ☎0131 663 6762
  Fax 0131 654 9019
  e-mail: bonnyrigg.library@midlothian.gov.uk

Senior Librarian David Stevenson BA MCLIP

- Danderhall Library, 1A Campview, Danderhall, Midlothian EH22 1QD
  ☎0131 663 9293
  e-mail: danderhall.library@midlothian.gov.uk
  Assistant i/c Ms Rachel Archibald
- Gorebridge Library, Hunterfield Road, Gorebridge, Midlothian EH23 4TT
  ☎(01875) 820630
  Fax (01875) 823657
  e-mail: gorebridge.library@midlothian.gov.uk
  Assistant i/c Ms Janette Hamilton
- Loanhead Library, George Avenue, Loanhead, Midlothian EH20 9HD
  ☎0131 440 0824
  e-mail: loanhead.library@midlothian.gov.uk
  Assistant i/c Ms Gillian Renwick
- Local Studies, 2 Clerk Street, Loanhead, Midlothian EH20 9DR
  ☎0131 271 3976
  Fax 0131 440 4635
  e-mail: local.studies@midlothian.gov.uk
  Local Studies Officer Dr Kenneth Bogle MA MCLIP PhD
- Mayfield Library, Stone Avenue, Mayfield, Dalkeith, Midlothian EH22 5PB
  ☎0131 663 2126
  e-mail: mayfield.library@midlothian.gov.uk
  Assistant i/c Ms Isobel Allen
- Newtongrange Library, St Davids, Newtongrange, Midlothian EH22 4LG
  ☎0131 663 1816
  Fax 0131 654 1990
  e-mail: newtongrange.library@midlothian.gov.uk
  Assistant i/c Ms Jacqueline Elliot
- Penicuik Library, The Penicuik Centre, Carlops Road, Penicuik, Midlothian EH26 9EP
  ☎(01968) 664050
  Fax (01968) 679408
  e-mail: penicuik.library@midlothian.gov.uk
  Senior Librarian Stephen Harris MA MSc
- Roslin Library, 9 Main Street, Roslin, Midlothian EH25 9LD
  ☎0131 448 2781
  e-mail: roslin.library@midlothian.gov.uk
  Assistant i/c Ms Lorraine Martin
- Woodburn Library, Dalkeith Comunity Centre, 6 Woodburn Road, Dalkeith, Midlothian EH22 2AR
  ☎0131 654 4323
  e-mail: woodburn.library@midlothian.gov.uk
  Senior Librarian Thomas Regan BA MCLIP

MORAY

Authority: The Moray Council
HQ Educational Services Department, Council Office, High Street, Elgin, Moray IV30 1BX
☎(01343) 562600 (enquiries), 01343 563398 (administration)

Fax (01343) 563478
url: www.moray.gov.uk
Libraries and Museums Manager G Alistair Campbell MA BCom MCLIP (e-mail: campbea@moray.gov.uk)

Central/largest library

Elgin Library, Cooper Park, Elgin, Moray IV30 1HS
☎(01343) 562600
Fax (01343) 562630
e-mail: elgin.library@moray.gov.uk
Principal Librarian (Central Services) Ms Sheila Campbell MCLIP (e-mail: sheila.campbell@moray.gov.uk)

Area libraries

- Buckie Library, Cluny Place, Buckie, Banffshire AB56 1HB
  ☎(01542) 832121
  Fax (01542) 835237
  e-mail: buckie.library@moray.gov.uk
  Senior Librarian (Buckie) Ms Eleanor Kidd MA MCLIP
- Forres Library, Forres House, High Street, Forres, Moray IV36 1BU
  ☎(01309) 672834
  Fax (01309) 675084
  e-mail: forres.library@moray.gov.uk
  Community Librarian (Forres) Mrs Rebecca Bolton BA(Hons) MLib (e-mail: rebecca.bolton@moray.gov.uk)
- Keith Library, Union Street, Keith, Banffshire AB55 5DP
  ☎(01542) 882223
  Fax (01542) 882177
  e-mail: keith.library@moray.gov.uk
  Senior Librarian (Keith) Ms Susan Butts MA(Hons) MCLIP

NORTH AYRSHIRE

Authority: North Ayrshire Council
HQ Library, 39-41 Princes Street, Ardrossan, Ayrshire KA22 8BT
☎(01294) 469137
Fax (01294) 604236
e-mail: libraryhq@north-ayrshire.gov.uk
url: www.north-ayrshire.gov.uk
Library and Information Services Manager Dr Audrey Sutton MA(Hons) DipLib PLD MCLIP (e-mail: asutton@north-ayrshire.gov.uk)
Library Operations Manager Mrs Marilyn Vint MCLIP (01294 469137; fax: 01294 604236; e-mail: mvint@north-ayrshire.gov.uk)
Lifelong Learning Manager Miss Sandra Kerr MCLIP (e-mail: skerr@north-ayrshire.gov.uk)
Reading and Branch Development Manager Paul Cowan BEd DipLib MCLIP (e-mail: pcowan@north-ayrshire.gov.uk)

Central/largest library

Irvine Library, 168 High Street, Irvine, Ayrshire KA12 8AN
☎(01294) 271295
Fax (01294) 313051
e-mail: irvinelibrary@north-ayrshire.gov.uk
Area Librarian Miss Mary-Anne Scott MCLIP

Area libraries

- Largs Library, Allanpark Street, Largs, Ayrshire KA30 9AS
  ☎(01475) 673309 (tel/fax)
  e-mail: largslibrary@north-ayrshire.gov.uk
  Area Librarian John West BA DipLib MCLIP
- Saltcoats Library, Springvale Place, Saltcoats, Ayrshire KA21 5LS
  ☎(01294) 469546 (tel/fax)
  e-mail: saltcoatslibrary@north-ayrshire.gov.uk
  Area Librarian Jim Macaulay MCLIP DipLib

NORTH LANARKSHIRE

Authority: North Lanarkshire Council
HQ Learning and Leisure Services, Municipal Buildings, Kildonan Street, Coatbridge, North Lanarkshire ML5 3BT
☎(01698) 332606
Fax (01698) 332624
url: www.northlan.gov.uk
Libraries and Information Manager Vacant
Bibliographic and Support Manager James Lindsay BA MCLIP (e-mail: lindsayj@northlan.gov.uk)

Central/largest library

Motherwell Library, 35 Hamilton Road, Motherwell, North Lanarkshire ML1 3BZ
☎(01698) 332626
Fax (01698) 332625
Information Services Manager Charles Bennett BA MCLIP (e-mail: bennettc@northlan.gov.uk)
Lending Services Manager Mrs Catriona Wales BA MCLIP (e-mail: walesc@northlan.gov.uk)

Area libraries

- Coatbridge Library, 25 Academy Street, Coatbridge, North Lanarkshire ML5 3AW
  ☎(01236) 424150
  Fax (01236) 437997
  Lending Services Manager Central Danny McGuinness MCLIP (e-mail: mcguinnessd@northlan.gov.uk)
- Cumbernauld Library, 8 Allander Walk, Cumbernauld, North Lanarkshire G67 6EE
  ☎(01236) 725664
  Fax (01236) 458350

Lending Services Manager North Mrs Wendy Bennett BA MCLIP (e-mail: bennettw@northlan.gov.uk)

ORKNEY

Authority: Orkney Islands Council
HQ The Orkney Library and Archive, 44 Junction Road, Kirkwall, Orkney KW15 1AG
☎(01856) 873166 (enquiries and administration)
Fax (01856) 875260
e-mail: general.enquiries@orkneylibrary.org.uk
url: www.orkneylibrary.org.uk
Library and Archive Manager Gary Amos (e-mail: gary.amos@orkneylibrary.org.uk)
Principal Librarian Ms Karen Walker BA (e-mail: karen.walker@orkneylibrary.org.uk)
Principal Archivist Ms Alison Fraser (e-mail: alison.fraser@orkneylibrary.org.uk)

PERTH AND KINROSS

Authority: Perth and Kinross Council
HQ The A K Bell Library, York Place, Perth, Perthshire PH2 8EP
☎(01738) 444949
Fax (01738) 477010
e-mail: library@pkc.gov.uk
url: www.pkc.gov.uk/library
Community Libraries Manager Ms Caroline Beaton (e-mail: cfbeaton@pkc.gov.uk)
Senior Children's Librarian Ms Morag Kelly MA DipLib MCLIP (e-mail: makelly@pkc.gov.uk)

Area libraries

- Auchterarder Library, Aytoun Hall, Chapel Wynd, Auchterarder, Perthshire PH3 1BL
  ☎(01764) 663850
  Fax (01764) 663917
  Community Librarian Mrs Kirsty Mayall BA, Mrs Lesley Paul
- Blairgowrie Library, 46 Leslie Street, Blairgowrie, Perthshire PH10 6AW
  ☎(01250) 872905 (tel/fax)
  Community Librarian Simon McGowan MA
- Crieff Library, 6 Comrie Street, Crieff, Perthshire PH7 4AX
  ☎(01764) 653418
  Fax (01764) 657116
  Community Librarian Ms Marilyn Gordon BA
- Kinross Library, 27 High Street, Kinross, Kinross-shire KY13 8AW
  ☎(01577) 864202
  Library Assistant in Charge Ms Marion Garden
- Scone Library, Sandy Road, Scone, Perth, Perthshire PH2 6LJ
  ☎(01738) 553029 (tel/fax)
  Community Librarian Mrs Elaine Wallace BA, Ms Fiona Soutar

Community libraries

- Aberfeldy Library, Bank Street, Aberfeldy, Perthshire PH15 2BB

☎(01887) 820475
Library Assistant in Charge Mrs Sue Bennett

- Alyth Library, Airlie Street, Alyth, Blairgowrie, Perthshire PH11 8AH
  ☎(01828) 632731
  Library Assistant in Charge Mrs E Carnegie
- Birnam Library, The Institute, Station Road, Birnam, Dunkeld, Perthshire PH8 0DS
  ☎(01350) 727971
  Library Assistant in Charge Mrs M Quigley
- Comrie Library, Drummond Street, Comrie, Perthshire PH6 2DS
  ☎(01764) 670273
  Library Assistant in Charge Mrs M Donald
- Coupar Angus Library, Town Hall, Union Street, Coupar Angus, Blairgowrie, Perthshire PH13 9AE
  ☎(01828) 627090
  Library Assistant in Charge Mrs S Smith
- Pitlochry Library, 26 Atholl Road, Pitlochry, Perthshire PH16 5BX
  ☎(01796) 474919
  Library Assistant in Charge Mrs G Grant
- West Mill Street Library, West Mill Street, Perth PH1 5QP
  ☎(01738) 638436
  Library Assistant in Charge Mrs M Harris

RENFREWSHIRE

Authority: Renfrewshire Council
HQ Library Services, 8A Seedhill Road, Paisley, Renfrewshire PA1 1AJ
☎0141 840 3003
Fax 0141 840 3004
e-mail: libraries.els@renfrewshire.gov.uk
url: www.renfrewshire.gov.uk
Acting Library Manager Ms Jenifer McFarlane BA MCLIP

Central/largest library

Central Library (Lending), High Street, Paisley, Renfrewshire PA1 2BB
☎0141 887 3672
Fax 0141 887 6468
Person in Charge Ms Elaine Finlay BA DipLib MCLIP

Central Library (Reference), High Street, Paisley, Renfrewshire PA1 2BB
☎0141 889 2360
Fax 0141 887 6468
Contact David Weir BA DipLib MCLIP

Community libraries

- Bargarran Community Library, Community Hall, Barrhill Road, Erskine, Renfrewshire PA8 6BS
  ☎0141 812 2841
  Fax 0141 812 5265
  Contact Ms Gill Robinson

- Bishopton Community Library, 22 Greenock Road, Bishopton, Renfrewshire PA7 5JW
  ☎(01505) 862136
  Fax (01505) 862265
  e-mail: libraries.els@renfrewshire.gov.uk
  Contact Ms Janet Clasper
- Bridge of Weir Community Library, Main Street, Bridge of Weir, Renfrewshire PA11 3NR
  ☎(01505) 612220
  Fax (01505) 615052
  Contacts Ms Fiona Lochhead, Ms Evelyn Gilchrist
- Elderslie Community Library, Village Hall, Stoddart Square, Elderslie, Renfrewshire PA5 9AS
  ☎(01505) 322055
  Fax (01505) 327857
  Contact Bryan Smith
- Erskine Community Library, Bridgewater Place, Erskine, Renfrewshire PA8 7AA
  ☎0141 812 5331
  Fax 0141 812 4977
  Contact Ms Alison Horsburgh BLib MCLIP
- Ferguslie Park Community Library, Tannahill Centre, Blackstoun Road, Paisley, Renfrewshire PA3 1NT
  ☎0141 887 6404
  Fax 0141 849 0003
  Contact Andrew Givan MA(Hons) MSc MCLIP
- Foxbar Community Library, Ivanhoe Road, Paisley, Renfrewshire PA2 0JZ
  ☎(01505) 812353
  Fax (01505) 816989
  Contact Ms Ann White MCLIP
- Gallowhill Community Library, Netherhill Road, Paisley, Renfrewshire PA3 4SF
  ☎0141 889 1195
  Fax 0141 889 0034
  Contact Ms Christine Storie BA MCLIP
- Glenburn Community Library, Fairway Avenue, Paisley, Renfrewshire PA2 8DX
  ☎0141 884 2874
  Fax 0141 884 5758
  Contact Ms Janis McIntyre DipHE MCLIP
- Johnstone Community Library, Houston Court, Johnstone, Renfrewshire PA5 8DL
  ☎(01505) 329726
  Fax (01505) 336657
  e-mail: libraries.els@renfrewshire.gov.uk
- Johnstone Community Library, Houston Court, Johnstone, Renfrewshire PA5 6DL
  ☎(01505) 329726
  Fax (01505) 336657
  Contact Ms Jane Gourlay BA MCLIP
- Linwood Community Library, Ardlamont Square, Linwood, Renfrewshire PA3 2DE
  ☎(01505) 325283
  Fax (01505) 336150
  Contact Ms Linda Henderson MCLIP

- Lochwinnoch Community Library, Old School, High Street, Lochwinnoch, Renfrewshire PA12 6AB
  ☎(01505) 842305
  Fax (01505) 843780
  Contact Ms Margaret Sweenie
- Ralston Community Library, Community Centre, Allanton Road, Paisley, Renfrewshire PA1 3BL
  ☎0141 882 1879
  Fax 0141 882 2325
  Contacts Ms Kay Wright, Ms Pauline Chisholm
- Renfrew Community Library, Paisley Road, Renfrew, Renfrewshire PA4 8LJ
  ☎0141 886 3433
  Fax 0141 886 1660
  e-mail: libraries.els@renfrewshire.gov.uk
  Contacts Ms Moira Reid BA MCLIP, Ms Margaret Winters BA MCLIP
- Todholm Community Library, Lochfield Road, Paisley, Renfrewshire PA2 7JB
  ☎0141 887 3012
  Fax 0141 889 6167
  Contact Ms Debbie McBride
- Toy Library, Ivanhoe Road, Paisley, Renfrewshire PA2 0JZ
  ☎(01505) 812353
  Fax (01505) 816989
  Contacts Ms Anne Butterfield, Ms Sandra McCabe
- Mobile Libraries, Netherhill Road, Paisley, Renfrewshire PA3 4SF
  ☎0141 889 1195
  Fax 0141 889 0034
  Contact Ms Maureen Wallace

SCOTTISH BORDERS

Authority: Scottish Borders Council
HQ Scottish Borders Library Service, St Mary's Mill, Selkirk TD7 5EW
☎(01750) 20842
Fax (01750) 22875
url: www.scotborders.gov.uk
Head of Community Services Alan Hasson MA MBA DipLib MCLIP MIMgt
Library and Information Services Manager Ms Margaret Menzies BA MLib MCLIP
Community and Operations Librarian Ms Gillian McNay MA MCLIP DipLib
Information Systems Librarian Ms Sheena Milne MA MCLIP DipLib
Young People's Services Co-ordinator Ms Gill Swales BA MCLIP DipLib (e-mail: gswales@scotborders.gov.uk)

Area libraries

- Galashiels Library, Lawyer's Brae, Galashiels, Selkirkshire TD1 3JQ
  ☎(01896) 752512
  Fax (01896) 753575
  e-mail: libgalashiels@scotborders.gov.uk
  Area Librarian Miss Caroline R Letton MA FSA(Scot) MCLIP DipLib

- Hawick Library, North Bridge Street, Hawick, Roxburghshire TD9 9QT
  ☎(01450) 372637
  Fax (01450) 370991
  e-mail: libhawick@scotborders.gov.uk
  Area Librarian John Beedle BA MCLIP
- Peebles Library, Chambers Institute, High Street, Peebles, Peeblesshire EH45 8AG
  ☎(01721) 720123
  Fax (01721) 724424
  e-mail: libpeebles@scotborders.gov.uk
  Area Librarian Paul Taylor BSc FSA MCLIP

Branch libraries

- Coldstream Library, Gateway Centre, Coldstream, Scottish Borders TD12 4AE
  ☎(01890) 883314 (tel/fax)
  e-mail: libcoldstream@scotborders.gov.uk
  Branch Librarian Vacant
- Duns Library, 49 Newtown Street, Duns, Berwickshire TD11 3AU
  ☎(01361) 882622
  Fax (01361) 884104
  e-mail: libduns@scotborders.gov.uk
  Branch Librarian Ms Joan B Sanderson BA MCLIP
- Earlston Library, High School, Earlston, Scottish Borders TD4 6ED
  ☎(01896) 849282
  Fax (01896) 848918
  e-mail: libearlston@scotborders.gov.uk
  Branch Librarian Mrs Anne Taitt
- Eyemouth Library, Manse Road, Eyemouth, Scottish Borders TD14 5JE
  ☎(01890) 750300
  Fax (01890) 751633
  e-mail: libeyemouth@scotborders.gov.uk
  Branch Librarian Mrs Joan Thomas, Mrs Alison Fowler
- Innerleithen Library, Buccleuch Street, Innerleithen, Scottish Borders EH44 6LA
  ☎(01896) 830789 (tel/fax)
  e-mail: libinnerleithen@scotborders.gov.uk
  Branch Librarian Mrs Elaine Hogarth
- Jedburgh Library, Castlegate, Jedburgh, Scottish Borders TD8 6AS
  ☎(01835) 863592 (tel/fax)
  e-mail: libjedburgh@scotborders.gov.uk
  Branch Librarian Mrs Carol Chisholm
- Kelso Library, Bowmont Street, Kelso, Roxburghshire TD5 7JH
  ☎(01573) 223171
  Fax (01573) 226618
  e-mail: libkelso@scotborders.gov.uk
  Branch Librarian Mrs Ruth Holmes MSc MCLIP
- Local Studies, St Mary's Mill, Selkirk TD7 5EW
  ☎(01750) 20842
  Fax (01750) 22875
  Librarian Miss Helen Darling BA(Hons) MCLIP (e-mail: hdarling@scotborders.gov.uk)

- Melrose Library, 18 Market Square, Melrose, Scottish Borders TD6 9PN
  ☎(01896) 823052 (tel/fax)
  e-mail: libmelrose@scotborders.gov.uk
  Branch Librarian Mrs Mairi Wight
- Selkirk Library, Ettrick Terrace, Selkirk TD7 4LE
  ☎(01750) 20267 (tel/fax)
  e-mail: libselkirk@scotborders.gov.uk
  Branch Librarian Jamie McIntyre MA(Hons) PGDipILS

SHETLAND ISLANDS

Authority: Shetland Islands Council
HQ Shetland Library, Lower Hillhead, Lerwick, Shetland ZE1 0EL
☎(01595) 743868 (enquiries and administration)
Fax (01595) 694430
e-mail: shetlandlibrary@sic.shetland.gov.uk
Online catalogue: http://library.shetland.gov.uk/TalisPrism
Library and Information Services Manager Ms Silvija Crook (e-mail: silvija.crook@sic.shetland.gov.uk)
Support Services Librarian Douglas Garden (e-mail: douglas.garden@sic.shetland.gov.uk)
Customer Services Librarian Ms Karen Fraser (e-mail: karen.fraser@sic.shetland.gov.uk)
Secretary/Administration Assistant Mrs Agnes Anderson (e-mail: agnes.anderson@sic.shetland.gov.uk)
Administration Assistant Miss Katrina Williamson (e-mail: katrina.a.williamson@sic.shetland.gov.uk)
Systems Librarian Miss Aileen Paterson (e-mail: aileen.paterson@sic.shetland.gov.uk)
Young People's Services Librarian Mrs Morag Nicolson BA DipLib MCLIP (e-mail: morag.nicolson@sic.shetland.gov.uk)

SOUTH AYRSHIRE

Authority: South Ayrshire Council
HQ Library HQ, 26 Green Street, Ayr KA8 8AD
☎(01292) 288820
Fax (01292) 619019
url: www.south-ayrshire.gov.uk
Acting Libraries Manager Ms Jean Inness MA(Hons) DipLib MCLIP (e-mail: jean.inness@south-ayrshire.gov.uk)

Central/largest library

Carnegie Library, 12 Main Street, Ayr KA8 8ED
☎(01292) 286385
Fax (01292) 611593
e-mail: carnegie.library@south-ayrshire.gov.uk

SOUTH LANARKSHIRE

Authority: South Lanarkshire Council
HQ Libraries Service, Education Resources, Council Offices, Almada Street, Hamilton, South Lanarkshire ML3 0AA
☎(01698) 454545
Fax (01698) 454465
url: www.southlanarkshire.gov.uk
Libraries Manager Ms D Barr BA MCLIP MIMgt (01698 454412; e-mail: diana.barr@southlanarkshire.gov.uk)
Information Services Co-ordinator John McGarrity BA MCLIP (01698 452220; e-mail: john.mcgarrity@library.s-lanark.org.uk)
Service Development Co-ordinator Ms Frances Roberts BA MCLIP (01698 452144; e-mail: frances.roberts@library.s-lanark.org.uk)
Literacy Development Co-ordinator Ms Margaret Cowan MCLIP (01355 248581; e-mail: margaret.cowan@southlanarkshire.gov.uk)

Central/largest library

East Kilbride Central Library, 40 The Olympia, East Kilbride, South Lanarkshire G74 1PG
☎(01355) 220046
Fax (01355) 229365
e-mail: libek@library.s-lanark.org.uk
Libraries Co-ordinator D Leitch MCLIP

Divisional libraries

- Hamilton Central Library, 98 Cadzow Street, Hamilton, South Lanarkshire ML3 6HQ
  ☎(01698) 452299
  Fax (01698) 286334
  e-mail: libhc@library.s-lanark.org.uk
  Libraries Co-ordinator Ms Fiona Renfrew MCLIP

STIRLING

Authority: Stirling Council
HQ Library HQ, Springkerse Industrial Estate, Borrowmeadow Road, Stirling FK7 7TN
☎(01786) 432383 (enquiries/administration)
Fax (01786) 432395
e-mail: libraryheadquarters@stirling.gov.uk
url: www.stirling.gov.uk
Head of Libraries, Learning, Communities and Culture Mrs Susan Carragher BA(Hons) MCLIP (01786 443388) (Based at Stirling Council, Viewforth, Stirling FK8 2ET)
Library and Archives Services Manager Robert Ruthven MA DipLIS MCLIP (01786 432380)
Area Librarian Ms Elizabeth Farr BA MCLIP (01786 432389)
Operations Librarian Andrew Muirhead MA MLitt MCLIP (01786 432386)

Central/largest library

Central Library, Corn Exchange Road, Stirling FK8 2HX

☎(01786) 432106/7 (enquiries), (01786) 432108 (administration)
Fax (01786) 473094
e-mail: centrallibrary@stirling.gov.uk
Service Development Librarian, Children's and Youth Libraries Steven J Dolman BA(Hons) MCLIP (01786 432108)

WEST DUNBARTONSHIRE

Authority: West Dunbartonshire Council
HQ West Dunbartonshire Libraries, Levenford House, Helenslee Road, Dumbarton G82 4AH
☎(01389) 608041 (enquiries and administration)
Fax (01389) 608044
url: www.wdcweb.info
Director, Education & Cultural Services Ms Liz McGinlay (Based at Council Offices, Garshake Road, Dumbarton G82 3PU)
Manager, Lifelong Learning Ken Graham
Section Head, Libraries Miss Fiona MacDonald MA(Hons) DipLib MCLIP
Senior Officer, Young People's Services Ms Anne Louise Anglim BA(Hons) MCLIP (e-mail: annelouise.anglim@west-dunbarton.gov.uk)

Area libraries

- Clydebank Library, Dumbarton Road, Clydebank, Dumbarton G81 1XH
  ☎0141 952 1416 (enquiries)
  Fax 0141 951 8275
  Area Librarians Ms Maureen Lyden, Ms Laura Wilson BA(Hons) MCLIP
- Dumbarton Library, Strathleven Place, Dumbarton G82 1BD
  ☎(01389) 763129 (enquiries), (01389) 608038 (administration)
  Fax (01389) 607302
  Area Librarian Ms Fiona Matheson MCLIP

WEST LOTHIAN

Authority: West Lothian Council
HQ Library HQ, Connolly House, Hopefield Road, Blackburn, West Lothian EH47 7HZ
☎(01506) 776336 (enquiries), (01506) 776342 (administration)
Fax (01506) 776345
e-mail: library.info@westlothian.gov.uk
url: www.westlothian.gov.uk/libraries
Library Services Manager Mrs Jeanette Castle MA(Hons) DipILS MCLIP (e-mail: jeanette.castle@westlothian.gov.uk)
Support Services Manager Ms Anne Hunt MA(Hons) DipLib MCLIP (01506 776325; e-mail: anne.hunt@westlothian.gov.uk)
Area Manager Mrs Irene Brough (01506 776327; e-mail: irene.brough@westlothian.gov.uk)
Acting Area Manager Mrs Hilda Gibson MCLIP (01506 776350; e-mail: hilda.gibson@westlothian.gov.uk), Mrs Mary Shelton MCLIP (01506 776350; e-mail: mary.shelton@westlothian.gov.uk)

Central/largest library

Carmondean Library, Carmondean Centre, Livingston, West Lothian EH54 8PT
☎(01506) 777602 (enquiries)
e-mail: carmondean.lib@wled.org.uk
Library Manager Ms Cathy MacIntyre BA MSc(Econ) MCLIP (e-mail: cathy.macintyre@wled.org.uk)

Branch libraries

- Almondbank Library, The Mall, Craigshill, Livingston, West Lothian EH54 5EJ
  ☎(01506) 777500
  e-mail: almondbank.lib@wled.org.uk
  Library Manager Ms Helen Dobie MA DipLib MCLIP (e-mail: helen.dobie@wled.org.uk)
- Armadale Library, West Main Street, Armadale, West Lothian EH48 3JB
  ☎(01501) 678400
  Fax armadale.lib@wled.org.uk
  Library Manager Mrs Betty Hunter MCLIP (e-mail: betty.hunter@wled.org.uk)
- Bathgate Library, 66 Hopetoun Street, Bathgate, West Lothian EH48 4PD
  ☎(01506) 776400
  e-mail: bathgate.lib@wled.org.uk
  Library Managers Mrs Anne Mackintosh BA MCLIP (e-mail: anne.mackintosh@wled.org.uk), Mrs Margaret Armstrong MCLIP (e-mail: margaret.armstrong@wled.org.uk) (job-share)
- Blackburn Connected, Mill Centre, Blackburn, West Lothian EH47 7LQ
  ☎(01506) 776500
  e-mail: blackburn.lib@wled.org.uk
  Library Manager Mrs Fiona Aitken MSc(Econ) ILS (e-mail: fiona.aitken@wled.org.uk)
- Blackridge Library, Craig Inn Centre, Blackridge, West Lothian EH48 3SP
  ☎(01501) 752396
  e-mail: blackridge.lib@wled.org.uk
  Library Manager Ms Moira McCabe (e-mail: moira.mccabe@wled.org.uk)
- Broxburn Library, West Main Street, Broxburn, West Lothian EH52 5RH
  ☎(01506) 775600
  e-mail: broxburn.lib@wled.org.uk
  Library Manager Ms Catherine Lauriol MA MSc(Econ) MCLIP (e-mail: catherine.lauriol@wled.org.uk)
- East Calder Library, Main Street, East Calder, West Lothian EH53 0EJ
  ☎(01506) 883633
  e-mail: eastcalder.lib@wled.org.uk
  Library Manager Ms Gillian Downie BA MCLIP (e-mail: gillian.downie@wled.org.uk)
- Fauldhouse Library, Lanrigg Road, Fauldhouse, West Lothian EH47 9JA
  ☎(01501) 770358
  e-mail: fauldhouse.lib@wled.org.uk
  Library Manager Ms Marilyn James (e-mail: marilyn.james@wled.org.uk)
- Lanthorn Library, Lanthorn Centre, Kenilworth Rise, Dedridge, Livingston, West Lothian EH54 6NY
  ☎(01506) 777700
  e-mail: lanthorn.lib@wled.org.uk

Library Manager Ms Gillian Downie BA MCLIP (e-mail: gillian.downie@wled.org.uk)

- Linlithgow Library, The Vennel, Linlithgow, West Lothian EH49 7EX
  ☎(01506) 775490
  e-mail: linlithgow.lib@wled.org.uk
  Library Manager Mrs Kay Ali BA MCLIP (e-mail: kay.ali@wled.org.uk)
- Public Reference Library, West Lothian College, Almondvale Cresent, Livingston, West Lothian EH54 7EP
  ☎(01506) 427601
  Library Manager Ms Linda Hartley (e-mail: linda.hartley@west-lothian.ac.uk)
- Pumpherston Library, Pumpherston Primary School, 18 Uphall Station Road, Pumpherston, West Lothian EH53 0LP
  ☎(01506) 435837
  e-mail: pumpherston.lib@wled.org.uk
  Library Manager Mrs Ruth Forsythe MCS (e-mail: ruth.forsythe@wled.org.uk)
- West Calder Library, Main Street, West Calder, West Lothian EH55 8BJ
  ☎(01506) 871371
  e-mail: westcalder.lib@wled.org.uk
  Library Manager Ms Catherine Lauriol MA MSc(Econ) MCLIP (e-mail: catherine.lauriol@wled.org.uk)
- Whitburn Library, Union Road, Whitburn, West Lothian EH47 0AR
  ☎(01501) 678050
  e-mail: whitburn.lib@wled.org.uk
  Acting Library Manager Ms Sandra Valaitis (e-mail: sandra.valaitis@wled.org.uk)

WESTERN ISLES *see* COMHAIRLE NAN EILEAN SIAR

ANGLESEY, ISLE OF

Authority: Isle of Anglesey County Council
HQ Department of Education and Leisure, Parc Mownt, Fford Glanhwfa, Llangefni, Ynys Môn LL77 7EY
☎(01248) 752092 (enquiries); (01248) 752908 (administration)
Fax (01248) 752999
url: www.ynysmon.gov.uk
Corporate Director: Education and Leisure Richard Jones MA (01248 752900; e-mail: rpjed@ynysmon.gov.uk)
Head of Service: Lifelong Learning and Information John Rees Thomas BSc(Econ) DipLib MCLIP (01248 752908; e-mail: jrtlh@ynysmon.gov.uk)
Principal Librarian David Evans BA DipLib MCLIP
Archivist Ms Anne Venables BA DipAA (01248 752080)

Central/largest library

Llangefni Central Library, Lôn-y-Felin, Llangefni, Ynys Môn LL77 7RT
☎(01248) 752092
Fax (01248) 750197
e-mail: dhelh@ynysmon.gov.uk

Branch libraries

- Amlwch Library, Lôn Parys, Amlwch, Ynys Môn LL68 9EA
  ☎(01407) 830145 (tel/fax)
  e-mail: kbxlh@ynysmon.gov.uk
- Holyhead Library, Newry Fields, Holyhead, Ynys Môn LL65 1LA
  ☎(01407) 762917
  Fax (01407) 769616
  e-mail: kpxlh@ynysmon.gov.uk
- Menai Bridge Library, Ffordd y Ffair, Menai Bridge, Ynys Môn LL59 5AS
  ☎(01248) 712706 (tel/fax)
  e-mail: dbxlh@ynysmon.gov.uk
- Record Office, Shirehall, Glanhwfa Street, Llangefni, Ynys Môn LL77 7TW
  ☎(01248) 752083
  Fax (01248) 751289
  e-mail: archives@ynysmon.gov.uk

BLAENAU GWENT

Authority: Blaenau Gwent County Borough Council
HQ Library Headquarters, Leisure Services, Anvil Court, Church Street, Abertillery, Blaenau Gwent NP13 1DB
url: www.blaenau-gwent.gov.uk

Principal Librarian Mrs Sue White MCLIP (01495 355950; e-mail: sue.white@blaenau-gwent.gov.uk)
Development Manager Ms Karen Ross MCLIP (01495 354607; e-mail: karen.ross@blaenau-gwent.gov.uk)

Central/largest library

Ebbw Vale Library, 21 Bethcar Street, Ebbw Vale, Blaenau Gwent NP23 6HH
☎(01495) 303069
Fax (01495) 350547
e-mail: ebbw.vale.library@blaenau-gwent.gov.uk

Area libraries

- Abertillery Library, Station Hill, Abertillery, Blaenau Gwent NP13 1TE
  ☎(01495) 212332
  Fax (01495) 320995
  e-mail: abertillery.library@blaenau-gwent.gov.uk
- Blaina Library, Reading Institute, High Street, Blaina, Blaenau Gwent NP13 3BN
  ☎(01495) 290312 (tel/fax)
  e-mail: blaina.library@blaenau-gwent.gov.uk
- Brynmawr Library, Market Square, Brynmawr, Blaenau Gwent NP23 4AJ
  ☎(01495) 310045 (tel/fax)
  e-mail: brynmawr.library@blaenau-gwent.gov.uk
- Cwm Library, Canning Street, Cwm, Blaenau Gwent NP23 7RW
  ☎(01495) 370454 (tel/fax)
  e-mail: cwm.library@blaenau-gwent.gov.uk
- Llanhilleth Library, Workman's Institute, Llanhilleth, Blaenau Gwent NP13 2JH
  ☎(01495) 214485 (tel/fax)
  e-mail: llanhilleth.library@blaenau-gwent.gov.uk
- Tredegar Library, The Circle, Tredegar, Blaenau Gwent NP22 3PS
  ☎(01495) 722687
  Fax (01495) 717018
  e-mail: tredegar.library@blaenau-gwent.gov.uk

BRIDGEND

Authority: Bridgend County Borough Council
HQ Library and Information Service, Coed Parc, Park Street, Bridgend CF31 4BA
☎(01656) 754800
Fax (01656) 645719
e-mail: blis@bridgend.gov.uk
url: www.bridgend.gov.uk/libraries
Group Manager (Libraries, Information and Heritage) John C Woods BSc MCLIP (e-mail: woodsjc@bridgend.gov.uk)

Central/largest libraries

- Bridgend Lending Library, Wyndham Street, Bridgend CF31 1EF
  ☎(01656) 754830
  Fax (01656) 754829

e-mail: bridgendlib@bridgend.gov.uk
Branch Librarian Mrs Diana Apperley MA (e-mail: apperd@bridgend.gov.uk)
- Maesteg Library, North's Lane, Maesteg, Glamorgan CF34 9AA
☎(01656) 754835
Fax (01656) 754834
e-mail: maestlib@bridgend.gov.uk
Branch Librarian Ms Helen Pridham BA DipIS MCLIP (e-mail: morleh@bridgend.gov.uk)
- Pencoed Library, Penybont Road, Pencoed, Glamorgan CF35 5RA
☎(01656) 754840
Fax (01656) 754842
e-mail: penclib@bridgend.gov.uk
Branch Librarian Mrs Wendy Francis (e-mail: francwa@bridgend.gov.uk)
- Porthcawl Library, Church Place, Porthcawl, Glamorgan CF36 3AG
☎(01656) 754845
Fax (01656) 754847
e-mail: porthcawllib@bridgend.gov.uk
Branch Librarian Mrs Claire Williams MSc(Econ) MCLIP (e-mail: willicd1@bridgend.gov.uk)
- Pyle Library, Pyle Life Centre, Helig Fan, Pyle, Glamorgan CF33 6BS
☎(01656) 754850
Fax (01656) 754852
e-mail: pylelib@bridgend.gov.uk
Life Centre Manager Mrs Janet Arbery (e-mail: arberja@bridgend.gov.uk)
- Reference and Information Centre, Coed Parc, Park Street, Bridgend CF31 4BA
☎(01656) 754810
Fax (01656) 645719
e-mail: blis@bridgend.gov.uk
url: www.bridgend.gov.uk/libraries
Reference Librarian Mrs Lesley A Milne BA MCLIP (e-mail: milnela@bridgend.gov.uk)

CAERPHILLY

Authority: Caerphilly County Borough Council
HQ Lifelong Learning and Leisure, Unit 7, Woodfieldside Business Park, Penmaen Road, Pontllanfraith, Blackwood, Caerphilly NP12 2DG
☎(01495) 235587
Fax (01495) 235567
e-mail: libraries@caerphilly.gov.uk
url: www.caerphilly.gov.uk/learning/libraries
Principal Officer: Libraries Ms Mary Palmer MLib MCLIP
Assistant Director Peter Gomer

Area libraries

- Blackwood Library, 192 High Street, Blackwood, Caerphilly NP12 1AJ
☎(01495) 233000
Fax (01495) 233002
Area Manager: North Mrs Dianne Madhavan MCLIP

- Caerphilly Library, Morgan Jones Park, Caerphilly CF8 1AP
  ☎029 208 52543
  Fax 029 2086 5585
  Area Manager: South Mrs Yvonne Harris MCLIP
- Lifelong Learning and Leisure, Unit 4, Woodfieldside Business Park, Penmaen Road, Pontllanfraith, Blackwood, Caerphilly NP12 2DG
  ☎(01495) 235562
  Fax (01495) 235565
  Youth Services Manager Mrs Lesley Case MCLIP (e-mail: casel@caerphilly.gov.uk)
- Risca Library, Park Place, Risca, Caerphilly NP11 6AS
  ☎(01633) 600920
  Fax (01633) 600922
  Area Manager: Central Mrs Marion Davies MCLIP

CARDIFF

Authority: Cardiff Council
HQ Cardiff Libraries and Information Service, Central Library, John Street, Cardiff CF10 5BA
☎029 2038 2116
Fax 029 2087 1588
e-mail: centrallibrary@cardiff.gov.uk
url: www.cardiff.gov.uk/libraries
Operational Manager Lifelong Learning Ms Barbara Beedham (e-mail: b.beedham@cardiff.gov.uk)
Central Library Manager Rob Boddy BA MCLIP (e-mail: rboddy@cardiff.gov.uk)
Libraries and Information Development Manager Ms Elspeth Morris BA MCLIP (e-mail: emorris@cardiff.gov.uk)
Branch Libraries Manager Ms Fiona Bailey (e-mail: fbailey@cardiff.gov.uk)
Stock Manager Ms Linda Williams MCLIP (e-mail: lwilliams@cardiff.gov.uk)

CARMARTHENSHIRE

Authority: Carmarthenshire County Council
HQ Library HQ, Block 1, Parc Myrddin, Richmond Terrace, Carmarthen, Carmarthenshire SA31 1DS
☎(01267) 228203
Fax (01267) 238584
url: www.libraries.carmarthenshire.gov.uk
Head of Libraries and Community Learning Dewi P Thomas BA DipLib MCLIP (e-mail: dpthomas@sirgar.gov.uk)

Area libraries

- Ammanford Area Library, 3 Wind Street, Ammanford, Carmarthenshire SA18 3DN
  ☎(01269) 598150
  Fax (01269) 598151
  Area Librarian Myrddin Morgan BSc(Econ) DipLib MCLIP (e-mail: mymorgan@sirgar.gov.uk)

- Carmarthen Area Library, St Peter's Street, Carmarthen SA31 1LN
  ☎(01267) 224824
  Fax (01267) 221839
  Area Librarian William T Phillips BA DipLib MCLIP (e-mail: wtphillips@sirgar.gov.uk)
- Llanelli Area Library, Vaughan Street, Llanelli, Carmarthenshire SA15 3AS
  ☎(01554) 773538
  Fax (01554) 750125
  Area Librarian Mark Jewell BSc(Econ) (e-mail: mjewell@sirgar.gov.uk)

CEREDIGION

Authority: Ceredigion County Council
HQ Public Library, Corporation Street, Aberystwyth, Ceredigion SY23 2BU
☎(01970) 633703; 633716
Fax (01970) 625059
url: www.ceredigion.gov.uk
Assistant Director (Cultural Services) D Geraint Lewis MA MCLIP
County Libraries Officer W H Howells BA MLib MCLIP (e-mail: williamh@ceredigion.gov.uk)

Branch library

- Branch Library, Canolfan Teifi, Pendre, Ceredigion SA43 1JL
  ☎(01239) 612578
  Fax (01239) 612285
  e-mail: teifillb@ceredigion.gov.uk
  Branch Librarian D G Evans MCLIP

CONWY

Authority: Conwy County Borough Council
HQ Library, Information and Culture Service, Bodlondeb, Conwy LL32 8DU
☎(01492) 576140
Fax (01492) 592061
e-mail: lic@conwy.gov.uk
url: www.conwy.gov.uk/library
Head of Service Ms Rona Aldrich MLib MCLIP (e-mail: rona.aldrich@conwy.gov.uk)
Principal Librarian Ms Rhian G Williams BA DipLib MCLIP (01492 576139; e-mail: rhian.williams@conwy.gov.uk)
Corporate Information Manager David J Smith BA(Hons) DMS MCLIP MCMI (01492 576137; e-mail: david.smith@conwy.gov.uk)

Regional/community libraries

- Abergele Library, Market Street, Abergele, Abergele, Conwy LL22 7BP
  ☎(01745) 832638
  Fax (01745) 823376
  e-mail: llyfr.lib.abergele@conwy.gov.uk
- Colwyn Bay Library, Woodland Road West, Colwyn Bay, Conwy LL29 7DH
  ☎(01492) 532358

Fax (01492) 534474
e-mail: llyfr.lib.baecolwynbay@conwy.gov.uk

- Conwy Library, Civic Hall, Castle Street, Conwy LL32 6AY
☎(01492) 596242
Fax (01492) 582359
e-mail: llyfr.lib.conwy@conwy.gov.uk
- Llandudno Library, Mostyn Street, Llandudno, Conwy LL30 2RP
☎(01492) 574010/574020
Fax (01492) 876826
e-mail: llyfr.lib.llandudno@conwy.gov.uk
- Llanrwst Library, Plas yn Dre, Station Road, Llanrwst, Conwy LL26 0DF
☎(01492) 640043
e-mail: llyfr.lib.llanrwst@conwy.gov.uk

DENBIGHSHIRE

Authority: Denbighshire County Council
HQ Library Service, Directorate of Lifelong Learning, Yr Hen Garchar, Clwyd Street, Ruthin, Denbighshire LL15 1HP
☎(01824) 708204 (enquiries)
Fax (01824) 708202
url: www.denbighshire.gov.uk/libraries
Principal Librarian Robat Arwyn Jones BMus MCLIP DipLib (01824 708203; e-mail: arwyn.jones@denbighshire.gov.uk)

Central/largest library

Rhyl Library, Museum and Arts Centre, Church Street, Rhyl, Denbighshire LL18 3AA
☎(01745) 353814
Fax (01745) 331438
e-mail: rhyl.library@denbighshire.gov.uk
Principal Community Librarian Alastair Barber BSc DipLib MCLIP

FLINTSHIRE

Authority: Flintshire County Council
HQ Library and Information Service, Library Headquarters, County Hall, Mold, Flintshire CH7 6NW
☎(01352) 704400
Fax (01352) 753662
e-mail: libraries@flintshire.gov.uk
url: www.flintshire.gov.uk
Head of Libraries, Culture and Heritage L Rawsthorne MLib FCLIP MIMgt
Principal Librarian, Community Libraries and Arts Mrs S Kirby MCLIP (01352 704402)
Senior Information Librarian Mrs G Fraser BA MCLIP (01352 704416)
Lifelong Learning Librarian Mrs Gina Maddison BA MA MCLIP (e-mail: gina_maddison@flintshire.gov.uk)

Group libraries

- Broughton Library, Broughton Hall Road, Broughton, Nr Chester, Flintshire CH4 0QQ
  ☎(01244) 533727
  Community Librarian Miss Kathleen Morris BA DipLib MCLIP
- Buckley Library, Museum and Gallery, The Precinct, Buckley, Flintshire CH7 2EF
  ☎(01244) 549210
  Fax (01244) 548850
  Community Librarian Mrs Penelope Corbett MLib MCLIP
- Connah's Quay Library, Wepre Drive, Connah's Quay, Deeside, Flintshire CH5 4HA
  ☎(01244) 830485
  Fax (01244) 856672
  Community Librarian Mrs Carol A Guy BA MCLIP
- Flint Library, Church Street, Flint, Flintshire CH6 5AP
  ☎(01352) 703737
  Fax (01352) 731010
  Community Librarian Mrs Elizabeth A Martin BLib MCLIP
- Holywell Library, North Road, Holywell, Flintshire CH8 7TQ
  ☎(01352) 713157
  Fax (01352) 710744
  Community Librarian Mrs Catherine E Barber MCLIP, Mrs Morwenna Wallbank MCLIP
- Mold Library, Museum and Gallery, Earl Road, Mold, Flintshire CH7 1AP
  ☎(01352) 754791
  Fax (01352) 754655
  Community Librarian Miss Nia W Jones BLib MCLIP

GWYNEDD

Authority: Gwynedd Council
HQ Council Offices, Caernarfon, Gwynedd LL55 1SH
☎(01286) 679504
Fax (01286) 677347
e-mail: llyfrgell@gwynedd.gov.uk
url: www.gwynedd.gov.uk/library
Principal Librarian Hywel James BA DipLib MCLIP

Central/largest library

Caernarfon Library, Pavilion Hill, Caernarfon, Gwynedd LL55 1AS
☎(01286) 679463
Fax (01286) 671137
e-mail: llyfrgellcaernarfon@gwynedd.gov.uk
Community Services Librarian Mrs Eirlys Thomas MCLIP
User Services Manager Ms Nia Gruffydd MLib MCLIP (e-mail: NiaGruffydd@gwynedd.gov.uk)
Information Services Manager Alun Hughes Williams BA DipLib MCLIP (e-mail: AlunHughesWilliams@gwynedd.gov.uk)

Largest libraries

- Bangor Library, Ffordd Gwynedd, Bangor, Gwynedd LL57 1DT
  ☎(01248) 353479
  Fax (01248) 370149
  e-mail: llyfrgellbangor@gwynedd.gov.uk
  Library Services Promoter Ms Rhiannon Clifford Jones MCLIP
- Dolgellau Library, Ffordd y Bala, Dolgellau, Gwynedd LL40 2YF
  ☎(01341) 422771
  Fax (01341) 423560
  e-mail: llyfrgelldolgellau@gwynedd.gov.uk
  Information Librarian Elwyn Evans MCLIP
- Porthmadog Library, Stryd Wesla, Porthmadog, Gwynedd LL49 9BT
  ☎(01766) 514091
  Fax (01766) 513821
  e-mail: llyfrgellporthmadog@gwynedd.gov.uk
  South Gwynedd Community Librarian Ms Anna Yardley Jones BA DipLib MCLIP

MERTHYR TYDFIL

Authority: Merthyr Tydfil County Borough Council
HQ Central Library, High Street, Merthyr Tydfil CF47 8AF
☎(01685) 723057
Fax (01685) 370690
e-mail: library.services@merthyr.gov.uk
url: www.merthyr.gov.uk
Head of Libraries Geraint James BA MCLIP

Area libraries

- Dowlais Library, Church Street, Merthyr Tydfil CF48 3HS
  ☎(01685) 723051
  Fax (01685) 723051
  (Enquiries to Central Library)
- Treharris Library, Perrott Street, Treharris, Merthyr Tydfil CF46 5ET
  ☎(01443) 410517
  Fax (01443) 410675
  (Enquiries to Central Library)

MONMOUTHSHIRE

Authority: Monmouthshire County Council
HQ Libraries and Information Service, Chepstow Library, Manor Way, Chepstow, Monmouthshire NP16 5HZ
☎(01291) 635731 (enquiries), 01291 635649 (administration)
Fax (01291) 635736
url: http://libraries.monmouthshire.gov.uk
Principal Librarian Ms Ann Jones MLib MCLIP (e-mail: annjones@monmouthshire.gov.uk)

Area libraries

Bryn-a-Cwm Area

- Abergavenny Library, Baker Street, Abergavenny, Monmouthshire NP7 5BD
  ☎(01873) 735980
  Fax (01873) 735985
  e-mail: abergavennylibrary@monmouthshire.gov.uk
  Library Managers Ms Julia Greenway MCLIP (e-mail: juliagreenway@monmouthshire.gov.uk), Ms Alison Newsam BA DipLIS MCLIP (e-mail: alisonnewsam@monmouthshire.gov.uk)

Central Monmouthshire Area

- Monmouth Library, Rolls Hall, Whitecross Street, Monmouth NP25 3BY
  ☎(01600) 775215
  Fax (01600) 775218
  e-mail: monmouthlibrary@monmouthshire.gov.uk
  Library Manager Ms Vivienne Thomas BA BD MCLIP (e-mail: viviennethomas@monmouthshire.gov.uk)

Lower Wye Area

- Chepstow Library, Manor Way, Chepstow, Monmouthshire NP16 5HZ
  ☎(01291) 635730
  Fax (01291) 635736
  e-mail: chepstowlibrary@monmouthshire.gov.uk
  Library Manager Ms Margaret Stimson (e-mail: margaretstimson@monmouthshire.gov.uk)

Severnside Area

- Caldicot Library, Woodstock Way, Caldicot, Monmouthshire NP26 4DB
  ☎(01291) 426425
  Fax (01291) 426426
  e-mail: caldicotlibrary@monmouthshire.gov.uk
  Library Managers Richard Skinner MCLIP (e-mail: richardskinner@monmouthshire.gov.uk), Ms Valerie Jenkins (e-mail: valeriejenkins@monmouthshire.gov.uk)

NEATH PORT TALBOT

Authority: Neath Port Talbot County Borough Council
HQ Library and Information Services, Reginald Street, Velindre, Port Talbot SA13 1YY
☎(01639) 899829
Fax (01639) 899152
e-mail: npt.libhq@npt.gov.uk
url: www.npt.gov.uk
Cultural Services Co-ordinator J L Ellis BA MCLIP (e-mail: j.l.ellis@npt.gov.uk)

Central/largest libraries

- Neath Library, Victoria Gardens, Neath, Neath Port Talbot SA11 3BA

☎(01639) 644604/635017
Fax (01639) 641912
e-mail: neath.library@npt.gov.uk
Branch Library Manager Wayne John MCLIP (e-mail: w.john@npt.gov.uk)

- Port Talbot Library, Aberavon Shopping Centre (1st Floor), Port Talbot SA13 1PB
☎(01639) 763490/1
Fax (01639) 763489
e-mail: porttalbot.library@npt.gov.uk

NEWPORT

Authority: Newport City Council
HQ Community Learning and Libraries Service, Central Library, John Frost Square, Newport, Gwent NP20 1PA
☎(01633) 656656 (enquiries and administration)
Fax (01633) 414705
e-mail: central.library@newport.gov.uk
url: www.newport.gov.uk/libraries
Community Learning and Libraries Manager Mrs Gill John MBA MCLIP
Children and Young People's Services Manager Ms Tracey Paddon BSc(Hons) DipAppSc MCLIP

PEMBROKESHIRE

Authority: Pembrokeshire County Council
HQ County Library, Dew Street, Haverfordwest, Pembrokeshire SA61 1SU
☎(01437) 775241 (administration, enquiries); (01437) 775244 (Lending Library); (01437) 775248 (Reference Library)
Fax (01437) 767092
url: www.pembrokeshire.gov.uk
Cultural Services Manager Neil Bennett BSc DMS MCLIP (01437 775240; e-mail: neil.bennett@pembrokeshire.gov.uk)
Principal Librarian (Development) Mrs Anita Thomas MCLIP (e-mail: anita.thomas@pembrokeshire.gov.uk)
Principal Librarian (Service, Delivery & Training) Clive Richards MCLIP (e-mail: clive.richards@pembrokeshire.gov.uk)
Information/ICT Development Librarian Ms Sue Armour MCLIP (e-mail: sue.armour@pembrokeshire.gov.uk)
Stock & Reader Development Librarian Mrs Sandra Matthews MCLIP (01437 775243; e-mail: sandra.matthews@pembrokeshire.gov.uk)
Children's & Young People's Librarian Miss Pamela Harry (e-mail: pamela.harry@pembrokeshire.gov.uk)
Outreach, Social Inclusion & Marketing Librarian Mrs Eleri Evans MCLIP (e-mail: eleri.evans@pembrokeshire.gov.uk)
Local & Family History Librarian George Edwards MCLIP (01437 775245; e-mail: george.edwards@pembrokeshire.gov.uk)

Community libraries

- County Library, Dew Street, Haverfordwest, Pembrokeshire SA61 1SU
  ☎(01437) 775244
  Librarian in Charge Ms Gill Gilliland (e-mail: gill.gilliland@pembrokeshire.gov.uk)
- Fishguard Library, Fishguard Town Hall, Market Square, Fishguard, Pembrokeshire SA65 9HA
  ☎(01348) 872694 (tel/fax)
  Cultural Manager Ms Wendy Davies (e-mail: wendy.davies@pembrokeshire.gov.uk)
- Milford Haven Library, Hamilton Terrace, Milford Haven, Pembrokeshire SA73 3HP
  ☎(01646) 692892 (tel/fax)
  Senior Library Assistant Mrs Joan Cole
- Pembroke Dock Library, Water Street, Pembroke Dock, Pembrokeshire SA72 6DW
  ☎(01646) 686356
  Fax (01646) 687071
  Senior Library Assistant Stuart Croxford
- Tenby Library, Greenhill Avenue, Tenby, Pembrokeshire SA70 7LB
  ☎(01834) 843934 (tel/fax)
  Senior Library Assistant Mrs Julie Sutcliffe

POWYS

Authority: Powys County Council
HQ County Library HQ, Cefnllys Road, Llandrindod Wells, Powys LD1 5LD
☎(01597) 826860 (general enquiries)
Fax (01597) 826872
url: www.powys.gov.uk
County Librarian Miss Tudfil L Adams BA MCLIP

Library HQ, Cefnllys Lane, Llandrindod Wells, Powys LD1 5LD
☎(01597) 826864
Fax (01597) 826872
Principal Librarian (Field Services) Mrs Helen Edwards BLib MCLIP

Children and Schools Library HQ, Cefnllys Lane, Llandrindod Wells, Powys LD1 5LD
☎(01597) 826867
Fax (01597) 826872
Principal Librarian (Education, Schools and Children) Mrs Dianne Jones MCLIP

Main libraries

- Brecon Library, Ship Street, Brecon, Powys LD3 9AE
  ☎(01874) 623346
  Fax (01874) 622818
  Group Librarian Ms Deborah Cogger MCLIP
- Llandrindod Wells Library, Cefnllys Lane, Llandrindod Wells, Powys LD1 5LD
  ☎(01597) 826870
  Fax (01597) 826872
  Group Librarian Mrs Rebecca Pugh
- Newtown Library, Park Lane, Newtown, Powys SY16 1EJ

☎(01686) 626934
Fax (01686) 624935
Group Librarian Gareth Griffiths BA MCLIP

RHONDDA CYNON TAF

Authority: Rhondda Cynon Taf County Borough Council
HQ Education and Lifelong Learning, Ty Trevithick, Abercynon, Mountain Ash, Rhondda Cynon Taf CF45 4UQ
☎(01443) 744000
Fax (01443) 744023
url: www.rhondda-cynon-taf.gov.uk
Head of Libraries and Museums Ms Gill Evans BA DipLib MCLIP (01443 744029; e-mail: Gillian.M.Evans@rhondda-cynon-taff.gov.uk)
Library IT Manager Leon Hughes (01443 778951; e-mail: Leon.J.Hughes@rhondda-cynon-taff.gov.uk) (based at Treorchy Library)
Principal Librarian Mrs Norma Jones MSc MCLIP (01685 880060; e-mail: Norma.D.Jones@rhondda-cynon-taff.gov.uk) (based at Aberdare Library)
Area Manager North Mrs Ros Williams MSc MCLIP (01443 778952; e-mail: Ros.Williams@rhondda-cynon-taff.gov.uk) (based at Treorchy Library)
Area Manager South Mrs Lindsay Morris BA MCLIP (01443 492138; e-mail: Lindsay.M.Morris@rhondda-cynon-taff.gov.uk) (based at Pontypridd Library)
Children and Youth Services Librarian Ms Ceri Roberts MCLIP DipEd (01443 478463; e-mail: ceri.w.roberts@rhondda-cynon-taf.gov.uk) (based at Mountain Ash Library)

Largest library

Aberdare Library, Green Street, Aberdare, Rhondda Cynon Taf CF44 7AG
☎(01685) 880050
Fax (01685) 881181
Branch Librarian Ms Catherine Langdon BA MCLIP

Regional libraries

- Pontypridd Library, Library Road, Pontypridd, Rhondda Cynon Taf CF37 2DY
  ☎(01443) 486850
  Fax (01443) 493258
  Branch Librarian Ms Linda Jones MCLIP, Mrs Edwina Smart BA MCLIP (job-share)
- Treorchy Library, Station Road, Treorchy, Rhondda Cynon Taf CF42 6NN
  ☎(01443) 773204
  Fax (01443) 777047
  Branch Librarian Dean Price BSc(Econ)

SWANSEA

Authority: City and County of Swansea
HQ Library HQ, County Hall, Oystermouth Road, Swansea SA1 3SN
☎(01792) 636430
Fax (01792) 636235
e-mail: swansea.libraries@swansea.gov.uk

url: www.swansea.gov.uk/libraries
Strategic Manager: Libraries and Culture Vacant
Library Services Manager Steve Hardman BSc(Econ) (01792 636610; e-mail: steve.hardman@swansea.gov.uk)
Assistant Head of Libraries Ms Karen Bewen-Chappell MCLIP (01792 636809; e-mail: karen.bewen-chappell@swansea.gov.uk), Ms Caroline Tomlin BA DipLib MCLIP (01792 636809; e-mail: caroline.tomlin@swansea.gov.uk) (job share)
Principal Librarian: Resources and Reader Services Mrs Julie Clement BLib MCLIP (01792 636628; e-mail: julie.clement@swansea.gov.uk)
Principal Librarian: Customer Services and Operations Mrs Jayne Trumper BA DipLib MCLIP (01792 636938; e-mail: jayne.trumper@swansea.gov.uk)
Principal Librarian: Information and Learning Mark Hughes (01792 636329; e-mail: mark.hughes2@swansea.gov.uk)
Central Library Project and Operations Manager Ms Karen Gibbins MCLIP (01792 637176; e-mail: karen.gibbins@swansea.gov.uk)
Principal Librarian: Central Library and Development Ms Rebecca Williams BA(Hons) PGDip (01792 637132; e-mail: rebecca.williams@swansea.gov.uk)

Central/largest library

Swansea Library, Alexandra Road, Swansea SA1 5DX
☎(01792) 516750/516751
Fax (01792) 516759
e-mail: central.library@swansea.gov.uk
Library Manager Ms Kerry Pillai

Branch libraries

- Gorseinon Library, 15 West Street, Gorseinon, Swansea SA4 4AA
  ☎(01792) 516780
  Fax (01792) 516772
  e-mail: gorseinon.library@swansea.gov.uk
  Library Manager Mrs Carole Bonham
- Morriston Library, Treharne Road, Morriston, Swansea SA6 7AA
  ☎(01792) 516770
  Fax (01792) 516771
  e-mail: morriston.library@swansea.gov.uk
  Library Manager Peter Matthews
- Oystermouth Library, Dunns Lane, Mumbles, Swansea SA3 4AA
  ☎(01792) 368380
  Fax (01792) 369143
  e-mail: oystermouth.library@swansea.gov.uk
  Library Manager Vacant

TORFAEN

Authority: Torfaen County Borough Council
HQ Torfaen Libraries HQ, Civic Centre, Pontypool, Torfaen, Gwent NP4 6YB
☎(01633) 628941
Fax (01633) 628935

url: www.torfaen.gov.uk
Principal Librarian Mrs Christine George BA DipLib MCLIP

Central/largest library

Cwmbran Library, Gwent House, Cwmbran, Torfaen, Gwent NP44 1XQ
☎(01633) 483240
Fax (01633) 838609
e-mail: cwmbranlibrary@torfaen.gov.uk
Senior Librarian Ms Sandra Miller MCLIP

Group library

- Pontypool Library, Hanbury Road, Pontypool, Torfaen, Gwent NP4 6JL
  ☎(01495) 762820
  Fax (01495) 752530
  e-mail: pontypoollibrary@torfaen.gov.uk
  Senior Librarian Mark Tanner BA DipLib MCLIP

VALE OF GLAMORGAN

Authority: Vale of Glamorgan Council
HQ Directorate of Learning and Development, Civic Offices, Holton Road, Barry, Vale of Glamorgan CF63 4RU
☎(01446) 709381
url: www.valeofglamorgan.gov.uk/libraries
Chief Librarian Ms Sian E Jones BSc(Econ) MSc(Econ) MCLIP (e-mail: sjones@valeofglamorgan.gov.uk)
Principal Librarian Christopher Edwards BA DipLib MCLIP (e-mail: cdedwards@valeofglamorgan.gov.uk)

Central/largest library

County Library, King Square, Barry, Vale of Glamorgan CF63 4RW
☎(01446) 735722
Senior Librarian Ms Sandra Wildsmith MCLIP (e-mail: smwildsmith@valeofglamorgan.gov.uk)
Information Librarian Ms Katherine Owen MCLIP (e-mail: kowen@valeofglamorgan.gov.uk)

Main libraries

- Cowbridge Library, Old Hall, Cowbridge, Vale of Glamorgan CF7 7AH
  ☎(01446) 773941
  Community Librarian Ms Melanie Weeks (e-mail: mpweeks@valeofglamorgan.gov.uk)
- Dinas Powys Library, The Murch, Dinas Powys, Vale of Glamorgan CF64 4QU
  ☎029 2051 2556
  Community Librarian Ms Susan Sawyer (e-mail: ssawyer@valeofglamorgan.gov.uk)
- Llantwit Major Library, Boverton Road, Llantwit Major, Vale of Glamorgan CF61 9XZ
  ☎(01446) 792700
  Community Librarian Ms Ronni Allen MCLIP (e-mail: rallen@valeofglamorgan.gov.uk)

- Penarth Library, Stanwell Road, Penarth, Vale of Glamorgan CF64 2YT
  ☎029 2070 8438
  Senior Librarian Marcus Payne BA DipLib MCLIP (e-mail: mmpayne@valeofglamorgan.gov.uk)

WREXHAM

Authority: Wrexham County Borough Council
HQ Library, Learning and Culture Department, Ty Henblas, Queen's Square, Wrexham LL13 8AZ
☎(01978) 297430
Fax (01978) 297422
url: www.wrexham.gov.uk
Chief Leisure, Libraries and Culture Officer Alan Watkin BA DipLib FCLIP MIM FRSA
Libraries Officer Dylan Hughes BA DipLib MCLIP (01978 297442)

Central/largest library

Wrexham Library, Rhosddu Road, Wrexham LL11 1AU
☎(01978) 292090
Fax (01978) 292611
e-mail: reference.library@wrexham.gov.uk
Community Librarian Hedd ap Emlyn BA DipLib MCLIP

Group/branch libraries

- Brynteg Library, Quarry Road, Brynteg, Wrexham LL11 6AB
  ☎(01978) 759523
  Community Librarian Mrs Marina Thomas MCLIP
- Rhosllanerchrugog Library, Princes Road, Rhos, Wrexham LL14 1AB
  ☎(01978) 840328
  Community Librarian Miss Ann Hughes MA MCLIP

CROWN DEPENDENCIES

ALDERNEY

HQ Alderney Library, Church Street, Alderney, Channel Islands GY9
☎(01481) 824178
e-mail: info@alderneylibrary.org
url: www.alderneylibrary.org
Chairman, Alderney Committee Mrs Joyce Whitehead
Children's Room Mrs Liz Bowles
(Alderney Library is a voluntary organization)

GUERNSEY

HQ Guille-Allès Library, Market Street, St Peter Port, Guernsey, Channel Islands GY1 1HB
☎(01481) 720392
Fax (01481) 712425
e-mail: ga@library.gg
url: www.library.gg
Chief Librarian Miss Maggie Falla BA MA MLib MCLIP (e-mail: maggiefalla@library.gg)
Head of Services to Education and Young People Mrs Jane Falla BA DipLib MCLIP (e-mail: jfalla@library.gg)

Priaulx Library, Candie Road, St Peter Port, Guernsey, Channel Islands GY1 1UG
☎(01481) 721998
Fax (01481) 713 804
e-mail: priaulx.library@gov.gg
url: www.priaulxlibrary.com
Chief Librarian Ms Amanda Bennett MA MCLIP
Deputy Chief Librarian Ms Sue Lakes DipLib CMS MCLIP
(The Priaulx Library is a reference and lending library specializing in local history and family history research in the Channel Islands)

ISLE OF MAN

HQ Henry Bloom Noble Library, Douglas Corporation, 10/12 Victoria Street, Douglas, Isle of Man IM1 2LH
☎(01624) 696461
Fax (01624) 696400
e-mail: enquiries@douglas.gov.im
url: www.douglas.gov.im
Borough Librarian Mrs Jan Macartney BA(Hons) MCLIP (e-mail: jmacartney@douglas.gov.im)

Castletown Library, Farrants Way, Castletown, Isle of Man IM9 1NR
☎(01624) 829355

Fax (01624) 829355
e-mail: library@castletown.org.im
Librarian Ms Pauline Cringle

Family Library and Mobile Library, Nobles Hall, Westmoreland Road, Douglas, Isle of Man IM1 1RL
☎(01624) 673123
Fax (01624) 671043
Librarian (Junior Service) Ms Mary Cousins (e-mail: m.cousins@doe.sch.im)
Mobile Librarian Mrs Sandra Henderson MCLIP (e-mail: s.henderson@doe.sch.im)

George Herdman Library, Bridson Street, Port Erin, Isle of Man IM9 6AL
☎(01624) 832365
Librarian Miss Angela Dryland BSc (e-mail: drylandangela@yahoo.co.uk)

Onchan Library, Willow House, 61-69 Main Road, Onchan, Isle of Man IM3 1AJ
☎(01624) 621228 (tel/fax)
e-mail: onchan.library@onchan.org.im
url: www.library.onchan.org.im
Librarian Mrs Pam Hand

Ramsey Town Library, Town Hall, Parliament Square, Ramsey, Isle of Man IM8 1RT
☎(01624) 810146
e-mail: rtc@mcb.net
Librarian Paul Boulton BA

Ward Library, 38 Castle Street, Peel, Isle of Man IM5 1AL
☎(01624) 843533
e-mail: ward_library@hotmail.com
Librarian Mrs Carol Horton

JERSEY

HQ Jersey Library, Halkett Place, St Helier, Jersey, Channel Islands JE2 4WH
☎(01534) 448700 (enquiries), (01534) 448701 (reference), (01534) 448714 (administration)
Fax (01534) 448730
e-mail: je.library@gov.je
url: www.gov.je/library
Chief Librarian Mrs Pat Davis MCLIP

Public Libraries in the Republic of Ireland

CARLOW

Authority: Carlow County Council
HQ Carlow Central Library, Tullow Street, Carlow, Republic of Ireland
☎(00 353 59) 917 0094
Fax (00 353 59) 914 0548
e-mail: library@carlowcoco.ie
url: www.carlow.ie
County Librarian Tom King MA DipLib
Senior Executive Librarian Ms Deirdre Condron BComm DipLib
Executive Librarian Ms Carmel Flahavan BA(Open) DipLib
Executive Librarian John Shortall BA MSc(Econ)

CAVAN

Authority: Cavan County Council
HQ Johnston Central Library, Farnham Street, Cavan, Republic of Ireland
☎(00 353 49) 437 8500/8501
Fax (00 353 49) 432 6987
e-mail: library@cavancoco.ie
url: www.cavancoco.ie
County Librarian Ms Josephine Brady BA DLIS
Executive Librarian Tom Sullivan DLIS
Assistant Librarians Mrs Teresa Treacy BA DLIS, Ms Emma Clancy BA DLIS
ICT Officer Brian Connolly

CLARE

Authority: Clare County Council
HQ Clare County Library HQ, Mill Road, Ennis, Co Clare, Republic of Ireland
☎(00 353 65) 684 2461/684 6350
Fax (00 353 65) 684 2462
e-mail: mailbox@clarelibrary.ie
url: www.clarelibrary.ie
County Librarian Noel Crowley FLAI

Central/largest library

De Valera Branch Library, Ennis, Co Clare, Republic of Ireland
☎(00 353 65) 684 6353

Area libraries

- Kilfinaghty Library, Church Street, Sixmile Bridge, Co Clare, Republic of Ireland
  ☎(00 353 61) 369678
- Kilrush Library, Kilrush, Co Clare, Republic of Ireland
  ☎(00 353 65) 905 1504
- The Library, Kilnasoolagh Park, Newmarket-on-Fergus, Co Clare, Republic of Ireland
  ☎(00 353 61) 368411
- The Library, The Lock House, Killaloe, Co Clare, Republic of Ireland

☎(00 353 61) 376062

- The Library, Ballard Road, Miltown Malbay, Co Clare, Republic of Ireland
  ☎(00 353 65) 708 4822
- Local Studies Centre, The Manse, Harmony Row, Ennis, Co Clare, Republic of Ireland
  ☎(00 353 65) 684 6271
- Sean Lemass Library, Town Centre, Shannon, Co Clare, Republic of Ireland
  ☎(00 353 61) 364266
- Sweeney Memorial Library, O'Connell Street, Kilkee, Co Clare, Republic of Ireland
  ☎(00 353 65) 905 6034
- The Library, The Square, Ennistymon, Co Clare, Republic of Ireland
  ☎(00 353 65) 7071245

CORK CITY

Authority: Cork City Council
HQ Cork City Libraries, Grand Parade, Cork, Republic of Ireland
☎(00 353 21) 492 4900
Fax (00 353 21) 427 5684
e-mail: libraries@corkcity.ie
url: www.corkcitylibraries.ie
City Librarian Liam Ronayne BCL DipLib ALAI

Branch libraries

- Bishopstown Library, Wilton, Cork, Republic of Ireland
  ☎(00 353 21) 492 4950
  Fax (00 353 21) 434 5428
  e-mail: bishopstown_library@corkcity.ie
- Douglas Library, Village Shopping Centre, Douglas, Cork, Republic of Ireland
  ☎(00 353 21) 492 4932
  Fax (00 353 21) 427 5684
  e-mail: douglas_library@corkcity.ie
- Hollyhill Library, Shopping Centre, Hollyhill, Cork, Republic of Ireland
  ☎(00 353 21) 492 4928
  Fax (00 353 21) 439 3032
  e-mail: hollyhill_library@corkcity.ie
- Mayfield Library, Old Youghal Road, Cork, Republic of Ireland
  ☎(00 353 21) 492 4935
  Fax (00 353 21) 427 5684
  e-mail: mayfield_library@corkcity.ie
- St Mary's Road Library, Cork, Republic of Ireland
  ☎(00 353 21) 492 4933
  Fax (00 353 21) 427 5684
  e-mail: stmarys_library@corkcity.ie
- Tory Top Road Library, Ballyphehane, Cork, Republic of Ireland
  ☎(00 353 21) 492 4934
  Fax (00 353 21) 427 5684
  e-mail: torytop_library@corkcity.ie

CORK COUNTY

Authority: Cork County Council
HQ Cork County Library, Model Business Park, Model Farm Road, Cork, Republic of Ireland
☎(00 353 21) 454 6499
Fax (00 353 21) 434 3254
e-mail: corkcountylibrary@corkcoco.ie
url: www.corkcoco.ie
County Librarian Ms Ruth Flanagan BA DipLib ALAI (e-mail: ruth.flanagan@corkcoco.ie)

DONEGAL

Authority: Donegal County Council
HQ Donegal County Library Admin. Centre, Rosemount, Letterkenny, Co Donegal, Republic of Ireland
☎(00 353 74) 912 1968 (enquiries and administration)
Fax (00 353 74) 912 1740
e-mail: library@donegalcoco.ie
url: www.donegallibrary.ie
County Librarian and Divisional Manager, Cultural Services Ms Eileen Burgess

Central/largest library

Central Library & Arts Centre, Oliver Plunkett Road, Letterkenny, Co Donegal, Republic of Ireland
☎(00 353 74) 912 4950
Fax (00 353 74) 912 4950
e-mail: central@donegallibrary.ie
Assistant Librarian Ms Maureen Kerr

DUBLIN

Authority: Dublin City Council
HQ Dublin City Council Public Libraries, Dublin City Library and Archive, 138–144 Pearse Street, Dublin 2, Republic of Ireland
☎(00 353 1) 674 4800
Fax (00 353 1) 674 4880
e-mail: dublinpubliclibraries@dublincity.ie
url: www.dublincity.ie
City Librarian and Director Ms Deirdre Ellis-King BA DipLib ALAI MPhil (e-mail: deirdre.ellis_king@dublincity.ie)
Deputy City Librarian Ms Margaret Hayes BA DipLib HDipEd ALAI

Central/largest library

Central Public Library, ILAC Centre, Henry Street, Dublin 1, Republic of Ireland
☎(00 353 1) 873 4333
Fax (00 353 1) 872 1451
e-mail: central.library@dublincity.ie

DÚN LAOGHAIRE–RATHDOWN

Authority: Dún Laoghaire–Rathdown County Council
HQ Public Library Service, Duncairn House, 14 Carysfort Avenue (First Floor), Blackrock, Co Dublin, Republic of Ireland
☎(00 353 1) 278 1788
Fax (00 353 1) 278 1792
e-mail: libraries@dlrcoco.ie
url: www.dlrcoco.ie/library
County Librarian Muiris Ó Raghaill BSc(Econ) MCLIP
Senior Executive Librarian, Bibliographic Services Ms Orla Gallagher BSocSc DLT
Senior Executive Librarian, Administration, Staff and Policy Co-ordination Ms Geraldine McHugh MA DLIS ALAI
Senior Executive Librarian (ICT) Ms Kathleen Guinan BA DLIS
Senior Executive Librarian, Culture Ms Mairead Owens BA DLIS
Librarian, Interlibrary Loans Ms Patricia Byrne BA DLIS
Senior Librarian, Finance Ms Lisa Larkin BA HDipLIS
Senior Librarian, Cataloguing Pat Walsh BA HDipEd DLIS
Senior Librarian, Schools and Youth Services Ms Carmel Kelly BA DLIS
Senior Librarian, Staff and Administration Ms Ciara Jones BA DLIS
Senior Librarian, Staff Library Ms Mary McCaughan BA DLIS

Branch libraries

- Blackrock Library, Main Street, Blackrock, Co Dublin, Republic of Ireland
  ☎(00 353 1) 288 8117
  e-mail: blackrocklib@dlrcoco.ie
  Senior Librarian Ms Eithne Prout BA DLIS
- Cabinteely Library, Old Bray Road, Cabinteely, Dublin 18, Republic of Ireland
  ☎(00 353 1) 285 5363
  e-mail: cabinteelylib@dlrcoco.ie
  Senior Librarian Ms Frances Fox BA DLIS
- Dalkey Library, Castle Street, Dalkey, Co Dublin, Republic of Ireland
  ☎(00 353 1) 285 5277
  e-mail: dalkeylib@dlrcoco.ie
  Senior Librarian Ms Susan Lynch BA DLIS
- Deansgrange Library, Clonkeen Drive, Deansgrange, Dublin 18, Republic of Ireland
  ☎(00 353 1) 285 0860
  e-mail: deansgrangelib@dlrcoco.ie
  Senior Librarian Tony Curran BA DLIS
  Librarian Ms Patricia Corish BA DLIS, Ms Audrey Geraghty BA DLIS
- Dun Laoghaire Library, Lower George's Street, Dun Laoghaire, Co Dublin, Republic of Ireland
  ☎(00 353 1) 280 1147
  e-mail: dunlaoghairelib@dlrcoco.ie
  Senior Librarian Ms Donagh Brennan BA DipLIS
- Dundrum Library, Upper Churchtown Road, Dublin 14, Republic of Ireland
  ☎(00 353 1) 298 5000
  e-mail: dundrumlib@dlrcoco.ie

Senior Librarian Don Griffin BA DLT
Librarian Ms Detta O'Connor BA HDipEd DLIS

- Sallynoggin Library, Senior College, Sallynoggin, Co Dublin, Republic of Ireland
  ☎(00 353 1) 285 0127
  e-mail: sallynogginlib@dlrcoco.ie
  Librarian Nigel Curtin BA DLIS
- Shankill Library, Library Road, Shankill, Co Dublin, Republic of Ireland
  ☎(00 353 1) 282 3081
  e-mail: shankilllib@dlrcoco.ie
  Librarian Ms Fionnuala Carton BA DLIS
- Stillorgan Library, St Laurence's Park, Stillorgan, Co Dublin, Republic of Ireland
  ☎(00 353 1) 288 9655
  e-mail: stillorganlib@dlrcoco.ie
  Senior Librarian Ms Marian Keyes BA MA DLIS
  Librarian Ms Anne Millane BA DLIS

FINGAL

Authority: Fingal County Council
HQ Fingal County Libraries, Lower Ground Floor, County Hall, Swords, Co Dublin, Republic of Ireland
☎(00 353 1) 890 5524
Fax (00 353 1) 890 5599
e-mail: libraries@fingalcoco.ie
url: www.fingalcoco.ie/libraries
County Librarian Paul Harris DLIS ALAI
Senior Executive Librarian (Personnel & Finance) Ms Phyllis Carter
Senior Executive Librarian (Bibliographic Services) Ms Rina Mullett
Senior Executive Librarian (Projects/Library Services Development) Ms Bernadette Fennell
Librarian (Development & PR) Ms Carmel Turner

Largest library

Blanchardstown Library, Civic Centre, Blanchardstown Centre, Dublin 15, Republic of Ireland
☎(00 353 1) 890 5560
Fax (00 353 1) 890 5571
e-mail: blanchlib@fingalcoco.ie
Senior Executive Librarian Ms Yvonne Reilly
Senior Librarians Ms Evelyn Conway (Children's), Ms Marion Coakley (Adult Lending), Ms Anne Finn (Reference & Research)

Branch libraries

- Balbriggan Library, St George's Square, Balbriggan, Co Dublin, Republic of Ireland
  ☎(00 353 1) 870 4401
  e-mail: balbrigganlibrary@fingalcoco.ie
  Senior Librarian Ms Assumpta Hickey
- Baldoyle Library, Strand Road, Baldoyle, Dublin 13, Republic of Ireland

☎(00 353 1) 890 6793
Fax (00 353 1) 832 3684
e-mail: baldoylelibrary@fingalcoco.ie
Senior Librarian Ms Catherine Keane

- County Archives, 11 Parnell Square, Dublin 1, Republic of Ireland
  ☎(00 353 1) 872 7968
  Fax (00 353 1) 878 6919
  e-mail: archives@fingalcoco.ie
  Archivist Colm McQuinn
- Housebound Services, Unit 34, Coolmine Industrial Estate, Coolmine, Dublin 15, Republic of Ireland
  ☎(00 353 1) 860 4290
  Fax (00 353 1) 822 1568
  e-mail: houseboundlibrary@finalcoco.ie
  Librarian Ms Josephine Knight
- Howth Library, Main Street, Howth, Co Dublin, Republic of Ireland
  ☎(00 353 1) 832 2130
  Fax (00 353 1) 832 2277
  e-mail: howthlibrary@fingalcoco.ie
  Librarian Ms Helen Hughes
- Local Studies, 11 Parnell Square, Dublin 1, Republic of Ireland
  ☎(00 353 1) 878 6910
  Fax (00 353 1) 878 6919
  e-mail: local.studies@fingalcoco.ie
  Librarian Jeremy Black
- Malahide Library, Main Street, Malahide, Co Dublin, Republic of Ireland
  ☎(00 353 1) 845 2026
  Fax (00 353 1) 845 2199
  e-mail: malahidelibrary@fingalcoco.ie
  Senior Librarian Ms Marjory Sliney
- Mobile Library Services, Unit 34, Coolmine Industrial Estate, Coolmine, Dublin 15, Republic of Ireland
  ☎(00 353 1) 822 1564
  Fax (00 353 1) 822 1568
  e-mail: mobilelibraries@fingalcoco.ie
  Senior Librarian Dermot Bregazzi
- Skerries Library, Strand Street, Skerries, Co Dublin, Republic of Ireland
  ☎(00 353 1) 849 1900
  Fax (00 353 1) 849 5142
  e-mail: skerrieslibrary@fingalcoco.ie
  Librarian Ms Geraldine Bollard
- Swords Library, Swords Shopping Centre, Rathbeale Road, Swords, Co Dublin, Republic of Ireland
  ☎(00 353 1) 840 4179
  Fax (00 353 1) 840 4417
  e-mail: swordslibrary@fingalcoco.ie
  Senior Librarian Charlie Quinn

GALWAY

Authority: Galway County Council
HQ Galway County Library HQ, Island House, Cathedral Square, Galway, Republic of Ireland
☎(00 353 91) 562471
Fax (00 353 91) 565039
e-mail: info@galwaylibrary.ie
url: www.galwaylibrary.ie
County Librarian Pat McMahon DipLib (e-mail: pmcmahon@galwaycoco.ie)
Senior Executive Librarians Ms Maureen Moran, Mrs Bernadette Kelly BA DipLib, Peter Rabbitt
Librarian, ICT John Fitzgibbon
Executive Librarian, Schools Mrs Josephine Vahey
Archivist Ms Patricia McWalter
Librarian, Branch System Ms Catherine Farragher

Central/largest library

Galway City Library, Hynes Building, St Augustine Street, Galway, Republic of Ireland
☎(00 353 91) 561666
Executive Librarian Martin Keating

Branch libraries

- Public Library, Fairgreen, Ballinasloe, Co Galway, Republic of Ireland
  ☎(00 353 90) 964 3464
  Executive Librarian Mrs Mary Dillon
- Public Library, Castlepark Road, Ballybane, Galway, Republic of Ireland
  ☎(00 353 91) 380590
  Executive Librarian Ms Siobhan Arkins
- Public Library, Clifden, Co Galway, Republic of Ireland
  ☎(00 353 95) 21092
  Senior Library Assistant Paul Keogh
- Public Library, Loughrea, Co Galway, Republic of Ireland
  Assistant Librarian Ms Anne Callanan
- Public Library, Oranmore, Co Galway, Republic of Ireland
  Staff Officer, Libraries John Lawlor
- Public Library, Portumna, Co Galway, Republic of Ireland
  ☎(00 353 90) 974 1261
  Senior Library Assistant Ms Teresa Tierney
- Public Library, Tuam, Co Galway, Republic of Ireland
  ☎(00 353 93) 24287
  Staff Officer, Libraries Ms Emer Donoghue
- Westside Library, Seamus Quirke Road, Galway City, Republic of Ireland
  ☎(00 353 91) 520616
  Executive Librarian Ms Cora Gunther

KERRY

Authority: Kerry County Council
HQ Kerry County Library, Moyderwell, Tralee, Co Kerry, Republic of Ireland
☎(00 353 66) 712 1200
Fax (00 353 66) 712 9202
e-mail: info@kerrycolib.ie
url: www.kerrycolib.ie
County Librarian Tommy O'Connor

Area libraries

- Ballybunion Branch Library, Ballybunion, Co Kerry, Republic of Ireland
  ☎(00 353 68) 27615
  e-mail: ballybunion@kerrycolib.ie
- Caherciveen Branch Library, Caherciveen, Co Kerry, Republic of Ireland
  ☎(00 353 66) 947 2287
  e-mail: caherciveen@kerrycolib.ie
- Castleisland Branch Library, Castleisland, Co Kerry, Republic of Ireland
  ☎(00 353 66) 714 1485
  e-mail: castleisland@kerrycolib.ie
- Dingle Branch Library, Dingle, Co Kerry, Republic of Ireland
  ☎(00 353 66) 915 1499
  e-mail: dingle@kerrycolib.ie
- Kenmare Branch Library, Kenmare, Co Kerry, Republic of Ireland
  ☎(00 353 64) 41416
  e-mail: kenmare@kerrycolib.ie
- Killarney Branch Library, Killarney, Co Kerry, Republic of Ireland
  ☎(00 353 64) 32655
  Fax (00 353 64) 36065
  e-mail: killarney@kerrycolib.ie
- Killorglin Branch Library, Killorglin, Co Kerry, Republic of Ireland
  ☎(00 353 66) 976 1272
  e-mail: killorglin@kerrycolib.ie
- Listowel Branch Library, Listowel, Co Kerry, Republic of Ireland
  ☎(00 353 68) 23044
  e-mail: listowel@kerrycolib.ie
- Local History and Archives Department, Moyderwell, Tralee, Co Kerry, Republic of Ireland
  ☎(00 353 66) 712 1200
  e-mail: localhistory@kerrycolib.ie; archives@kerrycolib.ie
- Mobile Library Services
  Contact details as HQ above

KILDARE

Authority: Kildare County Council
HQ Kildare County Library Service, Riverbank Arts Centre, Main Street, Newbridge, Co Kildare, Republic of Ireland

☎(00 353 45) 431109/431486 (enquiries)
Fax (00 353 45) 432490
e-mail: colibrary@kildarecoco.ie
url: www.kildare.ie
County Librarian Ms Breda Gleeson

Kildare Collections & Research Services, Athgarvan Road, Newbridge, Co Kildare, Republic of Ireland
☎(00 353 45) 449721 (enquiries)
e-mail: localhistory@kildarecoco.ie
Librarian in Charge Mario Corrigan

School Library Service, Kildare Business Park, Melitta Road, Co Kildare, Republic of Ireland
☎(00 353 45) 527080 (enquiries)
Librarian in Charge Ms Caroline Farrell

Mobile Library Service, Riverbank Arts Centre, Main Street, Newbridge, Co Kildare, Republic of Ireland
☎(00 353 45) 448303 (enquiries)
e-mail: mobilelib@kildarecoco.ie
Librarian in Charge Ms Catherine Rafferty

Main branch libraries

- Community Library, Town Hall, Athy, Co Kildare, Republic of Ireland
  ☎(00 353 45) 863 1144
  Fax (00 353 45) 863 1809
  Librarian in charge Ms Nuala Hartnett
- Branch Library, Main Street, Maynooth, Co Kildare, Republic of Ireland
  ☎(00 353 1) 628 5530
  Librarians in charge Ms Lorraine Daly, Ms June Branigan
- Community Library, St Patrick's Park, Celbridge, Co Kildare, Republic of Ireland
  ☎(00 353 1) 627 2207
  Librarian in charge Ms Aisling Donnelly
- Community Library, Newtown House, Leixlip, Co Kildare, Republic of Ireland
  ☎(00 353 1) 606 0050
  Librarian in Charge Ms Gillian Allen
- Community Library, Canal Harbour, Naas, Co Kildare, Republic of Ireland
  ☎(00 353 45) 879111
  Fax (00 353 45) 881766
  Librarian in Charge Mark Reid
- Community Library, Athgarvan Road, Newbridge, Co Kildare, Republic of Ireland
  ☎(00 353 45) 436453
  Librarian in Charge Ms Eoghan Lynch

KILKENNY

Authority: Kilkenny County Council
HQ Kilkenny County Library, 6 Rose Inn Street, Kilkenny, Republic of Ireland

☎(00 353 56) 779 4160 (enquiries, local studies, mobile, schools, administration)
Fax (00 353 56) 779 4168
e-mail: info@kilkennylibrary.ie
url: www.kilkennylibrary.ie
County Librarian James Fogarty DLIS ALAI (e-mail: jim.fogarty@kilkennylibrary.ie)
Senior Executive Librarian Ms Dorothy O'Reilly DLIS ALAI
Executive Librarian Declan Macauley BSc DLIS

Central/largest library

Kilkenny City Library, John's Quay, Kilkenny, Republic of Ireland
☎(00 353 56) 779 4174
e-mail: citylibrary@kilkennylibrary.ie
Acting Executive Librarian Ms Brenda Ward BA HDE DLIS

Area libraries

- Callan Library, Callan, Co Kilkenny, Republic of Ireland
  ☎(00 353 56) 779 4183
  e-mail: callan@kilkennylibrary.ie
  Branch Librarian Ms Helen Phillips
- Castlecomer Library, Kilkenny Street, Castlecomer, Co Kilkenny, Republic of Ireland
  ☎(00 353 56) 444 0561
  e-mail: castlecomer@kilkennylibrary.ie
  Staff Officer Ms Mary Morrissey
- Graiguenamanagh Library, Convent Road, Graiguenamanagh, Co Kilkenny, Republic of Ireland
  ☎(00 353 56) 779 4178
  e-mail: graiguenamanagh@kilkennylibrary.ie
  Acting Senior Library Assistant Ms Majella Byrne
- Loughboy Library, Loughboy Shopping Centre, Kilkenny, Republic of Ireland
  ☎(00 353 56) 779 4176
  e-mail: loughboy@kilkennylibrary.ie
  Senior Library Assistant Ms Catriona Kenneally
- Thomastown Library, Marshes Street, Thomastown, Co Kilkenny, Republic of Ireland
  ☎(00 353 56) 779 4331
  e-mail: tomlib@eircom.net
  Branch Librarian Ms Kay Cody
- Urlingford Library, The Courthouse, Urlingford, Co Kilkenny, Republic of Ireland
  ☎(00 353 56) 779 4182
  e-mail: urlingford@kilkennylibrary.ie
  Branch Librarians Ms Helen Muldowney, Ms Annette Purcell

LAOIS

Authority: Laois County Council
HQ Laois County Library, Aras An Chontae, JFL Avenue, Portlaoise, Co Laois, Republic of Ireland
☎(00 353 57) 867 4315
Fax (00 353 57) 867 4381

url: www.laois.ie/library
County Librarian Gerry Maher LLB(Hons) DLIS (e-mail: gmaher@laoiscoco.ie)

Central/largest library

Portlaoise Branch Library, Dunamase House, Lyster Square, Portlaoise, Co Laois, Republic of Ireland
☎(00 353 57) 862 2333
Executive Librarian Ms Jackie McIntyre

Branch libraries

- Abbeyleix Branch Library, Market House, Abbeyleix, Co Laois, Republic of Ireland
  ☎(00 353 57) 873 0020
  Branch Librarian Ms Catherine Hutchinson
- Clonaslee Branch Library, Clonaslee Heritage Centre, Clonaslee, Co Laois, Republic of Ireland
  ☎(00 353 57) 864 8437
  Branch Librarian Ms Maureen Cusack
- Mountmellick Branch Library, Irishtown, Mountmellick, Co Laois, Republic of Ireland
  ☎(00 353 57) 862 4733
  Branch Librarian Ms Fiona Lynch
- Mountrath Branch Library, Shannon Street, Mountrath, Co Laois, Republic of Ireland
  ☎(00 353 57) 875 6046
  Branch Librarian Ms Joan Phelan
- Portarlington Branch Library, Station Road, Portarlington, Co Laois, Republic of Ireland
  ☎(00 353 57) 864 3751
  Branch Librarian Ms Aoife Anton
- Rathdowney Branch Library, Mill Street, Rathdowney, Co Laois, Republic of Ireland
  ☎(00 353 505) 46852
  Branch Librarian Mrs Catherine Fitzpatrick
- Stradbally Branch Library, Court Square, Stradbally, Co Laois, Republic of Ireland
  ☎(00 353 57) 862 5005
  Branch Librarian Ms Julie Ann Stead
- Timahoe Branch Library, Timahoe, Co Laois, Republic of Ireland
  ☎(00 353 57) 862 7231
  Branch Librarian Ms Mairin Scully

LEITRIM (LEABHARLANN CHONTAE LIATROMA)

Authority: Leitrim County Council
HQ Leitrim County Library, Main Street, Ballinamore, Co Leitrim, Republic of Ireland
☎(00 353 71) 964 5582
Fax (00 353 71) 964 5572
e-mail: leitrimlibrary@eircom.net
url: www.leitrimlibrary.ie
County Librarian Seán Ó Suilleabháin DLT FLAI ALAI

LIMERICK CITY

Authority: Limerick City Council
HQ Limerick City Library, The Granary, Michael Street, Limerick, Republic of Ireland
☎(00 353 61) 407510
Fax (00 353 61) 411506
e-mail: citylib@limerickcity.ie
url: www.limerickcity.ie
City Librarian Ms Dolores Doyle BA FLAI ALAI (e-mail: ddoyle@limerickcity.ie)

LIMERICK COUNTY

Authority: Limerick County Council
HQ Limerick County Library HQ, 58 O'Connell Street, Limerick, Republic of Ireland
☎(00 353 61) 496526 (enquiries and administration)
Fax (00 353 61) 318570
e-mail: colibrar@limerickcoco.ie
County Librarian Damien Brady BA DLIS
Senior Executive Librarians Ms Anne Bennett BA DLIS, Ms Helen Walsh DLIS LAI (00 353 61 496536) (Children and Youth Libraries)

Central/largest library

Dooradoyle Branch Library, Crescent Shopping Centre, Dooradoyle Road, Limerick, Republic of Ireland
☎(00 353 61) 301101
Executive Librarian Ms Noreen O'Neill BA DLIS

Branch libraries

- Abbeyfeale Branch Library, Bridge Street, Abbeyfeale, Co Limerick, Republic of Ireland
  ☎(00 353 68) 32488
  Senior Library Assistant Mike Sweeney
- Adare Branch Library, Adare, Co Limerick, Republic of Ireland
  ☎(00 353 61) 396822
  Assistant Librarian Ms Margaret O'Reilly BA DLIS
- Foynes Branch Library, Foynes, Co Limerick, Republic of Ireland
  ☎(00 353 69) 65365
  Assistant Librarian Ms Sarah Prendiville DLIS
- Newcastlewest Branch Library, Newcastlewest, Co Limerick, Republic of Ireland
  ☎(00 353 69) 62273
  Executive Librarian Ms Aileen Dillane BA DLIS

LONGFORD

Authority: Longford County Council
HQ Longford County Library, Archives and Heritage Services, Town Centre, Longford, Republic of Ireland
☎(00 353 43) 41124
Fax (00 353 43) 48576

e-mail: library@longfordcoco.ie
url: www.longfordlibrary.ie
County Librarian Ms Mary Carleton-Reynolds DLIS ALAI

Central/largest library

Longford Library, Town Centre, Longford, Co Longford, Republic of Ireland
☎(00 353 43) 41125
e-mail: longfordlibrary@longfordcoco.ie
Librarian Willie O'Dowd BComm LLB MLIS

Branch libraries

- Ballymahon Library, Main Street, Ballymahon, Co Longford, Republic of Ireland
  ☎(00 353 90) 643 2546
  e-mail: ballymahonlibrary@longfordcoco.ie
  Branch Librarian Ms Carmel Kelly BA DLIS
- Drumlish Library, Drumlish, Co Longford, Republic of Ireland
  ☎(00 353 43) 24760
  e-mail: drumlishlibrary@longfordcoco.ie
  Branch Librarian Ms Isabella Mallon
- Edgeworthstown Library, Edgeworthstown, Co Longford, Republic of Ireland
  ☎(00 353 43) 71927
  e-mail: edgeworthstownlibrary@longfordcoco.ie
  Branch Librarian Ms Sheila Walsh
- Granard Library, Granard, Co Longford, Republic of Ireland
  ☎(00 353 43) 86164
  e-mail: granardlibrary@longfordcoco.ie
  Branch Librarian Ms Rosemary Gaynor
- Lanesboro Library, Lanesboro, Co Longford, Republic of Ireland
  ☎(00 353 43) 24760
  e-mail: lanesborolibrary@longfordcoco.ie
  Branch Librarian Ms Stella O'Sullivan

LOUTH

Authority: Louth
HQ Louth County Library, Roden Place, Dundalk, Co Louth, Republic of Ireland
☎(00 353 42) 935 3190
Fax (00 353 42) 933 7635
url: www.louthcoco.ie
County Librarian Miss Ann Ward BA DLT (e-mail: ann.ward@louthcoco.ie)

MAYO

Authority: Mayo County Council
HQ Mayo County Library, Library HQ, John Moore Road, Castlebar, Co Mayo, Republic of Ireland
☎(00 353 94) 904 7922 (enquiries and administration)
Fax (00 353 94) 902 4774

url: www.mayolibrary.ie
County Librarian Austin Vaughan BA DLIS (e-mail: avaughan@mayococo.ie)

Central/largest library

Mayo Central Library, The Mall, Castlebar, Co Mayo, Republic of Ireland
☎(00 353 94) 904 7925
Fax (00 353 94) 902 6491
Librarian Ms Paula Leavy McCarthy

MEATH

Authority: Meath County Council
HQ Meath County Library, Railway Street, Navan, Co Meath, Republic of Ireland
☎(00 353 46) 902 1134; 902 1451
e-mail: colibrar@meathcoco.ie
url: www.meath.ie/library
County Librarian Ciaran Mangan BA MLIS
Senior Executive Librarian Ms Geraldine Donnelly DLIS
Executive Librarians Ms Dympna Herward BA DLIS, Ms Frances Tallon MA DLIS (Local Studies Dept), Ms Yvonne Morrison BA DLIS (Navan Branch Library)

Branch libraries

- Ashbourne Library, 1-2 Killegland Court, Ashbourne, Co Meath, Republic of Ireland
  ☎(00 353 1) 835 8185
  Executive Librarian Ms Mary Murphy
- Athboy Library, Main Street, Athboy, Co Meath, Republic of Ireland
  ☎(00 353 46) 943 2539
  Branch Librarian Ms Teresa Doherty
- Duleek Library, Main Street, Duleek, Co Meath, Republic of Ireland
  ☎(00 353 41) 988 0709
  Library Assistant David Farnan
- Dunboyne Library, Castleview, Dunboyne, Co Meath, Republic of Ireland
  ☎(00 353 1) 825 1248
  Executive Librarian Tom French BA DLIS
- Dunshaughlin Library, Main Street, Dunshaughlin, Co Meath, Republic of Ireland
  ☎(00 353 1) 825 0504
  Senior Library Assistant Vacant
  Library Assistant Ms Fiona Smith
- Kells Library, Maudlin Street, Kells, Co Meath, Republic of Ireland
  ☎(00 353 46) 924 1592
  Branch Librarian Ms Rose Grimes
- Laytown Library, Laytown, Co Meath, Republic of Ireland
  Branch Librarian Ms Iris Cunningham
- Nobber Library, Nobber, Co Meath, Republic of Ireland
  ☎(00 353 46) 905 2732
  Branch Librarian Ms Imelda Griffin
- Oldcastle Library, Millbrook Road, Oldcastle, Co Meath, Republic of Ireland
  ☎(00 353 49) 854 2084

Senior Library Assistant Ms Anne Price

- Slane Library, Castle Hill, Slane, Co Meath, Republic of Ireland
  ☎(00 353 41) 982 4955
  Branch Librarian Ms Patricia McGrane
- Trim Library, High Street, Trim, Co Meath, Republic of Ireland
  ☎(00 353 46) 943 6014
  Executive Librarian Ms Maedhbh Rogan

MONAGHAN

Authority: Monaghan County Council
HQ Monaghan County Library, The Diamond, Clones, Co Monaghan, Republic of Ireland
☎(00 353 47) 51143
Fax (00 353 47) 51863
e-mail: moncolib@monaghancoco.ie
url: www.monaghan.ie
County Librarian Joe McElvaney DLIS (e-mail: jmcelvaney@monaghancoco.ie)
Senior Executive Librarian Ms Catherine Elliott BSocSc

Central/largest library

Monaghan Branch Library, North Road, Monaghan Town, Republic of Ireland
☎(00 353 47) 81830
Fax (00 353 47) 38688
Assistant Librarian Ms Karen McKenna (e-mail: kmckenna@monaghancoco.ie)

Branch libraries

- Ballybay Library, Main Street, Ballybay, Co Monaghan, Republic of Ireland
  ☎(00 353 42) 974 1256
  Branch Librarian Mrs Rosemary McDonnell
- Carrickmacross Branch Library, Market Square, Carrickmacross, Co Monaghan, Republic of Ireland
  ☎(00 353 42) 966 1148
  Senior Library Assistant Ms Breda Moore (e-mail: bmoore@monaghancoco.ie)
- Castleblayney Branch Library, Iontas Resource Centre, Castleblayney, Co Monaghan, Republic of Ireland
  ☎(00 353 42) 974 0281
  Branch Librarian Ms Pauline Duffy
- Clones Branch Library, The Diamond, Clones, Co Monaghan, Republic of Ireland
  ☎(00 353 47) 51143
  Fax (00 353 47) 51863
  Staff Officer Ms Catriona Lennon

OFFALY

Authority: Offaly County Council
HQ Offaly County Library, O'Connor Square, Tullamore, Co Offaly, Republic of Ireland
☎(00 353 57) 934 6834
Fax (00 353 57) 935 2769

e-mail: colibrar@offalycoco.ie
url: www.offaly.ie
County Librarian Ms Anne M Coughlan DLT MCLIP
Executive Librarian Diarmaid Bracken BA DLIS

ROSCOMMON

Authority: Roscommon County Council
HQ Roscommon County Library, Abbey Street, Roscommon, Republic of Ireland
☎(00 353 90) 663 7272/7274 (enquiries and administration)
Fax (00 353 90) 663 7101
url: www.roscommoncoco.ie/home.htm
County Librarian Richie Farrell BA DLIS (e-mail: rfarrell@roscommoncoco.ie)

Central/largest library

Roscommon Branch Library, Abbey Street, Roscommon, Republic of Ireland
☎(00 353 90) 663 7277
Fax (00 353 90) 663 7101
e-mail: roslib@eircom.net

Branch libraries

- Ballaghaderreen Branch Library, Barrack Street, Ballaghaderreen, Co Roscommon, Republic of Ireland
  ☎(00 353 94) 987 7044
  e-mail: ballaghaderreenlibrary@roscommoncoco.ie
  Senior Library Assistant Ms Deirdre Creighton
- Ballyforan Branch Library, Ballyforan, Co Roscommon, Republic of Ireland
  Branch Librarian Ms Rebecca Thompson
- Boyle Branch Library, The King House, Boyle, Co Roscommon, Republic of Ireland
  ☎(00 353 71) 966 2800
  e-mail: boylelibrary@roscommoncoco.ie
  Senior Library Assistant Matthew Gammon
- Castlerea Branch Library, Main Street, Castlerea, Co Roscommon, Republic of Ireland
  ☎(00 353 94) 962 0745
  e-mail: castlerealibrary@roscommoncoco.ie
  Branch Librarian Ms Maura Carroll
- Elphin Branch Library, Main Street, Elphin, Co Roscommon, Republic of Ireland
  ☎(00 353 71) 963 5775
  e-mail: ebllib@eircom.net
  Branch Librarian Ms Mary Walsh
- Strokestown Branch Library, Elphin Street, Strokestown, Co Roscommon, Republic of Ireland
  ☎(00 353 71) 963 4027
  e-mail: strokestownlibrary@roscommoncoco.ie
  Branch Librarian Ms Moya Lane

SLIGO

Authority: Sligo County Council
HQ Sligo County Library, The Westward Town Centre, Bridge Street, Sligo, Republic of Ireland
☎(00 353 71) 911 1850
Fax (00 353 71) 914 6798
e-mail: sligolib@sligococo.ie
url: www.sligolibrary.ie
County Librarian Donal Tinney MA DLIS ALAI
Senior Executive Librarian Ms Pauline Brennan DLIS
Executive Librarians Ms Ultan McNasser, Fran Hegarty DipLib

Central/largest library

Sligo Central Library, Stephen Street, Sligo, Republic of Ireland
☎(00 353 71) 911 1675
Fax (00 353 71) 914 6798
Executive Librarian Ms Patricia Keane

Branch library

- Tubbercurry Community Library, Teach Laighne, Humbert Street, Tubbercurry, Co Sligo, Republic of Ireland
  ☎(00 353 71) 911 1705
  Fax (00 353 71) 912 0446
  e-mail: tubbercurry@sligococo.ie
  Executive Librarian Ms Caroline Morgan FLAI

SOUTH DUBLIN

Authority: South Dublin County Council
HQ Unit 1, The Square Industrial Complex, Tallaght, Dublin 24, Republic of Ireland
☎(00 353 1) 459 7834
Fax (00 353 1) 459 7872
e-mail: library@sdublincoco.ie
url: www.southdublinlibraries.ie
Acting County Librarian Ian Stobbart

Central/largest library

County Library, County Hall, Tallaght, Dublin 24, Republic of Ireland
☎(00 353 1) 462 0073
Fax (00 353 1) 414 9207
e-mail: talib@sdublincoco.ie
Senior Executive Librarian Ms Maria Donohoe

Branch libraries

- Ballyroan Library, Orchardstown Avenue, Rathfarnham, Dublin 14, Republic of Ireland
  ☎(00 353 1) 494 1900
  Fax (00 353 1) 494 7083

e-mail: ballyroan@sdublincoco.ie
Senior Librarians Ms Rosena Hand, Ms Margaret Bentley

- Castletymon Library, Castletymon Shopping Centre, Tymon Road North, Tallaght, Dublin 24, Republic of Ireland
  ☎(00 353 1) 452 4888
  Fax (00 353 1) 459 7873
  e-mail: castletymon@sdublincoco.ie
  Librarian Ms Ann Dunne
- Clondalkin Library, Monastry Road, Clondalkin, Dublin 22, Republic of Ireland
  ☎(00 353 1) 459 3315
  Fax (00 353 1) 459 5509
  e-mail: clondalkin@sdublincoco.ie
  Acting Senior Librarian Vincent Allen
- John J Jennings Library, Stewarts Hospital, Palmerstown, Dublin 20, Republic of Ireland
  ☎(00 353 1) 626 4444 (ext 1129)
  Fax (00 353 1) 626 1707
  e-mail: johnjjlib@eircom.net
  Senior Librarian Ms Siobhan O'Neill
- Lucan Library, Superquinn Shopping Centre, Newcastle Road, Lucan, Co Dublin, Republic of Ireland
  ☎(00 353 1) 621 6422
  Fax (00 353 1) 621 6433
  e-mail: lucan@sdublincoco.ie
  Acting Senior Librarian Ms Mary Byron
- Mobile Library Service, Unit 1, The Square Industrial Complex, Tallaght, Dublin 24, Republic of Ireland
  ☎(00 353 1) 459 7834
  Fax (00 353 1) 459 7872
  e-mail: mobiles@sdublincoco.ie
  Senior Librarian Ms Breid Ryan
- Whitechurch Library, Taylor's Lane, Rathfarnham, Dublin 16, Republic of Ireland
  ☎(00 353 1) 493 0199
  e-mail: whitechurch@sdublincoco.ie
  Branch Librarian Ms Breda Bollard

TIPPERARY

Authority: County Tipperary Joint Libraries Committee
HQ Tipperary County Library, Castle Avenue, Thurles, Co Tipperary, Republic of Ireland
☎(00 353 504) 21555
Fax (00 353 504) 23442
e-mail: info@tipperarylibraries.ie
url: www.tipperarylibraries.ie
County Librarian Martin Maher

Branch libraries

- Borrisokane Library, Main Street, Borrisokane, Co Tipperary, Republic of Ireland
  ☎(00 353 67) 27199

Branch Librarian Mrs Frankie O'Carroll

- Cahir Library, The Square, Cahir, Co Tipperary, Republic of Ireland
  ☎(00 353 52) 42075
  Branch Librarian Mrs Ann Tuohy
- Carrick-on-Suir Library, Fair Green, Carrick-on-Suir, Co Tipperary, Republic of Ireland
  ☎(00 353 51) 640591 (tel/fax)
  Acting Senior Library Assistant Ms Orla O'Connor
- Cashel Library, Friar Street, Cashel, Co Tipperary, Republic of Ireland
  ☎(00 353 62) 63825
  Fax (00 353 62) 63948
  e-mail: cashel@tipperarylibraries.ie
  Assistant Librarian Ms Margaret Ryan
- Clonmel Library, Emmet Street, Clonmel, Co Tipperary, Republic of Ireland
  ☎(00 353 52) 24545
  Fax (00 353 52) 27336
  e-mail: clonmel@tipperarylibraries.ie
  Assistant Librarian Mrs Marie Boland
- Cloughjordan Library, Main Street, Cloughjordan, Co Tipperary, Republic of Ireland
  ☎(00 353 505) 42425
  Branch Librarian Mrs Marie Brady
- Killenaule Library, Slieveardagh Centre, River Street, Killenaule, Co Tipperary , Republic of Ireland
  ☎(00 353 52) 56156
  Branch Librarian Mrs Rena Lahart
- Nenagh Library, O'Rahilly Street, Nenagh, Co Tipperary, Republic of Ireland
  ☎(00 353 67) 34404
  Fax (00 353 67) 34405
  e-mail: nenagh@tipperarylibraries.ie
  Assistant Librarian Ms Breffni Hannon
- Roscrea Library, Birr Road, Roscrea, Co Tipperary, Republic of Ireland
  ☎(00 353 505) 22032 (tel/fax)
  Assistant Librarian Ms Aine Beausang
- Templemore Library, Old Mill Court, Templemore, Co Tipperary, Republic of Ireland
  ☎(00 353 504) 32555/6
  Fax (00 353 504) 32545
  e-mail: templemore@tipperarylibraries.ie
  Senior Library Assistant Pat Bracken
- Thurles Library, The Source, Cathedral Street, Thurles, Co Tipperary, Republic of Ireland
  ☎(00 353 504) 29720
  Fax (00 353 504) 21344
  e-mail: thurles@tipperarylibraries.ie
  Assistant Librarian Ms Ann Marie Brophy
- Tipperary Library, Dan Breen House, Tipperary, Republic of Ireland
  ☎(00 353 62) 51761 (tel/fax)
  Branch Librarian Ms Nollaig Butler, Ms Gerardine Hughes

WATERFORD CITY

Authority: Waterford City Council
HQ Central Library, Lady Lane, Waterford, Republic of Ireland
☎(00 353 51) 849839
Fax (00 353 51) 850031
e-mail: citylibrary@waterfordcity.ie
url: www.waterfordcity.ie/library
City Librarian Ms Jane Cantwell
Senior Executive Librarians Ms Mary Conway, Ms Katherine Collins
Executive Librarians Ms Kathleen Moran, Ms Melanie Cunningham, Ms Sinead O'Higgins
Assistant Librarians Ms Debbie Johnson, Ms Niamh Baldwin

Central/largest library

Central Library, Lady Lane, Waterford City, Waterford, Republic of Ireland
☎(00 353 51) 849975
Fax (00 353 51) 850031
e-mail: library@waterfordcity.ie
Senior Executive Librarian Ms Mary Conway

Other libraries

- Ardkeen Library, Ardkeen Shopping Centre, Dunmore Road, Waterford, Republic of Ireland
  ☎(00 353 51) 849755
  Fax (00 353 51) 874100
  e-mail: library@waterfordcity.ie
  Assistant Librarian Ms Melanie Cunningham
- Brown's Road Library, Paddy Brown's Road, Waterford, Republic of Ireland
  ☎(00 353 51) 860845
  e-mail: library@waterfordcity.ie

WATERFORD COUNTY

Authority: Waterford County Council
HQ Waterford County Library, West Main Street, Lismore, Co Waterford, Republic of Ireland
☎(00 353 58) 21370
e-mail: libraryhq@waterfordcoco.ie
url: www.waterfordcountylibrary.ie
County Librarian Donal Brady (e-mail: dbrady@waterfordcoco.ie)
Deputy Librarian Ms Kate Murphy (e-mail: kmurphy@waterfordcoco.ie)

Central/largest library

Dungarvan Branch Library, Davitt's Quay, Dungarvan, Dungarvan, Co Waterford, Republic of Ireland
☎(00 353 58) 41231
e-mail: dungarvanlibrary@waterfordcoco.ie
Executive Librarian Ger Croughan (e-mail: gcroughan@waterfordcoco.ie)

Area libraries

- Cappoquin Branch Library, Cappoquin, Waterford, Republic of Ireland
  ☎(00 353 58) 52263
  e-mail: cappoquinlibrary@waterfordcoco.ie
  Branch Librarian Mrs Mary Tobin
- Dunmore Branch Library, Dunmore East, Waterford, Republic of Ireland
  ☎(00 353 51) 383211
  e-mail: dunmorelibrary@waterfordcoco.ie
  Branch Librarian Ms Claire O Mullain
- Kilmacthomas Branch Library, Kilmacthomas, Waterford, Republic of Ireland
  ☎(00 353 51) 294270
  e-mail: kilmacthomaslibrary@waterfordcoco.ie
  Branch Librarian Ms Laura Kirwan
- Lismore Branch Library, Main Street, Lismore, Waterford, Republic of Ireland
  ☎(00 353 58) 21377
  e-mail: lismorelibrary@waterfordcoco.ie
  Senior Library Assistant Robert Drohan
- Portlaw Branch Library, The Square, Portlaw, Waterford, Republic of Ireland
  ☎(00 353 51) 387402
  e-mail: portlawlibrary@waterfordcoco.ie
  Librarian Ms Ger Murphy
- Tallow Branch Library, Convent Street, Tallow, Waterford, Republic of Ireland
  ☎(00 353 58) 56347
  e-mail: tallowlibrary@waterfordcoco.ie
  Branch Librarian Ms Sheila Curtin
- Tramore Branch Library, Market Square, Tramore, Waterford, Republic of Ireland
  ☎(00 353 51) 381479
  e-mail: tramorelibrary@waterfordcoco.ie
  Executive Librarian Ms Jean Webster

WESTMEATH

Authority: Westmeath County Council
HQ Westmeath County Library HQ, Dublin Road, Mullingar, Co Westmeath, Republic of Ireland
☎(00 353 44) 934 0781/2/3
Fax (00 353 44) 934 1322
url: www.westmeathcoco.ie/services/library/
County Librarian Miss Mary Farrell BA HDE DLIS ALAI (e-mail: mfarrell@westmeathcoco.ie)
Senior Executive Librarian Mrs Paula O'Dornan BA(Hons) PGDipLIS (e-mail: podornan@westmeathcoco.ie)

Branch libraries

- Aidan Heavey Public Library, Athlone Civic Centre, Church Street, Athlone, Co Westmeath, Republic of Ireland
  ☎(00 353 90) 644 2157/8/9
  e-mail: athlib@westmeathcoco.ie

Senior Executive Librarian Gearoid O'Brien DLIS FLAI ALAI (e-mail: gobrien@westmeathcoco.ie)

- Ballynacarrigy Library, 2 Kilmurray's Corner, Main Street, Ballynacarrigy, Co Westmeath, Republic of Ireland
  ☎(00 353 44) 937 3882
  e-mail: bnclib@westmeathcoco.ie
  Branch Librarian Ms Cecilia Connolly
- Castlepollard Library, Civic Offices, Mullingar Road, Castlepollard, Co Westmeath, Republic of Ireland
  ☎(00 353 44) 933 2199
  e-mail: cpdlib@westmeathcoco.ie
  Staff Officer Ms Nicola Brennan-Gavin (e-mail: ngavin@westmeathcoco.ie)
- Kilbeggan Library, Kilbeggan Civic Offices, The Square, Kilbeggan, Co Westmeath, Republic of Ireland
  ☎(00 353 57) 933 3148
  e-mail: killib@westmeathcoco.ie
  Senior Library Assistant Ms Edel Olcese
- Killucan Library, Rathwire Hall, Killucan, Co Westmeath, Republic of Ireland
  ☎(00 353 44) 937 4260
  Branch Librarian Ms Geraldine Corroon (e-mail: gcorroon@westmeathcoco.ie)
- Moate Library, The Courthouse, Main Street, Moate, Co Westmeath, Republic of Ireland
  ☎(00 353 90) 648 1888 (tel/fax)
  e-mail: moatelib@westmeathcoco.ie
  Branch Librarian Ms Lorna Farrell
- Mullingar Library, Church Avenue, Mullingar, Co Westmeath, Republic of Ireland
  ☎(00 353 44) 934 8278
  e-mail: mgarlib@westmeathcoco.ie
  Assistant Librarian Tony Cox DLIS (e-mail: tcox@westmeathcoco.ie)

WEXFORD

Authority: Wexford County Council
HQ Library Management Services, 6A Ardcavan Business Park, Ardcavan, Co Wexford, Republic of Ireland
☎(00 353 53) 912 4922/912 4928
Fax (00 353 53) 912 1097
e-mail: libraryhq@wexfordcoco.ie
url: www.wexford.ie
County Librarian Ms Fionnuala Hanrahan BA DLIS MLIS MCLIP MCLIPI

Central/largest library

Wexford Town Library, Selskar House, McCauley's Carpark, off Redmond Square, Co Wexford, Republic of Ireland
☎(00 353 53) 912 1637
Fax (00 353 53) 912 1639
e-mail: wexfordlib@wexfordcoco.ie
Librarian Ms Hazel Percival BA DLIS

Area libraries

- Bunclody Branch Library, Mill Wood, Carrigduff, Bunclody, Co Wexford, Republic of Ireland
  ☎(00 353 53) 937 5466
  Executive Librarian Ms Eileen Morrissey BA DLIS
- Enniscorthy Branch Library, Lymington Road, Enniscorthy, Co Wexford, Republic of Ireland
  ☎(00 353 53) 923 6055
  e-mail: enniscorthylib@wexfordcoco.ie
  Librarian Ms Clare Kelly BA DLIS
- New Ross Branch Library, Barrack Lane, New Ross, Co Wexford, Republic of Ireland
  ☎(00 353 51) 421877
  e-mail: newrosslib@eircom.net
  Senior Library Assistant Ms Joan Lambert

WICKLOW

Authority: Wicklow County Council
HQ Wicklow County Library, Library HQ, Boghall Road, Bray, Co Wicklow, Republic of Ireland
☎(00 353 1) 286 6566 (enquiries and administration)
Fax (00 353 1) 286 5811
e-mail: wcclhq@eircom.net
url: www.wicklow.ie
County Librarian Brendan Martin BA DLIS
Senior Executive Librarian (Schools and Outreach) Ms Noelle Murray BA DLIS
Senior Executive Librarian (Administration) Ms Carmel Moore DLIS
Executive Librarian (IT) Ms Mary O'Driscoll BSocSc DLIS

Largest library

Bray Public Library, Eglinton Road, Bray, Co Wicklow, Republic of Ireland
☎(00 353 1) 286 2600
Executive Librarian Ms Gillean Misstear BA MA

Area libraries

- Arklow Public Library, St Mary's Road, Arklow, Co Wicklow, Republic of Ireland
  ☎(00 353 402) 39977
  Assistant Librarian Ms Ciara Brennan
- Ballywaltrim Public Library, Boghall Road, Bray, Co Wicklow, Republic of Ireland
  ☎(00 353 1) 272 3205
  Assistant Librarian Ms Sharon Walsh
- Blessington Public Library, New Town Centre, Blessington, Co Wicklow, Republic of Ireland
  ☎(00 353 405) 891701
- Greystones Public Library, Church Road, Greystones, Co Wicklow, Republic of Ireland
  ☎(00 353 1) 287 3548
  Executive Librarian Ms Mary Murphy

- Wicklow Public Library, Market Square, Co Wicklow, Republic of Ireland
  ☎(00 353 404) 67025
  Assistant Librarian Ms Sharon Walsh

Libraries in Academic Institutions in the United Kingdom

ABERDEEN UNIVERSITY

Aberdeen University Library, Aberdeen University, Queen Mother Library, Meston Walk, Aberdeen AB24 3UE
☎(01224) 273403 (enquiries/help desk)
Fax (01224) 487048
e-mail: library@abdn.ac.uk
url: www.abdn.ac.uk/library
University Librarian Ms Chris Banks

Site libraries

- Medical Library, Aberdeen University, Polwarth Building, Foresterhill, Aberdeen AB25 2ZD
  ☎(01224) 681818 ext 52488 (enquiries), ext 52740 (administration)
  Fax (01224) 685157
  e-mail: medlib@abdn.ac.uk
  Site Services Manager Ms Melanie Bickerton BA
- Special Libraries and Archives, Aberdeen University, King's College, Aberdeen AB24 3SW
  ☎(01224) 272598 (enquiries)
  Fax (01224) 273891
  e-mail: speclib@abdn.ac.uk
  Manager, Historic Collections Alan Knox BSc PhD (e-mail: a.g.knox@abdn.ac.uk)
- Taylor Library and European Documentation Centre, Aberdeen University, Taylor Building, Aberdeen AB24 3UB
  ☎(01224) 272601 (law enquiries), 273334 (European Union enquiries), 273892 (administration)
  Fax (01224) 273893
  e-mail: lawlib@abdn.ac.uk
  Site Services Manager Ms Liz Mackie BA (e-mail: e.a.mackie@abdn.ac.uk)

UNIVERSITY OF ABERTAY DUNDEE

Information Services, University of Abertay Dundee, Bell Street, Dundee DD1 1HG
☎(01382) 308866
Fax (01382) 308877
e-mail: infodesk@abertay.ac.uk
url: http://vlib.abertay.ac.uk/
Depute Principal (Planning and Resources) Ivor G Lloyd BA DipLib MLib MCLIP (e-mail: i.lloyd@abertay.ac.uk)

ABERYSTWYTH UNIVERSITY

(formerly University of Wales Aberystwyth)

Hugh Owen Library, Aberystwyth University, Penglais, Aberystwyth, Ceredigion SY23 3DZ
☎(01970) 622399 (enquiries), (01970) 622391 (administration)
Fax (01970) 622404
e-mail: libinfo@aber.ac.uk

url: www.aber.ac.uk
Director of Information Services Mike Hopkins BA PhD MCLIP

Site/departmental libraries

- Law Library, Aberystwyth University, The Hugh Owen Building, Penglais, Aberystwyth, Ceredigion SY23 3DZ
  ☎(01970) 622401
  e-mail: libinfo@aber.ac.uk
  Librarian i/c Mrs Lillian Stevenson LLB DipLib MCLIP
- Old College Library, Aberystwyth University, Old College, King Street, Aberystwyth, Ceredigion SY23 2AX
  ☎(01970) 622130
  Librarian i/c Elgan Davies BA DipLib
- Physical Sciences Library (Mathematics, Computer Sciences and Physics), Aberystwyth University, 4th Floor, Physical Sciences Building, Penglais, Aberystwyth, Ceredigion SY23 3BZ
  ☎(01970) 622407
  e-mail: libinfo@aber.ac.uk
  Librarian i/c Mrs Tegwen Meredith
- Thomas Parry Library, Aberystwyth University, Llanbadarn Fawr, Aberystwyth, Ceredigion SY23 3AS
  ☎(01970) 622412 (enquiries), (01970) 622417 (administration)
  Fax (01970) 621868
  e-mail: parrylib@aber.ac.uk
  Librarian i/c Dr Jonathan Davies PhD

ANGLIA RUSKIN UNIVERSITY

University Library, Anglia Ruskin University, Chelmsford Campus, Bishop Hall Lane, Chelmsford, Essex CM1 1SQ
☎(01245) 493131
url: http://libweb.anglia.ac.uk
University Librarian Ms Nicky Kershaw BA CertEd MCLIP (0845 196 3763; e-mail: nicky.kershaw@anglia.ac.uk)
Assistant Director of Library Services (Essex) Ms Margaret March BA MA MCLIP (0845 196 4644; e-mail: m.march@anglia.ac.uk)
Assistant Director of Library Services (Systems and Central Services) Graham Howorth BA MSc MCLIP (0845 196 3145; e-mail: g.howorth@anglia.ac.uk)

University Library, Anglia Ruskin University, Cambridge Campus, East Road, Cambridge CB1 1PT
☎(01223) 363271
url: http://libweb.anglia.ac.uk
Assistant Director of Library Services (Cambridge) Roddie Shepherd BA DipLib MCLIP (0845 196 2310; e-mail: r.c.shepherd@anglia.ac.uk)

ARTS INSTITUTE AT BOURNEMOUTH

AIB Library Ltd, The Arts Institute at Bournemouth, Wallisdown Road, Poole, Dorset BH12 5HH
☎(01202) 363256
Fax (01202) 537729
e-mail: library@aib.ac.uk
url: www.aib.ac.uk
Head of Library and Information Services Ms Julia Waite BSc(Econ) MSc MCLIP FHEA (e-mail: jwaite@aib.ac.uk)

ASTON UNIVERSITY

Library & Information Services, Aston University, Aston Triangle, Birmingham B4 7ET
☎0121 204 4525 (enquiries), 0121 204 4509 (administration)
Fax 0121 204 4530
e-mail: library@aston.ac.uk
url: www.aston.ac.uk/lis/
Director Nick Smith BSc MSc PhD MCLIP
Head of Information Resources Mrs Jackie Brocklebank BA MIL DipLib MCLIP, Mrs Heather Whitehouse BSc DipInfSc(job share)
Head of Public Services Mrs Jill Lambert BSc DipLib MA MCLIP (e-mail: j.lambert@aston.ac.uk)
Head of Library Systems Mrs Zinat Bennett BSc PGDipLib MA MBA

BANGOR UNIVERSITY

(formerly University of Wales Bangor)

Library and Archives Service, Bangor University, College Road, Bangor, Gwynedd LL57 2DG
☎(01248) 382981 (enquiries), (01248) 383772 (secretary)
Fax (01248) 382979
e-mail: library@bangor.ac.uk; ill@bangor.ac.uk (interlibrary loans)
url: www.bangor.ac.uk/is/library
Head of Library and Archives Service Vacant
Librarians Gwyneth Haylock BA DipLib (e-mail: g.d.haylock@bangor.ac.uk), Mairwen Owen BA (e-mail: mairwen.owen@bangor.ac.uk), Marion Poulton BA MEd DipLib MCLIP (e-mail: m.poulton@bangor.ac.uk), John Wright BA DipILM (e-mail: john.wright@bangor.ac.uk)
User Support Officer Eileen Tilley MA CertEd MCLIP (e-mail: e.f.tilley@bangor.ac.uk),
Lending and Access Services Manager Tony Heaton (e-mail: t.heaton@bangor.ac.uk)
Systems and Technical Services Manager Mieko Yamaguchi BA MA DipLib (e-mail: m.yamaguchi@bangor.ac.uk)
University Archivist, Welsh and Special Collections Einion Wyn Thomas BA DAA (e-mail: e.w.thomas@bangor.ac.uk)

Site libraries

- Education Site Library, Bangor University, Safle'r Normal, Holyhead Road, Bangor, Gwynedd LL57 2PX
  ☎(01248) 383048
- Health Studies Library, Bangor University, Archimedes Centre, Technology Park, Wrexham LL13 7YP
  ☎(01978) 316370
- Health Studies Library, Bangor University, Fron Heulog, Holyhead Road, Bangor, Gwynedd LL57 2EF
  ☎(01248) 383131
- Law Library, Bangor University, College Road, Bangor, Gwynedd LL57 2DG
  ☎(01248) 382983
- Main Library, Bangor University, College Road, Bangor, Gwynedd LL57 2DG
  ☎(01248) 382983
- Ocean Sciences Library, Bangor University, Wolfson Building, Askew Street, Menai Bridge LL59 5EY
  ☎(01248) 382985
- Science Library, Bangor University, Adeilad Deiniol, Deiniol Road, Bangor, Gwynedd LL57 2UX
  ☎(01248) 382984

BATH SPA UNIVERSITY

Library, Bath Spa University, Newton Park, Newton St Loe, Bath BA2 9BN
☎(01225) 875490
Fax (01225) 875493
url: www.bathspa.ac.uk
Head of Library and Information Services Mrs Julie Parry MLib MCLIP (01225 875634; e-mail: j.parry@bathspa.ac.uk)
Head of Academic Library Services Nick Drew BA MLib MCLIP (01225 875477; e-mail: n.drew@bathspa.ac.uk)
Head of Library Systems Ms Ann Siswell BA DipLib MCLIP (01225 875678; e-mail: a.siswell@bathspa.ac.uk)
Information Managers Mrs Barbara Molloy BA MCLIP (01225 875430; e-mail: b.molloy@bathspa.ac.uk), Richard Taylor MCLIP (01225 875476; e-mail: r.taylor@bathspa.ac.uk)

Campus library

- Library, Bath Spa University, 8 Somerset Place, Bath BA1 5SF
  ☎(01225) 875648
  Fax (01225) 427080
  Campus Librarians Ms Helen Rayner BA(Hons) DipInf (01225 875648; e-mail: h.rayner@bathspa.ac.uk), Ms Nicola Morrison BA(Hons) MCLIP (01225 875648; e-mail: n.morrison@bathspa.ac.uk)

UNIVERSITY OF BATH

Library and Learning Centre, University of Bath, Bath BA2 7AY

☎(01225) 386835 (enquiries), (01225) 386084 (administration)
Fax (01225) 386229
e-mail: library@bath.ac.uk
url: www.bath.ac.uk/library
University Librarian Howard Nicholson MA MCLIP FRSA

UNIVERSITY OF BEDFORDSHIRE

Learning Resources Centre, University of Bedfordshire, Park Square, Luton, Beds LU1 3JU
☎(01582) 743488 (library), (01582) 489398 (administration)
Fax (01582) 489325
e-mail: geraldine.kiernan@beds.ac.uk (administration)
url: www.beds.ac.uk
Director of Learning Resources Tim Stone MA MCLIP (01582 489310; e-mail: tim.stone@beds.ac.uk)
Deputy Director of Learning Resources and Student Services Marcus Woolley (e-mail: marcus.woolley@beds.ac.uk)

Site libraries

- Healthcare Library, School of Acute Care/Midwifery, University of Bedfordshire, Luton and Dunstable Hospital, Lewsey Road, Luton, Beds LU4 0DT
  ☎(01582) 497296
- Healthcare Library, School of Community and Mental Health, University of Bedfordshire, Britannia Road, Bedford MK40 2NU
  ☎(01234) 792215
- Library, University of Bedfordshire, Polhill Campus, Polhill Avenue, Bedford MK41 9EA
  ☎(01234) 793189
  Fax (01234) 793209
- Putteridge Bury Resource Centre, University of Bedfordshire, Hitchin Road, Luton, Beds LU2 8LE
  ☎(01582) 489079

BELL COLLEGE *see* UNIVERSITY OF PAISLEY

BIRMINGHAM COLLEGE OF FOOD, TOURISM AND CREATIVE STUDIES

Birmingham College of Food, Tourism and Creative Studies, Summer Row, Birmingham B3 1JB
☎0121 604 1000
Fax 0121 608 7100
url: www.bcftcs.ac.uk
Head of Library Services Ms Stephanie Holliday MSc AdDipEd (e-mail: s.holliday@bcftcs.ac.uk)

Birmingham College of Food, Tourism and Creative Studies, Richmond House, Newhall Street, Birmingham B3 1PB

☎0121 604 1000
Fax 0121 608 7100
Library Manager Miss Debbie Findlay BA (e-mail: d.findlay@bcftcs.ac.uk)

UNIVERSITY OF BIRMINGHAM

Main Library, Information Services, University of Birmingham, Edgbaston, Birmingham B15 2TT
☎0121 414 5828 (enquiries)
Fax 0121 471 4691
url: www.is.bham.ac.uk
Director of Information Services (Acting) Ray Tier (e-mail: r.k.tier@bham.ac.uk)
Head of Library Services Ms Elizabeth Warner-Davies BSc DipLib DipHECouns

Site libraries

- Barber Fine Art Library, University of Birmingham, Edgbaston, Birmingham B15 2TT
  ☎0121 414 7334
  e-mail: fine-arts-library@bham.ac.uk
  Manager Ms Jean Scott BA DipLib
- Barber Music Library, University of Birmingham, Edgbaston, Birmingham B15 2TT
  ☎0121 414 5852
  e-mail: music-library@bham.ac.uk
  Manager Ms Jean Scott BA DipLib
- Barnes Library (Medicine, Health Sciences, Life Sciences), University of Birmingham, Edgbaston, Birmingham B15 2TT
  ☎0121 414 3567
  e-mail: ba-lib@bham.ac.uk
  Manager Ms Jean Scott BA DipLib
- Education Library, University of Birmingham, Edgbaston, Birmingham B15 2TT
  ☎0121 414 4869
  e-mail: edlib@bham.ac.uk
  Manager Ms Dorothy Vuong BSocSc PGDip
- European Resource Centre, University of Birmingham, Edgbaston, Birmingham B15 2TT
  ☎0121 414 3614
  Manager Geoff Price MCLIP
- Harding Law Library, University of Birmingham, Edgbaston, Birmingham B15 2TT
  ☎0121 414 5865
  Manager Geoff Price MCLIP
- Orchard Learning Resources Centre, University of Birmingham, Hamilton Drive, Weoley Park Road, Selly Oak, Birmingham B29 6QW
  ☎0121 415 8454
  e-mail: olrc@bham.ac.uk
  Manager Ms Dorothy Vuong BSocSc PGDip
- Ronald Cohen Dental Library, Birmingham Dental Hospital, University of Birmingham, St Chad's Queensway, Birmingham B4 6NN
  ☎0121 237 2859
  e-mail: dllib@bham.ac.uk
  Manager Ms Jean Scott BA DipLib

- Shakespeare Institute Library, University of Birmingham, Shakespeare Institute, Church Street, Stratford upon Avon, Warwicks CV37 6HP
  ☎(01789) 293384
  e-mail: silib@bham.ac.uk
  Manager Geoff Price MCLIP
- Special Collections, University of Birmingham, Edgbaston, Birmingham B15 2TT
  ☎0121 414 5838
  e-mail: special-collections@bham.ac.uk
  Head of Special Collections Ms Susan Worrall MA(Hons) MArchAd

BISHOP GROSSETESTE UNIVERSITY COLLEGE LINCOLN

(formerly Bishop Grosseteste College)

Sibthorp Library, Bishop Grosseteste University College Lincoln, Lincoln LN1 3DY
☎(01522) 583790
e-mail: library-enquiries@bishopg.ac.uk
url: www.bishopg.ac.uk
Director of Library and Knowledge Services Ms Emma Sansby BA(Hons) MA MCLIP (01522 583793; e-mail: emma.sansby@bishopg.ac.uk)
Assistant Librarians Ms Nicola Parry BA(Hons) MA AMBCS (01522 583744; e-mail: nicola.parry@bishopg.ac.uk), Ms Janice Morris BA MEd MCLIP (e-mail: j.m.morris@bishopg.ac.uk), Ms Susan Rodda BA (e-mail: susan.rodda@bishopg.ac.uk)

UNIVERSITY OF BOLTON

Eagle Learning Support Centre, University of Bolton, Deane Road, Bolton, Lancashire BL3 5AB
☎(01204) 903092 (enquiries), (01204) 903160 (administration)
Fax (01204) 903166
url: www.bolton.ac.uk/learning/
Head of Library Mrs Karen Senior BA MCLIP MLib (01204 903160; e-mail: k.senior@bolton.ac.uk)

BOURNEMOUTH UNIVERSITY

Library and Learning Centre, Bournemouth University, Talbot Campus, Fern Barrow, Poole, Dorset BH12 5BB
☎(01202) 965959 (enquiries), (01202) 965044 (administration)
Fax (01202) 965475
e-mail: jascott@bournemouth.ac.uk
url: www.bournemouth.ac.uk/library
University Librarian David Ball MA(Oxon) DipLib MLitt FCLIP MCMI

Site library

- Bournemouth House Library, Bournemouth University, Bournemouth House, 19 Christchurch Road, Bournemouth BH1 3LG

☎(01202) 965959 (enquiries)
Fax (01202) 967298
Service Development and Site Manager (IHCS Subject Librarian) Jonathan Hutchins MA(Cantab) DipLib MCLIP (01202 967350)

UNIVERSITY OF BRADFORD

J B Priestley Library, University of Bradford, Bradford BD7 1DP
☎(01274) 233301
Fax (01274) 233398
e-mail: library@bradford.ac.uk
url: www.brad.ac.uk/lss/library/
Director of Learner Support Services Ms Sara Marsh MA MCLIP (01274 233303)
University Librarian (Resources Management) Peter M Ketley BA MA (01274 233366; e-mail: p.m.ketley@bradford.ac.uk)

UNIVERSITY OF BRIGHTON

Information Services, University of Brighton, Cockcroft Building, Lewes Road, Brighton BN2 4GJ
☎(01273) 600900
Fax (01273) 642988
url: www.brighton.ac.uk/is/library.shtml
Director of Information Services Mark Toole MA(Cantab)

Central/largest library

The Aldrich Library, University of Brighton, Cockcroft Building, Lewes Road, Brighton BN2 4GJ
☎(01273) 642760
Fax (01273) 642988
e-mail: AskAldrich@brighton.ac.uk
Information Services Manager Ms Lyn Turpin MA MCLIP

Site libraries

- Falmer Library, University of Brighton, Village Way, Falmer, Brighton BN1 9PH
  ☎(01273) 643569
  Fax (01273) 643560
  e-mail: AskFalmer@brighton.ac.uk
  Information Services Manager Keith Baxter MBA
- Health Sciences Library, University of Brighton, District General Hospital, King's Drive, Eastbourne, West Sussex BN21 2UD
  ☎(01323) 417400 ext 4048
  e-mail: AskDGH@brighton.ac.uk
  Librarian-in-Charge Ms Sue Hardwick
- Queenwood Library, University of Brighton, Darley Road, Eastbourne, East Sussex BN20 7UN
  ☎(01273) 643682
  Fax (01273) 643825

e-mail: AskQueenwood@brighton.ac.uk
Information Services Manager Michael Ainscough BA MCLIP

- St Peter's House Library, University of Brighton, 16-18 Richmond Place, Brighton BN2 2NA
  ☎(01273) 643221
  Fax (01273) 607532
  e-mail: AskSPH@brighton.ac.uk
  Information Services Manager Mrs Louise Tucker BA

UNIVERSITY OF BRISTOL

Arts and Social Sciences Library, University of Bristol, Information Services, Tyndall Avenue, Bristol BS8 1TJ
☎0117 928 9000 ext 8000, 0117 928 8004 (administration)
Fax 0117 925 5334
e-mail: library-enquiries@bristol.ac.uk
url: www.bris.ac.uk/is
Director of Library Services Peter King BA MA PhD

Branch libraries

- Biological Sciences Library, University of Bristol, Woodland Road, Bristol BS8 1UG
  ☎0117 928 7943
- Chemistry Library, University of Bristol, School of Chemistry, Cantocks Close, Bristol BS8 1TS
  ☎0117 928 8984
- Continuing Education Library, University of Bristol, 10 Berkeley Square, Bristol BS8 1HH
  ☎0117 928 7177
- Dental Library, University of Bristol, Lower Maudlin Street, Bristol BS1 2LY
  ☎0117 928 4419
- Education Library, University of Bristol, 35 Berkeley Square, Bristol BS8 1JA
  ☎0117 928 7070
- Geography Library, University of Bristol, University Road, Bristol BS8 1SS
  ☎0117 928 8116
- Medical Library, University of Bristol, Medical School, University Walk, Bristol BS8 1TD
  ☎0117 928 7945
- Physics Library, University of Bristol, H. H. Wills Physics Laboratory, Tyndall Avenue, Bristol BS8 1TL
  ☎0117 928 7960
- Queen's Library (Engineering, Mathematics, Computer Science), University of Bristol, Queen's Building, University Walk, Bristol BS8 1TR
  ☎0117 928 7628
- Social Medicine Library, University of Bristol, Department of Social Medicine, Canynge Hall, Whiteladies Road, Bristol BS8 2PR
  ☎0117 928 7366
- Veterinary Science Library, University of Bristol, School of Veterinary Science, Churchill Building, Langford, Bristol BS40 5DU
  ☎0117 928 9205

- Wills Memorial Library (Law, Earth Sciences, EDC), University of Bristol, Wills Memorial Building, Queen's Road, Bristol BS8 1RJ
  ☎0117 954 5398

BRUNEL UNIVERSITY

Library, Brunel University, Middlesex UB8 3PH
☎(01895) 266154 (enquiries), (01895) 266177 (administration)
Fax (01895) 269741
e-mail: library@brunel.ac.uk
url: www.brunel.ac.uk/about/pubfac/library
Director of Library Services Nick Bevan BSc MSc(Econ) DipLib MSc(InfSc) MCLIP
Assistant Director: User Services and Staff Development Ms Liz Annetts BA MCLIP
Assistant Director: Systems and Resource Management Malcolm Emmett BSc MCLIP
Head of Collections John Aanonson BSc MSc MCLIP
Head of Academic Liaison Ms Angela Brady BA DipLib MCLIP

UNIVERSITY OF BUCKINGHAM

University Library, University of Buckingham, Hunter Street, Buckingham MK18 1EG
☎(01280) 814080
Fax (01280) 820312
e-mail: library@buckingham.ac.uk
url: www.buckingham.ac.uk

Site libraries

- Franciscan Library, University of Buckingham, London Road, Buckingham MK18 1EG
  ☎(01280) 814080
  Fax (01280) 828288
  Librarian (Law and Science) Miss Louise Hammond BSc
- Hunter Street Library, University of Buckingham, Hunter Street, Buckingham MK18 1EG
  ☎(01280) 814080
  Fax (01280) 820312
  Librarian (Business and Humanities) Miss Swee Har Newell BA DipLib LLB

BUCKINGHAMSHIRE CHILTERNS UNIVERSITY COLLEGE

Learning Resource Centre, Buckinghamshire Chilterns University College, Queen Alexandra Road, High Wycombe, Bucks HP11 2JZ
☎(01494) 522141 ext 5107 (enquiries), ext 3270 (administration)
Fax (01494) 450774
e-mail: hwlib@bcuc.ac.uk
url: www.bcuc.ac.uk
Head of Learning and Information Services Dr Helen Fletcher (ext 5064; e-mail: helen.fletcher@bcuc.ac.uk)
Learning Resources Manager Mrs Ann Badhams MCLIP (ext 3027; e-mail: ann.badhams@bcuc.ac.uk)

Campus libraries

- Campus Library, Buckinghamshire Chilterns University College, Wellesbourne Campus, Kingshill Road, High Wycombe, Bucks HP13 5BB
  ☎(01494) 522141 ext 4055
  Fax (01494) 450774
- Campus LRC, Buckinghamshire Chilterns University College, Chalfont Campus, Newland Park, Gorlands Road, Chalfont St Giles, Bucks HP8 4AD
  ☎(01494) 522141 ext 5137
  Fax (01494) 603082
  Learning Resources Manager Mrs Ann Badhams MCLIP (ext 3081; e-mail: ann.badhams@bcuc.ac.uk)

UNIVERSITY OF CAMBRIDGE

Cambridge University Library, University of Cambridge, West Road, Cambridge CB3 9DR
☎(01223) 333000
Fax (01223) 333160
e-mail: library@lib.cam.ac.uk
url: www.lib.cam.ac.uk
Librarian Peter K Fox MA AKC
Deputy Librarian Ms Anne Murray MA

Dependent libraries

- Betty and Gordon Moore Library, University of Cambridge, Wilberforce Road, Cambridge CB3 0WD
  ☎(01223) 765670
  Fax (01223) 765678
  e-mail: moore-library@lib.cam.ac.uk
  Librarian Michael L Wilson MA
- Central Science Library, University of Cambridge, Benet Street, Cambridge CB2 3PY
  ☎(01223) 334744
  Fax (01223) 334748
  e-mail: lib-csl-inquiries@lists.cam.ac.uk
  Librarian Michael L Wilson MA
- Squire Law Library, University of Cambridge, 10 West Road, Cambridge CB3 9DZ
  ☎(01223) 330077
  Fax (01223) 330048
  e-mail: squire@law.cam.ac.uk
  Librarian David F Wills BA MCLIP
- University Medical Library, University of Cambridge, Addenbrooke's Hospital, Hills Road, Cambridge CB2 0SP
  ☎(01223) 336757
  Fax (01223) 331918
  e-mail: library@medschl.cam.ac.uk
  url: www.medsch.cam.ac.uk/library/library.html
  Librarian Peter B Morgan MA MCLIP

College, Institute and Departmental

Cambridge Union Society
Keynes Library, Cambridge Union Society, 9(A) Bridge Street, Cambridge CB2 1UB
☎(01223) 566421
Fax (01223) 566444
e-mail: paa22@cam.ac.uk
url: www.cambridge-union.org
Senior Librarian Ms Patricia Aske MA
(Members only)

Christ's College
Library, Christ's College, Cambridge CB2 3BU
☎(01223) 334950/334905
Fax (01223) 334967
e-mail: library@christs.cam.ac.uk
url: www.christs.cam.ac.uk
College Librarian Miss Candace J E Guite MA(Ord) MCLIP LTCL MA (e-mail: cjeg2@cam.ac.uk)

Churchill College
Library, Churchill College, Storey's Way, Cambridge CB3 0DS
☎(01223) 336138
Fax (01223) 336160
url: www.chu.cam.ac.uk/members/library
Librarian Ms Mary Kendall MA MCLIP (e-mail: librarian@chu.cam.ac.uk)
(NB The Library is available to College Members only)

Clare College
- Fellows' Library, Clare College, Cambridge CB2 1TL
  ☎(01223) 333253
  Fax (01223) 765560
  url: www.clare.cam.ac.uk/academic/libraries/fellows-library.html
  Fellows' Librarian Dr Hubertus F Jahn PhD (e-mail: hfj21@cam.ac.uk)
- Forbes Mellon Library, Clare College, Cambridge CB3 9AJ
  ☎(01223) 333202
  Fax (01223) 765560
  e-mail: library@clare.cam.ac.uk
  url: www.clare.cam.ac.uk/academic/libraries/index.html
  Librarian Mrs Anne C Hughes MA

Corpus Christi College
- Butler Library, Corpus Christi College, Trumpington Street, Cambridge CB2 1RH
  ☎(01223) 338052
  Fax (01223) 338041
  e-mail: butler.library@corpus.cam.ac.uk
  url: www.corpus.cam.ac.uk
  Librarian Ms Iwona Krasodomska-Jones (e-mail: ik205@cam.ac.uk)

- Parker Library, Corpus Christi College, Trumpington Street, Cambridge CB2 1RH
  ☎(01223) 338025
  Fax (01223) 338041
  e-mail: parker-library@corpus.cam.ac.uk
  url: www.corpus.cam.ac.uk
  Librarian Dr Christopher de Hamel
  Sub-Librarian Mrs Gill Cannell (e-mail: gc110@cam.ac.uk)

Darwin College
Library, Darwin College, Silver Street, Cambridge CB3 9EU
☎(01223) 763547
Fax (01223) 335667
e-mail: librarian@dar.cam.ac.uk
url: www.dar.cam.ac.uk
Fellow Librarian Dr Catherine Boulter
Student Librarian Ms Alice Hall

Department of Land Economy Library
Mill Lane Library, Department of Land Economy Library, 8 Mill Lane, Cambridge CB2 1RX
☎(01223) 337110
Fax (01223) 337130
url: www.landecon.cam.ac.uk/library/library.htm
Librarian Ms Wendy Thurley BA ALAA (e-mail: wt10000@cam.ac.uk)
(Mill Lane Library also houses the Centre of Latin American Studies and the Centre of International Studies)

Downing College
The Maitland Robinson Library, Downing College, Regent Street, Cambridge CB2 1DQ
☎(01223) 334829 (enquiries), (01223) 335352 (College Librarian)
Fax (01223) 363852
url: www.dow.cam.ac.uk
Fellow Librarian Dr Marcus Tomalin PhD
College Librarian Ms Karen Lubarr BA

Emmanuel College
Library, Emmanuel College, Cambridge CB2 3AP
☎(01223) 334233
e-mail: library@emma.cam.ac.uk
url: www.emma.cam.ac.uk
College Librarian H C Carron BA MA MPhil PhD MCLIP
Assistant Librarian C E P Bonfield BA

Faculty of Education
Library and Information Service, Faculty of Education, 184 Hills Road, Cambridge CB2 2PQ
☎(01223) 767700 (enquiries)
Fax (01223) 767602
e-mail: library@educ.cam.ac.uk

url: www.educ.cam.ac.uk/library
Librarian Ms Angela Cutts BA DipLib MCLIP
Deputy Librarian Ms Emma Jane Batchelor BA DipILS MCLIP

Faculty of Music
Pendlebury Library of Music, Faculty of Music, 11 West Road, Cambridge CB3 9DP
☎(01223) 335182
Fax (01223) 335183
url: www.mus.cam.ac.uk
Librarian Ms Anna Pensaert LIC

Faculty of Oriental Studies
Library, Faculty of Oriental Studies, Sidgwick Avenue, Cambridge CB3 9DA
☎(01223) 335112 (enquiries)
Fax (01223) 335110
e-mail: library@oriental.cam.ac.uk
url: www.oriental.cam.ac.uk/guide1.html
Librarian Ms Françoise Simmons MA(Cantab) MA(UCL) (01223 335111)

Fitzwilliam College
Library, Fitzwilliam College, Cambridge CB3 0DG
☎(01223) 332042
Fax (01223) 477976
e-mail: library@fitz.cam.ac.uk
url: www.fitz.cam.ac.uk
Librarian Miss Marion A MacLeod MA DipLib

Girton College
Library, Girton College, Cambridge CB3 0JG
☎(01223) 338970
Fax (01223) 339890
e-mail: library@girton.cam.ac.uk
url: www-lib.girton.cam.ac.uk
Fellow and Librarian F Gandy BA MA MCLIP
Assistant Librarian J K Blackhurst MA MA MCLIP
Archivist K M Perry

Gonville and Caius College
Library, Gonville and Caius College, Cambridge CB2 1TA
☎(01223) 332419
e-mail: library@cai.cam.ac.uk
url: www.cai.cam.ac.uk/library/index.php
College Librarian M S Statham MA MCLIP
(Upper library open to members of the College only. Lower library open to scholars by appointment. All enquiries should be addressed to the College Librarian)

Homerton College
Library, Homerton College, Mary Allan Building, Hills Road, Cambridge CB2 8PH

☎(01223) 507259
url: www.homerton.cam.ac.uk
College Librarian Geoff Mizen (e-mail: gm10009@cam.ac.uk)
(Library restricted to use by Homerton College members only. Visits to the library by appointment only)

Institute of Criminology

Radzinowicz Library of Criminology, Institute of Criminology, Sidgwick Avenue, Cambridge CB3 9DT
☎(01223) 335375
Fax (01223) 335356
e-mail: crimlib@hermes.cam.ac.uk
url: www.crim.cam.ac.uk
Librarian Mrs M Gower MCLIP
Assistant Librarian S Feathers MPA BA

Jesus College

- Quincentenary Library, Jesus College, Jesus Lane, Cambridge CB5 8BL
  ☎(01223) 339451
  Fax (01223) 324910
  e-mail: quincentenary-library@jesus.cam.ac.uk
  url: www.jesus.cam.ac.uk/library.index.html
  Quincentenary Librarian Ms Rhona Watson BA(Hons) DipLib MCLIP
- The Old Library, Jesus College, Jesus Lane, Cambridge CB5 8BL
  ☎(01223) 339405
  Keeper of the Old Library Dr Stephen Heath
  Assistant to the Keeper and Archivist Dr Frances Willmoth
  (Apply in writing)

King's College Cambridge

Library, King's College Cambridge, Cambridge CB2 1ST
☎(01223) 331232
Fax (01223) 331891
e-mail: library@kings.cam.ac.uk
url: www.kings.cam.ac.uk/library/
Librarian Peter Jones

Lucy Cavendish College

Library, Lucy Cavendish College, Lady Margaret Road, Cambridge CB3 0BU
☎(01223) 332183
Fax (01223) 332178
e-mail: library@lucy-cav.cam.ac.uk
url: www.lucy-cav.cam.ac.uk
Librarian Ms C A Reid BSc MSc MCLIP
Assistant Librarian Ms J M Harris BA
(The Library is open only to the members of the College)

Magdalene College

- College Library, Magdalene College, Cambridge CB3 0AG
  ☎(01223) 332125
  e-mail: library@magd.cam.ac.uk
  url: www.magd.cam.ac.uk
  College Librarian N G Jones MA LLM PhD
  Sub-Librarian Ms Phillipa Grimstone
  (Open to College members only)
- Old Library and College Archives, Magdalene College, Cambridge CB3 0AG
  ☎(01223) 332125
  e-mail: library@magd.cam.ac.uk
  Keeper of the Old Library R Luckett MA PhD
  College Archivist R Hyam LittD
  Sub-Librarian Ms Phillipa Grimstone
  (Open to scholars by appointment only during term-time, plus July and August)
- Pepys Library, Magdalene College, Cambridge CB3 0AG
  ☎(01223) 332125
  e-mail: pepyslibrary@magd.cam.ac.uk
  url: www.magd.cam.ac.uk/pepys/
  Pepys Librarian R Luckett MA PhD
  Sub-Librarian Ms Phillipa Grimstone
  (Open Mon–Sat Oct–Mar: term-time only, 2.30–3.30pm; Apr–Aug 11.30–12.30 and 2.30–3.30pm. Scholars by appointment only during these hours.

New Hall

Rosemary Murray Library, New Hall, Huntingdon Road, Cambridge CB3 0DF
☎(01223) 762202
Fax (01223) 763110
e-mail: library@newhall.cam.ac.uk
url: www.newhall.cam.ac.uk/facilities/library/
Librarian Ms Alison Wilson BA MLitt MSc MCLIP
(Admittance to New Hall members only; for special collections, please write to the Librarian)

Newnham College

Library, Newnham College, Sidgwick Avenue, Cambridge CB3 9DF
☎(01223) 335740/335739
url: www.newn.cam.ac.uk/nclcl
Librarian Ms Deborah Hodder MA MCLIP (e-mail: librarian@newn.cam.ac.uk)

Pembroke College

Library, Pembroke College, Cambridge CB2 1RF
☎(01223) 338121
Fax (01223) 338163
e-mail: lib@pem.cam.ac.uk
url: www.pem.cam.ac.uk
Fellow Librarian N McBride
Librarian Ms Patricia Aske MA

Peterhouse
Ward and Perne Libraries, Peterhouse, Cambridge CB2 1RD
☎(01223) 338218 (Ward Library); (01223) 338233 (Perne Library)
e-mail: lib@pet.cam.ac.uk
url: www.pet.cam.ac.uk
Ward Librarian M S Golding MA
Assistant Librarian Ms E A McDonald BA MA MCLIP
Library Assistant Mrs E Grayton
Perne Librarian S H Mandelbrote MA
(Perne library by appointment only)

Queens' College
Library, Queens' College, Silver Street, Cambridge CB3 9ET
☎(01223) 335549, Porter's Lodge (01223) 335511
Fax (01223) 335522
e-mail: library@queens.cam.ac.uk
url: www.queens.cam.ac.uk
College Librarian Mrs Karen E Begg MSc(Econ) (e-mail: keb36@cam.ac.uk)
Fellow Librarian Dr Ian Patterson

Robinson College
Library, Robinson College, Cambridge CB3 9AN
☎(01223) 339124
url: www.robinson.cam.ac.uk
College Librarian Miss L Read MA BA MCLIP

St Catharine's College
Library, Saint Catharine's College, Cambridge CB2 1RL
☎(01223) 338343
Fax (01223) 338340
e-mail: librarian@caths.cam.ac.uk
url: www.caths.cam.ac.uk/library
Fellow Librarian Dr R S K Barnes
Librarian Mrs S N T Griffiths MA MCLIP (e-mail: sntg100@cam.ac.uk)

St Edmund's College
Library, Saint Edmund's College, Mount Pleasant, Cambridge CB3 0BN
☎(01223) 336250 (switchboard)
Fax (01223) 762822
url: www.st-edmunds.cam.ac.uk
Fellow Librarian Dr Peta Dunstan MA PhD (e-mail: librarian@st-edmunds.cam.ac.uk)
(Please write in with enquiries)

St John's College
Library, Saint John's College, Cambridge CB2 1TP
☎(01223) 338661 (administration), (01223) 338662 (enquiries)
Fax (01223) 337035

e-mail: library@joh.cam.ac.uk
url: www.joh.cam.ac.uk/library
Librarian Dr Mark Nicholls MA PhD

Scott Polar Research Institute
Library, Scott Polar Research Institute, Lensfield Road, Cambridge CB2 1ER
☎(01223) 336552
Fax (01223) 336549
e-mail: library@spri.cam.ac.uk
url: www.spri.cam.ac.uk
Librarian Mrs Heather E Lane MA(Oxon) DipLiS MCLIP (e-mail: hel20@cam.ac.uk)

Selwyn College
Library, Selwyn College, Grange Road, Cambridge CB3 9DQ
☎(01223) 335880
Fax (01223) 335837
e-mail: lib@sel.cam.ac.uk
url: www.sel.cam.ac.uk/library
College Librarian Mrs Sarah Stamford BA(Hons) MA
Assistant Librarian Michael P Wilson BA(Hons) MA

Sidney Sussex College
Library, Sidney Sussex College, Cambridge CB2 3HU
☎(01223) 338852
Fax (01223) 338884
e-mail: librarian@sid.cam.ac.uk
url: www.sid.cam.ac.uk/indepth/lib/library.html
Librarian Ms C E Roberts Lewis BSc(Econ) CertEd (e-mail: cer34@cam.ac.uk)

Section library
- Archive and Muniment Room, Sidney Sussex College, Cambridge CB2 3HU
  ☎(01223) 338824
  Fax (01223) 338884
  e-mail: archivist@sid.cam.ac.uk
  Archivist Nicholas J Rogers MA MLitt FSA (01223 338824; e-mail: njr1002@cam.ac.uk)

Trinity College
Library, Trinity College, Cambridge CB2 1TQ
☎(01223) 338488
Fax (01223) 338532
e-mail: jeb30@hermes.cam.ac.uk
url: www.trin.cam.ac.uk
Librarian Prof D J McKitterick FBA
(Undergraduate Library open to members of the College only. Wren Library: readers by appointment. Visitors: Mon–Fri 12–2pm; Sat 10.30–12.30, full term only)

Trinity Hall
Library, Trinity Hall, Trinity Lane, Cambridge CB2 1TJ
☎(01223) 332546
Fax (01223) 332537
e-mail: library@trinhall.cam.ac.uk
Director of Library Services Ms Dominique E Ruhlmann MA(Oxon) (e-mail: der1002@cam.ac.uk)
Library Assistant Mrs Diane FitzMaurice BA (e-mail: df226@cam.ac.uk)

Wolfson College
The Lee Library, Wolfson College, Barton Road, Cambridge CB3 9BB
☎(01223) 335965 (direct), (01223) 335900 (Porters' Lodge)
Fax (01223) 335908
e-mail: library@wolfson.cam.ac.uk
url: www.wolfson.cam.ac.uk/facilities/library
Librarian Mrs Anna Jones MA(Oxon) MA(Lond) MPhil(Cantab)

CANTERBURY CHRIST CHURCH UNIVERSITY

Library, Canterbury Christ Church University, North Holmes Road, Canterbury, Kent CT1 1QU
☎(01227) 782514 (enquiries), (01227) 782403 (administration)
Fax (01227) 767530
e-mail: lib1@canterbury.ac.uk
url: www.cant.ac.uk
Head of Library Services Pete Ryan BA(Hons) MCLIP (e-mail: pete.ryan@canterbury.ac.uk)

Site libraries

- Salomons Hayloft Library, Canterbury Christ Church University, David Salomons Estate, Broomhill Road, Southborough, Tunbridge Wells, Kent TN3 0TG
  ☎(01892 507514
  Fax (01892 507501
  e-mail: hayloftlibrary@canterbury.ac.uk
  Librarian Ms Andrea Ford BA DipLib MCLIP (e-mail: a.ford@canterbury.ac.uk)
- Salomons Mansion Library, Canterbury Christ Church University, David Salomons Estate, Broomhill Road, Southborough, Tunbridge Wells, Kent TN3 0TG
  ☎(01892) 507717
  Fax (01892) 507719
  e-mail: salomons_library@canterbury.ac.uk
  Site Librarian Mrs Kathy Chaney MCLIP (e-mail: kathy.chaney@canterbury.ac.uk)
- St Augustines Library, Canterbury Christ Church University, Burgate House, The Precincts, Canterbury, Kent CT1 2EH
  ☎(01227) 865338
  Librarian Ms Karen Erskine BA MCLIP (e-mail: karen.erskine@canterbury.ac.uk)
- Thanet Learning Centre, Canterbury Christ Church University, Northwood Road, Broadstairs, Kent CT10 2WA

☎(01843 609121
Fax (01843 609130
e-mail: thanetlc@canterbury.ac.uk
Learning Centre Manager Dennis Corn BSc (e-mail: dennis.corn@canterbury.ac.uk)

CARDIFF UNIVERSITY

Information Services, Cardiff University, 39-41 Park Place, Cardiff CF10 3BB
☎029 2087 4818
Fax 029 2037 1921
e-mail: library@cardiff.ac.uk
url: www.cf.ac.uk/insrv/libraries/index.html
Director of Information Services Martyn Harrow
University Librarian Mrs Janet Peters MA MLS MCLIP FHEA FRSA (029 2087 9362)

Site libraries

- Aberconwy Library, Cardiff University, PO Box 430, Cardiff CF24 0DE
  ☎029 2087 4770
  Fax 029 2087 6499
  e-mail: abcyliby@cardiff.ac.uk
  Library Manager Miss Sally Earney
- Archie Cochrane Library, Cardiff University, Llandough Hospital, Penarth, Cardiff CF64 2XX
  ☎029 2071 5497
  Fax 029 2071 6497
  e-mail: cochraneliby@cardiff.ac.uk
  Hospitals Librarian Mrs Rosemary Soper
- Architecture Library, Cardiff University, King Edward VII Avenue, Cardiff CF10 3NB
  ☎029 2087 5974
  Fax 029 2087 4192
  e-mail: archliby@cardiff.ac.uk
  Library Manager Mrs Alison Charles
- Arts and Social Sciences Library, Cardiff University, PO Box 430, Cardiff CF24 0DE
  ☎029 2087 4818
  Fax 029 2037 1921
  e-mail: assliby@cardiff.ac.uk
  Operational Services Manager Duncan Montgomery
- Biomedical Sciences Library, Cardiff University, PO Box 430, Cardiff CF24 0DE
  ☎029 2087 4090
  e-mail: biomedliby@cardiff.ac.uk
  Biomedical and Science Librarian Mrs Linda Davies
- Brian Cooke Dental Library, Cardiff University, 4th Floor, Dental School, Heath Park, Cardiff CF14 4XY
  ☎029 2074 2525
  Fax 029 2074 3834
  e-mail: dentliby@cardiff.ac.uk
  Dental Librarian Ms Jan Hooper
- Bute Library, Cardiff University, PO Box 430, Cardiff CF24 0DE

☎029 2087 4611
Fax 029 2087 4192
e-mail: buteliby@cardiff.ac.uk
Library Manager Mrs Alison Charles

- Cancer Research Wales Library, Cardiff University, Ground Floor, Cancer Research Wales Building, Velindre Hospital, Velindre Road, Whitchurch, Cardiff CF14 2TL
☎029 2031 6291
Fax 029 2031 6927
e-mail: library@velindre-tr-wales.nhs.uk
Library Manager Mrs Bernadette Coles
- Law Library, Cardiff University, PO Box 430, Cardiff CF24 0DE
☎029 2087 4971
Fax 029 2037 1921
e-mail: lawliby@cardiff.ac.uk
Operational Services Manager Duncan Montgomery
- Legal Practice Library, Cardiff University, PO Box 430, Cardiff CF24 0DE
☎029 2087 4942
e-mail: lpl@cardiff.ac.uk
Library Operations Manager Ms Jackie Kirk
- Music Library, Cardiff University, PO Box 430, Cardiff CF24 0DE
☎029 2087 4387
e-mail: musicliby@cardiff.ac.uk
Librarian Vacant
- Nursing and Healthcare Studies Library, Cardiff University, 2nd Floor, Ty Dewi Sant, Heath Park, Cardiff CF14 4XN
☎029 2074 2387
Fax 029 2075 6431
e-mail: healthcliby@cardiff.ac.uk
Nursing and Healthcare Studies Librarian Ms Meg Gorman
- Nursing and Midwifery Library, Cardiff University, Caerleon Education Centre, Grounds of St Cradoc's Hospital, Caerleon, Newport, Gwent NP18 3XR
☎(01633) 430919/436124
Fax (01633) 430717
e-mail: caerleon@cardiff.ac.uk
Library Manager Mrs Angela Bowyer
- Science Library, Cardiff University, PO Box 430, Cardiff CF24 0DE
☎029 2087 4085
Fax 029 2087 4995
e-mail: sciliby@cardiff.ac.uk
Biomedical and Science Librarian Mrs Linda Davies
- Senghennydd Library, Cardiff University, PO Box 430, Cardiff CF24 0DE
☎029 2087 4158
e-mail: sengliby@cardiff.ac.uk
Library Manager and Subject Librarian – Maths and Lifelong Learning
Ms Pauline Richards
- Sir Herbert Duthie Library, Cardiff University, B2, Heath Park, Cardiff CF14 4XN
☎029 2074 2875

Fax 029 2074 3651
e-mail: duthieliby@cardiff.ac.uk
Medical Librarian Mrs Lindsay Roberts

- Trevithick Library, Cardiff University, Po Box 430, Cardiff CF24 0DE
☎029 2087 4286
Fax 029 2087 4209
e-mail: trevliby@cardiff.ac.uk
Library Manager Mrs Ruth Thornton
- Whitchurch Postgraduate Centre Library, Cardiff University, Postgraduate Medical Centre, Whitchurch Hospital, Cardiff CF14 7XB
☎029 2033 6382
Fax 029 2052 0170
e-mail: whitliby@cardiff.ac.uk
Library Manager Mrs Eirian Kelly

UNIVERSITY OF CENTRAL ENGLAND IN BIRMINGHAM

Library and Learning Resources, University of Central England in Birmingham, Perry Barr, Birmingham B42 2SU
☎0121 331 5289 (enquiries), 0121 331 5300 (administration)
Fax 0121 356 2875
e-mail: kenrick.library.enquiry.desk@uce.ac.uk
url: http://library.uce.ac.uk
Director of Library and Learning Resources Ms Judith Andrews MA DipLib MCLIP (e-mail: judith.andrews@uce.ac.uk)

UNIVERSITY OF CENTRAL LANCASHIRE

Library and Learning Resource Services, University of Central Lancashire, Preston, Lancs PR1 2HE
☎(01772) 892284 (enquiries), (01772) 892260 (administration)
Fax (01772) 892937
e-mail: helpdesk@uclan.ac.uk 01772 892105
url: www.uclan.ac.uk
Director of Library and Learning Resource Services Kevin Ellard BA MA DMS MCLIP (01772 892261; e-mail: krellard@uclan.ac.uk)
Head of Information Services Jeremy Andrew BSc (01772 892264; e-mail: jsandrew@uclan.ac.uk)
Head of User Support Vacant
Head of Specialized Learning Resource Unit Ms K McCrea (01772 892294; e-mail: kmccrea@uclan.ac.uk)
Head of Specialized Learning Resource Unit Ms Kay Mason (01772 892294; e-mail: kmason1@uclan.ac.uk)
Acting Head of Bibliographic and Support Services Ms Sharon Whiteside (01772 892141; e-mail: smwhiteside@uclan.ac.uk)
Acting Head of Systems Stephen Mossop (01772 892692; e-mail: samossop@uclan.ac.uk)

Site libraries

- Blackburn Clinical Library, Education Centre, University of Central Lancashire, Blackburn Royal Infirmary, Bolton Road, Blackburn, Lancs BB2 3LR
  ☎(01254) 294312
  Fax (01254) 261504
  e-mail: lblackburn1@uclan.ac.uk
- Blackpool Clinical Library, University of Central Lancashire, Health Professionals Education Centre, Blackpool Victoria Hospital, Whinney Heys Road, Blackpool, Lancashire FY3 8NR
  ☎(01253) 303831
  Fax (01253) 303818
  e-mail: lblackpool1@uclan.ac.uk
- Burnley Clinical Library, Education Centre, University of Central Lancashire, Burnley General Hospital, Casterton Avenue, Burnley, Lancs BB10 2PQ
  ☎(01282) 474699
  Fax (01282) 838916
  e-mail: lburnley.uclan.ac.uk
- Ormskirk Clinical Library, Learning Resource Centre, University of Central Lancashire, Southport and Ormskirk District General Hospital, Wigan Road, Ormskirk, Lancs L39 2AZ
  ☎(01695) 656790
  Fax (01695) 581459
  e-mail: lormskirk@uclan.ac.uk
- Wigan Clinical Library, Wigan Education Centre, University of Central Lancashire, Bernard Surgeon Suite, RAE Infirmary, Wigan Lane, Wigan WN1 2NN
  ☎(01942) 822162
  Fax (01942) 829583
  e-mail: lwigan@uclan.ac.uk

CENTRAL SCHOOL OF SPEECH AND DRAMA

Learning and Information Services, Central School of Speech and Drama, Embassy Theatre, 64 Eton Avenue, London NW3 3HY
☎020 7559 3942 (enquiries)
Fax 020 7722 4132
e-mail: library@cssd.ac.uk
url: www.cssd.ac.uk
Head of Library Services Antony Loveland BA MA MCLIP (020 7559 3934; e-mail: a.loveland@cssd.ac.uk)
Head of Computer Services Vacant
Library Services Manager Peter Collett BA PGDipLib MCLIP (020 7559 3996; e-mail: p.collett@cssd.ac.uk)
Systems Manager Brian Harry BSc (020 7559 3969; e-mail: b.harry@cssd.ac.uk)

UNIVERSITY OF CHESTER

Learning and Information Services, University of Chester, Parkgate Road, Chester CH1 4BJ
☎(01244) 513300 (enquiries)

Fax (01244) 511325
url: www.chester.ac.uk/lr
Director of Learning and Information Services Brian Fitzpatrick BSc (ext 3303; e-mail: b.fitzpatrick@chester.ac.uk)
Deputy Director (Managed Learning Services) Henry Blackman BSc MBCS CITP MHEA (ext 3374; e-mail: h.blackman@chester.ac.uk)
Deputy Director (Health Libraries, Media and Desktop Services) Mrs Wendy Fiander BSc MA MCLIP FHEA (ext 1193; e-mail: w.fiander@chester.ac.uk)
Deputy Director (Academic and User Services) Mrs Angela Walsh BLib MA MCLIP (ext 3308; e-mail: a.walsh@chester.ac.uk)
Deputy Director (Warrington and Network Services) Nigel Williams MSc (ext 4211; e-mail: nigel.williams@chester.ac.uk)

Faculty of Health and Social Care Education Centre Libraries

- Bache Education Centre Library, University of Chester, Countess Way, Chester CH2 1BR
  ☎(01244) 512288
  Fax (01244) 382353
  Librarian Mrs Elisa Dowey BA MCLIP (e-mail: e.dowey@chester.ac.uk)
- JET (Joint Education and Training) Library, University of Chester, Leighton Hospital, Middlewich Road, Crewe, Cheshire CW1 4QJ
  ☎(01270) 612538
  Librarian Ms Clare Harman BSc(Econ) MSc(Econ) (e-mail: clare.harman@chester.ac.uk)
- McArdle Library, University of Chester, Arrowe Park Hospital, Upton, Wirral, Cheshire CH49 5PE
  ☎0151 604 7223 (tel/fax)
  Librarian Mrs Eileen Hume CertEd DipILM MA MCLIP (e-mail: mcardle.library@nhs.net)

UNIVERSITY OF CHICHESTER

Learning Resources Centre, University of Chichester, Bishop Otter Campus, College Lane, Chichester, West Sussex PO19 6PE
☎(01243) 816089 (enquiries), (01243) 816091 (administration)
Fax (01243) 816096
url: www.chi.ac.uk
Director of Information Services Terry A Hanson BA DipLib (01243 816150; e-mail: t.hanson@chi.ac.uk)
Head of Library Services Scott O Robertson MA MEd MCLIP (01243 816090; e-mail: s.robertson@chi.ac.uk)

Campus library

- Library, University of Chichester, Bognor Regis Campus, Upper Bognor Road, Bognor Regis, West Sussex PO21 1HR
  ☎(01243) 816099
  Fax (01243) 816081
  Campus Librarian Ms Norma Leigh BLib MA MCLIP (01243 816082; e-mail: n.leigh@chi.ac.uk)

CITY UNIVERSITY

University Library, City University, Northampton Square, London EC1V 0HB
☎020 7040 4061 (enquiries)
Fax 020 7040 8194
e-mail: library@city.ac.uk
url: www.city.ac.uk/library
Information Services Director Brendan Casey BA DipLib
Senior Associate Director Ms Liz Harris BA(Hons) MCLIP

Site libraries

- Learning Resource Centre, City University, Cass Business School, 106 Bunhill Row, London EC1Y 8TZ
  ☎020 7040 8787 (enquiries)
  Fax 020 7638 1080
  e-mail: cklib@city.ac.uk
  url: www.city.ac.uk/library/ckl
  Senior Associate Director Leslie Baldwin BA DipLib MCLIP
- Library and Information Services, City University, Inns of Court School of Law, 4 Gray's Inn Place, Gray's Inn, London WC1R 5DX
  ☎020 7400 3605 (enquiries)
  Fax 020 7831 3193
  e-mail: ltrc@icsl.ac.uk
  url: www.city.ac.uk/icsl/ltrc/
  Associate Director Paul Banks BA(Hons) DipLib MCLIP
- West Smithfield Site Library, City University, St Bartholomew's School of Nursing and Midwifery, 20 Bartholomew Close, London EC1A 7QN
  ☎020 7040 5759 (enquiries)
  url: www.city.ac.uk/library/sonm
  Associate Director Mrs Helen Alper MA MHSM MCLIP
- Whitechapel Site Library, City University, Alexandra Building, Philpot Street, London E1 2EA
  ☎020 7040 5859 (enquiries)
  url: www.city.ac.uk/library/sonm

COVENTRY UNIVERSITY

Lanchester Library, Coventry University, Frederick Lanchester Building, Gosford Street, Coventry CV1 5DD
☎024 7688 7575
Fax 024 7688 7525
url: www.coventry.ac.uk
University Librarian Pat Noon BA MBA DipLib MCLIP (e-mail: p.noon@coventry.ac.uk)

CRANFIELD UNIVERSITY

Kings Norton Library, Cranfield University, Cranfield, Beds MK43 0AL
☎(01234) 754444 (general enquiries)

Fax (01234) 752391
url: www.cranfield.ac.uk/library/
University Librarian Dr Hazel Woodward PhD BA MCLIP (e-mail: h.woodward@cranfield.ac.uk)
Deputy University Librarian Vacant

Other libraries

- Defence College of Management and Technology, Cranfield University, Library, Shrivenham, Swindon SN6 8LA
  ☎(01793) 785484 (general enquiries)
  Fax (01793) 785555
  e-mail: library2@cranfield.ac.uk
  Acting Director of Knowledge Services at Shrivenham Ms Darien Rossiter
- Management Information Resource Centre, Cranfield University, Cranfield, Beds MK43 0AL
  ☎(01234) 754440
  Fax (01234) 751806
  Information Services Manager John Harrington BA(Hons) MA DipLib MCLIP (e-mail: j.harrington@cranfield.ac.uk)

UNIVERSITY COLLEGE FOR THE CREATIVE ARTS AT CANTERBURY, EPSOM, FARNHAM, MAIDSTONE AND ROCHESTER

Head of Library and Learning Services Vanessa Crane MBA MCLIP (based at Maidstone)
Deputy Head of Library and Learning Services Rosemary Lynch MA MCLIP (based at Farnham)

Campus libraries

- Library, University College for the Creative Arts at Canterbury, Epsom, Farnham, Maidstone and Rochester, Canterbury Campus, New Dover Road, Canterbury, Kent CT1 3AN
  ☎(01227) 817302
  Fax (01227) 817500
  e-mail: www.ucreative.ac.uk
  College Librarian Mrs Annamarie McKie MA MCLIP (e-mail: amckie@ucreative.ac.uk)
- Library, University College for the Creative Arts at Canterbury, Epsom, Farnham, Maidstone and Rochester, Epsom Campus, Ashley Road, Epsom, Surrey KT18 5BE
  ☎(01372) 728811
  Fax (01372) 747050
  e-mail: www.ucreative.ac.uk
  College Librarian Mrs Christina Lewis BSc PGDip MCLIP (e-mail: clewis3@ucreative.ac.uk)
- Library, University College for the Creative Arts at Canterbury, Epsom, Farnham, Maidstone and Rochester, Farnham Campus, Falkner Road, Farnham, Surrey GU9 7DS
  ☎(01252) 722441

Fax (01252) 892616
e-mail: www.ucreative.ac.uk
Deputy Head of Library and Learning Services Ms Rosemary Lynch MA MCLIP (e-mail: rlynch@ucreative.ac.uk)
College Librarian Ms Gwynneth Wilkey BA MCLIP (e-mail: gwilkey@ucreative.ac.uk)

- Library, University College for the Creative Arts at Canterbury, Epsom, Farnham, Maidstone and Rochester, Maidstone Campus, Oakwood Park, Maidstone, Kent ME16 8AG
☎(01622) 620000
Fax (01622) 621100
e-mail: www.ucreative.ac.uk
Head of Library and Learning Services Ms Vanessa Crane MBA MCLIP (e-mail: vcrane@ucreative.ac.uk)
College Librarian Nicholas Ross BA(Hons) PGDip MCLIP (e-mail: nross@ucreative.ac.uk)
- Library, University College for the Creative Arts at Canterbury, Epsom, Farnham, Maidstone and Rochester, Rochester Campus, Fort Pitt, Rochester, Kent ME1 1DZ
☎(01634) 888734
Fax (01634) 888700
e-mail: www.ucreative.ac.uk
College Librarian Mrs Pauline Sowry BA PGDip(Ed) FHEA MCLIP (e-mail: psowry@ucreative.ac.uk)

UNIVERSITY OF CUMBRIA

(formerly St Martin's College and Cumbria Institute of the Arts)

Harold Bridges Library, University of Cumbria, Bowerham Road, Lancaster LA1 3JD
☎(01524) 384238
Fax (01524) 384588
url: www.cumbria.ac.uk/lis
Head of Learning and Information Services Ms Margaret Weaver BA MSc MCLIP FHEA (01524 384238; e-mail: margaret.weaver@cumbria.ac.uk)

Campus libraries

- Charlotte Mason Library, University of Cumbria, Rydal Road, Ambleside, Cumbria LA22 9BB
☎(01539) 430274
Fax (01539) 430371
e-mail: libamb@cumbria.ac.uk
Site Library Manager Ms Sarah Ruston BA(Hons) PGCE MCLIP (01539 430244; e-mail: sarah.ruston@cumbria.ac.uk)
- Harold Bridges Library, University of Cumbria, Bowerham Road, Lancaster LA1 3JD
☎(01524) 384319
Fax (01524) 384588
e-mail: liblan@cumbria.ac.uk
Site Library Manager Ms Lisa Toner BA DipLib MCLIP (01524 384682; e-mail: lisa.toner@cumbria.ac.uk)

- Library, University of Cumbria, Fusehill Street, Carlisle CA1 2HG
  ☎(01228) 616218
  Fax (01228) 616263
  e-mail: libcarfs@cumbria.ac.uk
  Site Library Manager Mrs Margaret Harper MCLIP (01228 616219; e-mail: margaret.harper@cumbria.ac.uk)
- Library, University of Cumbria, Brampton Road, Carlisle CA3 9AY
  ☎(01228) 400312
  e-mail: libcarbr@cumbria.ac.uk
  Site Library Manager Ms Clare Daniel BA MA MCLIP (01228 400325; e-mail: clare.daniel@cumbria.ac.uk)
- Library, University of Cumbria, Milbourne Street, Carlisle CA2 5XB
  ☎(01228) 616218 (for information on Milbourne Library)
  e-mail: libcarms@cumbria.ac.uk
  Site Library Manager David Singleton MA BSc(Hons) DipLib MCLIP (e-mail: david.singleton@cumbria.ac.uk)
- Library, University of Cumbria, Newton Rigg, Penrith, Cumbria CA11 0AH
  ☎(01228) 616218 (for information on Newton Rigg Library)
  e-mail: libpen@cumbria.ac.uk
  Site Library Manager David Singleton MA BSc(Hons) DipLib MCLIP (e-mail: david.singleton@cumbria.ac.uk)

CUMBRIA INSTITUTE OF THE ARTS *see* UNIVERSITY OF CUMBRIA

DARTINGTON COLLEGE OF ARTS

Library, Dartington College of Arts, Totnes, Devon TQ9 6EJ
☎(01803) 861651
Fax (01803) 861666
e-mail: library@dartington.ac.uk
url: www.dartington.ac.uk/informationandlearningservices/library/index.asp
Dean of Information and Learning Christopher Pressler BA(Hons) MA MSc MCLIP (e-mail: c.pressler@dartington.ac.uk)
Information Manager John Sanford (e-mail: j.sanford@dartington.ac.uk)

DE MONTFORT UNIVERSITY

Kimberlin Library, De Montfort University, The Gateway, Leicester LE1 9BH
☎0116 257 7165
Fax 0116 257 7046
url: www.library.dmu.ac.uk
Director of Library Services Ms Kathryn Arnold BA DipLib MCLIP (e-mail: karnold@dmu.ac.uk)
Academic Services Manager Ms Jo Webb MA Mlib MBA MCLIP ILTM FRSA (e-mail: jwebb@dmu.ac.uk)

Public Services Manager Richard Partridge BA(Hons) PGDipLIS (e-mail: rpartridge@dmu.ac.uk)
Technical Services Manager Alan Brine BA MSc MCLIP (e-mail: abrine@dmu.ac.uk)
Staffing and Quality Manager Ms Margaret Oldroyd BA(Hons) MLib MCLIP (e-mail: meo@dmu.ac.uk)

Campus library

- Charles Frears Campus Library, De Montfort University, 266 London Road, Leicester LE2 1RQ
  ☎0116 270 0661
  Fax 0116 270 9722
  Campus Librarian Ms Barbara Freeman BA MCLIP (e-mail: bfreeman@dmu.ac.uk)

UNIVERSITY OF DERBY

01332 591221

Learning and Information Services, University of Derby, Kedleston Road, Derby DE22 1GB
☎(01332) 591205
Fax (01332) 597767
e-mail: enquirydesk@derby.ac.uk
url: http://lib.derby.ac.uk/library/homelib.html
Director of Learning and Information Services Richard Maccabee MA (e-mail: r.maccabee@derby.ac.uk)
University Librarian Richard Finch MA DipLib DMS MCLIP (e-mail: r.j.finch@derby.ac.uk)
Head of Library ad Customer Operations Ms Pat Johnson (e-mail: p.a.johnson@derby.ac.uk)

Campus library

- Devonshire Learning Resource Centre, University of Derby, University of Derby Buxton, Buxton, Derbyshire SK17 6RY
  ☎(01332) 594633
  Manager Ms Maria Bennett (e-mail: m.a.bennett@derby.ac.uk)

DUNDEE UNIVERSITY

University Library, Dundee University, Small's Wynd, Dundee DD1 4HN
☎(01382) 384087 (enquiries), (01382) 384084 (administration)
Fax (01382) 229190
e-mail: library@dundee.ac.uk
url: www.dundee.ac.uk/Library
Librarian John Bagnall MA DipLib MCLIP

Site libraries

- Book and Paper Conservation Studio, Dundee University, Dundee DD1 4HN
  ☎(01382) 384094 (tel/fax)
  e-mail: conservation@dundee.ac.uk
  Senior Conservators Ms Vanessa Charles BA(Hons), Ms Philippa Sterlini BA(Hons)

- Duncan of Jordanstone Faculty of Art Library, Dundee University, Matthew Building, 13 Perth Road, Dundee DD1 4HT
  ☎(01382) 385255 (enquiries)
  Fax (01382) 229283
  e-mail: doj-library@dundee.ac.uk
  College Librarian Ms Marie Simmons BA MCLIP
- Law Library, Dundee University, Scrymgeour Building, Dundee DD1 4HN
  ☎(01382) 384100
  Fax (01382) 228669
  e-mail: law-library@dundee.ac.uk
  Librarian David Hart MA MCLIP
- Ninewells Medical and Nursing Library, Dundee University, Ninewells Hospital and Medical School, Dundee DD1 9SY
  ☎(01382) 632519
  Fax (01382) 566179
  e-mail: ninewells-medical-library@dundee.ac.uk
  Librarian Andrew Jackson BA(Hons) MCLIP
- Nursing and Midwifery Library, Fife Campus, Dundee University, Fife School of Nursing and Midwifery, Forth Avenue, Kirkcaldy, Fife KY2 5YS
  ☎(01382) 385930
  Fax (01382) 385931
  e-mail: snm-fife-library@dundee.ac.uk
  Librarian Ms Margaret Forrest MA(Hons) MSc DipLib FCLIP FSA(Scot)

UNIVERSITY OF DURHAM

University Library, University of Durham, Stockton Road, Durham DH1 3LY
☎0191 334 2968
Fax 0191 334 2971
e-mail: main.library@durham.ac.uk
url: www.dur.ac.uk/library
Librarian John T D Hall MA PhD

Departmental libraries

- Education Library, University of Durham, Leazes Road, Durham DH1 1TA
  ☎0191 334 8137
  Fax 0191 334 8311
  Site Supervisor Mrs Susan McBreen
- Palace Green Library, University of Durham, Law, Music, Archives & Special Collections, Palace Green, Durham DH1 3RN
  ☎0191 334 2932
  Fax 0191 334 2942
  Sub-Librarian, Heritage Collections Mrs Sheila M Hingley MA MCLIP
  Site Supervisor Mrs Anne E Farrow MA MCLIP
- Queen's Campus Library, University of Durham, Queen's Campus Section, University Boulevard, Stockton-on-Tees, Co Durham TS17 6BH
  ☎0191 334 0270
  Fax 0191 334 0271

e-mail: stockton.library@durham.ac.uk
Queen's Campus Library Manager Ms Jane A Hodgson

UNIVERSITY OF EAST ANGLIA

Library, University of East Anglia, Norwich NR4 7TJ
☎(01603) 592421 (enquiries), (01603) 592407 (administration)
Fax (01603) 591010
e-mail: library@uea.ac.uk
url: www.lib.uea.ac.uk
Director of Library and Learning Resources Ms Kitty Inglis BA DipLib (01603 592430; e-mail: k.inglis@uea.ac.uk)
Head of Collections Nicholas Lewis BA PGCE MA (01603 592382; e-mail: nicholas.lewis@uea.ac.uk)
Head of User Services Mrs Heather Wells BSc MSc MCLIP (01603 593440; e-mail: heather.wells@uea.ac.uk)
Faculty Librarian (Social Sciences) Ms Ellen Paterson BA MSc (e-mail: ellen.paterson@uea.ac.uk)
Faculty Librarian (Sciences) Dr Elizabeth Clarke BSc PhD (01603 591249; e-mail: e.clarke@uea.ac.uk)
Faculty Librarian (Arts and Humanities) Ms Sarah Elsegood BSc MCLIP ILTM
Faculty Librarian (Health) William Jones BSc DipLib MCLIP (01603 592412; e-mail: w.jones@uea.ac.uk)
Information Policy Officer David Palmer BA LLB MLS (01603 593523; e-mail: david.palmer@uea.ac.uk)
Technical Services Librarian Mrs Anne Baker BA MCLIP (01603 592429; e-mail: a.b.baker@uea.ac.uk)
User Services Points Manager Ms Catherine Baker BA (01603 593507; e-mail: catherine.baker@uea.ac.uk)
ICT Systems Director Iain Reeman (01603 592423; e-mail: i.reeman@uea.ac.uk)

UNIVERSITY OF EAST LONDON

Library and Learning Services, University of East London, 4–6 University Way, London E16 2RD
☎020 8223 3434 (enquiries), 020 8223 2619 (administration)
Fax 020 8223 2804
url: www.uel.ac.uk/lls
Director of Library and Learning Services and Head of Lifelong Learning Centres Prof Andrew McDonald FCLIP (020 8223 2620; e-mail: a.mcdonald@uel.ac.uk)
Head of Services Ms Cathy Walsh (020 8223 6460; e-mail: c.walsh@uel.ac.uk)
Head of Systems Ms Gurdish Sandhu (020 8223 6463; e-mail: g.sandhu@uel.ac.uk)
Academic Liaison and Skills Manager Ms Simone Okolo (e-mail: s.n.okolo@uel.ac.uk)
E-Resources Manager Vacant
Systems Manager Nick Jarrett (e-mail: n.p.jarrett@uel.ac.uk)

Campus library and learning centres

- Docklands Library and Learning Centre, University of East London, 4–6 University Way, London E16 2RD
  ☎020 8223 3434 (enquiries)
  Campus Library and Learning Centre Manager Ms Judith Preece BA MCLIP (e-mail: j.a.preece@uel.ac.uk)
- Duncan House Library and Learning Centre, University of East London, High Street, Stratford, London E15 2JA
  ☎020 8223 3346 (enquiries)
  Site Library and Learning Centre Manager Ms Maureen Azubike BA MCLIP (e-mail: m.azubike.uel.ac.uk)
- Stratford Library and Learning Centre, University of East London, University House, Romford Road, Stratford, London E15 4LZ
  ☎020 8223 4224 (enquiries)
  Campus Library and Learning Centre Manager Paul Chopra MA PGDipLib MCLIP (e-mail: p.chopra@uel.ac.uk)

EDGE HILL UNIVERSITY

Learning Services, Edge Hill University, St Helens Road, Ormskirk, Lancs L39 4QP
☎(01695) 584286 (enquiries), (01695) 584284 (administration)
Fax (01695) 584592
url: www.edgehill.ac.uk/ls/
Dean of Learning Services and Solstice Director Ms Alison Mackenzie (01695 584284; e-mail: alison.mackenzie@edgehill.ac.uk)
Academic Support Manager Ms Dawn McLoughlin (01695 584518; e-mail: mcloughd@edgehill.ac.uk)
Assistant Head of Learning Services Ms Maria Mirza (01695 584334; e-mail: maria.mirza@edgehill.ac.uk)

Site libraries

- Learning Services, Edge Hill University, Woodlands Campus, Southport Road, Chorley, Lancs PR7 1QR
  ☎(01257) 517136
  LRC Manager Ms Ruth Wilson BA DipLib MCLIP (01257 517137; e-mail: wilsonr@edgehill.ac.uk)
- The Library and Information Resource Centre, Edge Hill University, Clinical Sciences Centre, University Hospital Aintree, Longmoor Lane, Liverpool L9 7AL
  LIRC Manager Ms Rachel Bury BA(Hons) MCLIP (0151 529 5857; e-mail: buryr@edgehill.ac.uk)

EDINBURGH COLLEGE OF ART

Library, Edinburgh College of Art, Lauriston Place, Edinburgh EH3 9DF
☎0131 221 6182
Fax 0131 221 6293
url: www.lib.eca.ac.uk
Principal Librarian Wilson Smith MA DipLib (e-mail: w.smith@eca.ac.uk)

UNIVERSITY OF EDINBURGH

University of Edinburgh, George Square, Edinburgh EH8 9LJ
☎0131 650 3409 (Access and Lending Services); 0131 650 8379 (Special Collections)
Fax 0131 650 3380
e-mail: library@ed.ac.uk; libref@ed.ac.uk; eishelp@ed.ac.uk; is.helpdesk@ed.ac.uk
url: Library Online: www.lib.ed.ac.uk/
Director of Library Services Mrs Sheila E Cannell MA MCLIP (e-mail: s.cannell@ed.ac.uk)

Site libraries

- Law & Europa Library, University of Edinburgh, Old College, South Bridge, Edinburgh EH8 9YL
  ☎0131 650 2044
  Site and Services Supervisor Ms Teresa Jones (e-mail: teresa.jones@ed.ac.uk)
- Medical Libraries, University of Edinburgh, George Square, Edinburgh EH8 9LJ
  ☎0131 650 3690
  Fax 0131 650 3380
  Site and Services Supervisor Ms Claire Leach BSc(Hons) PGDipLib (e-mail: claire.leach@ed.ac.uk)
- Moray House Library (Education), University of Edinburgh, Dalhousie Land, St John Street, Edinburgh EH8 8AQ
  ☎0131 651 6193
  Fax 0131 557 3458
  Site and Services Supervisor David Fairgrieve MA DipLib MCLIP (e-mail: david.fairgrieve@ed.ac.uk)
- New College Library (Divinity), University of Edinburgh, Mound Place, Edinburgh EH1 2LU
  ☎0131 650 8957
  Fax 0131 650 7952
  Site and Services Supervisor Ms Sheila Dunn BA (e-mail: sheila.dunn@ed.ac.uk)
- Science Libraries, University of Edinburgh, West Mains Road, Edinburgh EH9 3JF
  ☎0131 650 5784
  Fax 0131 650 6702
  Site and Services Supervisor Ms Judy Melville BA(Hons) (e-mail: judith.melville@ed.ac.uk)
- Veterinary Libraries, University of Edinburgh, Summerhall, Edinburgh EH9 1QH
  ☎0131 650 6175
  Fax 0131 650 6593
  Site and Services Supervisor Ms Claire Leach BSc(Hons) PGDipLib (e-mail: claire.leach@ed.ac.uk)
  (site also at Easter Bush, Roslin, Midlothian EH25 9RG)

ESSEX UNIVERSITY

The Albert Sloman Library, Essex University, Wivenhoe Park, Colchester, Essex CO4 3SQ
☎(01206) 873188
Fax (01206) 872289

url: www.essex.ac.uk
Librarian Robert Butler MSc

UNIVERSITY OF EXETER

University Library, University of Exeter, Stocker Road, Exeter, Devon EX4 4PT
☎(01392) 263873 (enquiries), (01392) 263869 (administration)
Fax (01392) 263871
e-mail: library@exeter.ac.uk
url: www.exeter.ac.uk/library/
Director of Academic Services Ms Michele Shoebridge MA

Departmental libraries

- Law Library, University of Exeter, Amory Building, Rennes Drive, Exeter, Devon EX4 4RJ
  ☎(01392) 263356
- Old Library, University of Exeter, Prince of Wales Road, Exeter, Devon EX4 4PT
  ☎(01392) 264052
- St Luke's Campus Library, University of Exeter, Exeter, Devon EX1 2LU
  ☎(01392) 264785

Arab World Documentation Unit, University of Exeter, IAIS Building, Stocker Road, Exeter, Devon EX4 4ND
☎(01392) 264041

UNIVERSITY COLLEGE FALMOUTH

Learning Resources Centre, University College Falmouth, Tremough Campus, Treliever Road, Penryn, Cornwall TR10 9EZ
☎(01326) 370441
Fax (01326) 370437
e-mail: library@falmouth.ac.uk
url: www.falmouth.ac.uk
Head of Library and Information Services Ms Doreen Pinfold BA(Hons) PGDipLib MCLIP (e-mail: doreen.pinfold@falmouth.ac.uk)
Visual Resources Librarian Ms Rebecca Ball BA(Hons) PGDipLib (e-mail: rebeccab@falmouth.ac.uk)
User Services Librarian Ms Christina Lake MA (e-mail: christinal@falmouth.ac.uk)
Systems Librarian Steve Pellow BA(Hons) PGCE (e-mail: stevep@falmouth.ac.uk)
Technical Services Librarian Stephen Atkinson BSc DipLib MCLIP (e-mail: stephena@falmouth.ac.uk)
(Tremough Campus LRC also serves University of Exeter in Cornwall)

Library and Information Services, University College Falmouth, Woodlane Campus Library, Falmouth, Cornwall TR11 4RA
☎(01326) 213815
Fax (01326) 211205
e-mail: library@falmouth.ac.uk
url: www.falmouth.ac.uk

Head of Library and Information Services Ms Doreen Pinfold BA(Hons) PGDipLib MCLIP (e-mail: doreen.pinfold@falmouth.ac.uk)
Art and Design Librarian Roger Towe BA PGDipLib (e-mail: rogert@falmouth.ac.uk)
Technical Services Librarian Stephen Gibson BA (e-mail: stepheng@falmouth.ac.uk)
Campus Librarian Ms Rosalind Tyley MA

UNIVERSITY OF GLAMORGAN

Learning Resources Centre, University of Glamorgan, Pontypridd, Rhondda Cynon Taf CF37 1DL
☎(01443) 482625 (enquiries)
Fax (01443) 482629
e-mail: lrcenq@glam.ac.uk
url: www.glam.ac.uk/lrc
Director of Learning and Corporate Support Services Jeremy Atkinson BSc MPhil DipLib MCLIP
Head of Learning Resources Steve Morgan BA MEd MBA FCLIP

GLASGOW CALEDONIAN UNIVERSITY

Saltire Centre, Glasgow Caledonian University, Cowcaddens Road, Glasgow G4 0BA
☎0141 273 1000
Fax 0141 273 1183
e-mail: library@gcal.ac.uk
url: www.gcal.ac.uk/library
Director, Learner Support Tom Finnigan BSc PGCE DipEdComp MA MEd MIITT FHEA FRSA

GLASGOW SCHOOL OF ART

Library, Glasgow School of Art, 167 Renfrew Street, Glasgow G3 6RQ
☎0141 353 4551
Fax 0141 353 4670
url: www.gsa.ac.uk/library/
Head of Learning Resources Ms Catherine Nicholson MA DipLib MCLIP (e-mail: c.nicholson@gsa.ac.uk)

GLASGOW UNIVERSITY

University Library, Glasgow University, Hillhead Street, Glasgow G12 8QE
☎0141 330 6704/5 (enquiries), 0141 330 5634 (administration)
Fax 0141 330 4952
e-mail: library@lib.gla.ac.uk
url: www.lib.gla.ac.uk
University Librarian Ms Helen Durndell MA PGDipLib

Site/departmental libraries

- Adam Smith Library, Glasgow University, Adam Smith Building, Bute Gardens, Hillhead, Glasgow G12 8RT
  ☎0141 330 5648
  Librarian Kerr Ross
- Chemistry Branch, Glasgow University, Joseph Black Building, Glasgow G12 8QQ
  ☎0141 330 5502
  e-mail: library@lib.gla.ac.uk
  Librarian Mrs Denise Currie
- James Herriot Library, Glasgow University, Veterinary School, Garscube Estate, Bearsden, Glasgow G61 1QH
  ☎0141 330 5708
  e-mail: vetlib@lib.gla.ac.uk
  Librarian Mrs Maureen McGovern
- James Ireland Memorial Library, Glasgow University, Dental School and Hospital, Sauchiehall Street, Glasgow G2 3JZ
  ☎0141 211 9705
  e-mail: library@dental.gla.ac.uk
  Librarian Ms Beverley Rankin

UNIVERSITY OF GLOUCESTERSHIRE

Learning and Information Services, University of Gloucestershire, The Park Campus, Cheltenham, Glos GL50 2RH
☎(01242) 714273 01242 714224
Fax (01242) 715076
url: www.glos.ac.uk/lis
Head of Learning and Information Services Ms Ann Mathie BA MPhil MCLIP

Site libraries

- Francis Close Hall Learning Centre, University of Gloucestershire, Swindon Road, Cheltenham, Glos GL50 4AZ
  ☎(01242) 714600
  e-mail: lcinfofch@glos.ac.uk
  Learning Centre Manager Ms Sarah Kennedy
- Learning Centre, University of Gloucestershire, Urban Learning Foundation, Bede House, 56 East India Dock Road, London E14 6JE
  ☎020 7536 7002
  Fax 020 7536 0107
  e-mail: lcinfoulf@glos.ac.uk
- Oxstalls Learning Centre, University of Gloucestershire, Oxstalls Lane, Longlevens, Gloucester GL2 9HW
  ☎(01242) 175100
  e-mail: lcinfoox@glos.ac.uk
  Learning Centre Manager Ms Holly Comben
- Park Learning Centre, University of Gloucestershire, The Park Campus, Cheltenham, Glos GL50 2RH
  ☎(01242) 714333

e-mail: lcinfopark@glos.ac.uk
Learning Centre Manager Scott Jordan BA

- Pittville Learning Centre, University of Gloucestershire, Albert Road, Cheltenham, Glos GL52 3JG
  ☎(01242) 714900
  e-mail: lcinfopitt@glos.ac.uk
  Learning Centre Manager Terry Smith

UNIVERSITY OF GREENWICH

Maritime Greenwich Campus Library, University of Greenwich, Old Royal Naval College, Park Row, Greenwich, London SE10 9LS
☎020 8331 8000
url: www.gre.ac.uk/lib
Director of Information and Library Services Ms Maureen E Castens BSc MA MCLIP DMS (020 8331 8160; e-mail: m.castens@gre.ac.uk)
Head of Learning Services Ms Ann Murphy BA DipLib (020 8331 8196; e-mail: a.e.murphy@gre.ac.uk)

Campus libraries

- Avery Hill Campus Library, University of Greenwich, Bexley Road, London SE9 2PQ
  ☎020 8331 8484
  Fax 020 8331 8756
  Campus Librarian Ms Rosemary Moon BA DipLib (e-mail: r.m.moon@gre.ac.uk)
- Dreadnought Library, University of Greenwich, Maritime Greenwich Campus, Old Royal Naval College, Park Row, Greenwich, London SE10 9LS
  ☎020 8331 7788
  Fax 020 8331 7775
  Campus Librarian Ms Teri Harland BSc MCLIP (e-mail: c.m.harland@gre.ac.uk)
- Drill Hall Library, University of Greenwich, North Road, Chatham Maritime, Kent ME4 4TB
  ☎020 8331 9617
  Fax 020 8331 9837
  Drill Hall Library Manager Ms Virginia Malone

GUILDHALL SCHOOL OF MUSIC AND DRAMA

Library, Guildhall School of Music and Drama, Silk Street, Barbican, London EC2Y 8DT
☎020 7382 7178 (direct)
Fax 020 7786 9378 (direct)
e-mail: library@gsmd.ac.uk
url: www.gsmd.ac.uk
Senior Librarian Mrs Kate Eaton BA(Hons) MA MCLIP
Deputy Librarian Adrian Yardley BA(Hons) DipLib MCLIP

HARPER ADAMS UNIVERSITY COLLEGE

Library, Harper Adams University College, Edgmond, Newport, Shropshire TF10 8NB

☎(01952) 820280
e-mail: libhelp@harper-adams.ac.uk
url: www.harper-adams.ac.uk
Librarian Ms Kathryn Greaves BLib(Hons) MCLIP (e-mail: kgreaves@harper-adams.ac.uk)

HERIOT-WATT UNIVERSITY

University Library, Heriot-Watt University, Edinburgh EH14 4AS
☎0131 451 3571
Fax 0131 451 3164
e-mail: library@hw.ac.uk
url: www.hw.ac.uk/library
Librarian Michael Breaks BA DipLib (e-mail: m.l.breaks@hw.ac.uk)

UNIVERSITY OF HERTFORDSHIRE

Learning and Information Services, University of Hertfordshire, College Lane, Hatfield, Herts AL10 9AB
☎(01707) 284678
Fax (01707) 284666
e-mail: lisadmin@herts.ac.uk
url: www.herts.ac.uk/lis
Dean of Learning and Information Services Prof Di Martin MA DipLib MCLIP CertEd MCIPD (e-mail: d.martin@herts.ac.uk)

Learning resources centres

- Hatfield College Lane Campus Learning Resources Centre, University of Hertfordshire, College Lane, Hatfield, Herts AL10 9AB
  ☎(01707) 284678
  Campus LIS Manager Mrs Cathy Parr MA MCLIP
- Hatfield de Havilland Campus Learning Resources Centre, University of Hertfordshire, Hatfield, Herts AL10 9AB
  ☎(01707) 284678
  Campus LIS Manager Neil Allen BA MCLIP
  (post c/o College Lane address above)
- St Albans Campus Learning Resources Centre, University of Hertfordshire, 7 Hatfield Road, St Albans, Hertfordshire AL1 3RS
  ☎(01707) 284678
  Campus LIS Manager Nick Goodfellow MA MCLIP CertEd

UNIVERSITY OF HUDDERSFIELD

Library and Computing Centre, University of Huddersfield, Queensgate, Huddersfield, Yorkshire HD1 3DH
☎(01484) 473830 (enquiries), (01484) 473838 (administration)
Fax (01484) 472385
e-mail: lc@hud.ac.uk
url: www.hud.ac.uk

Director of Computing and Library Services Prof John Lancaster MPhil MCLIP
Head of Library Services Ms Sue White BA DipLib MCLIP
Head of Computing Services Brian Hackett BA MCLIP

UNIVERSITY OF HULL

The Brynmor Jones Library, University of Hull, Cottingham Road Campus, Cottingham Road, Kingston upon Hull HU6 7RX
☎(01482) 466581
Fax (01482) 466205
e-mail: libhelp@hull.ac.uk
url: www.hull.ac.uk/lib
Director of Academic Services and Librarian R G Heseltine BA DPhil DipLib

Campus library

- Keith Donaldson Library, University of Hull, Scarborough Campus, Filey Road, Scarborough, North Yorks YO11 3AZ
  ☎(01723) 357277
  Fax (01723) 357328
  e-mail: libhelp-scar@hull.ac.uk
  Head of Learning Resources (Scarborough) Ms A L Withey

ISLE OF MAN COLLEGE

Library, Isle of Man College, Homefield Road, Douglas, Isle of Man IM2 6RB
☎(01624) 648207
Fax (01624) 663675
e-mail: libiomc@manx.net
Senior Librarian Miss Carole Graham BA MCLIP MSc (e-mail: Carole.Graham@iomcollege.ac.im)
College Librarian Tim Kenyon BA MCLIP MA (e-mail: Tim.Kenyon@iomcollege.ac.im)

KEELE UNIVERSITY

Library Services, Keele University, Keele, Staffs ST5 5BG
☎(01782) 583535 (enquiries), (01782) 583232 office
Fax (01782) 584502
e-mail: libhelp@lib.keele.ac.uk
url: www.keele.ac.uk/depts/li
University Librarian P Reynolds MA MCLIP (e-mail: p.r.reynolds@keele.ac.uk)

Departmental library

- Health Library, Keele University, Clinical Education Centre, University Hospital of North Staffordshire, Newcastle Road, Stoke-on-Trent ST4 6QG
  ☎(01782) 556565
  Fax (01782) 556582
  Health Library Manager J Beard BA MCLIP (e-mail: j.d.beard@keele.ac.uk)

UNIVERSITY OF KENT

Templeman Library, University of Kent, University of Kent, Canterbury, Kent CT2 7NU
☎(01227) 823570 (enquiries), 823124 (administration)
Fax (01227) 823984
e-mail: library-enquiry@kent.ac.uk
url: www.kent.ac.uk/library
Director of Information Services John Sotillo BSc
Librarian Ms Carole Pickaver MSc(Econ) BA MCLIP

Site libraries

- Drill Hall Library, University of Kent at Medway, University of Kent, North Road, Chatham Maritime, Chatham, Kent ME4 4TB
  ☎(01634) 883742
  Library Manager Ms Virginia Malone
  (Shared library with Canterbury Christ Church University and University of Greenwich)
- Library, University of Kent Tonbridge Centre, University of Kent, Avebury Avenue, Tonbridge, Kent TN9 1TG
  ☎(01732) 352316
  Library Supervisor Mrs Denyse Straker

KINGSTON UNIVERSITY

Library Services, Kingston University, Penrhyn Road, Kingston upon Thames, Surrey KT1 2EE
☎020 8547 7101 (enquiries), 020 8547 7105 (administration)
Fax 020 8547 7111
e-mail: library@kingston.ac.uk
url: www.kingston.ac.uk/library
Director of Information Services Graham Bulpitt MA MCLIP CertEd (020 8547 7100; e-mail: g.bulpitt@kingston.ac.uk)
Head of Content Development Mrs Elizabeth Malone BA(Hons) DipLib MCLIP (020 8547 7814; e-mail: e.malone@kingston.ac.uk)
Head of Planning and Resources Simon Mackie (020 8547 7110; e-mail: s.mackie@kingston.ac.uk)

Campus libraries

- Library Services, Kingston University, Kingston Hill, Kingston upon Thames, Surrey KT2 7LB
  ☎020 8547 7384
  Fax 020 8547 7312
- Library Services, Kingston University, Knights Park, Kingston upon Thames, Surrey KT1 2QJ
  ☎020 8547 7057
  Fax 020 8547 8039
- Library Services, Kingston University, Penrhyn Road, Kingston upon Thames, Surrey KT1 2EE
  ☎020 8547 7101
  Fax 020 8547 8115

- Library Services, Kingston University, Roehampton Vale, Friars Avenue, London SW15 3DW
  ☎020 8547 7903 (tel/fax)

UNIVERSITY OF LANCASTER

University Library, University of Lancaster, Bailrigg, Lancaster LA1 4YH
☎(01524) 592517 (enquiries), 01524 592535 (administration)
Fax (01524) 65719
e-mail: lbrusrvs@exchange.lancs.ac.uk (Library user services)
url: www.libweb.lancs.ac.uk
University Librarian Ms Jacqueline Whiteside MA MCLIP FRSA (e-mail: j.whiteside@lancaster.ac.uk)

LEEDS COLLEGE OF MUSIC

Library, Leeds College of Music, 3 Quarry Hill, Leeds LS2 7PD
☎0113 222 3458 (enquiries), 0113 222 3477 (administration)
e-mail: library@lcm.ac.uk
url: www.lcm.ac.uk
Head of Library Services Ms Jay Glasby BA MCLIP (e-mail: j.glasby@lcm.ac.uk)
Jazz Archivist Ms Claire Marsh BMus MSc MCLIP (e-mail: c.marsh@lcm.ac.uk)

LEEDS METROPOLITAN UNIVERSITY

The Library, Leeds Metropolitan University, Leslie Silver Building, Civic Quarter, Leeds LS1 3HE
☎0113 812 3106
Fax 0113 812 6779
url: www/leedsmet.ac.uk/lis/lss
Head of Libraries and Learning Innovation Ms Jo Norry BA(Hons) MA DipLib PGDip MCLIP FHEA (0113 812 5966; e-mail: j.norry@leedsmet.ac.uk)

Campus libraries

- Civic Quarter Library, Leeds Metropolitan University, Leslie Silver Building, Woodhouse Lane, Leeds LS1 3HE
  ☎0113 812 3106
  Fax 0113 812 3123
  Service Manager: Libraries and Learning Innovation Ms Dilys Young BA DMS MSc(Econ) MLIS FHEA (0113 812 3975; e-mail: d.a.young@leedsmet.ac.uk)
- Harrogate College Library, Leeds Metropolitan University, Hornbeam Park, Harrogate, Yorkshire HG2 8QT
  ☎(01423) 878216/878213
  Campus Library Manager Arthur Sargeant MA BA(Hons) CertFE (0113 283 2600, ext 8282; e-mail: a.sargeant@leedsmet.ac.uk)
- Headingley Library, Leeds Metropolitan University, Beckett Park, Leeds LS6 3QS
  ☎0113 283 3164 (counter), 0113 283 7467 (enquiries)
  Fax 0113 283 3211

Service Manager: Libraries and Learning Innovation Ms Wendy Luker BA(Hons) PGDip MCLIP (0113 812 7468; e-mail: w.luker@leedsmet.ac.uk)

LEEDS TRINITY AND ALL SAINTS

(formerly Trinity and All Saints College)

Library, Leeds Trinity and All Saints, Brownberrie Lane, Horsforth, Leeds LS18 5HD
☎0113 283 7244
Fax 0113 283 7200
url: www.leedstrinity.ac.uk
Director of the Learning and Information Service Edward Brush BA(Hons) FIDPM (e-mail: e.brush@leedstrinity.ac.uk)
College Librarian Ms Elizabeth Murphy MA MCLIP (e-mail: e.murphy@leedstrinity.ac.uk)

UNIVERSITY OF LEEDS

University Library, University of Leeds, Leeds LS2 9JT
☎0113 343 6388 (general enquiries), 0113 343 5507 (administration)
Fax 0113 343 5561
e-mail: library@library.leeds.ac.uk
url: www.leeds.ac.uk/library/library.html
The Librarian/Head of the Brotherton Collection Ms Margaret Coutts MA(Glas) MA(Sheff) MCLIP

UNIVERSITY OF LEICESTER

University Library, University of Leicester, PO Box 248, University Road, Leicester LE1 9QD
☎0116 252 2043 (general enquiries), 0116 252 2031 (Librarian's secretary)
Fax 0116 252 2066
e-mail: libdesk@leicester.ac.uk
url: www.le.ac.uk/library/
University Librarian Mrs Christine Fyfe BA MA MBA

Site libraries

- Clinical Sciences Library, University of Leicester, Clinical Sciences Building, Leicester Royal Infirmary, PO Box 65, Leicester LE2 7LX
  ☎0116 252 3104
  Fax 0116 252 3107
  Clinical Sciences Librarian Miss Joanne E Dunham BA DipLib
- Education Library, University of Leicester, 21 University Road, Leicester LE1 7RF
  ☎0116 252 3738
  Fax 0116 252 5798

UNIVERSITY OF LINCOLN

University Library, Learning and Information Services, University of Lincoln, Brayford Pool, Lincoln LN6 7TS

☎(01522) 886222 (general enquiries)
Fax (01522) 886047
e-mail: phill@lincoln.ac.uk
url: www.lincoln.ac.uk
Head of Library and Information Services Ms Michelle Anderson BA(Hons) MA PGDip
Administrative Officer Ms Pat Hughes (e-mail: phughes@lincoln.ac.uk)

LIVERPOOL HOPE UNIVERSITY

Sheppard-Worlock Library, Liverpool Hope University, PO Box 95, Hope Park, Liverpool L16 9JD
☎0151 291 2000 (issue desk), 0151 291 2001 (administration), 0151 291 2041 (enquiries), 0151 291 2038 IT help desk
Fax 0151 291 2037
url: www.hope.ac.uk/library
Director of Library, Learning and Information Services (LLIS) Ms Linda J Taylor MEd BA MCLIP ILTM (0151 291 3528; e-mail: taylorl@hope.ac.uk)
Deputy Director Ms Susan Murray MA BSc MCLIP ILTM (0151 291 2002; e-mail: murrays@hope.ac.uk)
Academic Services Manager Ms Angela Duckworth BA MCLIP ILTM (0151 291 2008; e-mail: duckwoa@hope.ac.uk), Ms Ruth Keane MA BA BPhil DipLib MCLIP ILTM (0151 291 2008; e-mail: keaner@hope.ac.uk) (job-share)
Technical Services Manager Mrs Colette Hughes BA(Hons) MCLIP ILTM (0151 291 2016; e-mail: hughesc@hope.ac.uk)
Reader Services Manager Mrs Angela Griffiths BA MCLIP (0151 291 2018; e-mail: griffa@hope.ac.uk)

LIVERPOOL INSTITUTE FOR PERFORMING ARTS

Learning Services, Liverpool Institute for Performing Arts, Mount Street, Liverpool L1 9HF
☎0151 330 3111
Fax 0151 330 3110
url: www.lipa.ac.uk
Director of Information Services and Technical Support Ken O'Donoghue BA MA DLIS CertEd (0151 330 3250; e-mail: k.odonoghue@lipa.ac.uk)
Learning Services Manager Ms C Holmes BA(Hons) PGDipLib (0151 332 3111; e-mail: c.holmes@lipa.ac.uk)

LIVERPOOL JOHN MOORES UNIVERSITY

Learning and Information Services, Liverpool John Moores University, Aldham Robarts Learning Resource Centre, Maryland Street, Liverpool L1 9DE
☎0151 231 3544 or 3682
Fax 0151 231 3113
url: www.ljmu.ac.uk
Director of Learning and Information Services Ms Maxine Melling BA PGDipLib MLib MCLIP (0151 231 3682; e-mail: m.melling@ljmu.ac.uk)

ILL Unit, LJM University, New Century Building 52-56, Tithebarn St, L'pool L2 2SR

Computing Services Manager Graham Chan MSc BSc MCLIP (0151 231 4456; e-mail: g.k.chan@ljmu.ac.uk)
Customer Services Manager Mrs Brigid Badger BA DipLib (0151 231 3379; e-mail: b.j.badger@ljmu.ac.uk)
Facilities Services Manager Jim Ainsworth BA MCLIP (0151 231 4020/5300; e-mail: j.w.ainsworth@ljmu.ac.uk)
Academic Services Manager Ms Valerie Stevenson BA(Hons) (0151 231 3178; e-mail: v.stevenson@ljmu.ac.uk)

Site libraries

- Aldham Robarts Learning Resource Centre, Liverpool John Moores University, Maryland Street, Liverpool L1 9DE
  ☎0151 231 3634/3701
  Fax 0151 707 1307
  url: www.ljmu.ac.uk/lea/aldham/welcome.htm
- Avril Robarts Learning Resource Centre, Liverpool John Moores University, 79 Tithebarn Street, Liverpool L2 2ER
  ☎0151 231 4022
  Fax 0151 231 4479
  url: www.ljmu.ac.uk/lea/avril/welcome.htm
- I M Marsh Learning Resource Centre, Liverpool John Moores University, Barkhill Road, Liverpool L17 6BD
  ☎0151 231 5216
  Fax 0151 231 5378
  url: www.ljmu.ac.uk/lea/marsh

UNIVERSITY OF LIVERPOOL

University Library, University of Liverpool, Liverpool L69 3DA
☎0151 794 2679 (enquiries), 0151 794 2674 (administration)
Fax 0151 794 2681/5417
url: www.liv.ac.uk/library
University Librarian Phil Sykes BA MCLIP

Site libraries

- Continuing Education Library, University of Liverpool, 126 Mount Pleasant, Liverpool L69 3DA
  ☎0151 794 3285
  Continuing Education Librarian Ms Linda Crane BA MCLIP (e-mail: lcrane@liv.ac.uk)
- Harold Cohen Library (Science, Medicine, Engineering, Veterinary and Dental Science), University of Liverpool, Ashton Street, Liverpool L69 3DA
  ☎0151 794 5411
  Fax 0151 794 5417
  User Services Manager Mrs Laura Oldham BA DipLib (e-mail: loldham@liv.ac.uk)
- Law Library, University of Liverpool, Chatham Street, Liverpool L69 3DA
  ☎0151 794 2832
  e-mail: qlis07@liv.ac.uk
  Law Librarian Mrs Wendy Spalton BA DipLib

- Sydney Jones Library (Humanities, Social Sciences, Special Collections and Archives), University of Liverpool, Chatham Street, Liverpool L69 3DA
  ☎0151 794 2679
  Fax 0151 794 2681
  User Services Manager Ms Carol Kay BA MA DipLib MCLIP (e-mail: c.kay@liv.ac.uk)

LONDON CONTEMPORARY DANCE SCHOOL

Library, London Contemporary Dance School, The Place, 16 Flaxman Terrace, London WC1H 9AT
☎020 7121 1110
Fax 020 7121 1145
e-mail: library@theplace.org.uk
url: www.theplace.org.uk
Librarian Ms Sasi Del Bono (e-mail: sasi.delbono@theplace.org.uk)

LONDON METROPOLITAN UNIVERSITY

Calcutta House Library, London Metropolitan University, Calcutta House, Old Castle Street, London E1 7NT
☎020 7320 1185
Fax 020 7320 1182
url: www.londonmet.ac.uk
Head of Library Services Ms Julie Howell BSc(SocSci)Hons DipLib (020 7320 1170; e-mail: j.howell@londonmet.ac.uk)
Learning Resources Manager Ms Helen Dalton BSc MCLIP (e-mail: h.dalton@londonmet.ac.uk)

Commercial Road Library, London Metropolitan University, 41–71 Commercial Road, London E1 1LA
☎020 7320 1869
Fax 020 7320 2831
Learning Resources Manager Vacant

Holloway Road Library, London Metropolitan University, 236–250 Holloway Road, London N7 6PP
☎020 7133 2100
url: www.londonmet.ac.uk/library
Learning Resources Manager Peter Bowbeer BA(Hons) DipInfSci (020 7133 2089; e-mail: p.bowbeer@londonmet.ac.uk)
Academic Liaison Managers George Knapp BSc PGDipInf PGDipFilmSt (020 7133 2103; e-mail: g.knapp@londonmet.ac.uk)
Librarian, TUC Library Collections Ms Christine Coates MA MCLIP (020 7133 2260; e-mail: c.coates@londonmet.ac.uk), Crispin Partridge BA DipLib (020 7133 2720; e-mail: c.partridge@londonmet.ac.uk)

Ladbroke House Library, London Metropolitan University, Ladbroke House, 62–66 Highbury Grove, London N5 2AD

☎020 7133 5149
Fax 020 7133 5100
Library Resources Manager Ms Bridget Shersby BA (020 7133 5148; e-mail: b.shersby@londonmet.ac.uk)

Moorgate Library, London Metropolitan University, 84 Moorgate, London EC2M 6SQ
☎020 7320 1567
Fax 020 7320 1565
Learning Resources Manager Ms Laura Simmons (020 7320 1561; e-mail: l.simmons@londonmet.ac.uk)

(See also The Women's Library in Selected Government, National and Special Libraries section)

LONDON SOUTH BANK UNIVERSITY

Perry Library, London South Bank University, 250 Southwark Bridge Road, London SE1 6NJ
☎020 7815 6607 (enquiries), 020 7815 6602 (administration)
Fax 020 7815 6699
url: www.library.lsbu.ac.uk
Director of Centre for Learning Support and Development Robert Hall BA MA (e-mail: r.hall@lsbu.ac.uk)

Site libraries

- Library, London South Bank University, LSBU at Havering, Romford, Essex RM3 0BE
  ☎020 7815 5982
  Fax 020 7815 4786
  Site Manager Ms Patricia Noble MCLIP (e-mail: noblep@lsbu.ac.uk)
- Library, London South Bank University, Whipps Cross Education Centre, Whipps Cross Hospital, Leytonstone, London E11 1NR
  ☎020 7815 4747
  Fax 020 7815 4777
  Deputy Site Manager Ms Diana Watmough MCLIP CLTHE (e-mail: watmoudj@lsbu.ac.uk)

UNIVERSITY OF LONDON

Senate House Library, University of London, Senate House, Malet Street, London WC1E 7HU
☎020 7862 8461 (enquiries), 020 7862 8432 (administration)
Fax 020 7862 8480
e-mail: enquiries@shl.lon.ac.uk
url: www.ulrls.lon.ac.uk
Director, University of London Research Library Services David Pearson MA FCLIP FSA (020 7862 8410; e-mail: dpearson@lon.ac.uk)
Director, Academic Services, University of London Research Library Services Ian Snowley BA MBA FCLIP FRSA (020 7862 8415; e-mail: isnowley@lon.ac.uk)
Director, Technical Services, University of London Research Library Services Paul McLaughlin MA MCLIP (020 7862 8413; e-mail: pmclaughlin@lon.ac.uk)

Director, User Services, University of London Research Library Services
Ms Christine Muller BA MCLIP (020 7862 8412; e-mail: cmuller@lon.ac.uk)

(Includes libraries of the Institute of United States Studies, the Institute for English Studies and of the Australian and Canadian High Commissions)

Depository Library, University of London, Spring Rise, Egham, Surrey TW20 9PP
☎(01784) 434560 (tel/fax)
e-mail: shl.depository@london.ac.uk
Depository Librarian T West BA MCLIP (e-mail: twest@lon.ac.uk)
Any enquiries relating to the Depository Library should be directed to Paul McLaughlin (see above)

College, Institute and Departmental

Each College listed below is an independent self-governing institution funded, where applicable, by HEFCE, and awarding degrees of the University of London, of which each is a member.

Australian High Commission Library

See University of London, Senate House

Birkbeck

Library, Birkbeck, Malet Street, London WC1E 7HX
☎020 7631 6064 (administration), 020 7631 6063/6239 (enquiries)
Fax 020 7631 6066
e-mail: libhelp@bbk.ac.uk
url: www.bbk.ac.uk/lib/
Librarian Philip Payne BA HonFCLIP MCLIP (020 7631 6250; e-mail: p.payne@bbk.ac.uk)
Deputy Librarian Robert Atkinson MA DipLib MCLIP (020 7631 6366; e-mail: r.atkinson@bbk.ac.uk)

Visual Image Service (including Central Slide Library)
☎020 7679 7518
Fax 020 7679 1044
url: www.bbk.ac.uk/lib/about/hours/vis
Head of Visual Image Service Rodger Sykes BA MA (e-mail: r.sykes@bbk.ac.uk)

Canadian High Commission Library

See University of London, Senate House

Courtauld Institute of Art

Library, Courtauld Institute of Art, Somerset House, Strand, London WC2R 0RN
☎020 7848 2706 (enquiries)
Fax 020 7848 2887
url: www.courtauld.ac.uk
Kilfinan Librarian, Head of Libraries, Image Services and IT Antony Hopkins (e-mail: antony.hopkins@courtauld.ac.uk)

Goldsmiths

Library, Goldsmiths, New Cross, London SE14 6NW
☎020 7919 7150 (enquiries), 020 7919 7161 (administration)
Fax 020 7919 7165
e-mail: library@gold.ac.uk
url: http://libweb.gold.ac.uk
Librarian Ms Mary Nixon BA MA DipLib MCLIP

Heythrop College

Library, Heythrop College, Kensington Square, London W8 5HQ
☎020 7795 4250 (enquiries), 020 7795 4251 (administration)
Fax 020 7795 4253
e-mail: library@heythrop.ac.uk
url: www.heythrop.ac.uk
Librarian Christopher J Pedley SJ BA(Econ) BA MTh ThM MA (e-mail: c.pedley@heythrop.ac.uk)

Imperial College London

Central Library, Imperial College London, South Kensington, London SW7 2AZ
☎020 7594 8820 (enquiries), 020 7594 8816 (administration)
Fax 020 7594 8876
e-mail: library@imperial.ac.uk
url: www.imperial.ac.uk/library
Director of Library Services Ms Deborah Shorley BA FCLIP (020 7594 8880; e-mail: d.shorley@imperial.ac.uk)
Assistant Director, Faculty Support Services for Learning and Research Ms Liz Davis BSc MCLIP (020 7594 8877; e-mail: e.davis@imperial.ac.uk)
Assistant Director, e-Strategy and Information Resources Owen Stephens (020 7594 8829; e-mail: o.stephens@imperial.ac.uk)
Assistant Director, Administration and Planning Ms Susan Howard BA MSc DipLib MCLIP (020 7594 8622; e-mail: s.howard@imperial.ac.uk)

Departmental libraries

- Aeronautics Department Library, Imperial College London, South Kensington Campus, London SW7 2AZ
  ☎020 7594 5069
  Fax 020 7584 8120
- Chemical Engineering and Chemical Technology Department Library, Imperial College London, South Kensington Campus, London SW7 2AZ
  ☎020 7594 5598
  Fax 020 7594 5604
- Civil and Environmental Engineering Department Library, Imperial College London, South Kensington Campus, London SW7 2AZ
  ☎020 7594 6007
  Fax 020 7225 2716
- Electrical and Electronic Engineering Department Library, Imperial College London, South Kensington Campus, London SW7 2AZ

☎020 7594 6182
Fax 020 7823 8125

- Mathematics Library, Imperial College London, South Kensington Campus, London SW7 2AZ
  ☎020 7594 8542
  Fax 020 7594 8517

Medical libraries

- Charing Cross Campus Library, Imperial College London, Charing Cross Campus, St Dunstan's Road, London W6 8RP
  ☎020 7594 0755
  Fax 020 7594 0851
- Chelsea and Westminster Campus Library, Imperial College London, Chelsea and Westminster Campus, Fulham Road, London SW10 9NH
  ☎020 8746 8107
  Fax 020 8746 8215
- Hammersmith Campus Library, Imperial College London, Hammersmith Campus, Du Cane Road, London W12 0NN
  ☎020 8383 3246
  Fax 020 8383 2195
- Royal Brompton Campus Library, Imperial College London, Royal Brompton Campus, Dovehouse Street, London SW3 6LY
  ☎020 7351 8150
  Fax 020 7351 8117
- St Mary's Campus Library, Imperial College London, St Mary's Campus, Norfolk Place, London W2 1PG
  ☎020 7594 3692
  Fax 020 7402 3971
- Silwood Park Campus Library, Imperial College London, Silwood Park Campus, Buckhurst Road, Ascot, Berks SL5 7TE
  ☎(01491) 829112
  Fax (01491) 829123
- Wye Campus Library, Imperial College London, Wye Campus, High Street, Wye, Ashford, Kent TN25 5AH
  ☎020 7594 2915
  Fax 020 7594 2929

Institute for English Studies

See University of London, Senate House

Institute for the Study of the Americas

Latin American Studies Library, Institute for the Study of the Americas, School of Advanced Study, 31 Tavistock Square, London WC1H 9HA
☎020 7862 8501
Fax 020 7862 8971
e-mail: latam.lib@sas.ac.uk
url: http://americas.sas.ac.uk/library/
Library Operations Manager Ms Shereen Colvin (e-mail: shereen.colvin@lon.ac.uk)

Institute of Advanced Legal Studies

Library, Institute of Advanced Legal Studies, School of Advanced Study, 17 Russell Square, London WC1B 5DR
☎020 7862 5800
Fax 020 7862 5770
e-mail: ials@sas.ac.uk
url: www.ials.sas.ac.uk
Librarian Jules R Winterton BA LLB MCLIP
Deputy Librarian and Academic Services Manager David R Gee BA MA MCLIP
Information Systems Manager Steve J Whittle BA MA
Information Resources Manager Ms Lesley Young BA DipLib MCLIP

Institute of Cancer Research

Library, Institute of Cancer Research, Brookes Lawley Building, 15 Cotswold Road, Belmont, Sutton, Surrey SM2 5NG
☎020 8722 4230
Fax 020 8722 4323
e-mail: sutlib@icr.ac.uk
Librarian Barry Jenkins BA DipLib
Library Information Officer Mrs Sue Rogers BA MCLIP

Site library

- Library, Institute of Cancer Research, Chester Beatty Labs, 237 Fulham Road, London SW3 6JB
  ☎020 7153 5123
  Fax 020 7153 5143
  e-mail: fullib@icr.ac.uk
  url: www.icr.ac.uk
  Librarian Barry Jenkins BA DipLib
  Library Assistant Ms June Greenwood

Institute of Classical Studies

Institute of Classical Studies Library and Joint Library of the Hellenic and Roman Societies, Institute of Classical Studies, Senate House, Malet Street, London WC1E 7HU
☎020 7862 8709
Fax 020 7862 8724
url: http://icls.sas.ac.uk/library/home.htm
Librarian Colin H Annis MA MCLIP (e-mail: colin.annis@sas.ac.uk)

Institute of Commonwealth Studies

Library, Institute of Commonwealth Studies, 28 Russell Square, London WC1B 5DS
☎020 7862 8842 (library enquiries)
Fax 020 7862 8820
e-mail: icommlib@sas.ac.uk
url: http://commonwealth.sas.ac.uk
Information Resources Manager/Librarian David Clover DipLib MA (020 7862 8840; e-mail: david.clover@sas.ac.uk)

Institute of Education
Newsam Library and Archives, Institute of Education, 20 Bedford Way, London WC1H 0AL
☎020 7612 6080 (enquiries)
Fax 020 7612 6093
e-mail: lib.enquiries@ioe.ac.uk
url: www.ioe.ac.uk
Head of Library Services Stephen Pickles BA (020 7612 6064; e-mail: s.pickles@ioe.ac.uk)

Institute of Germanic and Romance Studies
(formerly Institute of Germanic Studies)
Germanic Studies Library, Institute of Germanic and Romance Studies, 29 Russell Square, London WC1B 5DP
☎020 7862 8967 (library)
Fax 020 7862 8970
e-mail: igslib@sas.ac.uk
url: http://igrs.sas.ac.uk/library/
Librarian William Abbey BA (020 7862 8969; e-mail: william.abbey@sas.ac.uk)

Institute of Historical Research
Library, Institute of Historical Research, School of Advanced Study, Senate House, Malet Street, London WC1E 7HU
☎020 7862 8760
Fax 020 7862 8762
e-mail: IHR.Library@sas.ac.uk
url: www.history.ac.uk/library/; http://catalogue.ulrls.lon.ac.uk
Librarian Robert Lyons BA DipLib

Institute of Ophthalmology and Moorfields Eye Hospital NHS Foundation Trust
Joint Library, Institute of Ophthalmology and Moorfields Eye Hospital NHS Foundation Trust, 11-43 Bath Street, London EC1V 9EL
☎020 7608 6814 (tel/fax)
e-mail: ophthlib@ucl.ac.uk
url: www.ucl.ac.uk/resources.php (then select joint library)
Librarian Ms Debbie Heatlie BA (020 7608 6815; e-mail: d.heatlie@ucl.ac.uk)
Assistant Librarian Vacant

Institute of United States Studies
See University of London, Senate House

King's College Institute of Psychiatry
Library, King's College Institute of Psychiatry, PO18 De Crespigny Park, London SE5 8AF
☎020 7848 0204
Fax 020 7848 0209
e-mail: spyllib@kcl.ac.uk
url: www.iop.ac.uk
Senior Librarian Ms Clare Martin BA MCLIP

King's College London
King's College London, 4th Floor, Waterloo Bridge Wing, Franklin-Wilkins Building, 150 Stamford Street, London SE1 9NN
☎020 7848 4480
Fax 020 7848 4457
e-mail: issenquiry@kcl.ac.uk
url: www.kcl.ac.uk/iss
Chief Information Officer and College Librarian Ms Karen Stanton (e-mail: karen.stanton@kcl.ac.uk)
Site Services Manager Mrs Vivien Robertson BA MCLIP (e-mail: vivien.robertson@kcl.ac.uk) (located at Chancery Lane: see Strand Campus below)
☎020 7848 2424
Fax 020 7848 2277

Guy's Campus
- Information Services Centre, King's College London, New Hunt's House, Guy's Campus, London SE1 1UL
  ☎020 7848 6600
  Fax 020 7848 6743

King's Denmark Hill Campus
- Information Services Centre, King's College London, Weston Education Centre, Cutcombe Road, London SE5 9RJ
  ☎020 7848 5541/5542
  Fax 020 7848 5550

Strand Campus
- Maughan Library & Information Services Centre, King's College London, Chancery Lane, London WC2A 1LR
  ☎020 7848 2313
  Fax 020 7848 2277
  Deputy Site Manager Ms Sally Brock

St Thomas' Campus
- Medical Library, King's College London, Block 9, Sherrington Building, St Thomas' Hospital, Lambeth Palace Road, London SE1 7EH
  ☎020 7188 3740
  Fax 020 7401 3932
  Deputy Site Manager Matthew Lawson

Waterloo Campus
- Information Services Centre, King's College London, Franklin-Wilkins Building, 150 Stamford Street, London SE1 9NH
  ☎020 7848 4378
  Fax 020 7848 4290
  Site Manager Ms Veronyka Carson (020 7848 4360; e-mail: veronyka.carson@kcl.ac.uk)

London Business School

- Library, London Business School, Regent's Park, London NW1 4SA
  ☎020 7000 7000 (switchboard)
  Fax 020 7706 1897
  e-mail: library@london.edu
  url: www.london.edu
  Director, Information Systems Russell Altendorff
  Head of Information Services Ms Helen Edwards BA MCLIP
  Deputy Head of Library Ms Gillian Dwyer (020 7000 7632; e-mail: gdwyer@london.edu)
- Business Information Service, London Business School, 25 Taunton Place, London NW1 6HB
  ☎020 7723 3404
  Fax 020 7706 1897
  e-mail: infoserve@london.edu
  url: www.bestofbiz.com
  Manager Ms Sue Watt DipLib MCLIP

(Note: Main postal address of the London Business School is Regent's Park, London NW1 4SA)

London School of Economics and Political Science

Library of the London School of Economics and Political Science (British Library of Political and Economic Science), London School of Economics and Political Science, 10 Portugal Street, London WC2A 2HD
☎020 7955 7229 (enquiries), 020 7955 7219 (administration)
Fax 020 7955 7454
e-mail: library.information.desk@lse.ac.uk
url: www.library.lse.ac.uk
Librarian and Director of IT Services Ms Jean Sykes MA MLitt DipLib MCLIP (020 7955 7218; e-mail: j.sykes@lse.ac.uk)
Head of Library Services Ms Maureen Wade BA DipLib MCLIP (020 7955 7224; e-mail: m.wade@lse.ac.uk)
Information Services Manager Ms Sarah Rosenblum MSc MCLIP (020 7955 7217; e-mail: s.rosenblum@lse.ac.uk)
Technical Services Manager Glyn Price BA DipLib MCLIP (020 7955 6755; e-mail: g.price@lse.ac.uk)
User Services Manager Ms Helen Cocker BA MPhil (020 7955 6336; e-mail: h.cocker@lse.ac.uk)
Archivist Ms Sue Donnelly BA DipArchiveAdmin (020 7955 7947; e-mail: document@lse.ac.uk)
Library IT Manager Tim Green DipCompStud (020 7955 6140; e-mail: t.green@lse.ac.uk)
Communications and Marketing Manager Ms Marysia Henty DipDM (020 7852 3525; e-mail: m.henty@lse.ac.uk)
Library Administrator and Project Coordinator Ms Val Straw BA PGCert(Prof Prac HE Admin) FAUA (020 7955 7238; e-mail: v.straw@lse.ac.uk)

London School of Hygiene & Tropical Medicine
Library, London School of Hygiene & Tropical Medicine, Keppel Street, London WC1E 7HT
☎020 7927 2276 (enquiries), 020 7927 2283 (administration)
Fax 020 7927 2273
e-mail: library@lshtm.ac.uk
url: www.lshtm.ac.uk/library/
Head of Library and Archives Service Ms Caroline Lloyd BA MA MCLIP (e-mail: caroline.lloyd@lshtm.ac.uk)

London School of Jewish Studies
Library, London School of Jewish Studies, Schaller House, 44A Albert Road, London NW4 2SJ
☎020 8203 6427
Fax 020 8203 6420
e-mail: enquiries@lsjs.ac.uk
Librarian Mrs Erla Zimmels DipLib

Moorfields Eye Hospital *see* University of London Institute of Ophthalmology and Moorfields Eye Hospital

Queen Mary
Library, Queen Mary, Mile End Road, London E1 4NS
☎020 7882 3300 (enquiries), 020 7882 3302 (administration)
Fax 020 8981 0028
e-mail: library@qmul.ac.uk
url: www.library.qmul.ac.uk/
Director of Library Services Ms Emma Bull BA(Hons) DipInf MCLIP
Main Library Manager Neil Entwistle BA MA MCLIP (020 7882 3304; e-mail: n.w.entwistle@qmul.ac.uk)
Medical Librarian Paul Hockney BSc MCLIP (020 7882 7114; e-mail: p.s.hockney@qmul.ac.uk)
Assistant Library Manager and Head of Subject Services Ms June Hayles BA MCLIP (020 7882 3323; e-mail: j.m.hayles@qmul.ac.uk)

Site libraries
- Medical and Dental Library (Whitechapel), Barts and the London School, Newark Street, London E1 2AT
  ☎020 7882 7112
  Fax 020 7882 7113
  e-mail: medlibs@qmul.ac.uk
- Medical Library (West Smithfield), St Bartholomew's Hospital, West Smithfield, London EC1A 7BA
  ☎020 7882 8188
  Fax 020 7601 7853

Royal Holloway
Library, Royal Holloway, University of London, Egham, Surrey TW20 0EX

☎(01784) 443823 (enquiries), 443334 (administration)
Fax (01784) 477670
e-mail: library@rhul.ac.uk
url: www.rhul.ac.uk (College); www.rhul.ac.uk/information-services/library/
Director of Information Services and Librarian Vacant
Deputy Librarian Vacant
Library Services Co-ordinator Matthew Brooke

Royal Veterinary College

Library, Royal Veterinary College, Royal College Street, London NW1 0TU
☎020 7468 5162
e-mail: library@rvc.ac.uk
url: www.rvc.ac.uk
Assistant Librarian Ms Kate Warner MA (e-mail: kwarner@rvc.ac.uk)

Campus library

- Hawkshead Campus Library, Royal Veterinary College, Eclipse Building, RVC, Hawkshead Lane, North Mimms, Hatfield, Herts AL9 7TA
  ☎(01707) 666457
  College Librarian Simon Jackson MA MCLIP (e-mail: sjackson@rvc.ac.uk)
  Senior Assistant Librarian Ms Elspeth Keith MCLIP

St George's, University of London

St George's Library, Saint George's, University of London, Hunter Wing, Cranmer Terrace, London SW17 0RE
☎020 8725 5466 (direct line)
Fax 020 8725 3863
e-mail: liblearn@sgul.ac.uk
url: www.sgul.ac.uk/depts/library/
Library Services Manager Ms Marina Logan Bruce BA(Hons) (e-mail: logan@sgul.ac.uk)

School of Oriental and African Studies

Library, School of Oriental and African Studies, Thornhaugh Street, Russell Square, London WC1H 0XG
☎020 7898 4163 (enquiries), 020 7898 4160 (library office)
Fax 020 7898 4159
url: www.soas.ac.uk/library/
Librarian Mrs Anne Poulson BA(Oxon) MA MPhil (020 7898 4161; e-mail: ap45@soas.ac.uk)

School of Pharmacy

Library, School of Pharmacy, 29–39 Brunswick Square, London WC1N 1AX
☎020 7753 5833
Fax 020 7753 5947
e-mail: library@pharmacy.ac.uk
url: www.pharmacy.ac.uk
Head of Library and Information Services Ms Michelle Wake BA MA MCLIP (e-mail: michelle.wake@pharmacy.ac.uk)

UCL (University College London)

UCL Library Services, UCL (University College London), Gower Street, London WC1E 6BT
☎020 7679 7700 (enquiries), 020 7679 7051 (administration)
Fax 020 7679 7373
e-mail: library@ucl.ac.uk
url: www.ucl.ac.uk/library
Director of UCL Library Services Paul Ayris MA PhD
Deputy Director of UCL Library Services: Group Manager, Academic Support Ms Elizabeth Chapman BA MA DipLib FECert FCLIP (020 7679 7907; e-mail: elizabeth.chapman@ucl.ac.uk)
Group Manager, IT Services Mrs Janet Cropper MSc DipLib (020 7679 7833; e-mail: j.cropper@ucl.ac.uk)
Group Manager, Planning and Resources Mrs Janet Percival MA DipArchAdmin (020 7679 7791; e-mail: j.percival@ucl.ac.uk)
Group Manager, Reader Services Vincent Matthews BSc(Econ) MA MA PhD (020 7679 2607; e-mail: v.matthews@ucl.ac.uk)
Group Manager, Bibliographic Services Ms Diana Mercer MSc DipLib (020 7679 2625; e-mail: d.mercer@ucl.ac.uk)

UCL Site libraries

- Information Centre, UCL Eastman Dental Institute, UCL (University College London), 256 Grays Inn Road, London WC1X 8LD
  ☎020 7915 1045/1262
  Fax 020 7915 1147
  e-mail: ic@eastman.ucl.ac.uk
  Librarian Ms Medwenna Buckland BA (e-mail: medwenna.buckland@ucl.ac.uk)
- Library and Information Services, UCL School of Slavonic and East European Studies, UCL (University College London), 16 Taviton Street, London WC1H 0BW
  ☎020 7679 8701
  e-mail: ssees-library@ssees.ucl.ac.uk
  Librarian and Director of Information Services Ms Lesley Pitman BA DipLib (e-mail: l.pitman@ssees.ucl.ac.uk)
- UCL Cruciform Library, UCL (University College London), Cruciform Building, Gower Street, London WC1E 6BT
  ☎020 7679 6079
  e-mail: clinscilib@ucl.ac.uk
  Librarian Ms Kate Cheney BA MSc MCLIP (e-mail: k.cheney@ucl.ac.uk)
- UCL Environmental Studies Library, UCL (University College London), Faculty of the Built Environment, Wates House, 22 Gordon Street, London WC1H 0QB
  ☎020 7679 4900
  e-mail: library@ucl.ac.uk
  Librarian Ms Suzanne Tonkin BA(Hons) MSc (e-mail: s.tonkin@ucl.ac.uk)
- UCL Human Communication Science Library (NICeST), UCL (University College London), UCL Dept of Human Communication Science, Remax House, 31/32 Alfred Place, London WC1E 7DP
  ☎020 7679 4207
  Fax 020 7713 0861
  e-mail: hcs.library@ucl.ac.uk

url: www.hcs.ucl.ac.uk
Librarian Ms Stevie Russell BA(Hons) DipLib (e-mail: s.russell@ucl.ac.uk)
(Temporary address until early 2008. Please check website for details)

- UCL Institute of Archaeology Library, UCL (University College London), 31–34 Gordon Square, London WC1H 0PY
☎020 7679 4788
e-mail: library@ucl.ac.uk
Librarian Robert Kirby MA (e-mail: r.kirby@ucl.ac.uk)
- UCL Institute of Child Health Library, UCL (University College London), 30 Guilford Street, London WC1N 1EH
☎020 7242 9789 ext 2424
Fax 020 7831 0488
e-mail: library@ich.ucl.ac.uk
Librarian John Clarke MA DipLib (e-mail: jclarke@ich.ucl.ac.uk)
- UCL Institute of Laryngology and Otology and RNID Library, UCL (University College London), Royal National Throat, Nose and Ear Hospital, Gray's Inn Road, London WC1X 8EE
☎020 7915 1445
e-mail: ilolib@ucl.ac.uk
Librarian Alex Stagg MA (e-mail: a.stagg@ucl.ac.uk)
- UCL Institute of Neurology, UCL (University College London), Rockefeller Medical Library, The National Hospital, Queen Square, London WC1N 3BG
☎020 7829 8709
Fax 020 7278 1371
e-mail: library@ion.ucl.ac.uk
Manager, Libraries and Computing Services (ION) and Librarian (Nat Hosp) Ms Louise Shepherd BA (e-mail: l.shepherd@ion.ucl.ac.uk)
- UCL Institute of Ophthalmology Library, UCL (University College London), 11–43 Bath Street, London EC1V 9EL
☎020 7608 6814 (tel/fax)
e-mail: ophthlib@ucl.ac.uk
Librarian Ms Debbie Heatlie BA (e-mail: d.heatlie@ucl.ac.uk)
- UCL Institute of Orthopaedics Library, UCL (University College London), Royal National Orthopaedic Hospital, Brockley Hill, Stanmore, Middlesex HA7 4LP
☎020 8909 5351
Fax 020 8954 1213
Librarian Ms Julie Noren MLS (e-mail: j.noren@ucl.ac.uk)
- UCL Library Special Collections, UCL (University College London), 140 Hampstead Road, London NW1 2BX
☎020 7679 5197
Fax 020 7679 5157
e-mail: spec.coll@ucl.ac.uk
Head of Special Collections Ms Gillian Furlong BA DipArchMan RMSA (e-mail: g.furlong@ucl.ac.uk)
- UCL Royal Free Hospital Medical Library, Royal Free and University College Medical School, UCL (University College London), Royal Free Hospital, Rowland Hill Street, Rowland Hill Street, London NW3 2PF

☎020 7794 0500 ext 3202
Fax 020 7794 3534
e-mail: library@medsch.ucl.ac.uk
Librarian Ms Betsy Anagnostelis BSc(Hons) MSc DipLib (e-mail: b.anagnostelis@medsch.ucl.ac.uk)

Warburg Institute

Library, Warburg Institute, School of Advanced Study, Woburn Square, London WC1H 0AB
☎020 7862 8935/6 (Reading Room)
Fax 020 7862 8939
e-mail: warburg.library@sas.ac.uk
url: http://warburg.sas.ac.uk
telnet (for library): catalogue.ulrls.lon.ac.uk
Librarian Prof Jill Kraye

LOUGHBOROUGH UNIVERSITY

Pilkington Library, Loughborough University, Loughborough, Leics LE11 3TU
☎(01509) 222360 (enquiries), (01509) 222353 (issue desk), (01509) 222341 (administration)
Fax (01509) 223993
e-mail: library@lboro.ac.uk
url: www.lboro.ac.uk/library; Contacts: www.lboro.ac.uk/library/contacts/index.html
University Librarian Mrs Mary Morley BA DipLib MCLIP

MANCHESTER METROPOLITAN UNIVERSITY

Library, Manchester Metropolitan University, All Saints, Manchester M15 6BH
☎0161 247 3096
Fax 0161 247 6349 0161 247 6645.
url: www.library.mmu.ac.uk
Head of Learning and Research Services Mrs Gill R Barry BA MSc MCLIP (0161 247 6101; e-mail: g.r.barry@mmu.ac.uk)
Faculty Librarian (Crewe & Alsager) Dr Margaret Robinson BA DipLib MCLIP (0161 247 5138; e-mail: m.g.robinson@mmu.ac.uk)

Site libraries

- Alsager Library, Manchester Metropolitan University, Hassall Road, Alsager, Stoke-on-Trent ST7 2HL
  ☎0161 247 5356
  Site Manager Ms Mary Pickstone BSc DipLib MCLIP (0161 247 5355; e-mail: m.pickstone@mmu.ac.uk)
- Aytoun Library, Manchester Metropolitan University, Aytoun Street, Manchester M1 3GH
  ☎0161 247 3093
  Library Services Manager David Matthews BA PGDip (0161 247 3091; e-mail: d.matthews@mmu.ac.uk)
- Crewe Library, Manchester Metropolitan University, Crewe Green Road, Crewe, Cheshire CW1 1DU
  ☎0161 247 5002

Site Manager Ms Lesley Harvey BA (0161 247 5012; e-mail: l.harvey@mmu.ac.uk)

- Didsbury Library, Manchester Metropolitan University, 799 Wilmslow Road, Manchester M20 8RR
  ☎0161 247 6126
  Library Services Manager Ms Jayne Evans BA MLib (0161 247 6120; e-mail: j.e.h.evans@mmu.ac.uk)
- Elizabeth Gaskell Library, Manchester Metropolitan University, Hathersage Road, Manchester M13 0JA
  ☎0161 247 6134
  Library Services Manager Ian Harter BSc DipLib (e-mail: i.harter@mmu.ac.uk)
- Hollings Library, Manchester Metropolitan University, Old Hall Lane, Manchester M14 6HR
  ☎0161 247 6119
  Library Services Manager Ian Harter BSc DipLib (e-mail: i.harter@mmu.ac.uk)

THE UNIVERSITY OF MANCHESTER

The John Rylands University Library, The University of Manchester, Main Library, Oxford Road, Manchester M13 9PP 0161 275 3741
☎0161 275 3751 (enquiries); 0161 275 3700 (administration)
url: www.manchester.ac.uk/library
University Librarian and Director of The John Rylands Library William G Simpson BA MA MCLIP FRSA (e-mail: bill.simpson@manchester.ac.uk); from January 2008, Ms Jan Wilkinson BA DipLib DMS FCLIP FRSA (e-mail: jan.wilkinson@manchester.ac.uk)
Deputy University Librarian (Information Resources and Academic Supoport) and Associate Director of The John Rylands Library Dr Diana M Leitch BSc PhD FRSC (e-mail: diana.leitch@manchester.ac.uk)
Deputy University Librarian (Infrastructure and Planning Support) and Associate Director of The John Rylands Library Dr Stella Butler BSc PhD AMA (e-mail: stella.butler@manchester.ac.uk)

Site libraries

- The John Rylands University Library, Special Collections Division, The University of Manchester, Main Library, Oxford Road, Manchester M13 9PP
  ☎0161 275 3764
  Head of Special Collections and Principal Keeper Dr Stella Butler BSc PhD AMA (e-mail: stella.butler@manchester.ac.uk)
- The Joule Library, The University of Manchester, PO Box 88, Sackville Street, Manchester M60 1QD
  ☎0161 306 4924
  Head of Public Services and Joule Site Librarian Ms Katy Woolfenden BA MA (e-mail: katy.woolfenden@manchester.ac.uk)
- The Eddie Davies Library, Manchester Business School, The University of Manchester, Booth Street West, Manchester M15 6PB
  ☎0161 275 6507 (enquiries), 0161 275 6500 (administration)
  Fax 0161 275 6505
  e-mail: libdesk@mbs.ac.uk
  url: www.mbs.ac.uk/services/library-services
  Librarian Ms Kathy Kirby MA MCLIP PGCE (e-mail: kathy.kirby@mbs.ac.uk)

MIDDLESEX UNIVERSITY

Learning Resources, Middlesex University, Sheppard Library, The Burroughs, Hendon, London NW4 6BT
☎020 8411 5234
Fax 020 8411 5163
url: www.lr.mdx.ac.uk
Pro Vice Chancellor, Head of Learning Resources and University Librarian William Marsterson MA MCLIP (020 8411 5234; e-mail: w.marsterson@mdx.ac.uk)
Assistant Head of Learning Resources Ms Judith Cattermole BA MCLIP (020 8411 6947; e-mail: j.cattermole@mdx.ac.uk)

Bibliographical Services, Middlesex University, Sheppard Library, The Burroughs, Hendon, London NW4 4BT
☎020 8411 5238 (direct)
e-mail: bibservices@mdx.ac.uk
Head of Systems and Bibliographic Services Alan Hopkinson MA FCLIP MBCS (e-mail: a.hopkinson@mdx.ac.uk)

Campus libraries

- Health Campus Library, Middlesex University, Chase Farm Education Centre, Chase Farm Hospital, The Ridgeway, Enfield, Middlesex EN2 8JL
  ☎020 8366 9112
  e-mail: libcf1@mdx.ac.uk
  Site Librarian Vacant
- Library, Middlesex University at Cat Hill, Middlesex University, Barnet, Herts EN4 8HT
  ☎020 8411 5042 (direct)
  e-mail: libch1@mdx.ac.uk
  Campus Librarian Ms Nazlin Bhimani BMus MA MCLIP
- Library, Middlesex University at Enfield, Middlesex University, Queensway, Enfield, Middlesex EN3 4SF
  ☎020 8411 5334 (direct)
  e-mail: liben1@mdx.ac.uk
  Campus Librarian Ms Kathy McGowan MA MCLIP
- Library, Middlesex University at Hendon, Middlesex University, The Burroughs, London NW4 4BT
  ☎020 8411 5852 (direct)
  e-mail: libhe1@mdx.ac.uk
  Campus Librarian Ms Hilary Cummings BSc DipLib, Mrs Caroline Fletcher BA (job-share)
- Library, Middlesex University at Trent Park, Middlesex University, Bramley Road, London N14 4XS
  ☎020 8411 5223 (direct)
  e-mail: libtp1@mdx.ac.uk
  Campus Librarian Ms Sue Fellows PGDipAS MCLIP

(The Health Campus libraries are also served by multidisciplinary libraries at: David Ferriman Library, North Middlesex Hospital, Sterling Way, London N18 1QX (020 8887

2223; e-mail: libnm1@mdx.ac.uk, libnm2@mdx.ac.uk) and The Archway Healthcare Library, Holborn Union Building, The Archway Campus, Highgate Hill, London N19 3UA (020 7288 3567; e-mail: libwh1@mdx.ac.uk, libwh2@mdx.ac.uk)

NAPIER UNIVERSITY

Main library

Craiglockhart Campus Library, Napier University, Craiglockhart Campus, Edinburgh EH14 1DJ
☎0131 455 4260
Fax 0131 455 4276
url: www.napier.ac.uk/
Director of Learning Information Services C Pinder BA MLib DipLib FCLIP (0131 455 4270)
Head of Customer Services and Deputy Director M Lobban MA DipLib DipEdTech MCLIP (0131 455 4272)
Head of Information Services M Jones BA DipLib MCLIP (0131 455 2693)
Research Support Advisor Dr D Cumming BSc DipLib MLib PhD MCLIP FGS (0131 455 2367; fax: 0131 455 2368)

Campus libraries

- Canaan Lane Library, Napier University, Canaan Lane Campus, Edinburgh EH9 2TB
  ☎0131 455 5616
  Fax 0131 455 5608
- Comely Bank Library, Napier University, Comely Bank Campus, Edinburgh EH4 2LD
  ☎0131 455 5319
  Fax 0131 455 5358
- Craighouse Library, Napier University, Craighouse Campus, Edinburgh EH10 5LG
  ☎0131 455 6020
  Fax 0131 455 6022
- Livingston Library, Napier University, Livingston Campus, West Lothian EH54 6PP
  ☎(01506) 523966
  Fax (01506) 523969
- Melrose Library, Napier University, Melrose Campus, Melrose, Scottish Borders TD6 9BS
  ☎(01896) 661632
  Fax (01896) 823869
- Merchiston Library, Napier University, Merchiston Campus, Edinburgh EH10 5DT
  ☎0131 455 2582
  Fax 0131 455 2377

NEWCASTLE UNIVERSITY

Robinson Library, Newcastle University, Newcastle upon Tyne NE2 4HQ
☎0191 222 7662 (enquiries), 0191 222 7674 (administration)
Fax 0191 222 6235
e-mail: library@newcastle.ac.uk
url: www.ncl.ac.uk/library/
Librarian Thomas W Graham MA PhD DipLib MCLIP
Deputy Librarian Wayne Connolly BA DipLib

Divisional libraries

- Law Library, Newcastle University, Newcastle Law School, 22-24 Windsor Terrace, Newcastle upon Tyne NE1 7RU
  ☎0191 222 7944
  Librarian Mrs Linda Kelly BA MCLIP
- The Walton Library (Medical and Dental), Newcastle University, The Medical School, Framlington Place, Newcastle upon Tyne NE2 4HH
  ☎0191 222 7550
  Librarian Ms Erika Gwynnett BA(Hons) MA DipLib

NEWMAN COLLEGE OF HIGHER EDUCATION

Library, Newman College of Higher Education, Genners Lane, Bartley Green, Birmingham B32 3NT
☎0121 476 1181 ext 2208
e-mail: library@newman.ac.uk
url: www.newman.ac.uk/library
Head of Library and Learning Services Ms Christine Porter BA MLib MCLIP (ext 2327; e-mail: c.porter@newman.ac.uk)

NORTH EAST WALES INSTITUTE OF HIGHER EDUCATION

Library, North East Wales Institute of Higher Education, Plas Coch, Mold Road, Wrexham LL11 2AW
☎(01978) 293250
Fax (01978) 293435
url: www.newi.ac.uk
User Services Manager Paul Jeorrett BA MCLIP (e-mail: p.jeorrett@newi.ac.uk)
Academic Liaison Co-ordinator Nicola Watkinson BSc MCLIP ILTM (e-mail: nicolaw@newi.co.uk)

UNIVERSITY OF NORTHAMPTON

Park Campus Library, University of Northampton, Boughton Green Road, Northampton NN2 7AL
☎(01604) 735500 ext 2477 (enquiries), ext 2041 (administration)
Fax (01604) 718819
url: www.northampton.ac.uk
Director of Information Services Ms Hilary Johnson BA MA MCLIP (ext 2045; e-mail: hilary.johnson@northampton.ac.uk)
Deputy Director, Academic Services Chris Powis BA MA MLib PGDipTHE MCLIP FHEA FRSA (ext 2229; e-mail: chris.powis@northampton.ac.uk)

Avenue Campus Library, University of Northampton, Maidwell Building, St George's Avenue, Northampton NN2 6JD
☎(01604) 735500 ext 3900
Fax (01604) 719618
Other details as above

NORTHERN SCHOOL OF CONTEMPORARY DANCE

Library, Northern School of Contemporary Dance, 98 Chapeltown Road, Leeds LS7 4BH
☎0113 219 3020
Fax 0113 219 3030
url: www.nscd.ac.uk
Librarian Miss Samantha King BA(Hons) MCLIP (e-mail: sam.king@nscd.ac.uk)
Counter Assistant Miss Ann Cawley (e-mail: ann.cawley@nscd.ac.uk)

NORTHUMBRIA UNIVERSITY

Library and Learning Services, Northumbria University, City Campus Library, Ellison Place, Newcastle upon Tyne NE1 8ST
☎0191 227 4125 (enquiries), 0191 227 4143 (administration)
Fax 0191 227 4563
url: www.unn.ac.uk/sd/central/library
Director of Library and Learning Services Prof Jane Core BA MLib MCLIP

Site library

- Coach Lane Library, Northumbria University, Coach Lane, Newcastle upon Tyne NE7 7XA
  ☎0191 215 6540
  Fax 0191 215 6560

NORWICH SCHOOL OF ART AND DESIGN

(Note: the library will be moving premises during 2007–8: see website for details.)
Library, Norwich School of Art and Design, 3–7 Redwell Street, Norwich NR2 4SN
☎(01603) 610561
Fax (01603) 615728
url: www.nsad.ac.uk
Librarian Tim Giles BA (e-mail: t.giles@nsad.ac.uk)
Assistant Librarians Ms Kitty Guiver MA MCLIP (e-mail: k.guiver@nsad.ac.uk), Ms Jan McLachlan BA(Hons) DipLIS (e-mail: j.mclachlan@nsad.ac.uk)

NOTTINGHAM TRENT UNIVERSITY

Libraries and Learning Resources, Nottingham Trent University, Goldsmith Street, Nottingham NG1 5LS
☎0115 848 6494
Fax 0115 848 2286
url: www.ntu.ac.uk
Director of Libraries and Knowledge Resources Ms Sue McKnight BBus MPA AALIA AFAIM (e-mail: sue.mcknight@ntu.ac.uk)

Site libraries

- The Boots Library, Nottingham Trent University, Goldsmith Street, Nottingham NG1 5LS

☎0115 848 2175 (enquiries)
Fax 0115 848 4425

- Brackenhurst Campus Library, Nottingham Trent University, Southwell Road, Southwell, Notts NG25 0QF
  ☎(01636) 817049 (enquiries)
  Fax (01636) 817077
- Clifton Campus Library, Nottingham Trent University, Clifton Lane, Nottingham NG11 8NS
  ☎0115 848 3570/6612
  Fax 0115 848 6304

UNIVERSITY OF NOTTINGHAM

Information Services, University of Nottingham, University Park, Nottingham NG7 2RD
url: www.nottingham.ac.uk/is
Chief Information Officer Stephen Pinfield MA MA MCLIP (0115 951 5109; e-mail: stephen.pinfield@nottingham.ac.uk)
Director, Customer Services Graham Moore BA (0115 951 4535; e-mail: graham.moore@nottingham.ac.uk)
Director, IT Systems Ms Lynne Tucker BSc (0115 951 3391; e-mail: lynne.tucker@nottinghamac.uk)

Library sites

- Business Library, University of Nottingham, Business School, Jubilee Campus, Wollaton Road, Nottingham NG8 1BB
  ☎0115 846 8069
  Fax 0115 846 8064
- Dennis Arnold Music Library, University of Nottingham, University Park, Nottingham NG7 2RD
  ☎0115 951 4596
  Fax 0115 951 4558
- Djanogly LRC (Education, Computer Science), University of Nottingham, Jubilee Campus, Wollaton Road, Nottingham NG8 1BB
  ☎0115 846 6700
  Fax 0115 846 6705
- George Green Library of Science and Engineering, University of Nottingham, University Park, Nottingham NG7 2RD
  ☎0115 951 4570
  Fax 0115 951 4578
- Greenfield Medical Library, University of Nottingham, Queen's Medical Centre, Nottingham NG7 2UH
  ☎0115 823 0555
  Fax 0115 823 0549
- Hallward Library (Arts and Humanities, Law, Social Sciences), University of Nottingham, University Park, Nottingham NG7 2RD
  ☎0115 951 4555
  Fax 0115 951 4558

- Hallward Library (Department of Manuscripts and Special Collections), University of Nottingham, King's Meadow Campus, Lenton Lane, Nottingham NG7 2NR
  ☎0115 951 4565
  Fax 0115 846 8651
  Keeper D B Johnston BA PhD DipLib (0115 951 4563)
- James Cameron-Gifford Library of Agricultural and Food Sciences, University of Nottingham, Sutton Bonington Campus, Sutton Bonington, nr Loughborough, Leics LE12 5RD
  ☎0115 951 6390
  Fax 0115 951 6389
- School of Nursing Library (Derby), University of Nottingham, Derby Centre, Derbyshire Royal Infirmary, London Road, Derby DE1 2QY
  ☎(01332) 347141 ext 2561
  Fax (01332) 290321
- School of Nursing Library (Mansfield), University of Nottingham, Mansfield Education Centre, Kings Mill Hospital, Mansfield Road, Sutton-in-Ashfield, Notts NG17 4JL
  ☎(01623) 465634
  Fax (01623) 465601
- Shakespeare Street Learning Resource Centre, University of Nottingham, Adult Education Centre, 14-22 Shakespeare Street, Nottingham NG1 4FQ
  ☎0115 951 6511
  Fax 0115 947 2977
- University of Nottingham at Derby Library, University of Nottingham, Derby Medical School, Derby City General Hospital, Uttoxeter Road, Derby DE22 3DT
  ☎(01332) 724650
  Fax (01332) 724647

OPEN UNIVERSITY

Library and Learning Resources Centre, Open University, Walton Hall, Milton Keynes MK7 6AA
☎(01908) 653138
Fax (01908) 653571
e-mail: oulibrary@open.ac.uk
url: www.open.ac.uk/library
Director of Library Services Mrs Nicky Whitsed MSc FCLIP (01908 653254; e-mail: n.whitsed@open.ac.uk)
Assistant Director of Library Services Ms Ann Davies BSc MSc (01908 652057; e-mail: ann.davies@open.ac.uk)
Head of Business Services Ms Mary Hunt MCLIP (01908 652672; e-mail: m.e.hunt@open.ac.uk)
Head of Library, Learning and Teaching Services Ms Patricia Heffernan BA(Hons) DipLib (01908 654850; e-mail: p.a.heffernan@open.ac.uk)
Head of Strategic and Service Development Ms Gill Needham BA(Hons) DipLib CertMan MSc(Econ) (01908 658369; e-mail: g.needham@open.ac.uk)

OXFORD BROOKES UNIVERSITY

Headington Library, Oxford Brookes University, Headington Campus, Gipsy Lane, Headington, Oxford OX3 0BP
☎(01865) 483156 (enquiries), (01865) 483130 (administration)
Fax (01865) 483998
e-mail: library@brookes.ac.uk
url: www.brookes.ac.uk/library
Director of Learning Resources and University Librarian Dr Helen M Workman PhD MCLIP (e-mail: h.workman@brookes.ac.uk)
Head of Academic Library Services Ms Jan Haines BLib MA DipM MCLIP ACIM (e-mail: jan.haines@brookes.ac.uk)
Head of Administration Tony Robbins BA MSc MCLIP (e-mail: tony.robbins@brookes.ac.uk)

Site libraries

- Harcourt Hill Library, Oxford Brookes University, Harcourt Hill Campus, Oxford OX2 9AT
  ☎(01865) 488222
  Fax (01865) 488224
  Head of Learning Resources: Harcourt Hill and Wheatley Ms Claire M Jeffery BSc DipLib DMS MCLIP (e-mail: cmjeffery@brookes.ac.uk)
- Wheatley Library, Oxford Brookes University, Wheatley Campus, Wheatley, Oxford OX33 1HX
  ☎(01865) 485869
  Fax (01865) 485750
  Head of Learning Resources: Harcourt Hill and Wheatley Ms Claire M Jeffery BSc DipLib DMS MCLIP (e-mail: cmjeffery@brookes.ac.uk)

UNIVERSITY OF OXFORD

Oxford University Library Services

Oxford University Library Services, Oxford University Library Services, Oxford
Bodley's Librarian and Director of University Library Services Dr Sarah E. Thomas PhD (e-mail: sarah.thomas@ox.ac.uk)
Librarian Emeritus Dr Reg P Carr MA FRSA BA MA(Man) MA(Camb) HonDLitt
Associate Director of University Library Services and Bodley's Librarian David E Perrow MA MCLIP

- Accessible Resources Acquisition and Creation Unit, Oxford University Library Services, University of Oxford, Osney One Building, Osney Mead, Oxford OX2 0EW
  ☎(01865) 283862
  Fax (01865) 793731
  e-mail: aracu@ouls.ox.ac.uk
  Director/Manager Ms Ruth Harris MA(Hons) MSc MCLIP
- Bodleian Library, University of Oxford, Broad Street, Oxford OX1 3BG
  ☎(01865) 277000

Fax (01865) 277182
e-mail: enquiries@bodley.ox.ac.uk
url: www.ouls.ox.ac.uk

- Bodleian Japanese Library, University of Oxford, 27 Winchester Road, Oxford OX2 6NA
☎(01865) 284506
Fax (01865) 284500
e-mail: japanese@bodley.ox.ac.uk
url: www.bodley.ox.ac.uk/dept/oriental/bjl.htm
Librarian Mrs Izumi Tytler MA
- Bodleian Law Library, University of Oxford, St Cross Building, Manor Road, Oxford OX1 3UR
☎(01865) 271462
Fax (01865) 271475
e-mail: law.library@bodley.ox.ac.uk
url: www.ouls.ox.ac.uk/law
Law Librarian Ms Ruth Bird BA TSTC GradDipLib (e-mail: ruth.bird@bodley.ox.ac.uk)
- Bodleian Library of Commonwealth and African Studies at Rhodes House, University of Oxford, Rhodes House, South Parks Road, Oxford OX1 3RG
☎(01865) 270908
Fax (01865) 270912
e-mail: rhodes.house.library@bodley.ox.ac.uk
Librarian i/c Ms L McCann
- Department for Continuing Education Library, University of Oxford, Rewley House, 1 Wellington Square, Oxford OX1 2JA
☎(01865) 270454
Fax (01865) 270309
e-mail: library@conted.ox.ac.uk
url: www.lib.ox.ac.uk
Librarian Ms S Pemberton BA DipLib MCLIP
- Department of Education Library, University of Oxford, 15 Norham Gardens, Oxford OX2 6PY
☎(01865) 274028 (library)
Fax (01865) 274027 (department)
e-mail: library@edstud.ox.ac.uk
url: www2.ouls.ox.ac.uk/edstud
Librarian Ms Kate Williams BA PGDipLib
- Department of Experimental Psychology, Library, University of Oxford, South Parks Road, Oxford OX1 3UD
☎(01865) 271312
Fax (01865) 310447
e-mail: library@psy.ox.ac.uk
url: www.psy.ox.ac.uk/library/
Librarian Ms Karine Barker
- English Faculty Library, University of Oxford, St Cross Building, Manor Road, Oxford OX1 3UQ
☎(01865) 271050
Fax (01865) 271054

e-mail: enquiries@efl.ox.ac.uk
url: www.ouls.ox.ac.uk/english
English Librarian Ms Sue Usher BA(Hons) DipLib MCLIP

- Faculty of Music Library, University of Oxford, St Aldate's, Oxford OX1 1DB
☎(01865) 276148 (enquiries)
Fax (01865) 286260
url: www.music.ox.ac.uk/library/
Subject Librarian Peter Ward Jones (e-mail: peter.wardjones@bodley.ox.ac.uk)
- History Faculty Library, University of Oxford, Broad Street, Oxford OX1 3DB
☎(01865) 277262
e-mail: library@history.ox.ac.uk
url: history.ouls.ox.ac.uk/history
Librarian Ms Isabel Holowaty BA(Hons) MSc (e-mail: isabel.holowaty@ouls.ox.ac.uk)
Deputy Librarian Ms Valerie Lawrence BA(Hons) DipLib (e-mail: valerie.lawrence@ouls.ox.ac.uk)
- Indian Institute Library, University of Oxford, New Bodleian Library, Broad Street, Oxford OX1 3BG
☎(01865) 277082
Fax (01865) 277182
e-mail: indian.institute@bodley.ox.ac.uk
Librarian Dr Gillian Evison MA MPhil DPhil
- Institute for Chinese Studies Library, University of Oxford, Walton Street, Oxford OX1 2HG
☎(01865) 280430
Fax (01865) 280431
e-mail: chinese.studies.library@bodley.ox.ac.uk
url: www.bodley.ox.ac.uk/dept/oriental/csl.htm
Librarian Minh Chung MA
- Latin American Centre, St Antony's College, University of Oxford, 1 Church Walk, Oxford OX2 6JF
☎(01865) 274483
Fax (01865) 274483
Librarian Mrs Nathalie Chaddock-Thomas (e-mail: nathalie.thomas@lac.ox.ac.uk)
- Oriental Institute Library, University of Oxford, Pusey Lane, Oxford OX1 2LE
☎(01865) 278202
Fax (01865) 278204
e-mail: library@orinst.ox.ac.uk
Librarian Martyn Minty MA MCLIP
- Philosophy Library, University of Oxford, 10 Merton Street, Oxford OX1 4JJ
☎(01865) 276927
Fax (01865) 276932
e-mail: phillib@bodley.ox.ac.uk
Librarian Dr Hilla A Wait MA DPhil
- Radcliffe Science Library, University of Oxford, Parks Road, Oxford OX1 3QP
☎(01865) 272800
Fax (01865) 272821
e-mail: rsl@ouls.ox.ac.uk

url: www.ouls.ox.ac.uk/rsl
Keeper of Scientific Books Dr Judith M Palmer MA PhD FCLIP MIIS

- Refugee Studies Centre, Library, University of Oxford, Queen Elizabeth House, 3 Worcester Street, Oxford OX1 2BX
☎(01865) 270298
Fax (01865) 270721
e-mail: rsclib@qeh.ox.ac.uk
url: www.rsc.ox.ac.uk
Librarian Ms Sarah Rhodes BA DipLib MA (e-mail: sarah.rhodes@qeh.ox.ac.uk)
(Postal address: 3 Mansfield Road, Oxford OX1 3TB)
- Sackler Library, University of Oxford, 1 St John Street, Oxford OX1 2LG
☎(01865) 278092
Fax (01865) 278098
e-mail: enquiries@saclib.ox.ac.uk; librarian@saclib.ox.ac.uk
url: www.saclib.ox.ac.uk
Librarian in Charge Dr Graham Piddock (e-mail: graham.piddock@ouls.ox.ac.uk)
(Access to the Library is limited to members of Oxford University and holders of Bodleian Library reader's tickets)
- Sainsbury Library, University of Oxford, Park End Street, Oxford OX1 1HP
☎(01865) 288880
Fax (01865) 288805
e-mail: library@sbs.ox.ac.uk
url: www.sbs.ox.ac.uk
Information Services Manager Ms Fiona Richardson
- Social Sciences Library, University of Oxford, Manor Road Building, Manor Road, Oxford OX1 3UQ
☎(01865) 271071 (Librarian), (01865) 271093 (Library)
Fax (01865) 271072
e-mail: library@ssl.ox.ac.uk
url: www.ssl.ox.ac.uk
Librarian Ms Margaret Robb BS MA MLS MCLIP (e-mail: margaret.robb@ouls.ox.ac.uk)
- Taylor Institution, Library, University of Oxford, St Giles, Oxford OX1 3NA
☎(01865) 278154 (office), 278158/278161 (main desk)
Fax (01865) 278165
e-mail: enquiries@taylib.ox.ac.uk
url: www.taylib.ox.ac.uk
Librarian i/c Ms Amanda Peters MA DipLib
(The Taylor Institution Modern Languages Faculty Library can also be found at this location; the Taylor Bodleian, Slavonic and Greek Library can be found at 47 Wellington Square, Oxford OX1 2JF; tel: 01865 270464)
- Theology Faculty Library, University of Oxford, 41 St Giles, Oxford OX1 3LW
☎(01865) 270731
e-mail: library@theology.ox.ac.uk
url: www.theology.ox.ac.uk
Librarian Ms Kate Alderson-Smith BA MA (e-mail: kate.alderson-smith@theology.ox.ac.uk)

- Vere Harmsworth Library (Rothermere American Institute), University of Oxford, 1A South Parks Road, Oxford OX1 3TG
  ☎(01865) 282700
  Fax (01865) 282709
  e-mail: vhl@bodley.ox.ac.uk
  Librarian Ms Margaret Robb BS MA MLS MCLIP (e-mail: margaret.robb@ouls.ox.ac.uk)
- Zoology Library, University of Oxford, Tinbergen Building, South Parks Road, Oxford OX1 3PS
  ☎(01865) 271141-3
  Fax (01865) 310447
  e-mail: enquiries.zoo@ouls.ox.ac.uk
  url: www.ouls.ox.ac.uk/isbes
  Librarian Roger Mills MA MCLIP

Health Care Libraries

- Cairns Library, University of Oxford, Oxford Radcliffe Hospitals NHS Trust, The John Radcliffe Hospital, Headley Way, Headington, Oxford OX3 9DU
  ☎(01865) 221936
  Fax (01865) 221941
  e-mail: library@hcl.ox.ac.uk
  url: www.ouls.ox.ac.uk/hcl
  Head of Health Care Libraries Donald M Mackay MA(Hons) MA MCLIP
- George Wiernik Library, University of Oxford, Research Institute, The Churchill Hospital, Oxford OX3 7LJ
  ☎(01865) 225815
  Fax (01865) 225834
  e-mail: library@hcl.ox.ac.uk
  url: www.ouls.ox.ac.uk/hcl
  Manager Donald M Mackay MA(Hons) MA MCLIP
- Health Care Library, University of Oxford, Old Road, Headington, Oxford OX3 7LG
  ☎(01865) 289409
  Fax (01865) 289406
  e-mail: old-road-library@hcl.ox.ac.uk
  Outreach Librarian Nia Wyn Robert

College, Institute and Departmental

All Souls College

Codrington Library, All Souls College, Oxford OX1 4AL
☎(01865) 279318
Fax (01865) 279299
e-mail: codrington.library@all-souls.ox.ac.uk
url: www.all-souls.ox.ac.uk
Librarian in Charge Dr Norma Aubertin-Potter BA PhD MCLIP

Balliol College
Library, Balliol College, Oxford OX1 3BJ
☎(01865) 277709
Fax (01865) 277803
e-mail: library@balliol.ox.ac.uk
url: www.balliol.ox.ac.uk
Librarian Dr P A Bulloch MCLIP FSA
Assistant Librarian Alan Tadiello BA

Brasenose College
Library, Brasenose College, Oxford OX1 4AJ
☎(01865) 277827
Fax (01865) 277831
e-mail: library@bnc.ox.ac.uk
url: www.bnc.ox.ac.uk
Fellow Librarian Dr Ed Bispham
College Librarian Ms Liz Kay

Campion Hall
Library, Campion Hall, Brewer Street, Oxford OX1 1QS
☎(01865) 286100
url: www.campion.ox.ac.uk
Librarian Revd Peter Edmonds BA STL LSS (01865 286106)
Assistant Librarian Laurence Weeks MA

Christ Church
Library, Christ Church, Oxford OX1 1DP
☎(01865) 276169
e-mail: library@chch.ox.ac.uk
url: www.chch.ox.ac.uk
Assistant Librarians Mrs J E McMullin MA MCLIP, Ms C M Neagu DPhil MCLIP

Corpus Christi College
Library, Corpus Christi College, Merton Street, Oxford OX1 4JF
☎(01865) 276744
Fax (01865) 276767
e-mail: library.staff@ccc.ox.ac.uk
url: www.ccc.ox.ac.uk/about/library/libraryhome.php
Librarian Miss Joanna Snelling MA MCLIP (e-mail: joanna.snelling@ccc.ox.ac.uk)

Exeter College
Library, Exeter College, Turl Street, Oxford OX1 3DP
☎(01865) 279600 (switchboard), (01865) 279657 (direct)
Fax (01865) 279630
e-mail: library@exeter.ox.ac.uk
url: www.exeter.ox.ac.uk
Fellow Librarian Dr H L Spencer DPhil
Sub-Librarian Ms Juliet Chadwick

Green College (at the Radcliffe Observatory)

Library, Green College (at the Radcliffe Observatory), Woodstock Road, Oxford OX2 6HG
☎(01865) 274788 (library), (01865) 274770 (lodge)
Fax (01865) 274796
url: http://library.green.ox.ac.uk
Assistant Librarian Ms Gill Edwards BSc (e-mail: gill.edwards@green.ox.ac.uk)

Harris Manchester College

Library, Harris Manchester College, Mansfield Road, Oxford OX1 3TD
☎(01865) 271016 (enquiries), (01865) 281472 (administration)
Fax (01865) 271012
e-mail: librarian@hmc.ox.ac.uk
url: www.hmc.ox.ac.uk
Fellow Librarian Ms Sue Killoran BA MA(Oxon) PGDipLib MCLIP

Hertford College

Library, Hertford College, Catte Street, Oxford OX1 3BW
☎(01865) 279409
Fax (01865) 279466
e-mail: library@hertford.ox.ac.uk
url: www.hertford.ox.ac.uk
Fellow Librarian Dr T C Barnard (e-mail: toby.barnard@hertford.ox.ac.uk)
Librarian Mrs Susan Griffin BA DipLib (e-mail: susan.griffin@hertford.ox.ac.uk)

Jesus College

Library, Jesus College, Oxford OX1 3DW
☎(01865) 279704
Fax (01865) 279687 (attn. Librarian)
e-mail: library@jesus.ox.ac.uk
url: www.jesus.ox.ac.uk
Fellow Librarian T J Horder MA PhD
College Librarian Miss S A Cobbold MA DipLib
Archivist Christopher Jeens BA DipArchAdmin (01865 279761)
(Visits by bona fide scholars are available only by prior appointment with the College Librarian or Archivist as appropriate)

Keble College

Library, Keble College, Oxford OX1 3PG
☎(01865) 272797
e-mail: library@keb.ox.ac.uk
url: www.keble.ox.ac.uk/about/library
Librarian Mrs Margaret Ann Sarosi BA HDipLib

Lady Margaret Hall

Library, Lady Margaret Hall, Norham Gardens, Oxford OX2 6QA
☎(01865) 274361
Fax (01865) 511069
url: www.lmh.ox.ac.uk

Librarian Miss Roberta Staples BA (e-mail: roberta.staples@lmh.ox.ac.uk)
Archivist Miss Anne Petrie MA MCLIP
(The library is for the use of members of college only, though bona fide researchers may be allowed access to books by arrangement with the Librarian)

Linacre College

Library, Linacre College, St Cross Road, Oxford OX1 3JA
☎(01865) 271661
Fax (01865) 271668
e-mail: library@linacre.ox.ac.uk
url: www.linacre.ox.ac.uk
Fellow Librarian Ms Margaret Robb BS MA MLS MCLIP (e-mail: margaret.robb@ouls.ox.ac.uk)
Assistant Librarian Mrs Emma Huber (e-mail: emma.huber@linacre.ox.ac.uk)

Lincoln College

Library, Lincoln College, Turl Street, Oxford OX1 3DR
☎(01865) 279831
e-mail: library@lincoln.ox.ac.uk
url: www.lincoln.ox.ac.uk
Librarian Mrs Fiona Piddock BA DipLib

Magdalen College

Library, Magdalen College, Oxford OX1 4AU
☎(01865) 276045 (direct)
Fax (01865) 276057
e-mail: library@magd.ox.ac.uk
url: www.magd.ox.ac.uk
Fellow Librarian Dr C Y Ferdinand BA MA MA MA DPhil
Assistant Librarian Mrs Hilary Pattison MA MA

Mansfield College

Library, Mansfield College, Mansfield Road, Oxford OX1 3TF
☎(01865) 270975
Fax (01865) 270970
url: www.mansfield.ox.ac.uk
Fellow Librarian Dr Kathryn Gleadle PhD (e-mail: kathryn.gleadle@mansfield.ox.ac.uk)
Librarian Ms Alma Jenner (e-mail: alma.jenner@mansfield.ox.ac.uk)

Merton College

Library, Merton College, Oxford OX1 4JD
☎(01865) 276380
Fax (01865) 276361
e-mail: library@admin.merton.ox.ac.uk
url: www.merton.ox.ac.uk
Librarian Ms Julia Walworth BA MA PhD
Assistant Librarian Mrs Catherine Lewis BA DipLib MCLIP

New College
Library, New College, Oxford OX1 3BN
☎(01865) 279580 (enquiries and administration)
Fax (01865) 279590
url: www.new.ox.ac.uk/the_library
Librarian Mrs Naomi van Loo MA BA MCLIP (e-mail: naomi.vanloo@new.ox.ac.uk)

Nuffield College
Library, Nuffield College, New Road, Oxford OX1 1NF
☎(01865) 278550
Fax (01865) 278621
e-mail: library-enquiries@nuffield.ox.ac.uk
url: www.nuffield.ox.ac.uk/library
Librarian Ms Elizabeth Martin DipLib MA MCLIP (e-mail: librarian@nuffield.ox.ac.uk)

Oriel College
Library, Oriel College, Oxford OX1 4EW
☎(01865) 276558 (direct)
e-mail: library@oriel.ox.ac.uk
url: www.oriel.ox.ac.uk
Librarian Mrs Marjory Szurko BA MRes DipLib MCLIP

Pembroke College
McGowin Library, Pembroke College, Oxford OX1 1DW
☎(01865) 276409 (direct)
Fax (01865) 276418
e-mail: library@pmb.ox.ac.uk
url: www.pmb.ox.ac.uk/library/index.html
Fellow Librarian Dr Christopher Melchert BA MA PhD
Librarian Mrs Lucie Walker MA BA BSc

Plant Sciences Library and Oxford Forest Information Service
Plant Sciences Library and Oxford Forest Information Service, Oxford University Library Services, South Parks Road, Oxford OX1 3RB
☎(01865) 275087
Fax (01865) 275095
e-mail: enquiries.plant@ouls.ox.ac.uk
url: www.ouls.ox.ac.uk/isbes

The Queen's College
Library, Queen's College, The, Oxford OX1 4AW
☎(01865) 279130
Fax (01865) 790819
e-mail: library@queens.ox.ac.uk
url: www.queens.ox.ac.uk/library
Librarian Ms Amanda Saville MA MCLIP (01865 279213)
Reader Services Librarian Ms Tessa Shaw BA DipLib

Technical Services Librarian Ms Lynette Dobson MA
Fellow Librarian Prof John Blair BA DPhil FSA
Historic Collections Assistant Mrs Veronika Vernier BA

Regent's Park College

Library, Regent's Park College, Pusey Street, Oxford OX1 2LB
☎(01865) 288120; (01865) 288142 (Angus Library direct line)
Fax (01865) 288121
e-mail: library@regents.ox.ac.uk
url: www.rpc.ox.ac.uk/; www.lib.ox.ac.uk/libraries/guides/REG.html
Librarian Andrew Hudson (e-mail: andrew.hudson@regents.ox.ac.uk)
(General College Library open to members of College only. The Angus Library, a research library for Baptist history, incorporating the former libraries of the Baptist Union of Great Britain and the Baptist Historical Society, and the archives of the Baptist Missionary Society on deposit, available by appointment to bona fide researchers)

St Anne's College

Library, Saint Anne's College, Woodstock Road, Oxford OX2 6HS
☎(01865) 274810
Fax (01865) 274899
e-mail: library@st-annes.ox.ac.uk
url: www.st-annes.ox.ac.uk/study/undergraduate/library.html
Librarian Dr David Smith MA DPhil MCLIP (e-mail: david.smith@st-annes.ox.ac.uk)

St Antony's College

Library, Saint Antony's College, Oxford OX2 6JF
☎(01865) 274480
Fax (01865) 274526
url: www.sant.ox.ac.uk
Librarian Ms R Campbell

St Benet's Hall

Library, Saint Benet's Hall, 38 St Giles, Oxford OX1 3LN
☎(01865) 280556
e-mail: michael.black@stb.ox.ac.uk
url: www.st-benets.ox.ac.uk
Master Father Felix Stephens OSB MA
Librarian Michael Black BSc MBA

St Catherine's College

Library, Saint Catherine's College, Manor Road, Oxford OX1 3UJ
☎(01865) 271707
e-mail: library@stcatz.ox.ac.uk
url: www.stcatz.ox.ac.uk
Librarian Dr Gervaise Rosser MA PhD
Assistant Librarian Mrs Sally Collins (e-mail: sally.collins@stcatz.ox.ac.uk)

St Cross College

Library, Saint Cross College, St Giles, Oxford OX1 3LZ
☎(01865) 278481
e-mail: librarian@stx.ox.ac.uk
url: www.stx.ox.ac.uk
Librarian Mrs Sheila Allcock BSc

St Edmund Hall

Library, Saint Edmund Hall, Queen's Lane, Oxford OX1 4AR
☎(01865) 279091
url: www.seh.ox.ac.uk
Librarian Ms Deborah Eaton BA MA (e-mail: deborah.eaton@seh.ox.ac.uk)
(The Library is for the use of members of St Edmund Hall only. Visitors welcome but only by prior application to the Librarian; groups shown round only during vacations.)

St Hilda's College

Library, Saint Hilda's College, Cowley Place, Oxford OX4 1DY
☎(01865) 276849 (general enquiries)
Fax (01865) 276816
e-mail: library@st-hildas.ox.ac.uk
url: www.st-hildas.ox.ac.uk
Librarian Miss Maria Croghan MA MCLIP (e-mail: maria.croghan@st-hildas.ox.ac.uk)

St Hugh's College

Library, Saint Hugh's College, St Margaret's Road, Oxford OX2 6LE
☎(01865) 274900 (enquiries), (01865) 274938 (administration)
Fax (01865) 274912
e-mail: library@st-hughs.ox.ac.uk
url: www.st-hughs.ox.ac.uk
Librarian Miss Deborah Quare BA MLitt MCLIP

St John's College

Library, Saint John's College, St Giles, Oxford OX1 3JP
☎(01865) 277300 (main lodge), (01865) 277330/1 (direct to library)
Fax (01865) 277435 (College office)
e-mail: library@sjc.ox.ac.uk
url: www.sjc.ox.ac.uk
Fellow Librarian Dr Malcolm Vale MA DPhil FRHistS
Librarian Mrs Catherine Hilliard MA MLIS (e-mail: catherine.hilliard@sjc.ox.ac.uk)
Library Administrator Mrs Ruth Ogden BA DipLib

St Peter's College

Library, Saint Peter's College, New Inn Hall Street, Oxford OX1 2DL
☎(01865) 278882
Fax (01865) 278855
e-mail: library@spc.ox.ac.uk
url: www.spc.ox.ac.uk
Librarian David Johnson MA(Lond) DPhil(Oxon) (e-mail: david.johnson@spc.ox.ac.uk)

Somerville College
Library, Somerville College, Oxford OX2 6HD
☎(01865) 270694
Fax (01865) 270620
e-mail: library@some.ox.ac.uk
url: www.some@ox.ac.uk
Librarian Miss Pauline Adams BLitt MA DipLib (01865 270694)
Assistant Librarian Miss Susan Purver MA DipLIS (01865 270694)

Templeton College
Information Centre, Templeton College, Kennington, Oxford OX1 5NY
☎(01865) 422564
Fax (01865) 422501
e-mail: infocent@templeton.oxford.ac.uk
url: www.templeton.ox.ac.uk
Information Centre and Library Manager Mrs E A H Yeates (on maternity leave 2007)
(Restricted access: enquiries to Information Centre helpdesk as above)

Trinity College
Library, Trinity College, Oxford OX1 3BH
☎(01865) 279863 (enquiries and administration)
Fax (01865) 279902
url: www.trinity.ox.ac.uk/college/library/
Librarian Ms Alison Felstead BA PGDipLib MCLIP (e-mail: alison.felstead@trinity.ox.ac.uk)

University College
Library, University College, Oxford OX1 4BH
☎(01865) 276621
e-mail: library@univ.ox.ac.uk
url: www.ox.ac.uk/univ
Fellow Librarian Dr Bill Child MA BPhil DPhil(Oxon)
College Librarian Miss Christine M Ritchie MA(Aber) MA(Lond) MCLIP

Wadham College
Library, Wadham College, Oxford OX1 3PN
☎(01865) 277900
Fax (01865) 277937
e-mail: library@wadh.ox.ac.uk
url: www.wadham.ox.ac.uk
Librarian Ms Sandra Bailey BA MA DipLib

Wolfson College
The Library, Wolfson College, Oxford OX2 6UD
☎(01865) 274076
e-mail: library@wolfson.ox.ac.uk
url: www.wolfson.ox.ac.uk/library/

Librarian Ms Fiona E Wilkes BA MA DipLib MCLIP
(Open to members of College and Common Room only)

Worcester College
Library, Worcester College, Walton Street, Oxford OX1 2HB
☎(01865) 278354/278370 (library); (01865) 278300 (porter's lodge)
Fax (01865) 278387
url: www.worc.ox.ac.uk
Librarian Dr Joanna Parker MA DPhil (e-mail: joanna.parker@worc.ox.ac.uk)

UNIVERSITY OF PAISLEY

(Bell College and University of Paisley merged on 1 August 2007)

Library, University of Paisley, High Street, Paisley, Renfrewshire PA1 2BE
☎0141 848 3758 (enquiries), 0141 848 3751 (administration)
Fax 0141 848 3761
e-mail: library@paisley.ac.uk
url: www.library.paisley.ac.uk/library
Acting University Librarian Ms Teresa Gilbert BA DipLib (e-mail: teresa.gilbert@paisley.ac.uk)

Site libraries

- Ayr Campus Library, University of Paisley, Beech Grove, Ayr KA8 0SR
  ☎(01292) 886345
  Fax (01292) 886288
  e-mail: libraryayr@paisley.ac.uk
  Librarian i/c: Ms Teresa Gilbert BA DipLib (e-mail: teresa.gilbert@paisley.ac.uk)
- Dumfries Campus Library, University of Paisley, Maxwell House, Crichton University Campus, Dumfries DG1 4UQ
  ☎(01387) 702084
  Fax (01387) 702082
  e-mail: dumfriescampuslibrary@bell.ac.uk
  Campus Librarian Ms Judith Anderson MA MCLIP
- Hamilton Campus Library, University of Paisley, Almada Street, Hamilton, Lanarkshire ML3 0JB
  ☎(01698) 894424
  Fax (01698) 286856
  College Librarian Ms Barbara Catt BA MCLIP (e-mail: b.catt@bell.ac.uk)
- RAH Campus Library, University of Paisley, Royal Alexandra Hospital, Corsebar Road, Paisley, Renfrewshire PA2 9BN
  ☎0141 314 7178
  Fax 0141 887 4962
  Acting Librarian Ms Tracey McKee

01752 232303

UNIVERSITY OF PLYMOUTH

Library, University of Plymouth, Drake Circus, Plymouth PL4 8AA

☎(01752) 232323/588588 (enquiries); (01752) 587100 (administration)
Fax (01752) 587101
url: www.plymouth.ac.uk/library
Director of Information and Learning Services Ms Penny Holland BA DipLib MCLIP (e-mail: penny.holland@plymouth.ac.uk)
Head of Learning and Research Support Ms Jane Gosling BSc DipLib MCLIP (e-mail: jane.gosling@plymouth.ac.uk)
Head of Customer Services Mike Pesterfield (e-mail: mike.pesterfield@plymouth.ac.uk)

UNIVERSITY OF PORTSMOUTH

University Library, University of Portsmouth, Cambridge Road, Portsmouth PO1 2ST
☎023 9284 3228/9 (enquiries), 023 9284 3222 (administration)
Fax 023 9284 3233
e-mail: library@port.ac.uk
url: www.port.ac.uk
University Librarian Ian Bonar BSc

QUEEN MARGARET UNIVERSITY, EDINBURGH
(formerly Queen Margaret University)

Learning Resource Centre, Queen Margaret University, Edinburgh, Queen Margaret University Drive, Musselburgh, East Lothian EH21 6UU
☎0131 474 0000
Fax 0131 474 0001
e-mail: Library_Enquiries@qmu.ac.uk
url: www.qmu.ac.uk/lb
Director of IS and the LRC Fraser Muir
Head of Library Services Mrs Jo Rowley BA(Hons) MSc MCLIP

QUEEN'S UNIVERSITY OF BELFAST

University Library, Queen's University of Belfast, Belfast BT7 1LS
☎028 9097 5020
Fax 028 9097 3072
url: www.qub.ac.uk/lib/
Director of Information Services John Gormley (e-mail: j.gormley@qub.ac.uk)
Assistant Director (Library Services) Ms Elizabeth Traynor BA MA MCLIP (e-mail: e.traynor@qub.ac.uk)

RAVENSBOURNE COLLEGE OF DESIGN AND COMMUNICATION

Library, Ravensbourne College of Design and Communication, Walden Road, Chislehurst, Kent BR7 5SN
☎020 8289 4974
Fax 020 8325 8320

url: www.rave.ac.uk
Director of Information Services Stephen A Bowman BA(Hons) MA FCLIP (e-mail: s.bowman@rave.ac.uk)
Media Services Officer Paul Rogers (e-mail: p.rogers@rave.ac.uk)
Information Services Officer Ms Dawn Fitzgerald BA MA (e-mail: d.fitzgerald@rave.ac.uk)
Library Services Officer Ms Rachel Todd BA MA (e-mail: r.todd@rave.ac.uk)

THE UNIVERSITY OF READING

Library, The University of Reading, Whiteknights, PO Box 223, Reading RG6 6AE
☎0118 378 8770 (enquiries), 0118 378 8773 (administration)
Fax 0118 378 6636
e-mail: library@reading.ac.uk
url: www.reading.ac.uk/library
University Librarian Mrs Julia Munro BSc MSc MBA MCLIP (0118 378 8774; e-mail: j.h.munro@reading.ac.uk)
Head of Collections Rupert Wood BPhil MA DipLib ILTM (0118 378 6784; e-mail: r.j.m.wood@reading.ac.uk)
Head of Systems and Services Miss Celia A Ayres BSc DipInfSc MCLIP (0118 378 8781; e-mail: c.a.ayres@reading.ac.uk)
Support Services Manager Ian Burn BA (0118 378 8775; e-mail: i.j.burn@reading.ac.uk)

Site library

- Bulmershe Library, The University of Reading, Bulmershe Court, Woodlands Avenue, Earley, Reading RG6 1HY
  ☎0118 378 8652
  Fax 0118 378 8651
  Bulmershe Librarian Gordon Connell MA MSc MCLIP (0118 378 5820; e-mail: g.connell@reading.ac.uk)

ROBERT GORDON UNIVERSITY

The Georgina Scott Sutherland Library, The Robert Gordon University, Garthdee Road, Aberdeen AB10 7QE
☎(01224) 263450
Fax (01224) 263455
e-mail: library@rgu.ac.uk
url: www.rgu.ac.uk/library
Director of Knowledge and Information Services Ms Carole Munro MA DipLib (e-mail: c.munro@rgu.ac.uk)
Associate Director, Operational Services Ms Judith Brown MA MCLIP (e-mail: j.brown@rgu.ac.uk)
Associate Director, Client Services Miss Margaret Buchan MA MCLIP (e-mail: m.buchan@rgu.ac.uk)
Associate Director, Technology Services Grant McDougall BA(Hons) DipIT MCLIP (e-mail: g.i.mcdougall@rgu.ac.uk)

Site library

- St Andrew Street Library, The Robert Gordon University, St Andrew Street, Aberdeen AB25 1HG
  ☎(01224) 262888
  Fax (01224) 262889
  e-mail: saslibrary@rgu.ac.uk
  url: www.rgu.ac.uk/library

ROEHAMPTON UNIVERSITY

Library and Learning Services Department, Roehampton University, Learning Resources Centre, Roehampton Lane, London SW15 5SZ
☎020 8392 3770 (enquiries), 020 8392 3053 (administration)
Fax 020 8392 3026
e-mail: enquiry.desk@roehampton.ac.uk
url: www.roehampton.ac.uk
University Librarian and Director of Learning Services Ms Sue Clegg BA MBA MCLIP (020 8392 3051; e-mail: s.clegg@roehampton.ac.uk)
Head of Library, Academic & Research Services and Deputy Librarian Adam Edwards BA MSc MCLIP (020 8392 3454; e-mail: adam.edwards@roehampton.ac.uk)
Head of LRC Operations Ms Michela Wilkins (020 8392 3211; e-mail: m.wilkins@roehampton.ac.uk)
Head of Library User Services Ms Faye Jackson (020 8392 3351; e-mail: f.jackson@roehampton.ac.uk)
Head of e-Learning Services Phil Cheeseman (020 8392 3874; e-mail: p.cheeseman@roehampton.ac.uk)

ROSE BRUFORD COLLEGE

Learning Resources Centre, Rose Bruford College, Lamorbey Park, Sidcup, Kent DA15 9DF
☎020 8308 2626
Fax 020 8308 0542
url: www.bruford.ac.uk
College Librarian Ms Kate Davies BSc(Hons) MA MCLIP (e-mail: kate.davies@bruford.ac.uk)
Assistant Librarian Ms Catherine Beach BD(Hons) MA (e-mail: catherine.beach@bruford.ac.uk)

ROYAL ACADEMY OF DRAMATIC ART

RADA Library, Royal Academy of Dramatic Art, 18 Chenies Street, London WC1E 7PA
☎020 7908 4878
e-mail: library@rada.ac.uk
url: www.rada.org
Library Manager James Thornton
Library Assistants Ms Clara Brennan-Bailey, Ms Alice Brickwood

ROYAL ACADEMY OF MUSIC

Library, Royal Academy of Music, Marylebone Road, London NW1 5HT
☎020 7873 7323 (enquiries and administration)
Fax 020 7873 7322
e-mail: library@ram.ac.uk
url: www.ram.ac.uk
Librarian Ms Kathryn Adamson BA MA DipLib HonARAM

ROYAL AGRICULTURAL COLLEGE

Library, Royal Agricultural College, Stroud Road, Cirencester, Glos GL7 6JS
☎(01285) 652531 ext 2274
Fax (01285) 889844
e-mail: library@rac.ac.uk
url: www.rac.ac.uk
Head of Library Services Peter Brooks BA MA PGCE MCLIP (01285 655214 ext 2276)

ROYAL COLLEGE OF ART

College Library, Royal College of Art, Kensington Gore, London SW7 2EU
☎020 7590 4224 (enquiries)
Fax 020 7590 4217
e-mail: library@rca.ac.uk
url: www.rca.ac.uk
Head of Information and Learning Services Peter Hassell MCLIP (e-mail: peter.hassell@rca.ac.uk)
Library Manager Ms Darlene Maxwell (e-mail: darlene.maxwell@rca.ac.uk)
Special Collections and Services Manager Neil Parkinson (e-mail: neil.parkinson@rca.ac.uk)

ROYAL COLLEGE OF MUSIC

Library, Royal College of Music, Prince Consort Road, London SW7 2BS
☎020 7591 4325
Fax 020 7589 7740
e-mail: library@rcm.ac.uk
url: www.rcm.ac.uk
Chief Librarian Ms Pamela Thompson BA (020 7591 4323; e-mail: pthompson@rcm.ac.uk)
Reference Librarian Dr Peter Horton (020 7591 4324; e-mail: phorton@rcm.ac.uk)

ROYAL COLLEGE OF NURSING OF THE UNITED KINGDOM

Library and Information Services (part of Information Research and Knowledge Management), Royal College of Nursing of the United Kingdom, 20 Cavendish Square, London W1G 0RN

☎020 7647 3610
Fax 020 7647 3420
e-mail: rcn.library@rcn.org.uk
url: www.rcn.org.uk
Learning and Development Manager – Information and Knowledge Management
Ms Jackie Cheeseborough BA(Hons) DipLib MCLIP
(Access for non-members is by appointment)

ROYAL NORTHERN COLLEGE OF MUSIC

Library, Royal Northern College of Music, 124 Oxford Road, Manchester M13 9RD
☎0161 907 5243
Fax 0161 273 7611
e-mail: library@rncm.ac.uk
url: www.rncm.ac.uk
Librarian Miss Anna Smart BA MA MCLIP HonRNCM
Deputy Librarian Geoffrey Thomason MusB MusM ARCM LTCL DipLib

ROYAL SCOTTISH ACADEMY OF MUSIC AND DRAMA

Whittaker Library, Royal Scottish Academy of Music and Drama, 100 Renfrew Street, Glasgow G2 3DB
☎0141 270 8268
Fax 0141 270 8353
e-mail: library@rsamd.ac.uk
url: www.rsamd.ac.uk/library
Head of Information Services Ms Caroline Cochrane (0141 270 8269; e-mail: c.cochrane@rsamd.ac.uk)

ROYAL WELSH COLLEGE OF MUSIC AND DRAMA

Library, Royal Welsh College of Music and Drama, Castle Grounds, Cathays Park, Cardiff CF10 3ER
☎029 2034 2854
Fax 029 2039 1304
url: library.rwcmd.ac.uk
Librarian Mrs Judith Agus BA BMus MCLIP (029 2039 1330; e-mail: judith.agus@rwcmd.ac.uk)

RUSKIN COLLEGE

Library, Ruskin College, Walton Street, Oxford OX1 2HE
☎(01865) 554331
Fax (01865) 554372
e-mail: library@ruskin.ac.uk

url: www.ruskin.ac.uk
Librarian Valerie Moyses BA(Hons) MCLIP DipLib
(Admission by appointment only)

UNIVERSITY OF ST ANDREWS

Library and Information Services, University of St Andrews, University Library, North Street, St Andrews, Fife KY16 9TR
☎(01334 462281 (enquiries and administration), 01334 462301 (library administration)
Fax (01334) 462282
e-mail: library@st-andrews/library
url: www.st-andrews/library
Director of Library Services Jon Purcell BA(Hons) MBA DMS DipLib MCLIP
Head of Collections Jeremy Upton MA DipLib BMus(Hons)
Head of Special Collections Norman Reid MA PhD

COLLEGE OF ST MARK AND ST JOHN

Library, College of St Mark and St John, Derriford Road, Plymouth PL6 8BH
☎(01752) 636845 (enquiries), (01752) 636700 ext 4206 (administration)
Fax (01752) 636820
e-mail: libraryenquiries@marjon.ac.uk
url: www.marjon.ac.uk
Head of Library Mrs Wendy Evans ILTA MCLIP (01752 636700 ext 4215; e-mail: wevans@marjon.ac.uk)

ST MARTIN'S COLLEGE *see* UNIVERSITY OF CUMBRIA

ST MARY'S UNIVERSITY COLLEGE TWICKENHAM

(formerly St Mary's College, Strawberry Hill)

Learning Resources Centre, St Mary's University College Twickenham, Waldegrave Road, Strawberry Hill, Twickenham, Middlesex TW1 4SX
☎020 8240 4097
Fax 020 8240 4270
e-mail: enquiry@smuc.ac.uk
url: www.smuc.ac.uk
Director of Information Services and Systems Ms Maire Lanigan BSc(Hons) DipLib
Assistant Director Martin Scarrott BA DipLib MCLIP ILTM

UNIVERSITY OF SALFORD

Information Services Division, University of Salford, Clifford Whitworth Building, Salford, Manchester M5 4WT
☎0161 295 2444

Sarum College Library, 19 the Close, Salisbury SP1 2EE
01722 424803

Fax 0161 295 5888
e-mail: isd-servicedesk@salford.ac.uk
url: www.isd.salford.ac.uk
Executive Director for Knowledge Management and Chief Information Officer Tony Lewis BA(Hons) MSc CEng MICE MIWEM
Associate Director (Services and Operations) Ms Liz Jolly BA(Hons) DipILS MCLIP FRSA
Associate Director (Liaison and Support) Mrs Julie Berry BA DMS MCLIP
Head of Learning Resources Mrs Wendy Carley BA MA MCLIP

Campus libraries

- Adelphi Library, University of Salford, Adelphi Building, Peru Street, Salford, Manchester M3 6EQ
  ☎0161 295 6084
  Fax 0161 295 6083
- Allerton Library, University of Salford, Allerton Building, Frederick Road, Salford, Manchester M6 6PU
  ☎0161 295 2435
  Fax 0161 295 2437
- Clifford Whitworth Library, University of Salford, Salford, Manchester M5 4WT
  ☎0161 295 5535
  Fax 0161 295 5888
- Irwell Valley Library, University of Salford, Irwell Valley Campus, Blandford Road, Salford, Manchester M6 6BD
  ☎0161 295 6083
  Fax 0161 295 2361

SCOTTISH AGRICULTURAL COLLEGE

The Agriculture Library, Scottish Agricultural College, Peter Wilson Building, King's Buildings, West Mains Road, Edinburgh EH9 3JG
☎0131 535 4117 (enquiries), 0131 535 4116 (administration)
Fax 0131 535 4246
e-mail: libraryed@sac.ac.uk
url: www.sac.ac.uk
Site Librarian Miss Ishbel K Leggat MA PGDipLib (e-mail: ishbel.leggat@sac.ac.uk)

Campus libraries

- SAC Aberdeen Library, Scottish Agricultural College, Ferguson Building, Craibstone Estate, Aberdeen AB21 9YA
  ☎(01224) 711057
  Fax (01224) 711291
  e-mail: libraryab@sac.ac.uk
  url: www.sac.ac.uk
  Head Librarian Mrs Elizabeth Buchan BA(Hons) (e-mail: elizabeth.buchan@sac.ac.uk)
- SAC Auchincruive Library, Scottish Agricultural College, Donald Hendrie Building, Ayr, Ayrshire KA6 5HW
  ☎(01292) 525209
  Fax (01292) 525211

e-mail: libraryau@sac.ac.uk
url: www.sac.ac.uk
Site Librarian Ms Elaine P Muir MA PGDipLib MCLIP (e-mail: elaine.muir@sac.ac.uk)

SHEFFIELD HALLAM UNIVERSITY

Learning and IT Services, Sheffield Hallam University, City Campus, Sheffield S1 1WB
☎0114 225 2103
Fax 0114 225 3859
e-mail: learning.centre@shu.ac.uk
url: www.shu.ac.uk/services/lits/index.html
Head of Information Services Ms B M Fisher MLib FCLIP (e-mail: b.m.fisher@shu.ac.uk)
Head of Business and Planning Services E Oyston BA MSc MCLIP

Campus Learning Centres

- Adsetts Centre, Sheffield Hallam University, Learning and IT Services, City Campus, Sheffield S1 1WB
  ☎0114 225 2109
  Fax 0114 225 3859
- Collegiate Learning Centre, Sheffield Hallam University, Learning and IT Services, Collegiate Crescent Campus, Sheffield S10 2BP
  ☎0114 225 2473
  Fax 0114 225 2476
- Psalter Lane Learning Centre, Sheffield Hallam University, Learning and IT Services, Psalter Lane Campus, Sheffield S11 8UZ
  ☎0114 225 2721
  Fax 0114 225 2717

THE UNIVERSITY OF SHEFFIELD

Main Library, The University of Sheffield, Western Bank, Sheffield S10 2TN
☎0114 222 7200 (general enquiries); 0114 222 7224 library (administration)
Fax 0114 222 7290
e-mail: library@sheffield.ac.uk
url: www.shef.ac.uk/library
Director of Library Services and University Librarian Martin J Lewis MA DipLib MCLIP

Major libraries

- Crookesmoor Library (Law), The University of Sheffield, Conduit Road, Sheffield S10 1FL
  ☎0114 222 7340
  Fax 0114 275 4620
  e-mail: lib-cml@sheffield.ac.uk
- Health Sciences Library, The University of Sheffield, Royal Hallamshire Hospital, Sheffield S10 2JF
  ☎0114 271 2030
  Fax 0114 278 0923
  e-mail: hsl.rhh@sheffield.ac.uk

- Health Sciences Library, The University of Sheffield, Northern General Hospital, Sheffield S5 7AU
  ☎0114 226 6800
  Fax 0114 226 6804
  e-mail: hsl.ngh@sheffield.ac.uk
- Information Commons, The University of Sheffield, 44 Leavygreave Road, Sheffield S3 7RD
  ☎0114 222 9999
  e-mail: infocommons@sheffield.ac.uk
- St George's Library (Engineering & Management), The University of Sheffield, Mappin Street, Sheffield S1 4DT
  ☎0114 222 7301
  Fax 0114 279 6406
  e-mail: sgl@sheffield.ac.uk

SOUTHAMPTON SOLENT UNIVERSITY

Mountbatten Library, Southampton Solent University, Southampton SO14 0RJ
☎023 8031 9681 (enquiries), 023 8031 9248 (administration)
Fax (023 8031 9672
url: www.solent.ac.uk/library/
Library and Learning Resources Manager Vacant
Library Services Manager Graeme Barber MSc BA(Hons) DipLib MCLIP (023 8031 9867; e-mail: graeme.barber@solent.ac.uk)

Site library

- Warsash Library, Southampton Solent University, Newtown Road, Warsash, Southampton SO31 9ZL
  ☎(01489) 556269

UNIVERSITY OF SOUTHAMPTON

023 8059 3456

Hartley Library, University of Southampton, Highfield, Southampton SO17 1BJ
☎023 8059 2180 (enquiries), 023 8059 3450 (administration)
Fax 023 8059 5451
e-mail: library@soton.ac.uk
url: www.library.soton.ac.uk/
University Librarian Mark Brown MA PhD DipLib DipMgmt MCLIP (023 8059 2677; e-mail: mlb@soton.ac.uk)
Deputy Librarian Richard Wake MA MA CertMgmt MCLIP (023 8059 2371; e-mail: rlw1@soton.ac.uk)
Head of Archives and Special Collections Christopher Woolgar BA PhD DipArchAdmin FSA FRHistS (023 8059 2721; e-mail: cmw@soton.ac.uk)

Site libraries

- Biomedical Sciences Library, University of Southampton, Biomedical Sciences Building, Bassett Crescent East, Highfield, Southampton SO16 7PX
  ☎023 8059 4215
  Fax 023 8059 3251

e-mail: bslenqs@soton.ac.uk
url: www.library.soton.ac.uk/bsl
Head of Biomedical Sciences Library Ms Gail McFarlane (e-mail: egm@soton.ac.uk)

- Health Services Library MP 883, University of Southampton, Level A, South Academic Block, Southampton General Hospital, Tremona Road, Southampton SO16 6YD
  ☎023 8079 6547
  Fax 023 8079 8939
  e-mail: hslib@soton.ac.uk
  url: www.library.soton.ac.uk/hsl
  Head of MHLS Library Services Ms Christine Fowler BSc(Hons) MA MCLIP (e-mail: c.a.fowler@soton.ac.uk)
- Library, University of Southampton, Winchester School of Art, Park Avenue, Winchester, Hants SO23 8DL
  ☎023 8059 6986
  e-mail: wsaenqs@soton.ac.uk
  url: www.library.soton.ac.uk/wsal
  Head of Library and Information Services Ms Linda Newington BA(Hons) PGDip MCLIP (e-mail: lan1@soton.ac.uk)
- National Oceanographic Library, University of Southampton, Southampton Oceanography Centre, Waterfront Campus, European Way, Southampton SO14 3ZH
  ☎023 8059 6111 (Marine Information and Advisory Service), 023 8059 6116 (general)
  Fax 023 8059 6115
  e-mail: mias@noc.soton.ac.uk (marine inf/adv serv); nol@noc.soton.ac.uk (general)
  url: www.soton.ac.uk/library/about/nol
  Head of Information Services Vacant

SPURGEON'S COLLEGE

Library, Spurgeon's College, 189 South Norwood Hill, London SE25 6DJ
☎020 8653 0850
Fax 020 8771 0959
e-mail: library@spurgeons.ac.uk
url: www.spurgeons.ac.uk
Librarian Mrs J C Powles BA MCLIP (e-mail: j.powles@spurgeons.ac.uk)

STAFFORDSHIRE UNIVERSITY

Information Services, Staffordshire University, PO Box 335, Beaconside, Stafford ST16 9DQ
☎(01782) 294000
Fax (01785) 353410
e-mail: library@staffs.ac.uk
url: www.staffs.ac.uk
Director of Information Services Ms Liz Hart BA(Hons) DipLib MBCS FCLIP (e-mail: l.hart@staffs.ac.uk)

Site libraries

- Health Library, Staffordshire University, School of Health, Royal Shrewsbury Hospital (North), Mytton Oak Road, Shrewsbury SY3 8XQ

☎(01743) 261440
Fax (01743) 261061
Subject and Learning Support Librarian Mrs Shirley Kennedy

- Law Library, Staffordshire University, Leek Road, Stoke-on-Trent, Staffs ST4 2DF
  ☎(01782) 294307
  Fax (01782) 294306
  Site Operations Manager Mrs Nicola Adams
- Nelson Library, Staffordshire University, PO Box 368, Beaconside, Stafford ST18 0YU
  ☎(01785) 353236
  Fax (01785) 251058
  Site Operations Manager Mrs Lynda Hawkins
- Thompson Library, Staffordshire University, PO Box 664, College Road, Stoke-on-Trent ST4 2XS
  ☎(01782) 295770
  Fax (01782) 295799
  Site Operations Manager Mrs Janice Broad

UNIVERSITY OF STIRLING

University Library, University of Stirling, Stirling FK9 4LA
☎(01786 467235 (Information Centre), 01786 467227 (administration)
Fax (01786) 466866
e-mail: library@stir.ac.uk
url: www.is.stir.ac.uk
Director of Information Services Peter Kemp MA PhD (e-mail: pk2@stir.ac.uk)

Campus library

- Highland Health Sciences Library, University of Stirling, Centre for Health Science, Old Perth Road, Inverness IV2 3JH
  ☎(01463) 255600
  Librarian Mrs A Gillespie BA DipLibStud MCLIP (e-mail: ag5@stir.ac.uk)

UNIVERSITY OF STRATHCLYDE

Andersonian Library, University of Strathclyde, Curran Building, 101 St James' Road, Glasgow G4 0NS
☎0141 548 3701 (enquiries), ext 4621 (administration)
Fax 0141 552 3304
e-mail: library@strath.ac.uk
url: www.lib.strath.ac.uk
Librarian and Director of Information Strategy Prof Derek Law DUniv MA DipLib FCLIP FKC FRSE (0141 548 4997; e-mail: d.law@strath.ac.uk)
Director of Library Services Keith R Davis BA DipLib (0141 548 4619; e-mail: k.r.davis@strath.ac.uk)

Constituent libraries

- Jordanhill Library, University of Strathclyde, 76 Southbrae Drive, Glasgow G13 1PP
  ☎0141 950 3300

Fax 0141 950 3150
e-mail: jordanhill.library@strath.ac.uk
Librarian David Alcock BA MA MCLIP (e-mail: d.alcock@strath.ac.uk)

UNIVERSITY OF SUNDERLAND

Student and Learning Support, University of Sunderland, Chester Road, Sunderland SR1 3SD
☎0191 515 2900 (enquiries) 0191 5152119.
Fax 0191 515 2904
url: www.sunderland.ac.uk ill@sunderland.ac.uk
Director of Student and Learning Support Ms Kirsten Black BA DipISTech (0191 515 3904)

Site libraries

- Ashburne Library, University of Sunderland, Sunderland SR2 7EG
  ☎0191 515 2119
  Fax 0191 515 3166
  Site Librarian Ms J Dodshon BA(Hons) DipLib (0191 515 2120; e-mail: jan.dodshon@sunderland.ac.uk)
- The Murray Library, University of Sunderland, Chester Road, Sunderland SR1 3SD
  ☎0191 515 2900
  Fax 0191 515 2904
  Assistant Director (Systems) Vacant
  Assistant Director (Services) Oliver Pritchard BA MA MA MCLIP (0191 515 2903)
  Site Librarian Ms J Archer BA (0191 515 3272; e-mail: julie.archer@sunderland.ac.uk)
- St Peter's Library, University of Sunderland, Prospect Building, St Peter's Riverside Campus, St Peter's Way, Sunderland SR6 0DD
  ☎0191 515 3059
  Fax 0191 515 3061
  Site Librarian Mrs E Astan BA MCLIP (e-mail: elizabeth.astan@sunderland.ac.uk)

UNIVERSITY OF SURREY

University Library, University of Surrey, George Edwards Building, Guildford, Surrey GU2 7XH
☎(01483 683325 (enquiries), 01483 689232 (administration)
Fax (01483) 689500
e-mail: library-enquiries@surrey.ac.uk
url: http://portal.surrey.ac.uk/library
Head of Library and Learning Support Services Mrs Jane Savidge MA MCLIP

UNIVERSITY OF SUSSEX

University Library, University of Sussex, Falmer, Brighton BN1 9QL
☎(01273) 678163 (enquiries), (01273) 877097 (administration)
Fax (01273) 678441
e-mail: library@sussex.ac.uk
url: www.sussex.ac.uk/library/

University Librarian Vacant
Head of Special Collections and Research Services Ms Dorothy Sheridan
Head of Information Services Ms Cath Morgan BEd(Hons) DipIS MCLIP
Head of Technical Services Adrian Hale
Head of Library Administration Ms Sally Faith

Institute of Development Studies, British Library for Development Studies, University of Sussex, Falmer, Brighton BN1 9RE
☎(01273) 678263 (enquiries)
Fax (01273) 873493
e-mail: blds@ids.ac.uk
url: http://blds.ids.ac.uk/blds
Librarian Ms Julie Brittain BA MA MCLIP

SPRU – The Keith Pavitt Library, University of Sussex, Freeman Centre, Falmer, Brighton BN1 9QE
☎(01273) 678066 (enquiries), (01273) 873528 (administration)
Fax (01273) 685865
e-mail: spru_library@sussex.ac.uk
url: www.sussex.ac.uk/spru/library; www.sprulib.central.sussex.ac.uk/ (for catalogue)
Information Services Manager Ms Barbara Merchant BSc MCLIP (e-mail: b.a.merchant@sussex.ac.uk)
Information Officer Ms Maureen Winder BA MSc MCLIP (e-mail: m.e.winder@sussex.ac.uk)

SWANSEA INSTITUTE OF HIGHER EDUCATION

Townhill Campus Library, Swansea Institute of Higher Education, Townhill Road, Swansea SA2 0UT
☎(01792) 482113
Fax (01792) 298017
e-mail: library2@sihe.ac.uk
url: www.sihe.ac.uk
Head of Library and Learning Resources Tony Lamb BA MCLIP GradCertEd (e-mail: tony.lamb@sihe.ac.uk)

Site libraries

- Dynevor Library, Swansea Institute of Higher Education, Dynevor Centre for Art, Design and Media, De La Beche Street, Swansea SA1 3EU
  ☎(01792) 481030
  Senior Assistant Librarian Ms Alison Williams BA MCLIP (e-mail: alison.williams@sihe.ac.uk)
- Owen Library, Swansea Institute of Higher Education, Mount Pleasant, Swansea SA1 6ED
  ☎(01792) 481000 ext 4221
  Site Librarian Ms Anne Harvey LLB (e-mail: anne.harvey@sihe.ac.uk)

SWANSEA UNIVERSITY (formerly University of Wales Swansea)

Library and Information Centre, Swansea University, Singleton Park, Swansea SA2 8PP
☎(01792) 295697 (enquiries), (01792) 295175 (administration)
Fax (01792) 295851
e-mail: library@swansea.ac.uk
url: www.swan.ac.uk/lis/index.htm
Director of Library and Information Services Christopher West MA BA MCLIP

Branch libraries

- Nursing Library, Swansea University, Morriston Hospital, Morriston, Swansea SA6 6NL
  ☎(01792) 703767
  e-mail: s.m.storey@swansea.ac.uk
  Health and Clinical Sciences Librarian Ms Lori D Havard MLS BA
- South Wales Miners' Library, Swansea University, Hendrefoelan Campus, Gower Road, Swansea SA2 7NB
  ☎(01792) 518603
  e-mail: miners@swansea.ac.uk
  Branch Librarian Ms Siân F Williams BSc MCLIP

UNIVERSITY OF TEESSIDE

Library and Information Services, Learning Resource Centre, University of Teesside, Middlesbrough TS1 3BA
☎(01642) 342100 (enquiries), (01642) 342103 (administration)
Fax (01642) 342190
e-mail: lisenquiries@tees.ac.uk
url: www.tees.ac.uk/lis/
Director of Library & Information Services Ian C Butchart MSc BA PGCE MCLIP (e-mail: ian.butchart@tees.ac.uk)

THAMES VALLEY UNIVERSITY

Learning and Research Support, Thames Valley University, St Mary's Road, Ealing, London W5 5RF
☎020 8231 2248 (enquiries), 020 8231 2246 (administration)
Fax 020 8231 2402
url: www.tvu.ac.uk/lrs
Head of Learning and Research Support John Wolstenholme BA (020 8231 2678; e-mail: john.wolstenholme@tvu.ac.uk)

Learning resource centres

- Crescent Road LRC, Thames Valley University, Crescent Road, Reading RG1 5RQ
  ☎0118 967 5360
  Resources Manager Andrew Noble (e-mail: andrew.noble@tvu.ac.uk)
- Kings Road LRC, Thames Valley University, Kings Road, Reading RG1 4HJ
  ☎0118 967 5060
  Fax 0118 967 5073

Resources Manager Andrew Noble (e-mail: andrew.noble@tvu.ac.uk)

- Paul Hamlyn LRC, Thames Valley University, Wellington Street, Slough SL1 1YG
  ☎(01753) 697536
  Fax (01753) 697538
  LRC Manager Michael Sharrocks (e-mail: michael.sharrocks@tvu.ac.uk)
- Royal Berkshire Hospital LRC, Thames Valley University, 4th Floor, Hanover House, 202 Kings Road, Reading RG1 4NN
  ☎0118 967 5560 (issue desk)
  Fax 0118 967 5561
  LRC Manager Felix Oliver-Tasker (0118 967 5562; e-mail: felix.oliver-tasker@tvu.ac.uk)
- St Mary's Road LRC, Thames Valley University, Ealing, London W5 5RF
  ☎020 8231 2401
  Fax 020 8231 2402
  LRC Manager David McGrath BA (e-mail: david.mcgrath@tvu.ac.uk)
- Westel House Health Sciences LRC, Thames Valley University, Westel House, 32 Uxbridge Road, Ealing, London W5 2BS
  ☎020 8280 5043
  Fax 020 8280 5045
  LRC Manager Ms Gillian Briggs (e-mail: gillian.briggs@tvu.ac.uk)

TRINITY AND ALL SAINTS COLLEGE *see* LEEDS TRINITY AND ALL SAINTS

TRINITY COLLEGE CARMARTHEN

Learning Resources Centre, Trinity College Carmarthen, College Road, Carmarthen SA31 3EP
☎(01267) 676780 (Library), (01267) 676786 (Teaching Resources Centre)
Fax (01267) 676766
e-mail: lrc@trinity-cm.ac.uk
url: www.trinity-cm.ac.uk/english/lrc
Director of Learning Resources Ms Sally Wilkinson BA DipLib MCLIP (e-mail: s.a.wilkinson@trinity-cm.ac.uk)

TRINITY LABAN

Jerwood Library of the Performing Arts, Trinity Laban, Trinity College of Music, King Charles Court, Old Royal Naval College, Greenwich, London SE10 9JF
☎020 8305 3950 (enquiries)
Fax 020 8305 9444
e-mail: library@tcm.ac.uk
url: www.tcm.ac.uk
Head Librarian Miss Claire Kidwell BA(Hons) MA (e-mail: ckidwell@tcm.ac.uk)
Administrator (Mander and Mitcheson Theatre Collection) Richard Mangan (020 8305 4426; e-mail: rmangan@tcm.ac.uk)
(Houses the Mander and Mitchenson Theatre Collection)

Library, Laban, Trinity Laban, Creekside, London SE8 3DZ
☎020 8691 8600 (switchboard)
Fax 020 8691 8400
e-mail: library@laban.co.uk
url: www.laban.org
Head of Library and Archives Ralph Cox

UHI MILLENNIUM INSTITUTE

UHI Library Services, UHI Millennium Institute, Executive Office, Ness Walk, Inverness IV3 5SQ
☎(01463) 279000
Fax (01463) 279001
url: www.uhi.ac.uk
Learning Resources Contact Ms Gillian Anderson BA MCLIP

Academic Partner libraries

- Argyll College UHI, Stewart Road, Campbeltown, Argyll PA28 6AT
  ☎(01631) 559670
  Learning Resources Contact Ms Liz Richardson
- Highland Theological College, High Street, Dingwall, Ross-shire IV15 9HA
  ☎(01349) 780215
  Fax (01349) 780001
  Learning Resources Contacts Martin Cameron BA DipLib MCLIP(Librarian), Fraser Jackson DipLib(Cataloguer)
- Inverness College UHI, 3 Longman Road, Longman Road South, Inverness IV1 1SA
  ☎(01463) 273248
  Fax (01463) 711977
  Learning Resources Contact Ms Sue Cromar BA DipLib MCLIP
- Lews Castle College UHI, Stornoway, Isle of Lewis, Hebrides HS2 0XR
  ☎(01851) 770408
  Fax (01851) 770007
  Learning Resources Contact Ms Jessie Murray MA MCLIP
- Lochaber College UHI, An Aird, Fort William, Lochaber, Inverness-shire PH33 6AN
  ☎(01397) 874277
  Fax (01397) 874001
  Learning Resources Contact Ms Sally Curran
- Moray College UHI, Moray Street, Elgin, Moray IV30 1JJ
  ☎(01343) 576206
  Fax (01343) 576001
  Learning Resources Contact Mrs Angie Mackenzie BA DipLib DipEdTech MCLIP
- NAFC Marine Centre, North Atlantic Fisheries College, Port Arthur, Scalloway, Shetland ZE1 0UN
  ☎(01595) 772350
  Fax (01595) 772001
  url: www.nafc.ac.uk
  Learning Resources Contact Ms Maureen Grant BSc(Hons)

- North Highland College UHI, Ormlie Road, Thurso, Caithness KW14 7EE
  ☎(01847) 889292
  Fax (01847) 889001
  Learning Resources Contact Ms Rhona Mason BA MLib MCLIP
- Orkney College UHI, East Road, Kirkwall, Orkney KW15 1LX
  ☎(01856) 569000
  Fax (01856) 569001
  Librarian Ms Anette Andersen (01856 569272)
- Perth College Library UHI, Crieff Road, Perth PH1 2NX
  ☎(01738) 877721
  Fax (01738) 631364
  e-mail: pc.LRCdesk@perth.uhi.ac.uk
  www.perth.ac.uk/library/index.htm
  Librarian Donald MacLean MA(Hons) PGDipILS ACLIB (e-mail: donald.maclean@perth.uhi.ac.uk)
- Sabhal Mòr Ostaig, Slèite, An t-Eilean Sgitheanach IV44 8RQ
  ☎(01471) 888431
  Fax (01471) 888001
  Ceannard an Leabharlainn Cairistìona Cain MA(Hons) MSc
- SAMS – Dunstaffnage Marine Laboratory, Dunbeg, by Oban, Argyll PA37 1QA
  ☎(01631) 559000
  Fax (01631) 559001
  Learning Resources Contact Ms Olga Kimmins BA(Hons)
- Shetland College UHI, Gremista, Lerwick, Shetland ZE1 0PX
  ☎(01595) 771258
  Fax (01595) 694830
  Learning Resources Contact Ms Sam Emmott BA MCLIP

UNIVERSITY OF ULSTER

LRC, University of Ulster, Shore Road, Jordanstown, Newtownabbey, Co Antrim BT37 0QB
☎028 9036 6370
Fax 028 9036 6849
url: www.ulster.ac.uk
Assistant Director, Library Mrs Elaine Urquhart MA DipLibInfoStud MCLIP (028 9036 6370; e-mail: ee.urquhart@ulster.ac.uk)

Campus libraries

- Library, University of Ulster at Belfast, University of Ulster, York Street, Belfast BT15 1ED
  ☎028 9026 7269
  Fax 028 9026 7278
  Belfast Campus Contact Mrs Marion Khorshidian BA DipLIS MCLIP (e-mail: m.khorshidian@ulster.ac.uk)
- Library, University of Ulster at Coleraine, University of Ulster, Cromore Road, Coleraine BT52 1SA
  ☎028 7032 4364
  Fax 028 7032 4928

Coleraine Campus Contact David McClure BA(Hons) DipEd DLS (e-mail: dj.mcclure@ulster.ac.uk)

- LRC, University of Ulster at Jordanstown, University of Ulster, Shore Road, Jordanstown, Newtownabbey, Co Antrim BT37 0QB
  ☎028 9036 6929
  Fax 028 9036 6849
  Jordanstown Campus Contact Mrs Mary McCullough BA DipLibStud (e-mail: m.mccullough@ulster.ac.uk)
- LRC, University of Ulster at Magee, University of Ulster, Northland Road, Londonderry BT48 7JL
  ☎028 7137 5386
  Fax 028 7137 5626
  Magee Campus Contact Mrs Stephanie McLaughlin BA LibStud (e-mail: sa.mclaughlin@ulster.ac.uk)

UNIVERSITY OF THE ARTS LONDON

Library and Learning Resources, University of the Arts London, 65 Davies Street, London W1K 5DA
☎020 7514 6000
url: www.arts.ac.uk/library
Director of Library and Learning Resources Ms Pat Christie BA MCLIP (020 7514 8072; e-mail: p.christie@arts.ac.uk)

College/site libraries

Camberwell College of Arts

Library and Learning Resources, Camberwell College of Arts, 43-45 Peckham Road, London SE5 8UF
☎020 7514 6349
Fax 020 7514 6324
Learning Resources Manager Peter Jennett MA MCLIP (e-mail: p.jennett@wimbledon.arts.ac.uk)

Central Saint Martins College of Art and Design

Library and Learning Resources, Central Saint Martins College of Art and Design, Southampton Row, London WC1B 4AP
☎020 7514 7037
Fax 020 7514 7033
url: www.csm.arts.ac.uk
Learning Resources Manager Ms Sarah Gilmour (e-mail: s.gilmour@csm.arts.ac.uk)

Library and Learning Resources, Central Saint Martins College of Art and Design, 107 Charing Cross Road, London WC2H 0DU
☎020 7514 7190
Fax 020 7514 7189
Assistant Learning Resources Manager Ms Arja Huxstep BA(Hons) MA DipLib

Chelsea College of Art and Design

Library and Learning Resources, Chelsea College of Art and Design, 16 John Islip Street, London SW1P 4JU
☎020 7514 7773/4
Fax 020 7514 7785
url: www.arts.ac.uk/library
Learning Resources Manager Ms Liz Ward BA MA

London College of Communication

Library and Learning Resources, London College of Communication, Elephant and Castle, London SE1 6SB
☎020 7514 8026 (enquiries), 020 7514 6587 (administration)
Fax 020 7514 6597
e-mail: libraryenquiries@lcc.arts.ac.uk
url: www.arts.ac.uk/library
Learning Resources Manager Ms Jacky Camroux MSc DipEdTech MCLIP (e-mail: j.camroux@lcc.arts.ac.uk)

London College of Fashion

Library and Learning Resources, London College of Fashion, 20 John Princes Street, Oxford Circus, London W1G 0BJ
☎020 7514 7455/7543
Fax 020 7514 7580
Learning Resources Manager Ms Diane Mansbridge BA MA MCLIP (e-mail: d.mansbridge@fashion.arts.ac.uk)

Wimbledon College of Art (formerly Wimbledon School of Art)

Library, Wimbledon College of Art, University of the Arts, London, Merton Hall Road, London SW19 3QA
☎020 7514 9690 (enquiries)
Fax 020 7514 9642
url: www.wimbledon.ac.uk
Learning Resources Manager Peter Jennett MA MCLIP (e-mail: p.jennett@wimbledon.arts.ac.uk)
Librarian Ms Helen Davies BA(Hons) MCLIP (e-mail: h.j.davies@wimbledon.arts.ac.uk)
Assistant Librarians Peter Crollie BA(Hons) (e-mail: p.crollie@wimbledon.arts.ac.uk), Ms Lorna Scott BA MCLIP (e-mail: l.a.scott@wimbledon.arts.ac.uk)

UNIVERSITY OF WALES ABERYSTWYTH *see* ABERYSTWYTH UNIVERSITY

UNIVERSITY OF WALES BANGOR *see* BANGOR UNIVERSITY

UNIVERSITY OF WALES INSTITUTE, CARDIFF

Library Division, University of Wales Institute, Cardiff, Llandaff Campus, Western Avenue, Cardiff CF5 2YB
☎029 2041 6240
Fax 029 2041 6908
url: www.uwic.ac.uk/library
Head of Library Division Paul Riley BA(Hons) MSc (029 2041 6240; e-mail: priley@uwic.ac.uk)

UNIVERSITY OF WALES LAMPETER

The Library, University of Wales Lampeter, Lampeter, Ceredigion SA48 7ED
☎(01570) 424772 (enquiries/Librarian)
Fax (01570) 424997
e-mail: library@lamp.ac.uk
url: www.lamp.ac.uk/library
Manager of Library Services Dr Andrew Prescott (e-mail: a.prescott@lamp.ac.uk)

UNIVERSITY OF WALES, NEWPORT

Learning and Information Services, University of Wales, Newport, Caerleon Campus, PO Box 179, Newport, Gwent NP18 3YG
☎(01633) 432842
Fax (01633) 432920
e-mail: lis@newport.ac.uk
url: http://lis.newport.ac.uk
Director of Library and Information Services Tony Rucinski (e-mail: tony.rucinski@newport.ac.uk)

Campus libraries

- Caerleon Campus, University of Wales, Newport, PO Box 179, Newport, Gwent NP18 3YG
  ☎(01633) 432294
  Head of Library Services Mrs Lesley May BA DipLib MCLIP PGCE FHEA (e-mail: lesley.may@newport.ac.uk)
- Allt-yr-yn Campus, University of Wales, Newport, PO Box 180, Newport, Gwent NP20 5XR
  ☎(01633) 432310
  Quality Manager Ms Dawne Leatherdale MBA MCLIP (e-mail: dawne.leatherdale@newport.ac.uk)

UNIVERSITY OF WALES SWANSEA *see* SWANSEA UNIVERSITY

UNIVERSITY OF WARWICK

Library, University of Warwick, Gibbet Hill Road, Coventry CV4 7AL
☎024 7652 4103
Fax 024 7652 4211
e-mail: library@warwick.ac.uk
url: www.warwick.ac.uk/go/library
Librarian Ms Anne Bell BA MA MCLIP

Site library

Warwick HRI Library, University of Warwick, Wellesbourne, Warwick CV35 9EF
☎024 7657 4973 (direct)
Fax 024 7657 4500
e-mail: wellesbourne.library@warwick.ac.uk
url: www.library.warwick.ac.uk
Biomedical Librarian Ms Samantha Johnson MA BA(Hons) DipLib MCLIP

UNIVERSITY OF THE WEST OF ENGLAND, BRISTOL

Library Services, University of the West of England, Bristol, Frenchay Campus, Coldharbour Lane, Bristol BS16 1QY
☎0117 328 2576 (enquiries), 0117 328 2404 (administration)
Fax 0117 328 2407
url: www.uwe.ac.uk/library
Head of Library Services Mrs Cathy Rex BSc DMS MAML MCLIP

UNIVERSITY OF WESTMINSTER

Information Systems and Library Services, University of Westminster, 115 New Cavendish Street, London W1W 6UW
☎020 7911 5095
Fax 020 7911 5093
url: www.wmin.ac.uk
Director of Information Systems and Library Services (ISLS) Ms Suzanne Enright BA DipLib MCLIP (e-mail: s.enright@wmin.ac.uk)

Campus libraries

- Cavendish Campus Library, University of Westminster, 115 New Cavendish Street, London W1W 6UW
  ☎020 7911 5000 ext 3613
  Fax 020 7911 5871
  Library Manager Ms Elaine Salter BA DipLib MLib (e-mail: e.salter@wmin.ac.uk)
- Harrow LRC, Harrow Campus, University of Westminster, Watford Road, Northwick Park, Harrow, Middlesex HA1 3TP
  ☎020 7911 5000 ext 4664
  Fax 020 7911 5952
  Library Manager Ms Carole Satchwell BA MCLIP (e-mail: c.satchwell@wmin.c.uk)

- Marylebone Campus Library, University of Westminster, 35 Marylebone Road, London NW1 5LS
  ☎020 7911 5000 ext 3212
  Fax 020 7911 5058
  Library Manager Ms Ann Sainsbury BA MCLIP (e-mail: a.sainsbury@wmin.ac.uk)
- Regent Campus Library, University of Westminster, 4–12 Little Titchfield Street, London W1W 7UW
  ☎020 7911 5000 ext 2537
  Fax 020 7911 5846
  Library Manager Ms Elaine Salter BA DipLib MLib (e-mail: e.salter@wmin.ac.uk)
- University Archives, University of Westminster, Regent Campus, 4–12 Little Titchfield Street, London W1W 7UW
  ☎020 7911 5000 ext 2524
  Fax 020 7911 5846
  Archivist Ms Elaine Penn MA DAA (e-mail: e.s.penn@wmin.ac.uk)

UNIVERSITY OF WINCHESTER 01962 827412

Library, University of Winchester, Sparkford Road, Winchester, Hants SO22 4NR
☎(01962) 827306
Fax (01962) 827443
url: www.winchester.ac.uk/library
Librarian David Farley BA(Hons) CertMan(OU) MCLIP (01962 827229; e-mail: david.farley@winchester.ac.uk)
Deputy Librarian Ms Liz Fletcher BA(Hons) MA (01962 827374; e-mail: liz.fletcher@winchester.ac.uk)
School Resources Librarian Ms Sybil Bunn BA MCLIP (e-mail: sybil.bunn@winchester.ac.uk)

UNIVERSITY OF WOLVERHAMPTON

Harrison Learning Centre, University of Wolverhampton, St Peter's Square, Wolverhampton WV1 1RH
☎(01902) 322300 (enquiries), 01902 322302 (administration)
Fax (01902) 322668
e-mail: lib@wlv.ac.uk
Director of Learning and Information Services Ms Fiona Parsons BA MLib PGCE (01902 322302) (located at Mill Building, Lichfield Street, Wolverhampton WV1 1SB)
Assistant Director of Learning and Information Services (Resources) Ms Fiona Mill MA DipLib, Mrs Irene Ordidge BSc DipLib (job-share)
Assistant Director of Learning and Information Services (Operational Development) Mrs Gill James BLib MCLIP

Site libraries

- Compton Learning Centre, University of Wolverhampton, Compton Road West, Wolverhampton WV3 9DX
  ☎(01902) 323642
  Fax (01902) 323702
  Learning Centre Manager Mrs Linda Thomas MCLIP

- Harrison Learning Centre, University of Wolverhampton, St Peter's Square, Wolverhampton WV1 1RH
  ☎(01902) 322300
  Fax (01902) 322194
  Learning Centre Manager Mrs Trish Fouracres BA(Hons) MA MCLIP
- Telford Learning Centre, University of Wolverhampton, Old Shifnal Road, Priorslee, Telford, Shropshire TF2 9NT
  ☎(01902) 323983
  Fax (01902) 323985
  Learning Centre Manager David W Clare BA MCLIP
- Walsall Learning Centre, University of Wolverhampton, Gorway, Walsall, West Midlands WS1 3BD
  ☎(01902) 323275
  Fax (01902) 323079
  Learning Centre Manager Ian Keepins BA(Hons) PGDipLib PGCert(Management)

School of Health site library

- Burton Learning Centre, University of Wolverhampton, Burton Nurse Education Centre, Belvedere Road, Burton upon Trent, Staffs DE13 0RB
  ☎(01283) 566333 ext 2217/2237
  Fax (01283) 515978
  Site Librarian Ms Liz Watson BA PGDipLib MCLIP
  Hybrid Services Manager John Dowd BA(Hons)

UNIVERSITY OF WORCESTER

Peirson Library, University of Worcester, Peirson Building, Henwick Grove, Worcester WR2 6AJ
☎(01905) 855341
Fax (01905) 855197
url: www.worcester.ac.uk
Director of Information and Learning Services Ms Anne Hannaford BA(Hons) DipLib (e-mail: a.hannaford@worc.ac.uk)
Issue Desk Manager Ms Lissa O'Grady (e-mail: l.o'grady@worc.ac.uk)

WRITTLE COLLEGE

Library, Writtle College, Chelmsford, Essex CM1 3RR
☎(01245) 424245
Fax (01245) 420456
e-mail: thelibrary@writtle.ac.uk
url: www.writtle.ac.uk
Head of Learning Information Services Mrs R M Hewings BSc(Econ) DMS DipLib MCLIP FHEA (ext 26009; e-mail: rachel.hewings@writtle.ac.uk)
Subject Librarian, Applied Science and Technology Ms Christina White BA DipLib (ext 26008; e-mail: christina.white@writtle.ac.uk)
Subject Librarian, Business Management and Horticulture Ms Tina Hohmann DipJng MLIS (ext 26008; e-mail: tina.hohmann@writtle.ac.uk)

YORK ST JOHN UNIVERSITY

(formerly York St John University College)

Library and Information Services, York St John University, Fountains Learning Centre, Lord Mayor's Walk, York YO31 7EX
☎(01904) 716700
Fax (01904) 716324
e-mail: library@yorksj.ac.uk
url: www.yorksj.ac.uk/library/learningcent/
College Librarian Tony Chalcraft BA MA MCLIP (01904 716701; e-mail: a.chalcraft@yorksj.ac.uk)
Deputy College Librarian Ms Helen Westmancoat BA MCLIP (e-mail: h.westmancoat@yorksj.ac.uk)
Academic Liaison Librarians Ms Jane Munks BA MCLIP (e-mail: j.munks@yorksj.ac.uk), John Hagart BA MCLIP (e-mail: j.hagart@yorksj.ac.uk), Ms Fiona Ware BA MCLIP (e-mail: f.ware@yorksj.ac.uk), Ms Lottie Alexander BA (e-mail: l.alexander@yorksj.ac.uk)
Acquisitions Librarian Bryan Jones BA (e-mail: b.jones@yorksj.ac.uk)
Special Collections Librarian Roger Wolfe BA (e-mail: r.wolfe@yorksj.ac.uk)
Database Librarian Ms Ruth Mardall BA MA (e-mail: r.mardall2@yorksj.ac.uk)

UNIVERSITY OF YORK

J B Morrell and Raymond Burton Libraries, University of York, Heslington, York YO10 5DD
☎(01904) 433865 (enquiries)
Fax (01904) 433866
e-mail: lib-enquiry@york.ac.uk
url: www.york.ac.uk/services/library/
University Librarian Stephen Town MA DipLib FCLIP

Branch/department libraries

- King's Manor Library, University of York, The King's Manor, York YO1 7EP
  ☎(01904) 433969
  Fax (01904) 433949
- Library and Information Service, University of York, Harrogate District Hospital Library, The Strayside Education Centre, Lancaster Park Road, Harrogate, Yorkshire HG2 7SX
  ☎(01423) 553104
  Fax (01423) 553097
  e-mail: hslibhg@york.ac.uk
  Manager of Library and Information Service Mrs Gillian Jarrett BA (e-mail: gj7@york.ac.uk)

Selected Government, National and Special Libraries in the United Kingdom

ACAS

Information Centre, ACAS, Brandon House, 180 Borough High Street, London SE1 1LW
☎020 7210 3911 (enquiries)
Fax 020 7210 3615
e-mail: library@acas.org.uk
url: www.acas.org.uk
Information Knowledge Manager Ms Mary Susan Barry BA DipLib MCLIP

Specialism(s): Advisory, conciliation and arbitration service. UK employment relations

ADVOCATES LIBRARY

Advocates Library, Parliament House, Edinburgh EH1 1RF
☎0131 260 5683 (enquiries), 0131 260 5637 (Librarian)
Fax 0131 260 5663 (9am–5pm weekdays)
e-mail: inqdesk@advocates.org.uk
url: www.advocates.org.uk
Senior Librarian Ms Andrea Longson BSc DipLib (e-mail: andrea.longson@advocates.org.uk)
(Open to members only. Non-members may access stock at the National Library of Scotland.)

Specialism(s): Law

ALDERSHOT MILITARY MUSEUM

Military Museum and Archive, Aldershot Military Museum, Evelyn Woods Road, Queens Avenue, Aldershot, Hants GU11 2LG
☎(01252) 314598
Fax (01252) 342942
url: www.hants.gov.uk/museum/aldershot
Curator Ms Sally Day BA MCLIP (e-mail: sally.1.day@hants.gov.uk)
(Accessible to enquirers by appointment)

Specialism(s): Military history; Local history

AMBLESS SOCIETY LIBRARY

Ambless Society Library, Shalom House, Lower Celtic Park, Enniskillen, Co Fermanagh BT74 6HP
☎028 6632 0320; Ambless Accident Supportline: 028 6632 0321 (tel/fax/smstext/voicemail/RBS)
Fax 028 6632 0320
url: www.ukselfhelp.info.ambless
Librarian John Wood

Specialism(s): Private research library working closely with the charity Ambless, which offers care and support to accident sufferers and their families

AMERICAN MUSEUM IN BRITAIN

Library, American Museum in Britain, Claverton Manor, Bath BA2 7BD
☎(01225) 823016
Fax (01225) 469160
e-mail: info@americanmuseum.org
url: www.americanmuseum.org
Librarian Mrs Anne Armitage BA (e-mail: anne.armitage@americanmuseum.org)

Specialism(s): American history and decorative arts; Religions, e.g. Shakers; North American Indians

AMGUEDDFA CYMRU – NATIONAL MUSEUM WALES

Library, Amgueddfa Cymru – National Museum Wales, Cathays Park, Cardiff CF10 3NP
☎029 2057 3202
Fax 029 2057 3216
e-mail: library@museumwales.ac.uk
url: www.museumwales.ac.uk
Librarian John R Kenyon BA MCLIP FSA FRHistS FSA(Scot)

Specialism(s): Archaeology; Fine and decorative arts; Botany; Geology; Zoology; Architecture; Welsh history and topography

THE ARMITT COLLECTION

The Armitt Collection, Rydal Road, Ambleside, Cumbria LA22 9BL
☎(01539) 431212
Fax (01539) 431313
e-mail: info@armitt.com
url: www.armitt.com
Collections Manager Ms Tanya Flower

Specialism(s): Specialist Lake District collection (literature, topography, natural history); Cumbria; Mountaineering; Kurt Schwitters; Beatrix Potter

ASSOCIATION OF COMMONWEALTH UNIVERSITIES

Reference Library, Association of Commonwealth Universities, Woburn House, 20–24 Tavistock Square, London WC1H 9HF
☎020 7380 6700
Fax 020 7387 2655
e-mail: info@acu.ac.uk
url: www.acu.ac.uk
Librarian Nicholas Mulhern MA MA DipLIS MCLIP

Specialism(s): Higher Education in the Commonwealth

BABRAHAM INSTITUTE

Library, The Babraham Institute, Babraham Research Campus, Cambridge CB22 3AT
☎(01223) 496214 (enquiries)
Fax (01223) 496027
e-mail: babraham.library@bbsrc.ac.uk
url: www.babraham.ac.uk
Librarian Miss Jennifer R Maddock BA DipLib MCLIP (01223 496235; e-mail: jennifer.maddock@bbsrc.ac.uk)
Library Assistants Ms Suzanne Morley BA MA, Mrs Arwen E Spicer BA

Specialism(s): Journals in Cell biology, Genetics, Immunology, Molecular biology and neuroscience

BANK OF ENGLAND

Information Centre, Bank of England, Threadneedle Street, London EC2R 8AH
☎020 7601 4715 (enquiries), 020 7601 4668 (administration)
Fax 020 7601 4356
e-mail: informationcentre@bankofengland.co.uk
url: www.bankofengland.co.uk
Information Centre Manager Ms Penny Hope BA MA MSc DipLib MCLIP

Specialism(s): Economics; Central banking

BG GROUP PLC

Information Centre, BG Group plc, Faraday Building 2, 100 Thames Valley Park Drive, Reading RG6 1PT
☎(0118) 929 2496 (enquiries and administration)
Fax (0118) 929 2414
url: www.bg-group.com
Information Analysts P Cronin (0118 929 2496; e-mail: padraig.cronin@bg-group.com), D Freemantle (0118 929 2497; e-mail: david.freemantle@bg-group.com)

Specialism(s): Reference collection, mainly energy industry

BIRMINGHAM AND MIDLAND INSTITUTE

The Birmingham Library, Birmingham and Midland Institute, 9 Margaret Street, Birmingham B3 3BS
☎0121 236 3591
Fax 0121 212 4577
e-mail: admin@bmi.org.uk
url: www.bmi.org.uk
Librarian Mrs Sheila Utley BA
(Private members' library)

Specialism(s): History; Literature; Natural history; Science; Travel; Fiction; Biography; Music

BISHOPSGATE FOUNDATION & INSTITUTE

Bishopsgate Library, Bishopsgate Foundation & Institute, 230 Bishopsgate, London EC2M 4QH
☎020 7392 9270
Fax 020 7392 9275
e-mail: library@bishopsgate.org.uk
url: www.bishopsgate.org.uk
Library Manager Jeff Abbott BA(Hons) (e-mail: jeffrey.abbott@bishopsgate.org.uk)
Archivist Stefan Dickers

Specialism(s): London history and topography; Labour history; 19thC trades union history; Co-operative movement; Freethought movement

BRITANNIA ROYAL NAVAL COLLEGE

College Library, Britannia Royal Naval College, Dartmouth, Devon TQ6 0HJ
☎(01803) 677278
Fax (01803) 677015
url: www.britannia.ac.uk
College Librarian Richard Kennell MCLIP (e-mail: brnc_lib1@nrta.mod.uk)
Deputy Librarian Ms Gill Smith (e-mail: brnc-lib2@nrta.mod.uk)
(Prior appointment necessary)

Specialism(s): Strategic studies; Naval history; Marine environment; Leadership

BRITISH ANTARCTIC SURVEY

Library, British Antarctic Survey, High Cross, Madingley Road, Cambridge CB3 0ET
☎(01223) 221617
Fax (01223) 362616
e-mail: baslib@bas.ac.uk
url: www.antarctica.ac.uk
Librarian Ms Christine Phillips MA MCLIP (e-mail: cmp@bas.ac.uk)

Specialism(s): Geology; Geophysics; Glaciology; Climatology; Upper atmosphere physics; Marine and terrestrial biology (all with accent on Antarctic region)

BRITISH BROADCASTING CORPORATION

BBC Information and Archives, British Broadcasting Corporation, 3rd Floor, BC3 Broadcast Centre, 201 Wood Lane, London W12 7TP
☎020 8008 2288
Fax 020 8008 2272
e-mail: customerservice@bbc.co.uk
url: www.bbc.co.uk; www.bbcmotiongallery.com; www.bbcworldwide.com
Head of Media Asset Management Ms Sarah Hayes

BRITISH COUNCIL

Information Centre, British Council, Bridgewater House, 58 Whitworth Street, Manchester M1 6BB
☎0161 957 7755
Fax 0161 957 7762
e-mail: general.enquiries@britishcouncil.org
url: www.britishcouncil.org
Textphone: 0161 957 7188
Manager Ms Lyndsey Kelly-Aberle
(For details of British Council information services in 109 countries and territories see website: www.britishcouncil.org.)

BRITISH DENTAL ASSOCIATION

BDA Information Centre, British Dental Association, 64 Wimpole Street, London W1G 8YS
☎020 7563 4545
Fax 020 7935 6492
e-mail: infocentre@bda.org
url: www.bda.org.uk
Head of Library Services R Farbey BA DipLib MCLIP (e-mail: r.farbey@bda.org)

BRITISH EMPIRE AND COMMONWEALTH MUSEUM

British Empire and Commonwealth Museum, Clock Tower Yard, Temple Meads, Bristol BS1 6QH
☎0117 925 4980
Fax 0117 925 4983
e-mail: admin@empiremuseum.co.uk
url: www.empiremuseum.co.uk
Director Dr Gareth Griffiths
Exhibition Floor Manager Ms Anne Lineen

Specialism(s): Commonwealth literature, archives and resources; Colonial and Empire history

BRITISH FILM INSTITUTE

BFI National Library, British Film Institute, 21 Stephen Street, London W1T 1LN
☎020 7255 1444 (information enquiry service), ext 4752 (administration)
Fax 020 7436 2338
e-mail: library@bfi.org.uk
url: www.bfi.org.uk/filmtvinfo/library
Head of Collections and Information Darren Long
Deputy (BFI National Library) David Sharp BA MCLIP (020 7957 8970)
(Incorporates Independent Television Commission Library collections)

Specialism(s): The moving image (national film and television collection and archives)

BRITISH GEOLOGICAL SURVEY

Library and Information Services, British Geological Survey, Kingsley Dunham Centre, Keyworth, Notts NG12 5GG
☎0115 936 3205 (enquiries), 0115 936 3472 (Chief Librarian)
Fax (0115 936 3015
e-mail: libuser@bgs.ac.uk
url: www.bgs.org.uk
Chief Librarian Ken Hollywood BA(Hons) DipLib MSc MCLIP

Branch libraries

- Library, British Geological Survey, Scottish Regional Office, Murchison House, West Mains Road, Edinburgh EH9 3LA
  ☎0131 667 1000, 0131 650 0322 (direct dial)
  Fax 0131 668 2683
  e-mail: mhlib@bgs.ac.uk
  Site Librarian Bob McIntosh BSc DipLib
- London Information Office, British Geological Survey, Natural History Museum, Exhibition Road, South Kensington, London SW7 2DE
  ☎020 7589 4090
  Fax 020 7584 8270
  e-mail: bgslondon@bgs.ac.uk
  Officer-in-Charge Ms Clare Tombleson (e-mail: cto@bgs.ac.uk)

BRITISH HOROLOGICAL INSTITUTE

Library, British Horological Institute, Upton Hall, Upton, Newark, Notts NG23 5TE
☎(01636) 813795
Fax (01636) 812258
e-mail: clocks@bhi.co.uk
url: www.bhi.co.uk
Librarian and Curator Viscount Alan Midleton FBHI

BRITISH LIBRARY

British Library, 96 Euston Road, London NW1 2DB
☎020 7412 7332 (general and visitor enquiries), 0870 444 1500 (switchboard)
url: www.bl.uk
Chairman Sir Colin Lucas
Chief Executive Mrs Lynne Brindley
Director of Human Resources Ms Mary Canavan
Director of Finance and Corporate Resources Steve Morris
Director of Scholarship and Collections Ronald Milne
Director of Strategic Marketing and Communications Ms Jill Finney
Director of e-Strategy and Information Systems Richard Boulderstone
Director of Operations and Services Phil Spence

Enquiry points
The following are based at 96 Euston Road, London NW1 2DB. Admission to the Library's London reading rooms is by pass only. Most of the Library's catalogues are available on its website, www.bl.uk. For general enquiries about the collection, reader services and advance reservations, tel: 020 7412 7676, e-mail: reader-services-enquiries@bl.uk
Other useful numbers/e-mail addresses
Reader Admissions (advice on who may use the Library and how to apply for a reader's pass)
☎020 7412 7677, e-mail: Reader-Admissions@bl.uk
Visitor Services (for general enquiries and details of exhibitions, events)
☎020 7412 7332, e-mail: Visitor-Services@bl.uk

Northern Site, British Library, Boston Spa, Wetherby, West Yorks LS23 7BQ
☎0870 444 1500
e-mail: dsc-customer-services@bl.uk

St Pancras Reading Rooms
Librarianship and Information Science Service (LIS)
☎020 7412 7676; e-mail: lis@bl.uk
Maps
☎020 7412 7702; e-mail: maps@bl.uk
Music Collections
☎020 7412 7772; e-mail: music-collections@bl.uk
Sound Archive
☎020 7412 7440; e-mail: sound-archive@bl.uk
Asia, Pacific and Africa Collections (formerly Oriental and India Office Collections)
☎020 7412 7873; e-mail: apac-enquiries@bl.uk
Philatelic
☎020 7412 7635; e-mail: philatelic@bl.uk
Rare Book Collections
☎020 7412 7676; e-mail: rare-books@bl.uk
Science, Technology and Medicine Information
☎020 7412 7676; e-mail: scitech@bl.uk
Manuscripts
☎020 7412 7513; e-mail: mss@bl.uk

Other Reading Rooms
British Library Newspapers, Colindale Avenue, London NW9 5HE
☎020 7412 7353/7356; e-mail: newspaper@bl.uk

For material in Document Supply
Boston Spa, Wetherby, West Yorks LS23 7BQ
☎(01937) 546060; e-mail: dsc-customer-services@bl.uk

BRITISH MEDICAL ASSOCIATION

BMA Library, British Medical Association, BMA House, Tavistock Square, London WC1H 9JP
☎020 7383 6625

Fax 020 7388 2544
e-mail: bma-library@bma.org.uk
url: www.bma.org.uk/library
Librarian Ms Jacky Berry

BRITISH MUSEUM

Anthropology Library, Centre for Anthropology, British Museum, Department of AOA, Great Russell Street, London WC1B 3DG
☎020 7323 8031
Fax 020 7323 8049
e-mail: anthropologylibrary@thebritishmuseum.ac.uk
Acting Senior Librarian Ms Lucia Navascues (020 7323 8069; e-mail: lnavascues@thebritishmuseum.ac.uk)
(The Anthropology Library in the British Museum is a major anthropological collection. It incorporates the stock of the former library of the Royal Anthropological Institute. It covers every aspect of anthropology–cultural anthropology (with emphasis on material culture), archaeology, biological anthropology, linguistics and such related fields as history, sociology, description and travel. It also houses a Pictorial Collection. The Library is open to researchers and the general public (proof of identity will be required).

Paul Hamlyn Library, British Museum, Great Russell Street, London WC1B 3DG
☎020 7323 8838
e-mail: collectionenquires@thebritishmuseum.ac.uk
url: www.thebritishmuseum.ac.uk
Paul Hamlyn Library Supervisor Charles Hoare (020 7323 8381; e-mail: choare@thebritishmuseum.ac.uk)
(The Paul Hamlyn Library is an open access public reference library on subjects relating to the Museum's collections, e.g. ancient history, archaeology, art history, museology. The Library is freely open to the public without any membership or prior appointment.)

BRITISH NATIONAL SPACE CENTRE

Information Unit, British National Space Centre, 151 Buckingham Palace Road, London SW1W 9SS
☎020 7215 0901 (enquiries)
Fax 020 7215 0936
e-mail: bnscinfo@bnsc.gsi.gov.uk
url: www.bnsc.gov.uk
Librarian Stuart Grayson BSc DipLib

Specialism(s): Space exploration, science and earth observation to support UK civil space activity

BRITISH PSYCHOLOGICAL SOCIETY

Psychology Library, British Psychological Society, Senate House Library, University of London, Malet Street, London WC1E 7HU
☎020 7862 8451/8461

Fax 020 7862 8480
e-mail: enquiries@shl.lon.ac.uk
url: www.shl.lon.ac.uk
Psychology Librarian, Senate House Library, University of London Mrs Susan E Tarrant BA MCLIP
(The BPS collection of periodicals is held at the Psychology Library and amalgamated with the University of London Library collection of psychology periodicals.)

BRITISH STANDARDS INSTITUTION

Library, British Standards Institution, 389 Chiswick High Road, London W4 4AL
☎020 8996 7004
Fax 020 8996 7005
e-mail: library@bsi-global.com
url: www.bsi-global.com
Resource Centre Manager David Mantle BSc(Hons) MSc
(The Library may be used for reference free of charge by members and students. For non-members there is a charge)

Specialism(s): Standards; Technical regulations; Quality and environmental management; Information security; Health & safety

BRITISH UNIVERSITIES FILM & VIDEO COUNCIL

Information Service, British Universities Film & Video Council, 77 Wells Street, London W1T 3QJ
☎020 7393 1500
Fax 020 7393 1555
e-mail: ask@bufvc.ac.uk
url: www.bufvc.ac.uk
Head of Information Luke McKernan PhD

Specialism(s): Film; Television; Radio

THE BRITTEN-PEARS LIBRARY

The Britten-Pears Library, The Red House, Golf Lane, Aldeburgh, Suffolk IP15 5PZ
☎(01728) 451700
Fax (01728) 453076
e-mail: library@brittenpears.org
url: www.brittenpears.org
Librarian Dr Christopher Grogan BMus PhD DipLIS (01728 451707)

BROMLEY HOUSE LIBRARY

Bromley House Library, Bromley House, Angel Row, Nottingham NG1 6HL
☎0115 947 3134
e-mail: enquiries@bromleyhouse.org
Librarian Mrs Carol Allison BSc DipLib MA MCLIP

(Subscription library also available to the public for reference purposes only, by prior appointment)

CANCER RESEARCH UK

Library and Information Services, Cancer Research UK, 44 Lincoln's Inn Fields, London WC2A 3PX
☎020 7269 3206 (enquiries), 020 7269 2868 (administration)
Fax 020 7269 3084
e-mail: lib.info@cancer.org.uk
url: www.science.cancerresearchuk.org/; www.cancerresearchuk.org/
LIS Resources Manager Chris Wilson BA DipLib (e-mail: chris.wilson@cancer.org.uk)

CANCERBACKUP

Library and Information Service, CancerBackup, 3 Bath Place, Rivington Street, London EC2A 3JR
☎020 7696 9003
Fax 020 7696 9002
url: www.cancerbackup.org.uk
Library and Information Service Manager Edward Wallace

CANTERBURY CATHEDRAL

Cathedral Library, Canterbury Cathedral, The Precincts, Canterbury, Kent CT1 2EH
☎(01227) 865287
e-mail: library@canterbury-cathedral.org
url: www.canterbury-cathedral.org/library.html
Cathedral Librarian K M C O'Sullivan MA MSc(Econ) MCLIP (e-mail: librarian@canterbury-cathedral.org)

Specialism(s): Theology; Liturgy; Church history; Local (Kentish) history; Anti-slavery movement; Catholic and anti-Catholic history; Natural history

CCLRC (COUNCIL FOR THE CENTRAL LABORATORY OF THE RESEARCH COUNCILS) *see* SCIENCE AND TECHNOLOGY FACILITIES COUNCIL

CENTRAL POLICE TRAINING AND DEVELOPMENT AUTHORITY *see* NATIONAL POLICING IMPROVEMENT AGENCY

CENTRE FOR ECOLOGY AND HYDROLOGY

Library, Centre for Ecology and Hydrology, Centre for Ecology and Hydrology Edinburgh, Bush Estate, Penicuik, Midlothian EH26 0QB
☎0131 445 4343
Fax 0131 445 3943
url: http://library.ceh.ac.uk
Librarian and Head of CEH Library Service Steve Prince BSc DipLib MCLIP (e-mail: sjpr@ceh.ac.uk)

Research station libraries

- Library, Centre for Ecology and Hydrology Banchory, Centre for Ecology and Hydrology, Hill of Brathens, Glassel, Banchory, Kincardineshire AB31 4BY
  ☎(01330) 826300
  Fax (01330) 823303
  Librarian Ms Alison Odds (e-mail: ao@ceh.ac.uk)
- Library, Centre for Ecology and Hydrology Bangor, Centre for Ecology and Hydrology, Orton Building, University of Wales, Deiniol Road, Bangor, Gwynedd LL57 2UP
  ☎(01248) 370045
  Fax (01248) 355365
  Librarian Ms Jackie Cooper (e-mail: jrco@ceh.ac.uk)
- Library, Centre for Ecology and Hydrology Lancaster, Centre for Ecology and Hydrology, Lancaster Environment Centre, Library Avenue, Bailrigg, Lancaster LA1 4AP
  ☎(01524) 595800
  Fax (01524) 61536
  Librarian Ms Jeanette Coward (e-mail: jcowa@ceh.ac.uk)
- Library, Centre for Ecology and Hydrology Monks Wood, Centre for Ecology and Hydrology, Abbots Ripton, Huntingdon, Cambs PE28 2LS
  ☎(01487) 773381
  Fax (01487) 773467
  Librarian Ms Pam Moorhouse (e-mail: pmo@ceh.ac.uk)
- Library, Centre for Ecology and Hydrology Oxford, Centre for Ecology and Hydrology, Mansfield Road, Oxford OX1 3SR
  ☎(01865) 281630
  Fax (01865) 281696
- Library, Centre for Ecology and Hydrology Wallingford, Centre for Ecology and Hydrology, Maclean Building, Crowmarsh Gifford, Wallingford, Oxon OX10 8BB
  ☎(01491) 838800
  Fax (01491) 692424
  Librarian Adrian Smith BSc AIMgt MCLIP (e-mail: apsm@ceh.ac.uk)

Specialism(s): Enviroment (esp. terrestrial and freshwater sciences)

CENTRE FOR POLICY ON AGEING

Library, Centre for Policy on Ageing, 25–31 Ironmonger Row, London EC1V 3QP
☎020 7553 6500
Fax 020 7553 6501
e-mail: cpa@cpa.org.uk

url: www.cpa.org.uk
Director Ms Gillian Crosby BA MCLIP (e-mail: gcrosby@cpa.org.uk)
Librarian Ms Ruth Hayes BA MCLIP
Information Officer Ms Kate Jones BA MCLIP

THE CHARTERED INSTITUTE OF LOGISTICS AND TRANSPORT IN THE UK

The Chartered Institute of Logistics and Transport in the UK, Earlstrees Court, Earlstrees Road, Corby, Northants NN17 4AX
☎(01536) 740112 or 740139 (library), (01536) 740100 (reception)
Fax (01536) 740102 (FAO Knowledge Centre Manager)
url: www.ciltuk.org.uk
Knowledge Centre Manager Peter Huggins MA (e-mail: peter.huggins@ciltuk.org.uk)
Database Administrator Ms Lynn Mentiply (e-mail: lynn.mentiply@ciltuk.org.uk)
Knowledge Centre Co-ordinator Ms Nicola Keane (e-mail: nicola.keane@ciltuk.org.uk)
(Access: free to Institute members and full-time students; a charge is made for non-member usage. London Reading Room open to members only – for details contact The Knowledge Centre Manager)

Specialism(s): Logistics; Supply-chain; Passenger transport

CHARTERED INSTITUTE OF PERSONNEL AND DEVELOPMENT

Library and Information Services, Chartered Institute of Personnel and Development, 151 The Broadway, London SW19 1JQ
☎020 8612 6210 (enquiries), 020 8612 6641 (administration)
Fax 020 8612 6232
e-mail: lis@cipd.co.uk
url: www.cipd.co.uk
Head of Library and Information Services Ms Barbara Salmon BA DipLib MCLIP

CHARTERED INSURANCE INSTITUTE

CII Knowledge Services, Chartered Insurance Institute, 20 Aldermanbury, London EC2V 7HY
☎020 7417 4415/4416
Fax 020 7972 0110
e-mail: knowledge@cii.co.uk
url: www.cii.co.uk
Head of Knowledge Services Robert Cunnew BA FCLIP

Specialism(s): Insurance, risk and related financial services

CHARTERED MANAGEMENT INSTITUTE

Management Information Centre, Chartered Management Institute, Management House, Cottingham Road, Corby, Northants NN17 1TT

☎(01536) 204222 (switchboard), (01536) 207400 (enquiries)
Fax (01536) 401013
e-mail: mic.enquiries@managers.org.uk
url: www.managers.org.uk
Member Services Manager Kevin Saunders
(Information services, principally to Institute members)

Specialism(s): Management theory, practice and techniques

CHETHAM'S LIBRARY

Chetham's Library, Long Millgate, Manchester M3 1SB
☎0161 834 7961
Fax 0161 839 5797
e-mail: librarian@chethams.org.uk
url: www.chethams.org.uk
Chetham's Librarian Michael Powell BD PhD

Specialism(s): Rare books; Local history

CILIP: THE CHARTERED INSTITUTE OF LIBRARY AND INFORMATION PROFESSIONALS

Information and Advice Team, CILIP: the Chartered Institute of Library and Information Professionals, 7 Ridgmount Street, London WC1E 7AE
☎020 7255 0620
Fax 020 7255 0501
e-mail: info@cilip.org.uk
url: www.cilip.org.uk
Textphone 020 7255 0505
Team Leader, Information and Advice Ms Jill Duffin MCLIP

Specialism(s): Library and information management

CILT, THE NATIONAL CENTRE FOR LANGUAGES

CILT Resources Library, CILT, the National Centre for Languages, 20 Bedfordbury, London WC2N 4LB
☎020 7379 5110
Fax 020 7379 5082
e-mail: library@cilt.org.uk
url: www.cilt.org.uk; http://www.cilt.org.uk/libcat (library catalogue)
Librarian Michael Hammond BA MCLIP

Note: CILT will be moving premises towards the end of 2007. Please see website for ongoing information.

Specialism(s): Language teaching methodology and materials

CIVIL AVIATION AUTHORITY

Corporate Services, Civil Aviation Authority, Aviation House, Gatwick Airport South, West Sussex RH6 0YR
☎(01293) 573048
e-mail: infoservices@caa.co.uk
url: www.caa.co.uk
CAA Management Systems Manager Ms Carol Cairns BA(Hons) DipLib MLib MCLIP (e-mail: carol.cairnssrg@caa.co.uk)
Library Manager Vagn Pedersen (01293 573966/01293 573181)

Specialism(s): UK aviation and aviation safety

COLLEGE OF OCCUPATIONAL THERAPISTS

Library, College of Occupational Therapists, 106–114 Borough High Street, Southwark, London SE1 1LB
☎020 7450 2303/2320/2316
Fax 020 7450 2364
e-mail: library@cot.co.uk
url: www.cot.org.uk
Librarian Ms Ann Mason BA(Hons) MCLIP
Deputy Librarian Ms Lorna Rutherford BA(Hons) PGDip
Assistant Librarian Andy Hughes BA(Hons) MA

COMMONWEALTH SECRETARIAT

Library, Commonwealth Secretariat, Marlborough House, Pall Mall, London SW1Y 5HX
☎020 7747 6164
Fax 020 7747 6168
e-mail: library@commonwealth.int
url: www.thecommonwealth.org
Librarian David Blake BA DipLib MSc MCLIP (e-mail: d.blake@commonwealth.int)

Specialism(s): The Commonwealth (politics, economics, health, education, science and gender)

COMPETITION COMMISSION

Information Centre, Competition Commission, Victoria House, Southampton Row, London WC1B 4AD
☎020 7271 0261
Fax 020 7271 0367
e-mail: info@cc.gsi.gov.uk
url: www.competition-commission.org.uk
Information Centre Manager Miss L J Fisher MA MCLIP
Press and Publicity Officer R Taylor
(Open to government libraries by appointment. Not open to the public, but deals with public telephone and written enquiries.)

CONSERVATIVE RESEARCH DEPARTMENT

Library, Conservative Research Department, Conservative Party, 30 Millbank, London SW1P 4DP
☎020 7222 9000 (main)
Fax 020 7984 8273
url: www.conservatives.com
Researcher Sheridan Westlake MA(Oxon) MSc MPhil
(Not open to the public)

Conservative Party Archive, Conservative Research Department, c/o Bodleian Library, Broad Street, Oxford OX1 3BG
☎(01865) 277046
e-mail: modern.papers@bodley.ox.ac.uk
url: www.conservativepartyarchive.org
Archivist Jeremy McIlwaine MArAd (01865 277181; e-mail: jeremy.mcilwaine@bodley.ox.ac.uk)

CORUS UK LTD, RESEARCH, DEVELOPMENT AND TECHNOLOGY

Knowledge and Library Services, Corus UK Ltd, Research, Development and Technology, Swinden Technology Centre, Moorgate, Rotherham, South Yorks S60 3AR
☎(01709) 820166
Fax (01709) 825464
e-mail: stc.library@corusgroup.com
url: www.corusgroup.com
Manager, Customised Information Services Ms Carol Patton (located at site library below)

Site library

Knowledge and Library Services, Corus UK Ltd, Research, Development and Technology, Teesside Technology Centre, PO Box 11, Eston Road, Grangetown, Middlesbrough, Cleveland TS6 6US
☎(01642) 382000
Fax (01642) 460321

Specialism(s): Steel engineering and manufacturing

COUNTRYSIDE AGENCY *see* NATURAL ENGLAND

COUNTRYSIDE COUNCIL FOR WALES (CYNGOR CEFN GWLAD CYMRU)

Library, Countryside Council for Wales (Cyngor Cefn Gwlad Cymru), Hafod Elfyn, Ffordd Penrhos, Bangor, Gwynedd LL57 2BQ

☎(01248) 385522
Fax (01248) 385510
e-mail: library@ccw.gov.uk
url: www.ccw.gov.uk
Librarian Ms Dwynwen Lloyd BA MCLIP

CPRE (CAMPAIGN TO PROTECT RURAL ENGLAND)

Library and Information Unit, CPRE (Campaign to Protect Rural England), 128 Southwark Street, London SE1 0SW
☎020 7981 2800
Fax 020 7981 2899
url: www.cpre.org.uk
Library and Information Services Officer Oliver Hilliam BA (e-mail: oliverh@cpre.org.uk)

Specialism(s): Planning; Environment; Transport

CROWN PROSECUTION SERVICE

Library Information Services, Crown Prosecution Service, 50 Ludgate Hill, London EC4M 7EX
☎020 7796 8320/8364
e-mail: cps.libraryinformationservices@cps.gsi.gov.uk
url: www.cps.gov.uk
CPS Librarian Robert Brall BA DipLib MCLIP (e-mail: robert.brall@cps.gsi.gov.uk)

CROWTHER CENTRE FOR MISSION EDUCATION

(formerly Partnership House Mission Studies Library)

Library, Crowther Centre for Mission Education, Church Mission Society, Watlington Road, Cowley, Oxford OX4 6BZ
☎(01865) 787552
Fax (01865) 776375
url: http://crowtherlib.soutron.com; www.cms-uk.org
Librarian Ms Margaret Acton (e-mail: margaret.acton@cms-uk.org)

Specialism(s): History and theology of mission of the Anglican Church

DEPARTMENT FOR BUSINESS, ENTERPRISE & REGULATORY REFORM (BERR)

(formerly Department of Trade and Industry (DTI))
Department for Business, Enterprise & Regulatory Reform (BERR), 1 Victoria Street, London SW1H 0ET
☎020 7215 5000 (switchboard)
Fax: 020 7215 5713

url: www.berr.gov.uk
Minicom 020 7215 6740
Assistant Director, Information Services Mrs Anne Bridge OBE MA MCLIP
Head of InfoSource Miss Alison Cotterill BLib(Hons) MA MCLIP

InfoSource, Department for Business, Enterprise & Regulatory Reform (BERR), 1 Victoria Street, London SW1H 0ET
☎020 7215 5006 (enquiries)
Fax 020 7215 5713
Information Services Manager (Research Services) Ms Diane Rowland BLib(Hons) MSc MCLIP
(Limited public access by prior appointment only)

DEPARTMENT FOR CHILDREN, SCHOOLS AND FAMILIES (DCSF) (formerly Department for Education and Skills (DFES)

Library, Department for Children, Schools and Families (DCSF), LG.01, Sanctuary Buildings, Great Smith Street, London SW1P 3BT
☎020 7925 5040 (enquiries)
Fax 020 7925 5085
e-mail: enquiries.library@dcsf.gsi.gov.uk
url: www.dcsf.gov.uk
Chief Librarian Ms Gill Baker (020 7925 5451; e-mail: gill.baker@dcsf.gsi.gov.uk)

Department for Children, Schools and Families (DCSF), W2, Moorfoot, Sheffield S1 4PQ
☎0114 259 3338 (enquiries)
Fax 0114 259 3564
e-mail: enquiries.library@dcsf.gsi.gov.uk

Departmental Public Enquiry Unit
☎0870 000 2288
e-mail: info@dcsf.gsi.gov.uk

Specialism(s): Education theory and policy

DEPARTMENT FOR COMMUNITIES AND LOCAL GOVERNMENT (DCLG)

Library and Information Services, Department for Communities and Local Government (DCLG), Department for Communities and Local Government, 2/H24 Ashdown House, 123 Victoria Street, London SW1E 6DE
☎020 7944 3039
Fax 020 7944 6098
url: www.communities.gsi.gov.uk
Knowledge Management Policy, Library and Information Services Branch Head Mrs Carol Gokce MSc MCLIP FLS

Specialism(s): Housing; Local Government; Planning

DEPARTMENT FOR CONSTITUTIONAL AFFAIRS (DCA) *see* MINISTRY OF JUSTICE

DEPARTMENT FOR CULTURE, MEDIA AND SPORT (DCMS)

Library, Department for Culture, Media and Sport (DCMS), 2-4 Cockspur Street, London SW1Y 5DH
☎020 7211 6200 (public enquiries), 020 7211 6041 (library administration)
Fax 020 7211 2170
e-mail: library@culture.gov.uk
url: www.culture.gov.uk
Manager Ms Abigail Humber BA(Hons) MA MCLIP

DEPARTMENT FOR EDUCATION AND SKILLS (DFES) *see* DEPARTMENT FOR CHILDREN, SCHOOLS AND FAMILES (DCSF)

DEPARTMENT FOR ENVIRONMENT, FOOD AND RURAL AFFAIRS (DEFRA)

Information Resource Centre, Department for Environment, Food and Rural Affairs (Defra), Lower Ground Floor, Ergon House, c/o Nobel House, 17 Smith Square, London SW1P 3JR
☎020 7238 6575
Fax 020 7238 6609
e-mail: defra.library@defra.gsi.gov.uk
url: www.defra.gov.uk
Head of Library and Translations Service and Chief Librarian Kevin Jackson BSc MCLIP
(Visitors must give 24 hours' notice)

Specialism(s): Environment; Farming; Food; Rural issues; Agriculture; Climate change and sustainable development

DEPARTMENT FOR INNOVATION, UNIVERSITIES AND SKILLS (DIUS)

For shared library services *see* Department for Children, Schools and Familes (DCSF). See website www.dius.gov.uk for further developments.

DEPARTMENT FOR INTERNATIONAL DEVELOPMENT (DFID)

E-library Services, Information Management Unit, Department for International Development (DFID), 1 Palace Street, London SW1E 5HE

☎020 7023 0574
Fax 020 7023 0223
e-mail: library@dfid.gov.uk
url: www.dfid.gov.uk
Business Information Specialist Ms Sharon Skelton BA(Hons)

Information Management Unit, Department for International Development (DFID), Alba Building, Abercrombie House, Eaglesham Road, East Kilbride, Glasgow G75 8EA

e-mail: library@dfid.gov.uk

DEPARTMENT FOR REGIONAL DEVELOPMENT

Library, Department for Regional Development, Room G-40, Clarence Court, 10–18 Adelaide Street, Belfast BT2 8GB
☎028 9054 1045/6
Fax 028 9054 1081
e-mail: library@drdni.gov.uk
url: www.drdni.gov.uk
Librarian Ms Fiona Sawey BA(Hons)
Assistant Librarian Ms Gillian Conroy MA(Hons) MA

DEPARTMENT FOR TRANSPORT (DFT)

Library and Information Services, Department for Transport (DfT), 2/H24 Ashdown House, 123 Victoria Street, London SW1E 6DE
☎020 7944 3039
Fax 020 7944 6098
url: www.dft.gov.uk
Knowledge Management Policy, Library and Information Services Branch Head Mrs Carol Gokce MSc MCLIP FLS

DEPARTMENT FOR WORK AND PENSIONS (DWP)

Adelphi Library and Information Centre, Department for Work and Pensions (DWP), Room 114, The Adelphi, 1–11 John Adam Street, London WC2N 6HT
☎020 7712 2500
Fax 020 7962 8491
e-mail: library@dwp.gsi.gov.uk
url: www.dwp.gov.uk
Head of Library and Information Services Graham Monk BA DipLib MCLIP
Senior Librarian and Deputy Head of Library and Information Services Ms Melanie Harris BA(Hons) DipLib MCLIP
Information Centre Manager Mrs Anoja Fernando
Acquisitions (Books) Librarian Philip Warnock MA DipLib MCLIP
Acquisitions (Serials) Librarian Ms Fiona Tyrrell BA(Hons) MCLIP
Cataloguer Alan Pratt BA(Hons) DipLib

Information Centre Sheffield, Department for Work and Pensions (DWP), Porterbrook House, 7 Pear Street, Sheffield S11 8JF
☎0114 259 6082
Information Centre Manager Ms Karen Gommersall

Legal Information Centre, Department for Work and Pensions (DWP), 4th Floor, New Court, 48 Carey Street, London WC2A 2LS
☎020 7412 1333
Fax 020 7412 1324
Acting Legal Information Manager Ms Elaine Varty BA DipLib MCLIP

DEPARTMENT OF HEALTH (DH)

Library, Department of Health (DH), Quarry House, Quarry Hill, Leeds LS2 7UE
☎0113 254 5080
Fax 0113 254 5084
e-mail: library.enquiries@dh.gsi.gov.uk
url: www.dh.gov.uk
Head of Library and Information Services Mrs Pek Lan Bower BA(Hons) DipLib MCLIP
Senior Librarian (London) Ms Melanie Peffer BA(Hons)
Senior Librarian (Leeds) Mrs Jennifer Goodfellow MA(Hons) MA MCLIP
Customer Services Librarian (Leeds) Mrs Natalie Gudgeon BSc(Hons)

Specialism(s): Public health, health services, health services policy and management, medicine, hospitals, social care

DEPARTMENT OF TRADE AND INDUSTRY (DTI) *see* DEPARTMENT FOR BUSINESS, ENTERPRISE & REGULATORY REFORM (BERR)

ENERGY INSTITUTE

Library and Information Service, Energy Institute, 61 New Cavendish Street, London W1G 7AR
☎020 7467 7113/4/5 (enquiries), 020 7467 7111 (administration)
Fax 020 7255 1472
e-mail: lis@energyinst.org.uk
url: www.energyinst.org.uk
Library and Information Service Manager Mrs C M Cosgrove BSc(Hons) BA MCLIP FEI
Senior Information Officer Chris L Baker BA(Hons) MEI
Information Officer Miss Catherine Hall BA(Hons) MA

ENGLISH FOLK DANCE AND SONG SOCIETY

Vaughan Williams Memorial Library, English Folk Dance and Song Society, Cecil Sharp House, 2 Regent's Park Road, London NW1 7AY

☎020 7485 2206 exts 29/33; Direct line 020 7241 8959
Fax 020 7284 0523
e-mail: library@efdss.org
url: www.efdss.org
Librarian Malcolm Taylor BA(Lib) MCLIP OBE
Assistant Librarian Ms Elaine Bradtke PhD, Ms Peta Webb BA

Specialism(s): Traditional music and folk culture

ENGLISH HERITAGE

Library, English Heritage, National Monuments Record Centre, Kemble Drive, Swindon SN2 2GZ
☎(01793) 414632
Fax (01793) 414801
e-mail: library@english-heritage.org.uk
url: www.english-heritage.org.uk
Senior Librarian Ms Felicity Gilmour MA(Hons)

Specialism(s): English archaeology and architecture

ENGLISH NATURE *see* NATURAL ENGLAND

ENGLISH-SPEAKING UNION

Page Memorial Library, English-Speaking Union, Dartmouth House, 37 Charles Street, London W1J 5ED
☎020 7529 1550
Fax 020 7495 6108
e-mail: library@esu.org
url: www.esu.org
Librarian/Information Officer Ms Gill Hale MEd MCLIP, Ms Jeanne Huse MCLIP

Specialism(s): Specialist collection on the USA (politics, sociology, history and literature (including fiction))

EQUALITY AND HUMAN RIGHTS COMMISSION (EHRC) (formerly Equal Opportunities Commission)

Library and Information Centre, Equality and Human Rights Commission (EHRC), 2nd Floor, Arndale House, Arndale Centre, Manchester M4 3AQ
☎0161 958 2000
Fax 0161 958 2001
url: www.ehrc.org.uk
Librarian David Sparrow BA(Hons) MA MCLIP (e-mail: david.sparrow@equalityrights.com)

Specialism(s): Library and information services across all equality strands: age, disability, gender, human rights, race, religion and belief, and sexual orientation. EHRC's mission is to reduce inequality, eliminate discrimination, strengthen good relations between people, and protect human rights.

EUROPEAN COMMISSION REPRESENTATION IN THE UNITED KINGDOM

Regional Outreach Section, The European Commission Representation in the United Kingdom, 8 Storey's Gate, London SW1P 3AT
☎020 7973 1992
Fax 020 7973 1900
url: http://ec.europa.eu/unitedkingdom
Librarian Mrs Marguerite-Marie Brenchley (e-mail: marguerite-marie.brenchley@ec.europa.eu)
(Enquiries may only be referred to this library via a recognized EPIC (European Public Information Centre, formerly known as PiR). For details of your nearest centre please contact your local library or check on the website)

Specialism(s): All EU legislation and information

FOOD STANDARDS AGENCY

The FSA Information Centre, Food Standards Agency, Aviation House, 125 Kingsway, London WC2B 6NH
☎020 7276 8181
Fax 020 7276 8069
e-mail: infocentre@foodstandards.gsi.gov.uk
url: www.food.gov.uk
Head of Information Section Ms Lorna Goodey BA(Hons)
Information Centre Manager Tony Timmons BA(Hons) DipLIS MCLIP
(Public access by appointment only)

Specialism(s): Food safety; Food science and nutrition.

FOREIGN AND COMMONWEALTH OFFICE

Ancell Library, Foreign and Commonwealth Office, Room E213, King Charles Street, London SW1A 2AH
☎020 7008 3925
Fax 020 7008 3270
e-mail: library.enquiries@fco.gov.uk
url: www.fco.gov.uk
Chief Librarian Ms Carryl Allardice BA HDipLib BA(Hons) MA MBA FCLIP

Departmental library

Legal Library, Foreign and Commonwealth Office, Room K168, King Charles Street, London SW1A 2AH
☎020 7008 1500 (switchboard)
Fax 020 7008 4259

Legal Librarian Ms Jane Crellin BA MA DipInf MCLIP (020 7008 3050; e-mail: jane.crellin@fco.gov.uk)

Specialism(s): International relations; International law; Diplomacy and politics

FORESTRY COMMISSION

Library, Forestry Commission, Forest Research Station, Alice Holt Lodge, Wrecclesham, Farnham, Surrey GU10 4LH
☎(01420) 22255, (01420) 526216 (direct line)
Fax (01420) 23653
e-mail: library@forestry.gsi.gov.uk
url: www.forestry.gov.uk; www.forestresearch.gov.uk
Librarian Miss Catherine Oldham BA MA DipLib MCLIP (e-mail: catherine.oldham@forestry.gsi.gov.uk)

Specialism(s): Forestry; Arboriculture; Plant sciences

FRANCIS SKARYNA BELARUSIAN LIBRARY AND MUSEUM

Francis Skaryna Belarusian Library and Museum, 37 Holden Road, London N12 8HS
☎020 8445 5358
Fax 020 8445 5358
e-mail: library@skaryna.org
url: www.skaryna.org
Librarian Mgr Alexander Nadson

Specialism(s): Books, periodicals and archives relating to Belarus

FRESHWATER BIOLOGICAL ASSOCIATION

Library, Freshwater Biological Association, Ferry House, Far Sawrey, Ambleside, Cumbria LA22 0LP
☎(01539) 442468
Fax (01539) 446914
url: www.fba.org.uk
Librarian I Pettman BSc (e-mail: ipettman@fba.org.uk)

Specialism(s): Freshwater biology; Water chemistry; Algology; Ichthyology

GEOLOGICAL SOCIETY OF LONDON

Library, Geological Society of London, Burlington House, Piccadilly, London W1J 0BG
☎020 7432 0999
Fax 020 7439 3470
e-mail: library@geolsoc.org.uk
url: www.geolsoc.org.uk
Librarian Miss S Meredith

GERMAN HISTORICAL INSTITUTE LONDON

Library, German Historical Institute London, 17 Bloomsbury Square, London WC1A 2NJ
☎020 7309 2019/2022 (enquiries), 020 7309 2020 (administration)
Fax 020 7309 2069/2072
e-mail: library@ghil.ac.uk
url: www.ghil.ac.uk
Head Librarian Dr Michael Schaich
Librarians Ms A-M Klauk, Ms C Meissmer, U Rieck

GOETHE-INSTITUT LONDON

Library, Goethe-Institut London, 50 Princes Gate, Exhibition Road, London SW7 2PH
☎020 7596 4040 (brief enquiries), 020 7596 4044 (information service)
Fax 020 7594 0230
e-mail: library@london.goethe.org
url: www.goethe.de/london
Head Librarian Mrs Elisabeth Pyroth (e-mail: pyroth@london.goethe.org)

Specialism(s): German culture, literature and language

GREATER LONDON AUTHORITY

Information Services, Greater London Authority, City Hall, The Queen's Walk, London SE1 2AA
☎020 7983 4000 (GLA switchboard), 020 7983 4455 (library enquiries)
Fax 020 7983 4674
e-mail: isinfo@london.gov.uk
url: www.london.gov.uk/gla/information-services
Head of Information Services Ms Annabel Davies BA(Hons) MCLIP
Information Manager Andy Land BA(Hons) PGDipIM MCLIP

GUILDFORD INSTITUTE

Library, Guildford Institute of the University of Surrey, Ward Street, Guildford, Surrey GU1 4LH
☎(01483) 562142
Fax (01483) 451034
e-mail: guildford-institute@surrey.ac.uk
Librarian Vacant

Specialism(s): General collection of literature, humanities and science work dating from late Victorian period to present; Local history collections of Surrey and Guildford. Lending service to members. Research enquiries welcomed by appointment.

HEALTH AND SAFETY EXECUTIVE

Information Management Unit, Health and Safety Executive, 1.G. Redgrave Court, Merton Road, Bootle, Merseyside L20 7HS

☎0151 951 4382
Fax 0151 951 3674
url: www.hse.gov.uk
Head of Information Management Unit Martin Davies (e-mail: martin.davies@hse.gsi.gov.uk)

Knowledge Centre

- Health and Safety Executive, Knowledge Centre, Redgrave Court, Merton Road, Bootle, Merseyside L20 7HS
  ☎0151 951 4382
  Fax 0151 951 3674
  Site Manager Ms Barbara Proctor MCLIP (e-mail: barbara.proctor@hse.gsi.gov.uk)

(General requests for information on health and safety at work should be referred to the HSE Infoline Tel: 0845 345 0055; Minicom: 0845 408 9577. Written enquiries to HSE Infoline, Caerphilly Business Park, Caerphilly CF83 3GG; e-mail: hse.infoline@natbrit.com; Fax: 0845 408 9566)

HEALTH MANAGEMENT LIBRARY

Health Management Library, Scottish Health Service Centre, Crewe Road South, Edinburgh EH4 2LF
☎0131 623 2535
Fax 0131 315 2369
e-mail: library@shsc.csa.scot.nhs.uk
url: www.healthmanagementonline.co.uk
Library Services Manager Mrs Gill Earl BA(Hons) MCLIP
Librarian Mrs Alison Bogle MA DipLib MCLIP

Specialism(s): Health care management

HEALTH PROTECTION AGENCY

Central Library, Centre for Emergency Preparedness and Response (CEPR), 61 Colindale Avenue, London NW9 5EQ
☎020 8327 7616 (enquiries), 020 8327 7617 (Librarian)
Fax 020 8200 7875
url: www.hpa.org.uk
Librarian David Keech BSc DipLib MCLIP (e-mail: david.keech@hpa.org.uk)

Site libraries

- Library, Centre for Emergency Preparedness and Response (CEPR), Porton Down, Salisbury, Wilts SP4 0JG
  ☎(01980) 612100 (switchboard)
  Librarian Ms Sue Goddard (01980 612711; e-mail: sue.goddard@hpa.org.uk)
- Library, Centre for Radiation, Chemical and Environmental Hazards (CRCE), Chilton, Didcot, Oxon OX11 0RQ
  ☎(01235) 831600 (switchboard)
  Librarian David Perry BA MCLIP (01235 822649; e-mail: david.perry@hpa.gov.uk)

Specialism(s): Microbiology, infectious diseases

HEREFORD CATHEDRAL

Library, Hereford Cathedral, The Cathedral, Hereford HR1 2NG
☎(01432) 374225/6
Fax (01432) 374220
e-mail: library@herefordcathedral.org
url: www.herefordcathedral.org/library.asp
Librarian Nicholas Baker (e-mail: nick.baker@herefordcathedral.org)
(Open to the public)

HIGH COMMISSION OF INDIA

Library, High Commission of India, India House, Aldwych, London WC2B 4NA
☎020 7632 3166 (Direct Line)
Fax 020 7632 3204
e-mail: info@hcilondon.net
Librarian Murari Lal
Hon Librarian Miss M S Travis
(Staff library only. Collection is for reference only; no interlibrary lending; visiting at the discretion of Head of Press and Information Department)

HIGHGATE LITERARY AND SCIENTIFIC INSTITUTION

Library, Highgate Literary and Scientific Institution, 11 South Grove, Highgate, London N6 6BS
☎020 8340 3343
Fax 020 8340 5632
e-mail: librarian@hlsi.net
url: www.hlsi.net
Librarian Ms Margaret Mackay DipLib BEd(Hons) MCLIP
(Public access allowed for reference)

Specialism(s): Biography; Fiction; London/local history; Samuel Taylor Coleridge; John Betjeman

HIGHWAYS AGENCY

Information Point, Highways Agency, Room 614, City Tower, Piccadilly Plaza, Manchester M1 4BE
☎0161 930 5518
Fax 0161 930 5572
e-mail: InformationCentre-Manchester@Highways.gsi.gov.uk
url: www.highways.gov.uk
Head of Library Services Steve Bunyan (e-mail: steve.bunyan@highways.gsi.gov.uk)

HISPANIC AND LUSO-BRAZILIAN COUNCIL

Canning House Library, Hispanic and Luso-Brazilian Council, 2 Belgrave Square, London SW1X 8PJ
☎020 7235 2303 ext 208
Fax 020 7838 9258
e-mail: library@canninghouse.com
url: www.canninghouse.com
Library and Information Services Manager Alan Biggins BSc DipLib MCLIP (e-mail: abiggins@canninghouse.com)

Specialism(s): Latin America, Spain, Portugal (history, literature, art, linguistics, culture, travel, sociology, politics and economics)

HISTORIC SCOTLAND

Technical Conservation, Research and Education (TCRE) Resource Centre, Historic Scotland, Room G55, Longmore House, Salisbury Place, Edinburgh EH9 1SH
☎0131 668 8642
Fax 0131 668 8669
e-mail: hs.resourcecentre@scotland.gsi.gov.uk
url: www.historic-scotland.gov.uk
Resource Centre Manager Ms Lisa Perry (e-mail: lisa.perry@scotland.gsi.gov.uk)

Specialism(s): Built heritage; History; Traditional building materials; Conservation science; Paintings conservation; Museums collections and conservation; Objects conservation

HM REVENUE AND CUSTOMS

Library Services, HM Revenue and Customs, 4W Ralli Quays, Stanley Street, Salford, Manchester M60 9LA
☎0161 827 0465
Fax 0161 827 0491
e-mail: libraryenquiries@hmrc.gsi.gov.uk
url: www.hmrc.gov.uk
Head of Library Service Ms Lorna Bankes BA(Hons) MCLIP

Department library

Library, HM Revenue and Customs, LG73, 100 Parliament Street, London SW1A 2BQ
☎020 7147 2193
Fax 020 7147 0232
e-mail: libraryenquiries@hmrc.gsi.gov.uk
url: www.hmrc.gov.uk
Senior Information Manager Mrs Marita Ewins

HM TREASURY AND CABINET OFFICE

Library and Information Service, HM Treasury and Cabinet Office, 1 Horse Guards Road, London SW1A 2HQ

☎020 7270 5270 (enquiries)
Fax 020 7270 5681
e-mail: library@hm-treasury.x.gsi.gov.uk
url: www.hm-treasury.gov.uk
Library Services Manager Ray Simpson

Specialism(s): Economics and finance; Public administration; Parliamentary material

HMS SULTAN

Library, HMS Sultan, Military Road, Gosport, Hants PO12 3BY
☎023 9254 2678
Fax 023 9254 2555
e-mail: sultan-librarian@nrta.mod.uk
url: www.royal-navy.mod.uk
Librarian Jim Quibell BA MCLIP
(Visits by arrangement)

Specialism(s): Mechanical, electrical, marine and aeronautical engineering; Naval science, technology and history

HOME OFFICE

Information Services Unit, Home Office, Communication Directorate, Lower Ground Floor, Seacole Building, 2 Marsham Street, London SW1P 4DF
☎020 7035 4041/2 (enquiries)
Fax 020 7035 4022
e-mail: library@homeoffice.gsi.gov.uk
url: www.homeoffice.gov.uk
Head of Customer Services Ms Jackie King
Head of Collections Management Ms Alice Laird

HOUSE OF COMMONS

Department of the Library, House of Commons, London SW1A 0AA
☎020 7219 4272
Fax 020 7219 5839
e-mail: hcinfo@parliament.uk
url: www.parliament.uk
Librarian of the House of Commons John Pullinger (e-mail: pullingerj@parliament.uk)
Head of the Information Office Stephen McGinness (e-mail: mcguinness@parliament.uk)
(There are specialist sections which deal with enquiries from Members of Parliament only. Outside enquirers should approach the Department's public interface, the House of Commons Information Office (contact details as above).)

HOUSE OF LORDS

Library, House of Lords, London SW1A 0PW

☎020 7219 5242 (enquiries), 020 7219 3240 (administration)
Fax 020 7219 6396
e-mail: hllibrary@parliament.uk
url: www.parliament.uk/about_lords/about_lords.cfm
Director of Information Services and Librarian Ms Elizabeth Hallam Smith PhD FSA FRSA FRHistS
Deputy Librarian Peter Davis PhD

HULTON/ARCHIVE – GETTY IMAGES

Hulton/Archive – Getty Images, Unique House, 21–31 Woodfield Road, London W9 2BA
☎020 7266 6900 (Research), 020 7579 5700 (Reception)
Fax 020 7266 3154
e-mail: archiveresearch@gettyimages.com
url: www.gettyimages.com
Picture Research Manager Ms Caroline Theakstone
Curator Ms Sarah McDonald

Specialism(s): Social history; Personalities; Entertainment; Sport; War; Royalty; Events up to 1980s

IGER (INSTITUTE OF GRASSLAND AND ENVIRONMENTAL RESEARCH)

Stapledon Library and Information Service, IGER (Institute of Grassland and Environmental Research), Plas Gogerddan, Ceredigion SY23 3EB
☎(01970) 823053 (library desk)
Fax (01970) 828357
e-mail: igerlib.igerlib-wpbs@bbsrc.ac.uk
url: www.iger.bbsrc.ac.uk
Institute Librarian Steve Smith BSc DipLib MCLIP (e-mail: stephen.smith@bbsrc.ac.uk)

Specialism(s): Grasses; Plant genetics, physiology and breeding; Livestock; Animal nutrition; Cell biology; Ecology

IMPERIAL WAR MUSEUM

Department of Printed Books, Imperial War Museum, Lambeth Road, London SE1 6HZ
☎020 7416 5342
Fax 020 7416 5246
e-mail: books@iwm.org.uk
url: www.iwm.org.uk
Keeper of Printed Books R Golland BA DipLib MCLIP
Head of Access Team Colin Bruce (020 7416 5465)
Head of Collections Development Team Ms M Wilkinson BA DipLib (020 7416 5348)
(Services: Reading Room (appointment required) Mon–Sat 10–5; telephone enquiry service Mon–Fri.)

Specialism(s): Conflicts since 1914 involving Great Britain and Commonwealth countries – military, civilian and social historical aspects. NB Reading Room access now includes IWM Sound Archive listening facilities.

INSTITUT FRANÇAIS D'ÉCOSSE (FRENCH INSTITUTE)

Library, Institut français d'Écosse (French Institute), 13 Randolph Crescent, Edinburgh EH3 7TT
☎0131 225 5366
Fax 0131 220 0648
e-mail: library@ifecosse.org.uk
url: www.ifecosse.org.uk
Librarian Ms Anne-Marie Usher, Ms Pascale Scott

Specialism(s): French language and culture

INSTITUT FRANÇAIS DU ROYAUME-UNI

The Multimedia Library, Institut français du Royaume-Uni, 17 Queensberry Place, London SW7 2DT
☎020 7073 1350
Fax 020 7073 1363
e-mail: library@ambafrance.org.uk
url: www.institut-francais.org.uk
Head Librarian Mme Anne-Elisabeth Buxtorf
Deputy Head Mme Chantal Morel

Children's Library, Institut français du Royaume-Uni, 32 Harrington Road, London SW7 3HD
☎020 7073 1350

Specialism(s): French literature, art, cinema, music, history and Free French Archives; press-cutting files on French current topics. Information services: CampusFrance for information on French education; SIR for general information on France

INSTITUTE FOR ANIMAL HEALTH

Library, Institute for Animal Health, Compton Laboratory, Compton, Newbury, Berks RG20 7NN
☎(01635) 577256
Fax (01635) 577304
url: www.iah.ac.uk
IAH Libraries Manager Mrs Chris Gibbons (e-mail: chris.gibbons@bbsrc.ac.uk)

Site library

Pirbright Library, Institute for Animal Health, Ash Road, Pirbright, Woking, Surrey GU24 0NF
☎(01483) 232441
Fax (01483) 232448
Library Assistant Mrs Gail van der Merwe (e-mail: gail.vandermerwe@bbsrc.ac.uk)

INSTITUTE OF ACTUARIES

Library, Institute of Actuaries, Napier House, 4 Worcester Street, Oxford OX1 2AW
☎(01865) 268206/7
Fax (01865) 268211
e-mail: libraries@actuaries.org.uk
url: www.actuaries.org.uk
Information Manager Ms Sally Grover MA MCLIP
Deputy Librarian Ms Fiona J McNeil BA MCLIP

Specialism(s): Actuarial science; Pensions; Insurance; Finance and investment; Demography

INSTITUTE OF CHARTERED ACCOUNTANTS IN ENGLAND AND WALES

Library and Information Service, Institute of Chartered Accountants in England and Wales, Chartered Accountants' Hall, PO Box 433, Moorgate Place, London EC2P 2BJ
☎020 7920 8620
Fax 020 7920 8621
e-mail: library@icaew.com
url: www.icaew.com/library
Head of Library and Information Services Ms S P Moore BA(Hons)Lib MCLIP
Business Process Manager N Williams BA(Hons)Lib MCLIP
Collection Development Manager Ms S Robertson MA MA MCLIP
(The Library is for members of the ICAEW and ICAEW registered students; ACT members and non-members by arrangement and paying a daily or weekly fee for access.)

Specialism(s): Accountancy; Auditing; Taxation; Law; Company information; Finance; Management; IT

INSTITUTE OF CHARTERED SECRETARIES AND ADMINISTRATORS

Information Centre, Institute of Chartered Secretaries and Administrators, 16 Park Crescent, London W1B 1AH
☎020 7580 4741*
Fax 020 7612 7034
e-mail: informationcentre@icsa.co.uk
url: www.icsa.org.uk
Information Centre Manager Ms Sheila Doyle
(*Technical enquiries should be sent by letter, fax or e-mail)

Specialism(s): Company law; Corporate governance; Company secretarial practice; Charity law

INSTITUTE OF CLINICAL RESEARCH

Resource Centre, Institute of Clinical Research, Thames House, Mere Park, Dedmere Road, Marlow, Bucks SL7 1PB

☎(01628) 899755
Fax (01628) 899766
e-mail: resources@icr-global.org
url: www.icr-global.org
Head of Information Services Ms Helena Korjonen-Close (01628 899764; e-mail: hkc@icr-global.org)

Specialism(s): Specialist subjects relate to nature of clinical research; Regulations; Ethical issues, the clinical trial process and the personal development of professionals involved in clinical research; Course materials, job descriptions and resource lists

INSTITUTE OF CONSERVATION

Institute of Conservation, 3rd Floor, Downstream Building, 1 London Bridge, London SE1 9BG
☎020 7785 3805
Fax 020 7785 3806
e-mail: info@icon.org.uk
url: www.icon.org.uk
Chief Executive Alastair McCapra

Chantry Library, Institute of Conservation, Grove Cottage, St Cross Road, Oxford OX1 3TZ
☎(01865) 251303
e-mail: library@ipc.org.uk
url: www.lib.ox.ac.uk/ipc-chantry/
Librarian James Andrews

Specialism(s): Book and paper conservation including bookbinding, book history, aspects of collection care such as general preservation, disaster mitigation, environmental control, exhibitions, pest management, security and storage. Note: The Chantry Library is administered by the Institute of Conservation. Information on the collection is available at the University of Oxford's online system OLIS (Oxford Libraries Information System).

INSTITUTE OF CONTEMPORARY STUDIES AND WIENER LIBRARY *see* WIENER LIBRARY INSTITUTE OF CONTEMPORARY HISTORY

INSTITUTE OF DIRECTORS

IOD Information Centre, Institute of Directors, 1 Pall Mall East, London SW1Y 5AU
☎020 7451 3100
Fax 020 7321 0145
e-mail: businessinfo@iod.com
url: www.iod.com/informationcentre
Head of Information and Advisory Services Mrs A Burmajster MA MCLIP

Specialism(s): Corporate governance; Directorship; Boardroom practice

INSTITUTE OF MATERIALS, MINERALS AND MINING

David West Library, Institute of Materials, Minerals and Mining, 1 Carlton House Terrace, London SW1Y 5DB
☎020 7451 7300 (switchboard)
Fax 020 7451 7406
url: www.iom3.org
Information and Library Co-ordinator Ms Hilda Kaune BA(Hons) DipLib (020 7451 7360 (direct); e-mail: hilda.kaune@iom3.org)
Information Officer Mrs Frances Perry BA (020 7451 7324 (direct); e-mail: frances.perry@iom3.org)

Specialism(s): Metals; Materials; Polymers and plastics; Ceramics; Composites; Packaging; Economic geology; Mining; Mineral processing; Extractive metallurgy

INSTITUTE OF OCCUPATIONAL MEDICINE

Library, Institute of Occupational Medicine, Research Avenue North, Riccarton, Edinburgh EH14 4AP
☎0870 850 5131
Fax 0870 850 5132
e-mail: info@iom-world.org
url: www.iom-world.org
Scientific Information Officer Ken Dixon MA(Hons) MA MCLIP

Specialism(s): Occupational medicine and environmental issues

INSTITUTE OF PSYCHOANALYSIS

Library, Institute of Psychoanalysis, 112a Shirland Road, Maida Vale, London W9 2EQ
☎020 7563 5008
Fax 020 7563 5001
e-mail: library@iopa.org.uk
url: www.psychoanalysis.org.uk
Librarian Saven Morris
Assistant Librarian Ms Hélène Martin

INSTITUTION OF CIVIL ENGINEERS

Library, Institution of Civil Engineers, 1 Great George Street, Westminster, London SW1P 3AA
☎020 7665 2251
Fax 020 7976 7610
e-mail: library@ice.org.uk
url: www.ice.org.uk
Head of Knowledge Transfer Michael Chrimes BA MLS MCLIP

THE INSTITUTION OF ENGINEERING AND TECHNOLOGY

Library, The Institution of Engineering and Technology, 2 Savoy Place, London WC2R 0BL
☎020 7240 1871; 020 7344 5461 (General Library Enquiries)
Fax 020 7344 8467
url: www.theiet.org
Manager of Library and Archives Services John Coupland BA MCLIP (020 7344 5451; e-mail: jcoupland@theiet.org)

Specialism(s): Electrical, electronic, control and manufacturing engineering; Telecommunications, computing and information technology

INSTITUTION OF MECHANICAL ENGINEERS

Information and Library Service, Institution of Mechanical Engineers, 1 Birdcage Walk, London SW1H 9JJ
☎020 7973 1274
Fax 020 7222 8762
e-mail: library@imeche.org.uk
url: www.imeche.org.uk/library
Head of Library Service Ms Sarah Rogers MA MCLIP
Information Officer Ms Katherine Dike MA
Librarian Mike Claxton BSc(Hons)
Archivists Ms Fenella Philpot MA MCLIP, Ms Laura Gardner MA

INSTITUTION OF OCCUPATIONAL SAFETY AND HEALTH

Technical Enquiry and Information Service, The Institution of Occupational Safety and Health, The Grange, Highfield Drive, Wigston, Leicester LE18 1NN
☎0116 257 3199; 0116 257 3100 (switchboard)
Fax 0116 257 3107
e-mail: techinfo@iosh.co.uk
url: www.iosh.co.uk
Information Service Co-ordinator Miss Anne Wells (e-mail: anne.wells@iosh.co.uk)

INSTITUTO CERVANTES

Library, Instituto Cervantes, 102 Eaton Square, London SW1W 9AN
☎020 7201 0757
Fax 020 7235 0329
e-mail: biblon@cervantes.es
url: www.cervantes.es; http://londres.cervantes.es
Chief Librarian David Carrión

Site library

Library, Instituto Cervantes, 326–330 Deansgate, Manchester M3 4FN

☎0161 661 4210 (direct)
Fax 0161 661 4203
e-mail: bibman@cervantes.es
Librarian José M Fernández

Specialism(s): Spanish culture, history, literature, language and teaching. A further site library (located in Dublin) can be found in the Academic, National and Special Libraries of the Republic of Ireland section.

THE INTERNATIONAL INSTITUTE FOR STRATEGIC STUDIES (IISS)

Library and Information Department, The International Institute for Strategic Studies (IISS), Arundel House, 13–15 Arundel Street, London WC2R 3DX
☎020 7395 9122 (library enquiries) or 020 7379 7676 (main switchboard)
Fax 020 7836 3108
e-mail: library@iiss.org
url: www.iiss.org/library
Chief Librarian Mrs Ellena Jamie MA(Oxon) MSc
Deputy Librarian Ms Catherine Micklethwaite BSc(Econ) MA
Assistant Librarian James Howarth BA MA MA

Specialism(s): International relations; War studies

INTERNATIONAL MARITIME ORGANIZATION

IMO Library Services, International Maritime Organization, 4 Albert Embankment, London SE1 7SR
☎020 7735 7611
Fax 020 7587 3348
url: www.imo.org
Librarian Mrs Marianne Harvey (ext 3164; e-mail: mharvey@imo.org)

Specialism(s): Maritime safety; Prevention of pollution from ships; Ship design; Navigation; Technical co-operation; Liability and compensation

ISLE OF MAN FAMILY HISTORY SOCIETY

Library, Isle of Man Family History Society, Derby Lodge, Derby Road, Peel, Isle of Man IM5 1HH
☎(01624) 843105
e-mail: iomfhs@manx.net
url: www.isle-of-man.com/interests/geneaology/fhs/
Librarian Mrs Doreen Quayle
(Open Tuesdays, Wednesdays and Saturday afternoons, 2–5pm)

ISLE OF MAN GOVERNMENT/LEGISLATURE OF THE ISLE OF MAN

Tynwald Library, Isle of Man Government/Legislature of the Isle of Man, Legislative Buildings, Douglas, Isle of Man IM1 3PW
☎(01624) 685520
Fax (01624) 685522
e-mail: library@tynwald.org.im
Librarian Geoffrey Clucas Haywood MCLIP
Deputy Librarian Ms Trudi Thompson BA
Library Executive Miss Shelley Walker

Specialism(s): Manx Parliamentary and Isle of Man Government publications and Isle of Man laws

ITALIAN CULTURAL INSTITUTE (ISTITUTO ITALIANO DI CULTURA)

Eugenio Montale Library, Italian Cultural Institute (Istituto Italiano di Cultura), 39 Belgrave Square, London SW1X 8NX
☎020 7235 1461 (switchboard), 020 7235 1461 ext 203 (library)/204 (information), 020 7396 4425 (library direct line)
Fax 020 7235 4618
e-mail: library.icilondon@esteri.it
url: www.icilondon.esteri.it
Librarian in charge Ms Maria Riccobono Reidy

Specialism(s): Italian culture and language; Literature and visual arts

JOINT SERVICES COMMAND AND STAFF COLLEGE

Library, Joint Services Command and Staff College, Faringdon Road, Watchfield, Swindon SN6 8TS
☎(01793) 788236
Fax (01793) 788281
e-mail: library.jscsc@defenceacademy.mod.uk
Head of Library Services C M Hobson MCLIP MBE

Specialism(s): Defence studies; International affairs; Military history

THE KENNEL CLUB

The Kennel Club Library & Art Gallery, The Kennel Club, 1–5 Clarges Street, London W1J 8AB
☎020 7518 1009
Fax 020 7518 1045
e-mail: library@thekennelclub.org.uk

url: www.thekennelclub.org.uk
Library and Collections Manager Ms Ciara Farrell BA HDipLIS
(Open Mondays to Fridays, 9.30 am–4.30 pm by appointment)

Specialism(s): Canine literature, registrations and show catalogues, canine art

KING'S FUND

Information and Library Service, King's Fund, 11–13 Cavendish Square, London W1G 0AN
☎020 7307 2568/9 (enquiries)
Fax 020 7307 2805
e-mail: library@kingsfund.org.uk
url: www.kingsfund.org.uk/library
Acting Information and Library Service Manager Ms Valerie Wildridge

Specialism(s): Health and social care policy/management

LABOUR PARTY

Communications Unit, Labour Party, Eldon House, Regents Centre, Newcastle upon Tyne NE3 3PW
☎08705 900200
Fax 0191 246 5136
url: www.labour.org.uk/contact
Communications Unit Manager Jim Harvey

Specialism(s): Labour Party and Government policy

LAMBETH PALACE LIBRARY

Lambeth Palace Library, London SE1 7JU
☎020 7898 1400
Fax 020 7928 7932
e-mail: lpl.staff@c-of-e.org.uk
url: www.lambethpalacelibrary.org; www.churchplansonline.org
Director of Libraries, Archives and Information Services Declan Kelly MSc MCLIP
(e-mail: declan.kelly@c-of-e.org.uk)
Librarian and Archivist Dr Richard Palmer PhD MCLIP

Specialism(s): History (particularly of the Church of England); Early printed mss; Archives of the Province of Canterbury; Liturgy; Bibliography; Architecture

Related libraries

Church of England Record Centre, 15 Galleywall Road, Bermondsey, London SE16 3PB
☎020 7898 1030
Fax 020 7394 7018
e-mail: archivist@c-of-e.org.uk
url: www.cofe.anglican.org/about/librariesandarchives
Archivist and Records Manager Philip Gale
(Reading room access via Lambeth Palace Library.)

Specialisms(s): Archives of the central organization of the Church of England, in particular the Church Commissioners; The Archbishops' Council; the General Synod.

Cathedral and Church Buildings Library, Church House, Great Smith Street, London SW1P 3NZ
☎020 7898 1884 (Tuesdays & Wednesdays)
Fax 020 7898 1881
e-mail: enquiries@ccc.c-of-e.org.uk
url: www.cofe.anglican.org/about/librariesandarchives

Specialism(s): Ecclesiastical architecture and archaeology; Church fittings and furnishings; Stained glass, organs, bells, monuments

LAW COMMISSION

Library, Law Commission, Conquest House, 37/38 John Street, Theobalds Road, London WC1N 2BQ
☎020 7453 1241 (enquiries), 020 7453 1242 (administration)
Fax 020 7453 1297
e-mail: library@lawcommission.gsi.gov.uk
url: www.lawcom.gov.uk
Librarian Keith Tree BA

THE LAW SOCIETY

Library, The Law Society, 113 Chancery Lane, London WC2A 1PL
☎0870 606 2511 (enquiries), 020 7320 5721 (administration)
Fax 020 7831 1687
e-mail: library@lawsociety.org.uk
url: www.library.lawsociety.org.uk
Online catalogue: www.catalyst.lawsociety.org.uk
Librarian and Head of Information Services Chris Holland BA MCLIP

Specialism(s): Law; Parliamentary material; Historical legal material

THE LIBRARY AND MUSEUM OF FREEMASONRY

The Library and Museum of Freemasonry, Freemasons' Hall, Great Queen Street, London WC2B 5AZ
☎020 7395 9257
Fax 020 7404 7418
e-mail: libmus@freemasonry.london.museum
url: www.freemasonry.london.museum
Director Ms Diane Clements
Librarian Martin Cherry BSc BA(Hons)
Curator Mark Dennis
Archivist Ms Susan Snell

LIBRARY FOR IRANIAN STUDIES

Library for Iranian Studies, The Woodlands Hall, Crown Street, London W3 8SA
☎020 8993 6384
Fax 020 8752 1300
url: www.iranianlibrary.org
Librarian Dr Mashala Ajoudani

LINCOLN CATHEDRAL

Library, Lincoln Cathedral, Minster Yard, Lincoln LN2 1PX
☎(01522) 561640
Fax (01522) 561641
url: www.lincolncathedral.com
Librarian Dr Nicholas Bennett (e-mail: librarian@lincolncathedral.com)

LINEN HALL LIBRARY

The Linen Hall Library, 17 Donegall Square North, Belfast BT1 5GB
☎028 9032 1707
Fax 028 9043 8586
e-mail: info@linenhall.com
url: www.linenhall.com
Librarian John Gray BA DLIS

Specialism(s): Irish history and culture

LINNEAN SOCIETY OF LONDON

Library, Linnean Society of London, Burlington House, Piccadilly, London W1J 0BF
☎020 7434 4479
Fax 020 7287 9364
e-mail: library@linnean.org
url: www.linnean.org
Librarian Ms G Douglas BSc FLS (e-mail: gina@linnean.org)
Deputy Librarian Mrs Lynda Brooks BA DipLib MCLIP (e-mail: lynda@linnean.org)
Assistant Librarian (Content Management) Ben Sherwood MA (e-mail: ben@linnean.org)

Specialism(s): Natural history; Taxonomy; Evolutionary ecology; History of natural history; Conservation and environment

LITERARY AND PHILOSOPHICAL SOCIETY OF NEWCASTLE UPON TYNE

Library, Literary and Philosophical Society of Newcastle upon Tyne, 23 Westgate Road, Newcastle upon Tyne NE1 1SE
☎0191 232 0192

Fax 0191 261 4494
e-mail: library@litandphil.org.uk
url: www.litandphil.org.uk
Librarian Ms Kay Easson MA DipLib MCLIP

Specialism(s): Humanities

LONDON CHAMBER OF COMMERCE AND INDUSTRY

Information Centre, London Chamber of Commerce and Industry, 33 Queen Street, London EC4R 1AP
☎020 7248 4444 (members only)
Fax 020 7203 1863
e-mail: info@londonchamber.co.uk
url: www.londonchamber.co.uk
Information Officer Jim Padget

Specialism(s): General business information

LONDON LIBRARY

London Library, 14 St James's Square, London SW1Y 4LG
☎020 7930 7705
Fax 020 7766 4766
e-mail: membership@londonlibrary.co.uk
url: www.londonlibrary.co.uk
Librarian Miss Inez T P A Lynn BA MLitt MCLIP

Specialism(s): History; Literature; The arts; Related subjects in major European languages

LONDON METROPOLITAN ARCHIVES

Library, London Metropolitan Archives, 40 Northampton Road, London EC1R 0HB
☎020 7332 3820
Fax 020 7833 9136
e-mail: ask.lma@cityoflondon.gov.uk
url: www.cityoflondon.gov.uk
Principal Archivist E Scudder

Specialism(s): London (local government history; social history)

LONDON TRANSPORT MUSEUM

Library, London Transport Museum, 39 Wellington Street, Covent Garden, London WC2E 7BB
☎020 7565 7280
Fax 020 7565 7252
e-mail: library@ltmuseum.co.uk

url: www.ltmuseum.co.uk
Library and Information Services Manager Ms Caroline Warhurst BA MCLIP
Librarian Ms Helen Kent MA
(Visitors by appointment)

Specialism(s): History and development of London's transport from 1800 to present day; information about Transport for London, London Transport and predecessor companies; special emphasis on the development of art, architecture and design in London Transport

MANX NATIONAL HERITAGE

Library, Manx National Heritage, Manx Museum, Douglas, Isle of Man IM1 3LY
☎(01624) 648000
Fax (01624) 648001
e-mail: library@mnh.gov.im
url: www.gov.im/mnh
Librarian/Archivist Roger M C Sims BA DAA DPESS RMSA FSA (e-mail: Roger.Sims@mnh.gov.im)
Librarian Alan G Franklin MA MCLIP (e-mail: alan.franklin@mnh.gov.im)
Archivist Ms Wendy Thirkettle BA DipAS (e-mail: Wendy.Thirkettle@mnh.gov.im)

Specialism(s): History and development of the Isle of Man; Combined local studies, Archive and diocesan record office

MARINE BIOLOGICAL ASSOCIATION

National Marine Biological Library, Marine Biological Association, Citadel Hill, Plymouth PL1 2PB
☎(01752) 633266
Fax (01752) 633102
e-mail: nmbl@mba.ac.uk
url: www.mba.ac.uk/nmbl/
Head of Library and Information Services Miss Linda Noble BSc MCLIP (01752 633270; e-mail: lno@mba.ac.uk)

Specialism(s): Marine sciences including marine biology, pollution, oceanography and chemistry; fisheries; dating back to 19th century

MARX MEMORIAL LIBRARY

Marx Memorial Library, 37A Clerkenwell Green, London EC1R 0DU
☎020 7253 1485
Fax 020 7251 6039
e-mail: info@marx-memorial-library.org
url: www.marx-memorial-library.org
Librarian Dr John Callow

MARYLEBONE CRICKET CLUB

MCC Library, Marylebone Cricket Club, Lord's Ground, St John's Wood, London NW8 8QN
☎020 7616 8657
Fax 020 7616 8659
e-mail: museum@mcc.org.uk
url: www.mcc.org.uk
Curator Adam Chadwick (020 7616 8655)
Archivist and Historian Ms Glenys Williams BA MPhil (020 7616 8656)

MET OFFICE

National Meterological Library, Met Office, FitzRoy Road, Exeter, Devon EX1 3PB
☎(01392) 884841 (enquiries)
e-mail: metlib@metoffice.gov.uk
url: www.metoffice.gov.uk
Library Information Manager Graham Bartlett
Library and Archive Manager Ms Sara Osman MA MSc MCLIP

National Meteorological Archive, Met Office, Great Moor House, Bittern Road, Sowton, Exeter, Devon EX2 7NL
☎(01392) 360987
e-mail: metarc@metoffice.gov.uk
url: www.metoffice.gov.uk
Archive Information Manager Ian MacGregor
Assistant Archivist Ms Kate Strachan
(Open to the public)

MINISTRY OF DEFENCE

MOD Information Services, Ministry of Defence, Ground Floor, Zone D, Main Building, Whitehall, London SW1A 2HB
☎020 7218 4445 (general enquiries), 020 7218 4184 (administration)
Fax 020 7218 5413
e-mail: info-svcslibrary-office@mod.uk
url: www.mod.uk
Chief Librarian Patrick Ryan BA MBA MCLIP (020 7218 0266; fax: 020 7218 5430; e-mail: patrick.ryan893@mod.uk)

Site library

Library, Ministry of Defence, Room 1410, Kentigern House, 65 Brown Street, Glasgow G2 8EX
☎0141 224 2500/1
Fax 0141 224 2257
e-mail: library@khinf.demon.co.uk
Librarian Ms Margaret Gair BA(Hons) DipLib MCLIP

MINISTRY OF JUSTICE

(formerly Department for Constitutional Affairs (DCA))

HQ Library, Ministry of Justice, Selborne House, 54 Victoria Street, London SW1E 6QW
☎020 7210 1671/1656
Fax 020 7210 1617
e-mail: moj.library@justice.gsi.gov.uk
url: www.justice.gov.uk
Librarian Miss Christine Younger BLib MCLIP

MORRAB LIBRARY

Morrab Library, Morrab Gardens, Penzance, Cornwall TR18 4DA
☎(01736) 364474 (tel/fax)
url: www.morrablibrary.co.uk
Librarian Mrs Annabelle Read (e-mail: morrablibrary@hotmail.co.uk)
(Available on payment of an annual subscription or a daily fee)

Specialism(s): Cornish literature and history; Napoleonic collection

MUSEUM OF LONDON

Library, Museum of London, London Wall, London EC2Y 5HN
☎0870 444 3852
Fax 0870 444 3853
e-mail: info@museumoflondon.org.uk
url: www.museumoflondon.org.uk
Librarian Ms Sally Brooks MA MCLIP
(Readers by appointment only)

MUSEUM OF WELSH LIFE (AMGUEDDFA WERIN CYMRU) *see* ST FAGANS: NATIONAL HISTORY MUSEUM

THE NATIONAL ARCHIVES

Archive and Library, National Archives, Kew, Richmond, Surrey TW9 4DU
☎020 8392 5200
Fax 020 8487 9207
url: www.nationalarchives.gov.uk; (enquiry form: www.nationalarchives.gov.uk/contact/form/)
Chief Executive (Keeper of the Public Record Office and Historical Manuscripts Commissioner) Ms Natalie Ceeney
Director of Public Services and Marketing James Strachan
Head of Readers and Customer Services Jeff Smith (e-mail: jeff.smith@nationalarchives.gov.uk)

Head of National Advisory Service Nicholas Kingsley (e-mail: nick.kingsley@nationalarchives.gov.uk)
Head of Resource Centre and Library Ms Helen Pye-Smith MA (e-mail: helen.pye-smith@nationalarchives.gov.uk)

NATIONAL ARMY MUSEUM

Templer Study Centre, National Army Museum, Royal Hospital Road, London SW3 4HT
☎020 7730 0717 ext 2306
Fax 020 7823 6573
e-mail: info@national-army-museum.ac.uk
url: www.national-army-museum.ac.uk
Head of Department of Printed Books Michael Ball MA AMA
Head of Archives, Photographs, Film and Sound Alastair Massie MA DPhil
Head of Fine and Decorative Art Miss Jenny Spencer-Smith MA AMA
(Open Thursday and Friday 10am–5pm and 1st and 3rd Saturdays of each month 10am–5pm, except Bank Holiday weekends)

Specialism(s): Military history; British army; Indian and Commonwealth armies

NATIONAL ART LIBRARY

Word and Image Department, National Art Library, Victoria and Albert Museum, Cromwell Road, South Kensington, London SW7 2RL
☎020 7942 2400 (enquiries)
Fax 020 7942 2401
e-mail: nal.enquiries@vam.ac.uk
url: www.vam.ac.uk/nal
Deputy Keeper and Chief Librarian John Meriton BA(Hons) MA DipLib FCLIP FRSA

Site library

Archive of Art and Design, National Art Library, Blythe House, 23 Blythe Road, West Kensington, London W14 0QF
☎020 7603 1514
Fax 020 7602 0980
e-mail: archive@vam.ac.uk
Archivist Ms Alexia Kirk

NATIONAL ASSEMBLY FOR WALES

Members' Library, National Assembly for Wales, Assembly Parliamentary Service, Cardiff Bay, Cardiff CF99 1NQ
☎029 2089 8629
url: www.wales.gov.uk
Resources Manager Mrs Stephanie Wilson (e-mail: stephanie.wilson@wales.gsi.gov.uk)

Specialism(s): Information resources to support the work of Assembly Members, also the Members' Research Services, which provide a confidential research and information service to individual Assembly Members and the Assembly's Committees

NATIONAL CHILDREN'S BUREAU

Library and Information Service, National Children's Bureau, 8 Wakley Street, London EC1V 7QE
☎020 7843 6008 (enquiry line)
Fax 020 7843 6007
e-mail: library@ncb.org.uk
url: www.ncb.org.uk
Head of Library & Information Ms Nicola Hilliard BA MCLIP

NATIONAL COAL MINING MUSEUM FOR ENGLAND

Library, National Coal Mining Museum for England, Caphouse Colliery, New Road, Overton, West Yorks WF4 4RH
☎(01924) 848806
Fax (01924) 840694
e-mail: info@ncm.org.uk
url: www.ncm.org.uk
Curatorial Librarian Ms Anisha Christison BSc(Hons) MSc MCLIP, Mrs Judith Dennis BA MSc MCLIP (e-mail: curatorial.librarian@ncm.org.uk)

NATIONAL GALLERY

Libraries and Archive, The National Gallery, Trafalgar Square, London WC2N 5DN
☎020 7747 2830
Fax 020 7747 2892
e-mail: lad@ng-london.org.uk
url: www.nationalgallery.org.uk
Head of Libraries and Archive Ms Elspeth Hector MA MCLIP (e-mail: elspeth.hector@ng-london.org.uk)
Archivist Alan Crookham (e-mail: alan.crookham@ng-london.org.uk)
(Readers by appointment only)

Specialism(s): Western European painting 1200–1900

NATIONAL HERITAGE LIBRARY

National Heritage Library, 313–315 Caledonian Road, London N1 1DR
☎020 7609 9639
Founder Director M McNiel
(A comprehensive reference collection covering every aspect of the landscape and culture of the British Isles: open by appointment only)

Specialism(s): The arts; Environmental, historical, industrial and transport sites

NATIONAL INSTITUTE FOR HEALTH AND CLINICAL EXCELLENCE (NICE)

Information Services, National Institute for Health and Clinical Excellence (NICE), Clinical and Public Health Directorate, MidCity Place, 71 High Holborn, London WC1V 6NA
☎020 7067 5800
Fax 020 7067 5801
e-mail: nice@nice.org.uk
url: www.nice.org.uk
Associate Director for Information Services Dr Sarah Cumbers (e-mail: sarah.cumbers@nice.org.uk)

Specialism(s): Evidence-based healthcare; Health technology evaluation; Clinical guidelines; Evidence-based public health

NATIONAL INSTITUTE FOR MEDICAL RESEARCH (MEDICAL RESEARCH COUNCIL)

Library, National Institute for Medical Research (Medical Research Council), The Ridgeway, Mill Hill, London NW7 1AA
☎020 8816 2228
Fax 020 8816 2230
e-mail: library@nimr.mrc.ac.uk
url: www.nimr.mrc.ac.uk/library
Librarian Frank Norman BSc DipLib MCLIP

Specialism(s): Physiology; Neuroscience; Immunology; Microbiology; Molecular biology; Cell biology; Biochemistry; Structural biology; Developmental biology

NATIONAL INSTITUTE OF ADULT CONTINUING EDUCATION (NIACE)

Library, National Institute of Adult Continuing Education (NIACE), 21 De Montfort Street, Leicester LE1 7GE
☎0116 204 4200
Fax 0116 204 4253
e-mail: information@niace.org.uk
url: www.niace.org.uk
Librarian Ms Helen Kruse BA(Hons) MCLIP
Information Co-ordinator Andy Kail

NATIONAL INSTITUTE OF ECONOMIC AND SOCIAL RESEARCH

Library, National Institute of Economic and Social Research, 2 Dean Trench Street, Smith Square, London SW1P 3HE
☎020 7222 7665

Fax 020 7654 1900
e-mail: library@niesr.ac.uk
url: www.niesr.ac.uk
Librarian Ms Patricia Oliver BA MCLIP (020 7654 1907; e-mail: poliver@niesr.ac.uk)

NATIONAL LIBRARY FOR THE BLIND *see* RNIB NATIONAL LIBRARY SERVICE

NATIONAL LIBRARY OF SCOTLAND

National Library of Scotland, George IV Bridge, Edinburgh EH1 1EW
☎0131 623 3700
Fax 0131 623 3701
e-mail: enquiries@nls.uk
url: www.nls.uk
Librarian Martyn Wade MA MLib MCLIP

Branch/regional libraries

- Inter-Library Services, National Library of Scotland, 33 Salisbury Place, Edinburgh EH9 1SL
  ☎0131 623 3985
  Fax 0131 623 3984
  e-mail: ils@nls.uk
- Map Library, National Library of Scotland, 33 Salisbury Place, Edinburgh EH9 1SL
  ☎0131 623 3970
  Fax 0131 623 3971
  e-mail: maps@nls.uk

Specialism(s): Scottish history and culture

NATIONAL LIBRARY OF WALES: LLYFRGELL GENEDLAETHOL CYMRU

National Library of Wales: Llyfrgell Genedlaethol Cymru, Aberystwyth, Ceredigion SY23 3BU
☎(01970) 632800
Fax (01970) 615709
e-mail: holi@llgc.org.uk
url: www.llgc.org.uk
Librarian Andrew Green MA DipLib MCLIP

Specialism(s): Legal deposit library housing books, mss, maps, photographs, paintings, audiovisual and electronic materials; an important digitization and exhibitions programme

NATIONAL MARITIME MUSEUM

Caird Library, National Maritime Museum, Greenwich, London SE10 9NF

☎020 8312 6673/8624
Fax 020 8312 6599
e-mail: library@nmm.ac.uk; manuscripts@nmm.ac.uk
url: www.nmm.ac.uk
Head of Library and Manuscripts Mrs Jill Terrell BSc DipLib MCLIP
Reader Services Librarian Ms Tanya Kirk BA(Hons) MA
Digital Resources Librarian Ms Renée Orr BA MA MLIS
Manuscripts Archivist Mrs Daphne Knott BA DipArch

Specialism(s): Maritime history; Horology; Astronomy; Shipbuilding; Navigation

NATIONAL MEDIA MUSEUM

(formerly National Museum of Photography, Film and Television)

Royal Photographic Society Collection, National Media Museum, Bradford BD1 1NQ
☎(01274) 202030 (switchboard)
Fax (01274) 772325
url: www.nationalmediamuseum.org.uk
Curator of Photographs Dr Jane Fletcher (01274 203398; e-mail: jane.fletcher@nationalmediamuseum.org.uk)
(Prior appointment essential for members and non-members)

NATIONAL MUSEUMS SCOTLAND

Library, National Museums Scotland, Chambers Street, Edinburgh EH1 1JF
☎0131 247 4137 (enquiries)
Fax 0131 247 4311
e-mail: library@nms.ac.uk
url: www.nms.ac.uk
Head of Information Services Ms Evelyn Simpson (e-mail: e.simpson@nms.ac.uk)
Library Services Manager Andrew Martin MA DipLib FSAScot (e-mail: a.martin@nms.ac.uk)

Branch library

Library, National Museums Scotland, National War Museum of Scotland, The Castle, Edinburgh EH1 2NG
☎0131 247 4409

Specialism(s): Decorative arts; Archaeology; Ethnography; History of science and technology; Natural sciences; Museology; Military history

NATIONAL PHYSICAL LABORATORY

Library, National Physical Laboratory, Hampton Road, Teddington, Middlesex TW11 0LW
☎020 8943 6417
Fax 020 8614 0424
e-mail: library@npl.co.uk
url: www.npl.co.uk

Librarian Ian O'Leary MA DLIS (020 8943 6809)

Specialism(s): Physics; Material science; Mathematics; Metrology

NATIONAL POLICING IMPROVEMENT AGENCY

(formerly Central Police Training and Development Authority)

National Police Library, National Policing Improvement Agency, Bramshill, Hook, Hants RG27 0JW
☎(01256) 602650 (enquiries), (01256) 602100 (main switchboard)
Fax (01256) 602285
e-mail: library@npia.pnn.police.uk
url: www.npia.police.uk
Chief Librarian Mrs Sue King MCLIP (e-mail: sue.king@npia.pnn.police.uk)

NATIONAL PORTRAIT GALLERY

Heinz Archive and Library, National Portrait Gallery, 2 St Martin's Place, London WC2H 0HE
☎020 7321 6617
Fax 020 7306 0056
e-mail: archiveenquiry@npg.org.uk
url: www.npg.org.uk
Head of Archive and Library Robin K Francis BSc(Hons) MA MCLIP
Librarian Ms Gabriele Popp
(Readers by appointment only)

Specialism(s): British portraiture

NATIONAL RAILWAY MUSEUM

Research Centre, National Railway Museum, Leeman Road, York YO26 4XJ
☎(01904) 621261 (switchboard); (01904) 686235 (enquiries)
Fax (01904) 611112
e-mail: nrm.researchcentre@nmsi.ac.uk
url: www.nrm.org.uk
Collections Access Manager Richard Taylor BA MArAd RMSA (01904 686289; e-mail: richard.taylor@nmsi.ac.uk)

NATIONAL SCIENCE LEARNING CENTRE

National Science Learning Centre, University of York, Heslington, York, North Yorks YO10 5DD
☎(01904) 328314
Fax (01904) 328328
url: www.slcs.ac.uk/national
Resource Centre Co-ordinator Andrew Jones (e-mail: a.jones@slcs.ac.uk)

Specialism(s): High quality professional development for everyone in the teaching of science, in primary and secondary schools and FE colleges across the UK.

NATIONAL UNION OF TEACHERS

Library and Information Unit, National Union of Teachers, Hamilton House, Mabledon Place, London WC1H 9BD
☎020 7380 4713
Fax 020 7387 8458
url: www.teachers.org.uk
Information Officer Ms Janet Friedlander BA MCLIP (e-mail: j.friedlander@nut.org.uk)
Information Assistant Mrs Kate Burry BA MCLIP (e-mail: k.burry@nut.org.uk)

NATIONAL YOUTH AGENCY

Information Centre, National Youth Agency, Eastgate House, 19–23 Humberstone Road, Leicester LE5 3GI
☎0116 242 7350 (enquiries and administration)
Fax 0116 242 7444
e-mail: dutydesk@nya.org.uk
url: www.nya.org.uk
Library Officer Ms Jo Poultney BA (e-mail: jop@nya.org.uk)
(Reference only. Personal visitors welcome, by appointment))

Specialism(s): Young people, the youth service and youth affairs.

NATURAL ENGLAND

(formerly Countryside Agency and English Nature)

Information and Library Services, Natural England, Northminster House, Northminster Road, Peterborough PE1 1UA
☎(01733) 455094 (library enquiry desk), 455000 (switchboard)
Fax (01733) 468834
e-mail: library@naturalengland.org.uk; further contact details can be found at enquiries@naturalengland.org.uk
url: www.naturalengland.org.uk
Team Leader Peter Wingate

Specialism(s): Sustainable use and management of the natural environment; biodiversity; wildlife; landscapes; access and recreation; conservation of marine and coastal environments

NATURAL HISTORY MUSEUM

Library, Natural History Museum, Cromwell Road, London SW7 5BD
☎020 7942 5460 (general enquiries)
Fax 020 7942 5559
e-mail: library@nhm.ac.uk
url: www.nhm.ac.uk
Head of Library and Information Services Graham Higley BSc
The Library is divided into four specialist sections at South Kensington: General & Zoology (020 7942 5460); Botany (020 7942 5685); Entomology (020 7942 5751) and Earth Sciences (020 7942 5476).

Site library

- Ornithology and Rothschild Library, Natural History Museum Tring, Akeman Street, Tring, Herts HP23 6AP
  ☎020 7942 6156
  Fax 020 7942 6150
  e-mail: ornlib@nhm.ac.uk
  url: www.nhm.ac.uk/tring/index.html
  Assistant Librarian Ms Alison Harding MA MSc MCLIP

NETWORK RAIL INFRASTRUCTURE LTD

Network Rail HQ Library, Network Rail Infrastructure Ltd, 2nd Floor Library, 40 Melton Street, London NW1 2EE
☎020 7557 8062
Fax 020 7557 9150
url: www.networkrail.co.uk
Librarian Ms Sue Peters (e-mail: sue.peters@networkrail.co.uk)
(Not open to the public but queries welcomed from professional organizations and researchers.)

Specialism(s): UK railway history, legislation, engineering, health and safety

NHS HEALTH SCOTLAND

Library, NHS Health Scotland, The Priory, Canaan Lane, Edinburgh EH10 4SG
☎0845 912 5442 (enquiries) - Scotland only), 0131 536 5582 (administration), textphone 0131 536 5593
Fax 0131 536 5502
e-mail: library.enquiries@health.scot.nhs.uk
url: www.healthscotland.com/library
Library Services Manager Ms Sharon Jamieson BA(Hons) MSc DipLIS MCLIP
Librarian Ms Julia Green BA DipLib MSc

Specialism(s): Public health; Health promotion and education

NHS NATIONAL SERVICES SCOTLAND

Information Services Division, NHS National Services Scotland, Gyle Square, 1 South Gyle Crescent, Edinburgh EH12 9EB
☎0131 275 6423
Fax 0131 275 7607
e-mail: isdlib@isd.csa.scot.nhs.uk
url: www.isdscotland.org/
Manager, ISD Library Services Alan Jamieson MA DipLib MCLIP (e-mail: alan.jamieson@nhs.net)

Specialism(s): Health statistics; Official circulars; Media monitoring

NORTHERN IRELAND ASSEMBLY

Library, Northern Ireland Assembly, Parliament Buildings, Stormont, Belfast BT4 3XX
☎028 9052 1250
Fax 028 9052 1922
e-mail: issuedesk.library@niassembly.gov.uk
url: www.ni-assembly.gov.uk
Resource Team Librarian George D Woodman BA DipLib MCLIP (028 9052 1250; e-mail: george.woodman@niassembly.gov.uk)

Specialism(s): Legislation and official publications relating especially to N Ireland, government, politics and Irish history

NORTHERN IRELAND OFFICE

Library, Northern Ireland Office, 11 Millbank, London SW1P 4PN
☎020 7210 0253
Fax 020 7210 0212
url: www.nio.gov.uk
Records Officer Ms Claire O'Neill (e-mail: claire.o'neill@nio.x.gsi.gov.uk)

OFFICE FOR NATIONAL STATISTICS

National Statistics Information and Library Service, Office for National Statistics, Room 1.001, Government Buildings, Cardiff Road, Newport, Gwent NT10 8XG
☎(01633) 812129
Fax (01633) 812599
e-mail: info@statistics.gov.uk
url: www.statistics.gov.uk
Chief Librarian Ian Bushnell BA MCLIP (01633 813033; e-mail: ian.bushnell@ons.gsi.gov.uk)
(This library is open to the public by appointment only)

OFFICE OF FAIR TRADING

Library and Information Centre, Office of Fair Trading, Ground Floor, Fleetbank House, 2-6 Salisbury Square, London EC4Y 8JX
☎020 7211 8938/9. For general OFT enquiries 020 7211 8000; OFT Publications orderline 0800 389 3158
Fax 020 7211 8940
e-mail: enquiries@oft.gsi.gov.uk
url: www.oft.gov.uk
Head of Library and Information Services Martin Shrive BA(Hons) MCLIP

OFFICE OF RAIL REGULATION

Library, Office of Rail Regulation, 1 Kemble Street, London WC2B 4AN
☎020 7282 2001 (direct)
Fax 020 7282 2118

e-mail: rail.library@orr.gsi.gov.uk
url: www.rail-reg.gov.uk
Librarian Ms Sue MacSwan BA MSc

OFFICE OF THE PARLIAMENTARY AND HEALTH SERVICE OMBUDSMAN (OFFICE OF THE PARLIAMENTARY COMMISSIONER FOR ADMINISTRATION AND HEALTH SERVICE COMMISSIONER FOR ENGLAND)

Library and Information Service, Office of the Parliamentary and Health Service Ombudsman (Office of the Parliamentary Commissioner for Administration and Health Service Commissioner for England), 19th Floor, Millbank Tower, Millbank, London SW1P 4QP
☎020 7217 4104
Fax 020 7217 4940
e-mail: library@ombudsman.org.uk
url: www.ombudsman.org.uk
Librarian Ms Deanne Mitchell BA DipLib MCLIP

Specialism(s): Ombudsman issues; Maladministration

OFGEM (OFFICE OF GAS AND ELECTRICITY MARKETS)

Research and Information Centre, OFGEM (Office of Gas and Electricity Markets), 9 Millbank, London SW1P 3GE
☎020 7901 7003
Fax 020 7901 7378
e-mail: library@ofgem.gov.uk
url: www.ofgem.gov.uk
Librarian Keith Smith
Assistant Librarian Ms Emma Davis
(Open 2pm–4.30pm Monday to Friday. By appointment only: 24 hours notice required.)

OFWAT (OFFICE OF WATER SERVICES)

Library and Information Services, OFWAT (Office of Water Services), Centre City Tower, 7 Hill Street, Birmingham B5 4UA
☎0121 625 1373 (general enquiries)
Fax 0121 625 1300
e-mail: enquiries@ofwat.gsi.gov.uk
url: www.ofwat.gov.uk
Librarian and Information Services Manager Ms Jackie Cranmer BSc MCLIP (0121 625 1361)

OMNIBUS SOCIETY

The John F Parke Memorial Library, The Omnibus Society, 100 Sandwell Street, Walsall, West Midlands WS1 3EB
☎(01922) 629358
e-mail: omnibussoc@easynet.co.uk
url: www.omnibussoc.org
Librarian Alan Mills (01922 631867 (tel/fax); e-mail: alanavrilmills@hotmail.com)
(Manned by volunteers, the Library is currently open to casual callers on Wednesdays (09.15–16.15), although other appointments can be made by prior arrangement.)

Specialism(s): Road passenger transport; Unique collection of timetables

ORDNANCE SURVEY

Library and Information Centre, Ordnance Survey, Room C128, Romsey Road, Southampton SO16 4GU
☎023 8079 2334
Fax 023 8079 2879
e-mail: library@ordnancesurvey.co.uk
url: www.ordnancesurvey.co.uk
Librarian Ms Cathy Layton BSc(Econ) (e-mail: cathy.layton@ordnancesurvey.co.uk)

PARTNERSHIP HOUSE MISSION STUDIES LIBRARIES *see* CROWTHER CENTRE FOR MISSION EDUCATION

THE PENSIONS REGULATOR

Library, The Pensions Regulator, Napier House, Trafalgar Place, Brighton BN1 4DW
☎(01273) 627745
Fax (01273) 627760
url: www.thepensionsregulator.gov.uk
Information Manager Ms Clare Butler (e-mail: clare.butler@thepensionsregulator.gov.uk)
(The Library is not open to the public.)

PIRA INTERNATIONAL

Information Services, PIRA International, Cleeve Road, Leatherhead, Surrey KT22 7RU
☎(01372) 802050 (enquiries)
Fax (01372) 802239
e-mail: infocentre@pira-international.com
url: www.intertechpira.com/www.piranet.com
Information Scientist Ms Jan Brophy MSc MCLIP

Specialism(s): Papermaking; Printing; Packaging; Publishing

PLUNKETT FOUNDATION

Library, Plunkett Foundation, The Quadrangle, Woodstock, Oxon OX20 1LH
☎(01993) 810730
Fax (01993) 810849
e-mail: info@plunkett.co.uk
url: www.plunkett.co.uk
Research and Communications Manager Mike Perry

Specialism(s): Focus on history and practice of cooperatives and rural enterprise; Agriculture

PLYMOUTH PROPRIETARY LIBRARY

Plymouth Proprietary Library, Alton Terrace, 111 North Hill, Plymouth PL4 8JY
☎(01752) 660515
Librarian John R Smith

Specialism(s): 19th- and early 20th-century classical fiction (available to members only)

POETRY LIBRARY

Poetry Library, Level 5, Royal Festival Hall, South Bank Centre, London SE1 8XX
☎020 7921 0943/0664
Fax 020 7921 0939
e-mail: info@poetrylibrary.org.uk
url: www.poetrylibrary.org.uk; www.poetrymagazines.org.uk
Acting Head Librarian Ms Miriam Valencia, Chris McCabe

POLISH LIBRARY

Polish Library, 238-246 King Street, London W6 0RF
☎020 8741 0474
Fax 020 8741 7724
e-mail: bibliotekapolska@posklibrary.fsnet.co.uk; polish.library@posk.org
Librarian Mrs Jadwiga Szmidt MA

PORTICO LIBRARY AND GALLERY

The Portico Library and Gallery, 57 Mosley Street, Manchester M2 3HY
☎0161 236 6785
Fax 0161 236 6785
url: www.theportico.org.uk
Librarian Miss Emma Marigliano BA(Hons) (e-mail: librarian@theportico.org.uk)
(Tours by arrangement. Nineteenth-century stock available for scholarly research. Gallery open to the public.)

PROUDMAN OCEANOGRAPHIC LABORATORY

Library, Proudman Oceanographic Laboratory, Joseph Proudman Building, 6 Brownlow Street, Liverpool L3 5DA
☎0151 795 4800
Fax 0151 795 4801
url: www.pol.ac.uk
Head of Information and Communications Ms Nadina McShane BA (e-mail: nm@pol.ac.uk)
Assistant Librarian Andrew J Kennedy BA MPhil MA

Specialism(s): Oceanography and marine science

QINETIQ

Information Centre, Qinetiq, Winfrith Technology Centre, Building A22, Dorchester, Dorset DT2 8XJ
☎(01305) 212218
url: www.qinetiq.com
Information Analyst Ms Wendy Gubbels BA (e-mail: wrgubbels@qinetiq.com)

Specialism(s): Sonar and oceanography

RELIGIOUS SOCIETY OF FRIENDS IN BRITAIN (QUAKERS)

Library, Religious Society of Friends in Britain (Quakers), Friends House, 173–177 Euston Road, London NW1 2BJ
☎020 7663 1135
Fax 020 7663 1001
e-mail: library@quaker.org.uk
url: www.quaker.org.uk/library
Librarian Ms Heather Rowland BA MCLIP

Specialism(s): Quakerism; Peace and pacifism; Anti-slavery

RESEARCH COUNCILS UK (formerly The Research Councils)

Research Councils UK, Polaris House, North Star Avenue, Swindon, Wilts SN2 1SZ
☎(01793) 442000 (enquiries)
Fax (01793) 442042
url: www.rcuk.ac.uk

The following research councils are based at this site:

- Biotechnology and Biological Sciences Research Council (BBSRC), Research Councils UK, Polaris House, North Star Avenue, Swindon, Wilts SN2 1UH
  url: www.bbsrc.ac.uk
  Information Officer Mrs Carol Milner (01793 414679; e-mail: carol.milner@bbsrc.ac.uk)

- Economic and Social Research Council (ESRC), Research Councils UK, Polaris House, North Star Avenue, Swindon, Wilts SN2 1UJ
  url: www.esrc.ac.uk
  Information Officer Ms Debbie Stalker (01793 413051; e-mail: debbie.stalker@esrc.ac.uk)
- Engineering and Physical Sciences Research Council (EPSRC), Research Councils UK, Polaris House, North Star Avenue, Swindon, Wilts SN2 1ET
  ☎(01793) 444100 (helpline)
  e-mail: infoline@esprc.ac.uk
  url: www.epsrc.ac.uk
- Natural Environment Research Council (NERC), Research Councils UK, Polaris House, North Star Avenue, Swindon, Wilts SN2 1EU
  url: www.nerc.ac.uk
  Information Officer John Mason (01793 411782; e-mail: jsma@nerc.ac.uk)

RNIB NATIONAL LIBRARY SERVICE

(formerly National Library for the Blind and Royal National Institute of the Blind)

RNIB National Library Service, Far Cromwell Road, Bredbury, Stockport, Cheshire SK6 2SG
☎0845 762 6843
Fax 0161 355 2098
e-mail: cservices@rnib.org.uk
url: www.rnib.org.uk/reading
Head Ms Helen Brazier MA MCLIP (0161 355 2004; e-mail: helen.brazier@rnib.org.uk)
Manager Ms Pat Beech MCLIP (0161 355 2005)
(RNIB National Library Service offers a comprehensive range of books and accessible information for adults and children with sight loss. Books are posted free of charge using the Articles for the Blind service.)

Specialism(s): Talking Books: the UK's largest collection (13,000) titles of unabridged audio books on CD, both fiction and non-fiction; Braille and Moon books: Europe's largest collection of touch-reading material including tactile imagery; Books in large print (16pt type) and giant print (24pt type); Braille Music Library: 14,000 Braille music scores (the largest collection outside the USA) plus books about music and music theory; Online reference services: free access to online accessible reference materials including dictionaries, encyclopedias, journals and newspapers; Online catalogues, e-mail discussion group and web message boards for book lovers, reader magazines and help with choosing books; RNIB Research Library: the most comprehensive UK collection of print material relating to sight loss (tel: 020 7391 2052).

RNID

RNID Library, RNID, UCL Ear Institute, 330–332 Gray's Inn Road, London WC1X 8EE
☎020 7915 1553 (also for Minicom)
Fax 020 7915 1443
e-mail: rnidlib@ucl.ac.uk
url: www.ucl.ac.uk/library/rnid

Librarian Alex Stagg MA (e-mail: a.stagg@ucl.ac.uk)

Specialism(s): Audiology; Deaf studies

ROTHAMSTED LIBRARY – ROTHAMSTED RESEARCH

Rothamsted Library – Rothamsted Research, Harpenden, Herts AL5 2JQ
☎(01582) 763133
Fax (01582) 760981
e-mail: res.library@bbsrc.ac.uk
url: www.rothamsted.bbsrcc.ac.uk/resources/library/
Librarian Mrs S E Allsopp BA DipLib (e-mail: liz.allsopp@bbsrc.ac.uk)

Specialism(s): Arable crops research; Sustainable land development

ROYAL ACADEMY OF ARTS

Library, Royal Academy of Arts, Burlington House, Piccadilly, London W1J 0BD
☎020 7300 5737 (enquiries), 020 7300 5740 (administration)
Fax 020 7300 5765
e-mail: library@royalacademy.org.uk
url: www.royalacademy.org.uk
Head of Library Services Adam Michael Waterton
Assistant Librarian Mrs Linda Macpherson BA(Hons) MA MA MCLIP

Specialism(s): British art and artists from 18th century to present; History of the Academy since 1768

ROYAL AERONAUTICAL SOCIETY

Library, Royal Aeronautical Society, 4 Hamilton Place, London W1J 7BQ
☎020 7670 4362
Fax 020 7670 4359
url: www.aerosociety.com
Library Head Brian Riddle (e-mail: brian.riddle@raes.org.uk)

Specialism(s): Extensive collection of material relating to the development and recent technical advances in aeronautics, aviation and aerospace technology

ROYAL AIR FORCE COLLEGE

College Library, Royal Air Force College, Cranwell, Sleaford, Lincs NG34 8HB
☎(01400) 266329
Fax (01400) 266266
e-mail: college011@btconnect.com
College Librarian & Archivist Ms Mary Guy BA(Hons) DipLib MCLIP (e-mail: collegelibrarian@cranwell.raf.mod.uk)

ROYAL AIR FORCE MUSEUM

Royal Air Force Museum, Grahame Park Way, Hendon, London NW9 5LL
☎020 8205 2266 ext 4873
Fax 020 8200 1751
e-mail: research@rafmuseum.org
url: www.rafmuseum.org
Senior Keeper P J V Elliott MA BSc MCLIP
(Prior appointment necessary)

Specialism(s): Military aviation

ROYAL ASTRONOMICAL SOCIETY

Library, Royal Astronomical Society, Burlington House, Piccadilly, London W1J 0BQ
☎020 7734 3307/4582
Fax 020 7494 0166
e-mail: info@ras.org.uk
url: www.ras.org.uk
Librarian Peter D Hingley BA MCLIP RD (e-mail: pdh@ras.org.uk)
(Enquiries in writing or by e-mail preferred, access by appointment)

Specialism(s): Extensive archive and rare book collection covering astronomy and geophysics.

ROYAL AUTOMOBILE CLUB

Library, Royal Automobile Club, 89 Pall Mall, London SW1Y 5HS
☎020 7747 3398
Fax 0870 460 6285
e-mail: library@royalautomobileclub.co.uk
url: www.royalautomobileclub.co.uk/guestarea/rac.asp?s=FA&ss=LI
Librarian Trevor G Dunmore

Specialism(s): History of motoring and motor sport

ROYAL BOTANIC GARDEN, EDINBURGH

Library, Royal Botanic Garden, Edinburgh, 20A Inverleith Row, Edinburgh EH3 5LR
☎0131 248 2853 (enquiries), 0131 248 2850 (administration)
Fax 0131 248 2901
e-mail: library@rbge.ac.uk
url: www.rbge.org.uk
Head of Library Mrs Jane Hutcheon BSc MCLIP (e-mail: j.hutcheon@rbge.ac.uk)

Specialism(s): Botany; Horticulture; Garden history and botanical art

ROYAL BOTANIC GARDENS, KEW

Library, Art & Archives, Royal Botanic Gardens, Kew, Richmond, Surrey TW9 3AE

☎020 8332 5414
Fax 020 8332 5430
e-mail: library@kew.org
url: www.rbgkew.org.uk
Head of Library, Art and Archives Christopher Mills BA MA DipLib MCLIP (020 8332 5412; e-mail: c.mills@rbgkew.org.uk)

ROYAL COLLEGE OF PHYSICIANS AND SURGEONS OF GLASGOW

Library, Royal College of Physicians and Surgeons of Glasgow, 232–242 St Vincent Street, Glasgow G2 5RJ
☎0141 227 3241 (enquiries), 0141 221 6072 (administration)
Fax 0141 221 1804
e-mail: library@rcpsg.ac.uk
url: www.rcpsg.ac.uk
Head of Library and Heritage Mrs Carol Parry BA(Hons) DAA FETC (e-mail: carol.parry@rcpsg.ac.uk)
Assistant Librarian Mrs Valerie McClure MA(Hons) MSc (e-mail: valerie.mcclure@rcpsg.ac.uk)

Specialism(s): History of medicine

ROYAL COLLEGE OF PHYSICIANS OF EDINBURGH

Library, Royal College of Physicians of Edinburgh, 9 Queen Street, Edinburgh EH2 1JQ
☎0131 225 7324
Fax 0131 220 3939
e-mail: library@rcpe.ac.uk
url: www.rcpe.ac.uk
Librarian, Historic Library Project Iain A Milne MLib MCLIP

ROYAL COLLEGE OF PHYSICIANS OF LONDON

Library, Royal College of Physicians of London, 11 St Andrews Place, Regent's Park, London NW1 4LE
☎020 7224 1539 (direct)
Fax 020 7486 3729
e-mail: infocentre@rcplondon.ac.uk
url: www.rcplondon.ac.uk
Minicom 020 7486 5687
Manager, Heritage Centre Ms Caroline Moss-Gibbons BLib(Hons) PGCE (020 7935 1174 ext 315; e-mail: caroline.moss-gibbons@rcplondon.ac.uk)
Manager, Information Centre Mrs Julie Beckwith BA MSc MCLIP (020 7935 1174 ext 317; e-mail: julie.beckwith@rcplondon.ac.uk)

Specialism(s): UK health policy; History of medicine

ROYAL COLLEGE OF PSYCHIATRISTS

Library and Information Service, Royal College of Psychiatrists, 17 Belgrave Square, London SW1X 8PG
☎020 7235 2351 ext 138/152
Fax 020 7259 6303
e-mail: infoservices@rcpsych.ac.uk
url: www.rcpsych.ac.uk
Library and Information Manager Ms Sally Blake

Specialism(s): Antiquarian psychiatry textbooks dating from 15th century

ROYAL COLLEGE OF SURGEONS OF ENGLAND

Library and Lumley Study Centre, Royal College of Surgeons of England, 35–43 Lincoln's Inn Fields, London WC2A 3PE
☎020 7869 6555/6556 (enquiries), 020 7405 3474 (College switchboard)
Fax 020 7405 4438
e-mail: library@rcseng.ac.uk
url: www.rcseng.ac.uk
Head of Library and Information Services Mrs Thalia Knight MA MA DipLib MCLIP
Information Services Manager Tom Bishop BA(Hons) MA
Records and Archives Manager Ms Beth Astridge BA(Hons) MA

ROYAL COLLEGE OF VETERINARY SURGEONS

RCVS Trust Library, Royal College of Veterinary Surgeons, Belgravia House, 62–64 Horseferry Road, London SW1P 2AF
☎020 7222 2021
Fax 020 7202 0751
e-mail: library@rcvstrust.org.uk
url: www.rcvstrust.org.uk
Librarian Ms Liz Murray (e-mail: l.murray@rcvstrust.org.uk)

ROYAL COMMISSION ON THE ANCIENT AND HISTORICAL MONUMENTS OF WALES

Publications and Outreach Branch, Royal Commission on the Ancient and Historical Monuments of Wales, Crown Building, Plas Crug, Aberystwyth, Ceredigion SY23 1NJ
☎(01970) 621200
Fax (01970) 627701
e-mail: nmr.wales@rcahmw.gov.uk
url: www.rcahmw.gov.uk
Secretary Dr Peter Wakelin
Librarian and Head of Reader Services Ms Patricia Moore BA MCLIP

Specialism(s): Archaeology; Architectural history and heritage of Wales

ROYAL ENGINEERS ARCHIVES AND LIBRARY

(formerly Royal Engineers Library)

Royal Engineers Archives and Library, Ravelin Building, Brompton Barracks, Chatham, Kent ME4 4UG
☎(01634) 822221
Fax (01634) 822419
url: www.remuseum.org.uk
Senior Curator Ms R Cheney

ROYAL ENTOMOLOGICAL SOCIETY

Library, Royal Entomological Society, The Mansion House, Chiswell Green Lane, St Albans, Herts AL2 3NZ
☎(01727) 899387
Fax (01727) 894797
e-mail: lib@royensoc.co.uk
url: www.royensoc.co.uk
Librarian Mrs Val McAtear BA(Hons)Lib

ROYAL GEOGRAPHICAL SOCIETY (WITH THE INSTITUTE OF BRITISH GEOGRAPHERS)

Foyle Reading Room, Royal Geographical Society (with the Institute of British Geographers), 1 Kensington Gore, London SW7 2AR
☎020 7591 3044
Fax 020 7591 3001
e-mail: enquiries@rgs.org
url: www.rgs.org
Principal Librarian E Rae MA DipLIS
Deputy Librarian Miss J C Turner BA(Hons)
Map Librarian D McNeill BA

Specialism(s): Geography; Travel; Exploration

ROYAL HORTICULTURAL SOCIETY

The Lindley Library, Royal Horticultural Society, 80 Vincent Square, London SW1P 2PE
☎020 7821 3050
Fax 020 7828 3022
e-mail: library.london@rhs.org.uk
url: www.rhs.org.uk
Librarian and Archivist Dr Brent Elliott BA MA PhD

ROYAL INSTITUTE OF BRITISH ARCHITECTS

British Architectural Library, Royal Institute of British Architects, 66 Portland Place, London W1B 1AD

☎020 7307 3707 (24-hr recorded information service); 020 7580 5533 (switchboard)
Fax 020 7631 1802
e-mail: info@inst.riba.org
url: www.architecture.com
Public information line (calls 50p per min): (0906) 302 0400
Director Dr Irena Murray
Deputy Director Ms Jane Oldfield BSc MA MCLIP

Branch library
British Architectural Library Drawings and Archives Collection, Royal Institute of British Architects, Henry Cole Wing, Victoria and Albert Museum, Exhibition Road, London SW7 2RL
☎020 7307 3708 (Study Room)
e-mail: drawings&archives@inst.riba.org
Associate Director and Curator of Drawings C Hind
Assistant Director, Drawings and Archives Ms Eleanor Gawne

ROYAL INSTITUTE OF INTERNATIONAL AFFAIRS

Library, Royal Institute of International Affairs, Chatham House, 10 St James's Square, London SW1Y 4LE
☎020 7957 5723 (enquiries)
Fax 020 7957 5710
e-mail: libenquire@chathamhouse.org.uk
url: www.chathamhouse.org.uk
Senior Librarian Mrs M Bone BSc (020 7314 3610; e-mail: mbone@chathamhouse.org.uk)

Specialism(s): International affairs; Politics; Economics; Security; Environment

ROYAL INSTITUTE OF NAVIGATION

Library, Royal Institute of Navigation, 1 Kensington Gore, London SW7 2AT
☎020 7591 3133
Fax 020 7591 3131
e-mail: editor@rin.org.uk
url: www.rin.org.uk
Librarian Tony Fyler
(The library is free to members and open to the public on an appointment-only basis)

Specialism(s): Land, sea and air navigation

ROYAL INSTITUTION OF CHARTERED SURVEYORS

Library and Information Services, Royal Institution of Chartered Surveyors, 12 Great George Street, Parliament Square, London SW1P 3AD
☎0870 333 1600 ext 3714; 020 7334 3714

Fax: 020 7334 3784
e-mail: contactrics@rics.org; library@rics.org
url: www.rics.org
Acting Head of Library and Information Services Ms Cathy Linacre BA DipLib MCLIP (020 7334 3748; e-mail: clinacre@rics.org

ROYAL INSTITUTION OF GREAT BRITAIN

Library, Royal Institution of Great Britain, 21 Albemarle Street, London W1S 4BS
☎020 7670 2939
Fax 020 7629 3569
e-mail: ril@ri.ac.uk
url: www.rigb.org
Head of Collections and Heritage Prof Frank James (020 7670 2924; e-mail: fjames@ri.ac.uk)

(Please note that the Library will be closed until Spring 2008)

ROYAL INSTITUTION OF NAVAL ARCHITECTS

Library, Royal Institution of Naval Architects, 10 Upper Belgrave Street, London SW1X 8BQ
☎020 7235 4622
Fax 020 7259 5912
e-mail: hq@rina.org.uk
url: www.rina.org.uk
Librarian Graeme Mitchell

ROYAL MILITARY ACADEMY SANDHURST

Central Library, Royal Military Academy Sandhurst, Camberley, Surrey GU15 4PQ
☎(01276) 412367
Fax (01276) 412538
url: www.atra.mod.uk/atra/rmas
Senior Librarian Andrew Orgill MA DipLib MCLIP (e-mail: senlibrarian@rmas.mod.uk)

Specialism(s): Military history and international affairs

ROYAL NATIONAL INSTITUTE OF THE BLIND *see* RNIB NATIONAL LIBRARY SERVICE

ROYAL PHARMACEUTICAL SOCIETY OF GREAT BRITAIN

Library, Royal Pharmaceutical Society of Great Britain, 1 Lambeth High Street, London SE1 7JN
☎020 7735 9141 (switchboard); 020 7572 2300 (direct)
Fax 020 7572 2499

e-mail: library@rpsgb.org
url: www.rpsgb.org
Head of Information Centre Roy T Allcorn BSc MCLIP
Librarian Ms Sarah Butler BA MA MCLIP
Assistant Librarian Miss Karen Poole BA MSc

Specialism(s): Pharmacy; Medicines; Therapeutics; Historical information; Pharmaceutical science

ROYAL SOCIETY

Library, Royal Society, 6–9 Carlton House Terrace, London SW1Y 5AG
☎020 7451 2606
Fax 020 7930 2170
e-mail: library@royalsoc.ac.uk
url: www.royalsoc.ac.uk
Head of Library and Information Services Keith Moore MA

ROYAL SOCIETY FOR THE PREVENTION OF ACCIDENTS

Information Centre, Royal Society for the Prevention of Accidents, Edgbaston Park, 353 Bristol Road, Birmingham B5 7ST
☎0121 248 2063/6
Fax 0121 248 2001
e-mail: infocentre@rospa.com
url: www.rospa.com
Information Services Manager Mrs Lisa Lawson BSocSc MA (0121 248 2063; e-mail: llawson@rospa.com)

ROYAL SOCIETY OF CHEMISTRY

Library and Information Centre, Royal Society of Chemistry, Burlington House, Piccadilly, London W1J 0BA
☎020 7440 3373 (direct)
Fax 020 7287 9798
e-mail: library@rsc.org
url: www.rsc.org/library
Manager, Library and Archival Services Nigel Lees MSc MCLIP

ROYAL SOCIETY OF MEDICINE

Library, Royal Society of Medicine, 1 Wimpole Street, London W1G 0AE
☎020 7290 2940 (enquiries), 020 7290 2931 (administration)
Fax 020 7290 2939 (requests), 020 7290 2976 (administration)
e-mail: library@rsm.ac.uk
url: www.rsm.ac.uk
Director of Library Services Wayne Sime BSc(Econ) MCLIP

ROYAL STATISTICAL SOCIETY

Library, Royal Statistical Society, 12 Errol Street, London EC1Y 8LX
☎020 7638 8998
url: www.rss.org.uk
Consultant Archivist Ms Janet Foster (e-mail: j.foster@rss.org.uk)
(Pre-1800 books and Society archives. Viewing by appointment only)

Albert Sloman Library, Royal Statistical Society, University of Essex, Wivenhoe Park, Colchester, Essex CO4 3SQ
☎(01206) 873181/873172 (enquiries)
Deputy Librarian Nigel Cochrane (e-mail: nigelc@essex.ac.uk)
Assistant Librarian Ms Sandy Macmillen (e-mail: amacmi@essex.ac.uk)
(Houses the historical collection of the RSS)

Specialism(s): Statistics; Social history

ROYAL TOWN PLANNING INSTITUTE

Library, Royal Town Planning Institute, 41 Botolph Lane, London EC3R 8DL
☎020 7929 9452
e-mail: library@rtpi.org.uk
url: www.rtpi.org.uk
Information Manager Miss M Wyatt BA

RSA

Library, RSA, 8 John Adam Street, London WC2N 6EZ
☎020 7451 6945
e-mail: library@rsa.org.uk
url: www.theRSA.org/library
Head of Knowledge Management Ms Joan Simpson

Archive, RSA, 8 John Adam Street, London WC2N 6EZ
☎020 7451 6847
e-mail: archive@rsa.org.uk
url: www.theRSA.org/archive
Archivist Rob Baker
(Access by appointment)

ST DEINIOL'S RESIDENTIAL LIBRARY

St Deiniol's Residential Library, Church Lane, Hawarden, Flintshire CH5 3DF
☎(01244) 532350
Fax (01244) 520643
e-mail: deiniol.warden@btconnect.com
url: www.st-deiniols.org
Warden The Very Revd P B Francis MTheol

Librarian Miss P J Williams BA DipLib
(Modern residential accommodation is available at modest charges. Day readers welcome. Testimonial required)

Specialism(s): This is a residential library specializing in theology, history and Victorian studies. The collection of over 250,000 volumes includes W E Gladstone's personal library.

ST FAGANS: NATIONAL HISTORY MUSEUM

(formerly Museum of Welsh Life (Amgueddfa Werin Cymru))

Library, St Fagans: National History Museum, St Fagans, Cardiff CF5 6XB
☎029 2057 3446
Fax 029 2057 3490
url: www.museumwales.ac.uk/en/196/
Librarian Niclas L Walker MA DipLib MCLIP (e-mail: nic.walker@museumwales.ac.uk)

Specialism(s): Material, social and cultural history of Wales

SCIENCE AND TECHNOLOGY FACILITIES COUNCIL

(formerly CCLRC (Council for the Central Laboratory of the Research Councils))

Chadwick Library, Science and Technology Facilities Council, Daresbury Laboratory, Daresbury Science and Innovation Campus, Warrington, Cheshire WA4 4AD
☎(01925) 603397
Fax (01925) 603779
e-mail: library@dl.ac.uk
url: www.e-science.stfc.ac.uk/services/library
Library Services Development Manager Mrs Debbie Franks BSc MCLIP (01925 603189)

Library, Rutherford Appleton Laboratory, Science and Technology Facilities Council, Harwell Science and Innovation Campus, Didcot, Oxon OX11 0QX
☎(01235) 445384 (general enquiries)
Fax (01235) 446403
e-mail: library@rl.ac.uk
url: www.e-science.stfc.ac.uk/services/library
Library Systems Development Manager Mrs Catherine Jones BSc MCLIP (01235 445402)

SCIENCE FICTION FOUNDATION COLLECTION

Science Fiction Foundation Collection, University of Liverpool Library, PO Box 123, Liverpool L69 3DA
☎0151 794 2696 (library)
Fax 0151 794 2681
url: www.sfhub.ac.uk
Librarian/Administrator Andy Sawyer MPhil MCLIP (0151 794 3142; e-mail: a.sawyer@liverpool.ac.uk)

SCIENCE MUSEUM LIBRARY

Science Museum Library, Imperial College Road, London SW7 5NH
☎020 7942 4242
Fax 020 7942 4243
e-mail: smlinfo@nmsi.ac.uk
url: www.sciencemuseum.org.uk (enter Library in search box)
Head of Library & Archives Rupert N Williams (e-mail: rupert.williams@sciencemuseum.org.uk)
Site Librarian (London) Ian E D Carter BSc DipLib MCLIP (e-mail: ian.carter@nmsi.ac.uk)

Site library

Science Museum Library, Science Museum Swindon, Hackpen Lane, Wroughton, Swindon SN4 9NS
Site Librarian (Swindon) Nicholas J Wyatt (e-mail: nick.wyatt@sciencemuseum.org.uk)

(A national library for the history and public understanding of science and technology, open free to the public for reference. Some services are run jointly with Imperial College London Central Library. Services are expected to resume in late 2007 following the completion of new facilities in Swindon and reconfiguration of the Library & Archives across the two sites; however details are not available at time of going to press: please check web pages for latest information.)

SCOTTISH ASSOCIATION FOR MARINE SCIENCE

Library, Dunstaffnage Marine Laboratory, Dunbeg, by Oban, Argyll PA37 1QA
☎(01631) 559000
Fax (01631) 559001
e-mail: samslibrary@sams.ac.uk
Librarian Ms Olga Kimmins BA(Hons) (e-mail: olga.kimmins@sams.ac.uk)

SCOTTISH ENTERPRISE

The Knowledge Exchange, Scottish Enterprise, 150 Broomielaw, Glasgow G2 8LU
☎0141 248 2700 (main), 0141 228 2268 (direct line)
Fax 0141 228 2818
url: www.scottish-enterprise.com
Manager Mrs Gail Rogers MA DipLib (e-mail: gail.rogers@scotent.co.uk)

Specialism(s): Business information

SCOTTISH EXECUTIVE

Information and Library Services Centre, Scottish Executive, Y Spur, Saughton House, Broomhouse Drive, Edinburgh EH11 3XD
☎0131 244 4556
Fax 0131 244 4545
e-mail: SELibrary@scotland.gsi.gov.uk

Head of Information Management Unit Ms Ann Robertson

Specialism(s): Scottish Executive and official publications

SCOTTISH NATURAL HERITAGE

Library Services, Scottish Natural Heritage, 2 Anderson Place, Edinburgh EH6 5NP
☎0131 446 2479 (enquiries), 0131 446 2478 (library management)
Fax 0131 446 2405
e-mail: library@snh.gov.uk
url: www.snh.org.uk
Library Manager Paul Longbottom MCLIP (e-mail: paul.longbottom@snh.gov.uk)

Library Services, Scottish Natural Heritage, Great Glen House, Leachkin Road, Inverness IV3 8NW
☎(01463) 725290 (enquiries); (01463) 725291 (library management)
Fax (01463) 725067

SCOTTISH PARLIAMENT

Scottish Parliament Information Centre (SPICe), Scottish Parliament, Edinburgh EH99 1SP
☎0131 348 5300
Fax 0131 348 5378
e-mail: spice@scottish.parliament.uk
url: www.scottish.parliament.uk
Head of Research and Information Services Ms Patsy Richards

SIGNET LIBRARY

Signet Library, Parliament Square, Edinburgh EH1 1RF
☎0131 225 4923
Fax 0131 220 4016
e-mail: library@wssociety.co.uk
url: www.signetlibrary.co.uk
Director of Information Services and Librarian Ms Elaine Bird BSc(Hons) MCLIP

Specialism(s): Scottish law

SOCIÉTÉ JERSIAISE

Lord Coutanche Library, Société Jersiaise, 7 Pier Road, St Helier, Jersey, Channel Islands JE2 4XW
☎(01534) 730538 (enquiries), (01534) 633392 (administration)
Fax (01534) 888262
e-mail: library@societe-jersiaise.org
url: www.societe-jersiaise.org
Librarian Mrs Brenda Ross MA(Hons)

Specialism(s): Local studies; Local and family history; Maps, prints, newspapers and ephemera

SOCIETY FOR COOPERATION IN RUSSIAN AND SOVIET STUDIES

Library, Society for Cooperation in Russian and Soviet Studies, 320 Brixton Road, London SW9 6AB
☎020 7274 2282
Fax 020 7274 3230
e-mail: ruslibrary@scrss.org.uk
url: www.scrss.org.uk
Hon Librarian John Cunningham

Specialism(s): Literature, arts and history of Russia/Soviet Union in the 20th century

SOCIETY OF ANTIQUARIES OF LONDON

Library, Society of Antiquaries of London, Burlington House, Piccadilly, London W1J 0BE
☎020 7479 7084
Fax 020 7287 6967
e-mail: library@sal.org.uk
url: www.sal.org.uk
Librarian Bernard Nurse MA FSA MCLIP

Specialism(s): Archaeology; Antiquities and historic monuments in Britain and Europe

SOCIETY OF GENEALOGISTS

Library, Society of Genealogists, 14 Charterhouse Buildings, Goswell Road, London EC1M 7BA
☎020 7251 8799
Fax 020 7250 1800
e-mail: library@sog.org.uk
url: www.sog.org.uk; online catalogue at www.sog.org.uk/sogcat
Librarian Ms Sue Gibbons BA MCLIP (e-mail: librarian@sog.org.uk)

Specialism(s): Family, local and national history; Topography; Biography; Heraldry; Demography

SUPREME COURT LIBRARY

Supreme Court Library, Royal Courts of Justice, Department for Constitutional Affairs, Strand, London WC2A 2LL
☎020 7947 6587 (enquiries), 020 7947 7198 (administration)
Fax 020 7947 6661
url: www.hmcourts-service.gov.uk; www.dca.gov.uk
Supreme Court Librarian Ms J M Robertson BA MCLIP

TATE LIBRARY AND ARCHIVE

The Hyman Kreitman Research Centre, Tate Library and Archive, Tate Bri'
London SW1P 4RG
☎020 7887 8838
Fax 020 7887 3952
e-mail: research.centre@tate.org.uk
url: www.tate.org.uk/research/researchservices
Head of Library and Archive Ms Kate Sloss BA PGDip MCLIP
Archivist Ms Sue Breakell MA MArAd
Reader Services Manager Tim Pate BA(Hons) MSc(Hons) ILM
(Opening hours: 10am–6pm, Mon–Fri)

Specialism(s): British art and international modern art

TAVISTOCK AND PORTMAN NHS FOUNDATION TRUST

Library, Tavistock and Portman NHS Foundation Trust, 120 Belsize Lane, London NW3 5BA
☎020 7435 7111 (switchboard); 020 8938 2520 (direct line)
Fax 020 7447 3734
e-mail: library@tavi-port.org
url: www.tavi-port.org
Head of Library Services Ms Angela Douglas MCLIP BSc MA

Specialism(s): Psychoanalysis; Psychotherapy; Educational psychology

THEATRE MUSEUM

The Theatre Museum Research Department, Theatre Museum, 1E Tavistock Street, London WC2E 7PR
☎020 7943 4700; 020 7943 4735 (enquiries); 020 7943 4727 (reading room)
Fax 020 7943 4777
e-mail: tmenquiries@vam.ac.uk
url: www.theatremuseum.org
Head of Information Services and Collections Management Ms C Hudson BA MCLIP
(Note: The Theatre Museum's reading room and research department is now located in Kensington Olympia, although the postal address is as above.)

Specialism(s): Performing arts; Stage design

TPS CONSULT LTD

The Information Centre, TPS Consult Ltd, Centre Tower, Whitgift Centre, Croydon CR9 0AU
☎020 8256 4110
Fax 0870 128 4894
url: www.tpsconsult.co.uk

Marketing and Information Services Manager Gursel Ziynettin (e-mail: ziynettin.gursel@tpsconsult.co.uk)

Specialism(s): Construction and design

TRADES UNION CONGRESS

TUC Library Collections, Trades Union Congress, Holloway Road Learning Centre, London Metropolitan University, 236–250 Holloway Road, London N7 6PP
☎020 7133 2260
Fax 020 7133 2529
e-mail: tuclib@londonmet.ac.uk
url: www.londonmet.ac.uk/libraries/tuc; www.unionhistory.info
Librarian Ms Christine Coates MA MCLIP (e-mail: c.coates@londonmet.ac.uk)

Specialism(s): Trade unions; Industrial relations; Politics; Economic history; International affairs

UNITED STATES EMBASSY

Information Resource Center, United States Embassy, 24 Grosvenor Square, London W1A 1AE
☎020 7894 0925 (10am–12 noon (public enquiries)), 020 7499 9000 ext 2643 (administration)
Fax 020 7629 8288
e-mail: reflond@state.gov
url: www.london.usembassy.gov
Director Ms Anna Girvan

Specialism(s): US government and foreign policy; Current affairs

VETERINARY LABORATORIES AGENCY

Library, Veterinary Laboratories Agency, New Haw, Addlestone, Surrey KT15 3NB
☎(01932) 357314 (enquiries), (01932) 357603 (administration)
Fax (01932) 357608
e-mail: enquiries@vla.defra.gsi.gov.uk
url: www.vla.gov.uk
Librarian and Agency Records Officer Mrs Heather Hulse BA(Hons)
Library Services Manager Vacant

Specialism(s): Veterinary science and medicine; Animal husbandry; Diseases of commercial farm animals

WELLCOME LIBRARY

Wellcome Library, 183 Euston Road, London NW1 2BE
☎020 7611 8722
url: http://library.wellcome.ac.uk

Librarian Ms Frances Norton DipLib MA
Head of User Services Ms Wendy Fish BA DipLib

History of Medicine/Science and Society collections
☎020 7611 8722 (enquiries)
Fax 020 7611 8369
e-mail: library@wellcome.ac.uk
Wellcome Images
☎020 7611 8348
Fax 020 7611 8577
e-mail: images@wellcome.ac.uk
Moving Image and Sound Collections
☎020 7611 8766
Fax 020 7611 8765
e-mail: misc@wellcome.ac.uk

Specialism(s): History of medicine and allied science subjects

WELSH ASSEMBLY GOVERNMENT

Assembly Library & Publications Service, Welsh Assembly Government, Information and Management Division, Cathays Park, Cardiff CF10 3NQ
☎029 2082 5440
e-mail: assemblylibraryservice@wales.gsi.gov.uk
url: www.wales.gov.uk
Head of the Assembly Library & Publications Service Ms Rebecca Davies (e-mail: rebecca.davies12@wales.gsi.gov.uk)

Specialism(s): Welsh government publications

WESTMINSTER ABBEY

Muniment Room and Library, Westminster Abbey, London SW1P 3PA
☎020 7654 4830
Fax 020 7654 4827
e-mail: library@westminster-abbey.org
url: www.westminster-abbey.org
Librarian Dr Tony Trowles MA DPhil (e-mail: tony.trowles@westminster-abbey.org)

Specialism(s): History of Westminster Abbey; Coronations; Theology (pre-1800)

WIENER LIBRARY INSTITUTE OF CONTEMPORARY HISTORY

(formerly Institute of Contemporary Studies and Wiener Library)

Wiener Library Institute of Contemporary History, 4 Devonshire Street, London W1W 5BH
☎020 7636 7247
Fax 020 7436 6428

e-mail: library@wienerlibrary.co.uk
url: www.wienerlibrary.co.uk
Librarian Ms Katharina Hübschmann
Director Ben Barkow
Education Officer Ms Katherine Klinger

Specialism(s): Holocaust; Third Reich; Fascism; Modern German–Jewish history; Anti-semitism

WILLIAM SALT LIBRARY

William Salt Library, 19 Eastgate Street, Stafford ST16 2LZ
☎(01785) 278372
Fax (01785) 278414
e-mail: william.salt.library@staffordshire.gov.uk
url: www.staffordshire.gov.uk/salt
Librarian Mrs Thea Randall BA DAS

Specialism(s): Staffordshire local history

DR WILLIAMS'S LIBRARY

Dr Williams's Library, 14 Gordon Square, London WC1H 0AR
☎020 7387 3727
e-mail: enquiries@dwlib.co.uk
url: www.dwlib.co.uk
Director of Dr Williams's Trust and Library D L Wykes BSc PhD FRHistS
(The Congregational Library at 15 Gordon Square is administered by Dr Williams's Library, to whom any application should be made. Other details are the same)

Specialism(s): History and theology of religious dissent

THE WOMEN'S LIBRARY

The Women's Library, London Metropolitan University, Old Castle Street, London E1 7NT
☎020 7320 2222
Fax 020 7320 2333
e-mail: enquirydesk@thewomenslibrary.ac.uk
url: www.thewomenslibrary.ac.uk
Head of Library Services Ms Beverley Kemp

Specialism(s): Women's history; Women's studies

WORKING CLASS MOVEMENT LIBRARY

Working Class Movement Library, Jubilee House, 51 The Crescent, Salford, Manchester M5 4WX
☎0161 736 3601
Fax 0161 737 4115
e-mail: enquiries@wcml.org.uk

url: www.wcml.org.uk
Librarian/Keeper Ms Lynette Cawthra MA DipLib MCLIP
Library Assistant Michael Weaver

Specialism(s): Labour history; Trades Unions; Communism; Socialism; Labour Party; ILP; Anarchism; Working class autobiography

YORK MINSTER

Library, York Minster, Dean's Park, York YO1 7JQ
☎(01904) 625308 (library); (01904) 611118 (archives)
Fax (01904) 611119
url: http://libcat0.york.ac.uk/F> (online library catalogue)
Librarian John S Powell MA MCLIP (e-mail: jsp5@york.ac.uk)
Archivist Peter Young MA
(Library open to the public Mon–Fri 9am–5pm; Archives open to the public Mon–Wed 9am–5pm)

Specialism(s): History; Theology; Church history; Early printed books; Yorkshire history; Stained glass; York Minster archives

ZOOLOGICAL SOCIETY OF LONDON

Library, Zoological Society of London, Regent's Park, London NW1 4RY
☎020 7449 6293
Fax 020 7586 5743
e-mail: library@zsl.org
url: www.zsl.org; http://library.zsl.org (library catalogue)
Librarian Ms A Sylph MSc MCLIP

Specialism(s): Zoology; Animal conservation

Academic, National and Special Libraries in the Republic of Ireland

ARCHBISHOP MARSH'S LIBRARY

Archbishop Marsh's Library, St Patrick's Close, Dublin 8, Republic of Ireland
☎(00 353 1) 454 3511 (enquiries and administration)
Fax (00 353 1) 454 3511
url: www.marshlibrary.ie
Keeper Dr Muriel McCarthy MA LLD (e-mail: keeper@marshlibrary.ie)
(Archbishop Marsh's Library is a 300-year-old research library with a magnificent collection of 16th and 17th century books. The library also has a book conservation bindery, which includes a flat paper conservation service.)

CDVEC CURRICULUM DEVELOPMENT UNIT

Library/Resource Centre, CDVEC Curriculum Development Unit, Sundrive Road, Crumlin, Dublin 12, Republic of Ireland
☎(00 353 1) 453 5487
Fax (00 353 1) 453 7659
url: www.curriculum.ie
Librarian Ms Eva Hornung DiplBibl MLIS ALAI MCLIP (e-mail: eva.hornung@cdu.cdvec.ie)

CENTRAL CATHOLIC LIBRARY

Central Catholic Library, 74 Merrion Square, Dublin 2, Republic of Ireland
☎(00 353 1) 676 1264 (enquiries and administration)
Fax (00 353 1) 678 7618
e-mail: catholicresearch@eircom.net
url: www.catholiclibrary.ie
Librarian Ms Teresa Whitington MA DLIS PhD

CHESTER BEATTY LIBRARY

Chester Beatty Library, Dublin Castle, Dublin 2, Republic of Ireland
☎(00 353 1) 407 0750
Fax (00 353 1) 407 0760
e-mail: info@cbl.ie
url: www.cbl.ie
Director and Librarian Dr Michael Ryan (e-mail: mryan@cbl.ie)
Reference Librarian Ms Celine Ward BA MLIS (e-mail: cward@cbl.ie)

AN CHOMHAIRLE LEABHARLANNA (THE LIBRARY COUNCIL)

Research Library, An Chomhairle Leabharlanna (The Library Council), 53-54 Upper Mount Street, Dublin 2, Republic of Ireland
☎(00 353 1) 678 4900/676 1167
Fax (00 353 1) 676 6721

e-mail: info@librarycouncil.ie
url: www.librarycouncil.ie
Research & Information Officer Alun Bevan MLib (00 353 1 678 4905; e-mail: abevan@librarycouncil.ie)

DUBLIN CITY UNIVERSITY

Library, Dublin City University, Dublin 9, Republic of Ireland
☎(00 353 1) 700 5418 (enquiries); (00 353 1) 700 5212 (administration)
Fax (00 353 1) 700 5010
url: www.dcu.ie/~library/
Director of Library Services Paul Sheehan (e-mail: paul.sheehan@dcu.ie)

DUBLIN INSTITUTE OF TECHNOLOGY

Central Services Unit, Dublin Institute of Technology, Rathmines Road, Dublin 6, Republic of Ireland
☎(00 353 1) 402 7800 (enquiries), 7801 (administration)
Fax (00 353 1) 402 7802
e-mail: csu.library@dit.ie
url: www.dit.ie/library
Head of Library Services Dr Philip Cohen BA MSc PhD DipLib MCLIP (e-mail: philip.cohen@dit.ie)
Senior Librarian, Collection Development Ms Ann McSweeney BA DLIS MLIS (00 353 1 402 7804; e-mail: ann.mcsweeney@dit.ie)
Senior Librarian, Systems Development Ms Ursula Gavin BA DLIS MLIS (00 353 1 402 7805; e-mail: ursula.gavin@dit.ie)
Faculty Librarian Ms Yvonne Desmond BA DLIS (00 353 1 402 7807; e-mail: yvonne.desmond@dit.ie)

Library, Dublin Institute of Technology, Bolton Street, Dublin 1, Republic of Ireland
☎(00 353 1) 402 3681
Fax (00 353 1) 402 3995
e-mail: bst.library@dit.ie
Faculty Librarian Peter Cahalane BA DipLib (00 353 1 402 3682; e-mail: peter.cahalane@dit.ie)

Library, Dublin Institute of Technology, Kevin Street, Dublin 8, Republic of Ireland
☎(00 353 1) 402 4894 (general enquiries)
Fax (00 353 1) 402 4651
e-mail: kst.library@dit.ie
Acting Faculty Librarian Brendan Devlin BA DLIS MLIS MA (00 353 1 402 4631; e-mail: brendan.devlin@dit.ie)

Library, Dublin Institute of Technology, Cathal Brugha Street, Dublin 1, Republic of Ireland
☎(00 353 1) 402 4423/4 (enquiries and administration)
Fax (00 353 1) 402 4499
e-mail: cbs.library@dit.ie

Faculty Librarian Brian Gillespie BA DipLib (00 353 1 402 4361; e-mail: brian.gillespie@dit.ie)

Library, Dublin Institute of Technology, 40-45 Mountjoy Square, Dublin 1, Republic of Ireland
☎(00 353 1) 402 4108
Fax (00 353 1) 402 4290
e-mail: mjs.library@dit.ie
Faculty Librarian Ms Ann Wrigley BA DLIS (00 353 1 402 4128; e-mail: ann.wrigley@dit.ie)

Library, Dublin Institute of Technology, Aungier Street, Dublin 2, Republic of Ireland
☎(00 353 1) 402 3068/9
Fax (00 353 1) 402 3289
e-mail: ast.library@dit.ie
Faculty Librarian Ms Anne Ambrose BA DLIS (00 353 1 402 3067; e-mail: anne.ambrose@dit.ie)

Library, Dublin Institute of Technology, Learning and Teaching Centre, 14 Upper Mount Street, Dublin 2, Republic of Ireland
☎(00 353 1) 402 7889
Fax (00 353 1) 676 7243
e-mail: ltc.library@dit.ie
Faculty Librarian Brian Gillespie BA DipLib (00 353 1 402 4361; e-mail: brian.gillespie@dit.ie)
Librarian Ms Diana Mitchell BA(Hons)

Music and Drama Library, Dublin Institute of Technology, Lower Rathmines Road, Dublin 6, Republic of Ireland
☎(00 353 1) 402 3461
Fax (00 353 1) 402 7854
e-mail: rmh.library@dit.ie
Faculty Librarian Ms Ann Wrigley BA DLIS (00 353 1 402 4128; e-mail: ann.wrigley@dit.ie)
Acting Librarian Ms Kathy Egan BA HDipEd DipLib MA

ECONOMIC AND SOCIAL RESEARCH INSTITUTE

Library, Economic and Social Research Institute, Whitaker Square, Sir John Rogerson's Quay, Dublin 2, Republic of Ireland
☎(00 353 1) 863 2000
Fax (00 353 1) 863 2100
url: www.esri.ie
Chief Librarian Ms Sarah Burns BSocSc (e-mail: sarah.burns@esri.ie)
Assistant Librarian Kevin Dillon BA DipLIS (e-mail: kevin.dillon@esri.ie)

ENTERPRISE IRELAND

Client Knowledge Services, Enterprise Ireland, Glasnevin, Dublin 9, Republic of Ireland
☎(00 353 1) 808 2325
Fax (00 353 1) 837 8854
e-mail: infocentre@enterprise-ireland.com
url: www.enterprise-ireland.com
Head of Department Lorcan O'Sullivan
Librarian in Charge Ms Sandra King BA (00 353 1 808 2380; e-mail: sandra.king@enterprise-ireland.com)

INSTITUTO CERVANTES

Library, Instituto Cervantes, Lincoln House, Lincoln Place, Dublin 2, Republic of Ireland
☎(00 353 1) 631 1515
Fax (00 353 1) 631 1599
e-mail: bibdub@cervantes.es
url: http://dublin.cervantes.es
Chief Librarian Ms Francisca Segura Pérez

NATIONAL ARCHIVES

National Archives, Bishop Street, Dublin 8, Republic of Ireland
☎(00 353 1) 407 2300
Fax (00 353 1) 407 2333
e-mail: mail@nationalarchives.ie
url: www.nationalarchives.ie
Director Dr David Craig
(Formed by the amalgamation of the Public Record Office of Ireland and the State Paper Office.)

NATIONAL COLLEGE OF ART AND DESIGN

Library, National College of Art and Design, 100 Thomas Street, Dublin 8, Republic of Ireland
☎(00 353 1) 636 4357
Fax (00 353 1) 636 4387
url: www.ncad.ie/library
Librarian Edward Murphy BA DipLib MLIS (e-mail: murphye@ncad.ie)

NATIONAL GALLERY OF IRELAND

Archive, National Gallery of Ireland, Merrion Square West, Dublin 2, Republic of Ireland
☎(00 353 1) 663 3508 (direct)
Fax (00 353 1) 661 5372
url: www.nationalgallery.ie
Archivist Ms Leah Benson BA HDipArch (e-mail: lbenson@ngi.ie)
(Opening hours 10–5 Mon–Fri by appointment)

Centre for the Study of Irish Art, National Gallery of Ireland, Merrion Square West, Dublin 2, Republic of Ireland
☎(00 353 1) 632 5517
Fax (00 353 1) 661 5372
e-mail: csia@ngi.ie
url: www.nationalgallery.ie
Administrator Dr Brendan Rooney

Fine Art Library, National Gallery of Ireland, Merrion Square West, Dublin 2, Republic of Ireland
☎(00 353 1) 663 3546 (direct)
Fax (00 353 1) 661 5372
e-mail: library@ngi.ie
url: www.nationalgallery.ie
Librarian Ms Andrea Lydon MA DLIS
(Opening hours 10–5 Mon–Fri by appointment)

Yeats Archive, National Gallery of Ireland, Merrion Square West, Dublin 2, Republic of Ireland
☎(00 353 1) 632 5500
Fax (00 353 1) 661 5372
e-mail: yeats@ngi.ie
url: www.nationalgallery.ie
Yeat Curator Dr Roisin Kennedy

NATIONAL LIBRARY OF IRELAND

National Library of Ireland, Kildare Street, Dublin 2, Republic of Ireland
☎(00 353 1) 603 0200
Fax (00 353 1) 676 6690
e-mail: info@nli.ie
url: www.nli.ie
Director Aongus Ó hAonghusa BSc MPA
Keeper (Printed and Visual Collections) Ms Colette O'Flaherty BA DipArchiv
Keeper (Systems) Brian McKenna BA
Keeper (Genealogical Office) Fergus Mac Giolla Easpaig MA DipArchiv
Keeper (Manuscripts) Gerard Lyne MA DipLIS HDipEd
Keeper (Administration) Temporary Ms Colette Byrne BA
Keeper (Outreach and Preservation) Ms Catherine Fahy BA DipLIS

National Photographic Archive

National Photographic Archive, Photographic Collection, Meeting House Square, Temple Bar, Dublin 2, Republic of Ireland
☎(00 353 1) 603 0374
Fax (00 353 1) 677 7451
e-mail: photoarchive@nli.ie
url: www.nli.ie
Curator Ms Sara Smyth BA DipLIS

NATIONAL UNIVERSITY OF IRELAND, GALWAY

James Hardiman Library, National University of Ireland, Galway, University Road, Galway, Republic of Ireland
☎(00 353 91) 492540 (administration), 493005 (information point)
Fax (00 353 91) 522394; 494528 (interlibrary loans)
e-mail: library@nuigalway.ie
url: www.library.nuigalway.ie
Chief Librarian Ms Marie Reddan DipLib DipSyAn FLAI MCLIP (00 353 91 493159; e-mail: marie.reddan@nuigalway.ie)
Deputy Librarian John Cox MA DipLib (00 353 91 493715; e-mail: john.cox@nuigalway.ie)
Systems Administrator Peter Corrigan BA DipLIS (00 353 91 492497; e-mail: peter.corrigan@nuigalway.ie)
Reader Services Ms Ann Mitchell BA HDipEd DipLIS (00 353 91 492738; e-mail: ann.mitchell@nuigalway.ie)
Bibliographic Services Ms Monica Crump BA MLIS (00 353 91 493765; e-mail: monica.crump@nuigalway.ie)
Information Services Niall McSweeney BA HDipinEd DipLib (00 353 91 493915; e-mail: niall.mcsweeney@nuigalway.ie)

Branch libraries

- Medical Library, National University of Ireland, Galway, Clinical Sciences Institute, University Road, Galway, Republic of Ireland
  ☎(00 353 91) 493601
  Fax (00 353 91) 494517
  Medical Librarian Timothy Collins BSc HDipEd DipLib DipSyAn FCLIP MIInfSc (00 353 91 492791; e-mail: tim.collins@nuigalway.ie)
- Nursing Library, National University of Ireland, Galway, IDA Business Park, Lower Dangan, Galway, Republic of Ireland
  ☎(00 353 91) 495228/495229
  Fax (00 353 91) 495562
  Nursing Librarian Ms Maire Ó hAodha BA DipLIS AHIP (e-mail: maire.ohaodha@nuigalway.ie), Ms Kate Kelly BA DipLIS AHIP (e-mail: kate.kelly@nuigalway.ie)

NATIONAL UNIVERSITY OF IRELAND, MAYNOOTH

The Library, National University of Ireland, Maynooth, Co Kildare, Republic of Ireland
☎(00 353 1) 708 3884
Fax (00 353 1) 628 6008
e-mail: library.information@nuim.ie
url: http://library.nuim.ie
Librarian Miss Agnes Neligan BA HDipEd MCLIP ALAI
Deputy Librarian Ms Helen Fallon MA DLIS
Sub-Librarian Ms Valerie Seymour BA(Mod) MCLIP

OIREACHTAS LIBRARY & RESEARCH SERVICE

Oireachtas Library & Research Service, Houses of the Oireachtas, Leinster House, Kildare Street, Dublin 2, Republic of Ireland
☎(00 353 1) 618 3000 (switchboard), (00 353 1) 618 4701/4702 (enquiries)
Fax (00 353 1) 618 4109
e-mail: lib@oireachtas.ie
url: www.oireachtas.ie
Head of Library and Research Services Ms Madelaine Dennison BSocSc MCLIP (00 353 1 4735; e-mail: madelaine.dennison@oireachtas.ie)
Head of Library Ms Maura Corcoran (00 353 1 618 4733; e-mail: maura.corcoran@oireachtas.ie)
Head of Research Ms Maria Fitzsimons (00 353 1 618 4734; e-mail: maria.fitzsimons@oireachtas.ie)

REPRESENTATIVE CHURCH BODY

Library, Representative Church Body, Braemor Park, Churchtown, Dublin 14, Republic of Ireland
☎(00 353 1) 492 3979
Fax (00 353 1) 492 4770
e-mail: library@ireland.anglican.org
url: www.ireland.anglican.org/
Librarian & Archivist Dr Raymond Refaussé BA PhD (e-mail: raymond.refausse@rcbdub.org)

ROYAL COLLEGE OF SURGEONS IN IRELAND

The Mercer Library, Royal College of Surgeons in Ireland, Mercer Street Lower, Dublin 2, Republic of Ireland
☎(00 353 1) 402 2407 (enquiries); 402 2411 (administration)
Fax (00 353 1) 402 2457
e-mail: library@rcsi.ie
url: www.rcsi.ie/library
Librarian Mrs Kate Kelly (e-mail: katekelly@rcsi.ie)

Branch library

RCSI Library, Royal College of Surgeons in Ireland, Beaumont Hospital, Beaumont Road, Dublin 9, Republic of Ireland
☎(00 353 1) 809 2531
Fax (00 353 1) 836 7396
e-mail: bhlibrary@rcsi.ie
Librarian Sean Hughes MA DLIS (e-mail: seanfhughes@rcsi.ie)

ROYAL DUBLIN SOCIETY

Library, Royal Dublin Society, Merrion Road, Ballsbridge, Dublin 4, Republic of Ireland
☎(00 353 1) 240 7274

Fax (00 353 1) 660 4014
e-mail: library@rds.ie
url: www.rds.ie/library
Library Director Ms Joanna Quinn BA(Mod) DBS DLIS MA (00 353 1 240 7299; e-mail: joanna.quinn@rds.ie)

ROYAL IRISH ACADEMY

Library, Royal Irish Academy, 19 Dawson Street, Dublin 2, Republic of Ireland
☎(00 353 1) 676 2570/676 4222
Fax (00 353 1) 676 2346
e-mail: library@ria.ie
url: www.ria.ie
Librarian Ms Siobhán Fitzpatrick (e-mail: s.fitzpatrick@ria.ie)
Deputy Librarian Dr Bernadette Cunningham MA DipLib (e-mail: b.cunningham@ria.ie)

TEAGASC (AGRICULTURE AND FOOD DEVELOPMENT AUTHORITY)

Library, TEAGASC (Agriculture and Food Development Authority), Ashtown Food Research Centre, Ashtown, Dublin 15, Republic of Ireland
☎(00 353 1) 805 9500 (switchboard); (00 353 1) 805 9577 (library)
Fax (00 353 1) 805 9550
url: www.teagasc.ie
Librarian Ms Maire Caffrey BSc DipLIS (e-mail: maire.caffrey@teagasc.ie)

Research libraries

- Library, TEAGASC (Agriculture and Food Development Authority), Moorepark Food Research Centre, Fermoy, Co Cork, Republic of Ireland
  ☎(00 353 25) 42222
  Fax (00 353 25) 42340
  Librarian Ms Siobhan Keating (e-mail: siobhan.keating@teagasc.ie)
- Library, TEAGASC (Agriculture and Food Development Authority), Johnstown Castle Agricultural Research Centre (environment), Wexford, Republic of Ireland
  ☎(00 353 53) 917 1200
  Fax (00 353 53) 914 2213
  Librarian Ms Eleanor Spillane (e-mail: eleanor.spillane@teagasc.ie)
- Library, TEAGASC (Agriculture and Food Development Authority), Oak Park Research Centre (crops production), Carlow, Republic of Ireland
  ☎(00 353 59) 917 0200
  Fax (00 353 59) 914 2423
  Librarian Ms Philomena Kelly (e-mail: philomena.kelly@teagasc.ie)
- Library, TEAGASC (Agriculture and Food Development Authority), Grange Research Centre (beef production), Dunsany, Co Meath, Republic of Ireland
  ☎(00 353 46) 906 1100 (switchboard); (00 353 1) 906 1151 (library)
  Fax (00 353 46) 902 6154
  Librarian Ms Ann Gilsenan (e-mail: ann.gilsenan@teagasc.ie)

TRINITY COLLEGE DUBLIN

Library, Trinity College Dublin, College Street, Dublin 2, Republic of Ireland
☎(00 353 1) 896 1127 (general enquiries); (00 353 1) 896 1661 (Librarian's office)
Fax (00 353 1) 896 3774
e-mail: library@tcd.ie
url: www.tcd.ie/library/
Librarian and College Archivist Robin Adams MA BA DipLib (e-mail: radams@tcd.ie)
Deputy Librarian Ms Jessie Kurtz BA BEd MLS (e-mail: jessie.kurtz@tcd.ie)

Departmental libraries

- John Stearne Medical Library, Trinity College Dublin, St James's Hospital, James's Street, Dublin 8, Republic of Ireland
  ☎(00 353 1) 896 2109
  Fax (00 353 1) 453 6087
  Medical Librarian David Mockler BSc DLIS (e-mail: mocklerd@tcd.ie)
- Science and Engineering Library, Trinity College Dublin, College Street, Dublin 2, Republic of Ireland
  ☎(00 353 1) 896 1805
  Fax (00 353 1) 896 3774
  Site Librarian Ms Arlene Healy BA MLIS (e-mail: arlene.healy@tcd.ie)

UNIVERSITY COLLEGE CORK

The Boole Library, University College Cork, College Road, Cork, Republic of Ireland
☎(00 353 21) 490 2794
Fax (00 353 21) 427 3428
e-mail: library@ucc.ie
url: www.booleweb.ucc.ie
Librarian John FitzGerald BA MPhil DLIS (00 351 21 490 2281/2851; fax: 00 353 21 490 3119; e-mail: j.fitzgerald@ucc.ie)

Branch/department library

Cork University Hospital Library, University College Cork, Cork University Hospital, Wilton Road, Cork, Republic of Ireland
☎(00 353 21) 490 2976
Fax (00 353 21) 434 5826
e-mail: CUH.Library@ucc.ie
Hospital Librarian Ms Una Ni Chonghaile (e-mail: u.nichonghaile@ucc.ie)

UNIVERSITY COLLEGE DUBLIN

UCD James Joyce Library, University College Dublin, Belfield, Dublin 4, Republic of Ireland
☎(00 353 1) 716 7583 (enquiries); (00 353 1) 716 7694 (administration)
Fax (00 353 1) 283 7667
e-mail: library@ucd.ie
url: www.ucd.ie/library/
Chief Librarian Sean Phillips BA MCLIP ALAI (e-mail: sean.phillips@ucd.ie)

Deputy Librarian Miss Pauline Corrigan BA DipLib ALAI (e-mail: pauline.corrigan@ucd.ie)

Site libraries

- UCD Library, University College Dublin, Health Sciences Building, Belfield, Dublin 4, Republic of Ireland
  ☎(00 353 1) 716 6572
  Fax (00 353 1) 716 6451
  Librarian i/c Peter Hickey BA DipLib (e-mail: peter.hickey@ucd.ie)
- UCD Library, University College Dublin, Veterinary Sciences Centre, Belfield, Dublin 4, Republic of Ireland
  ☎(00 353 1) 716 6208
  Fax (00 353 1) 716 6267
  Librarian i/c Diarmuid Stokes (e-mail: diarmuid.stokes@ucd.ie)
- UCD Library, University College Dublin, Smurfit Graduate School of Business, Blackrock, Co Dublin, Republic of Ireland
  ☎(00 353 1) 716 8069
  Fax (00 353 1) 716 8011
  Librarian i/c John Steele BA DipLib MLIS FLAI (e-mail: john.steele@ucd.ie)
- UCD Richview Library, University College Dublin, Richview, Clonskeagh, Dublin 14, Republic of Ireland
  ☎(00 353 1) 716 2741
  Fax (00 353 1) 283 0329
  Librarian i/c Ms Julia Barrett BMus DipLib (e-mail: julia.barrett@ucd.ie)

UNIVERSITY OF LIMERICK

Library and Information Services, University of Limerick, Limerick, Republic of Ireland
☎(00 353 61) 202166 (enquiries); 202156 (administration)
Fax (00 353 61) 213090
e-mail: libinfo@ul.ie
url: www.ul.ie
Director, Library and Information Services Ms Gobnait O'Riordan MA DLIS

Schools and Departments of Information and Library Studies

This information is subject to change. For a list of institutions that offer currently accredited courses, please visit the CILIP website, www.cilip.org.uk.

ABERYSTWYTH UNIVERSITY

Department of Information Studies, Aberystwyth University, Llanbadarn Fawr, Aberystwyth, Ceredigion SY23 3AS
☎(01970) 622188
Fax (01970) 622190
e-mail: dis-dept@aber.ac.uk
url: www.dis.aber.ac.uk
Head of Department Dr Gayner Eyre BA PhD MCLIP AALIA

UNIVERSITY OF BRIGHTON

The School of Computing, Mathematical and Information Sciences, University of Brighton, Watts Building, Lewes Road, Moulsecoomb, Brighton BN2 4GJ
☎(01273) 643500 (switchboard); (01273) 642428
Fax (01273) 642405
url: www.cmis.brighton.ac.uk
Head of School Dr John Taylor BSc PhD CMath FIMA (e-mail: john.taylor@brighton.ac.uk)
Head of Research Prof Peter G B Enser BA(Econ) MTech PhD MBCS CITP HonFCLIP (e-mail: p.g.b.enser@brighton.ac.uk)
Head of Division of Information and Media Studies Dr David S Horner BSc MSc PhD (e-mail: d.s.horner@brighton.ac.uk)

CITY UNIVERSITY

Department of Information Science, City University, School of Informatics, Northampton Square, London EC1V 0HB
☎020 7040 8381
Fax 020 7040 8584
e-mail: dis@soi.city.ac.uk
url: www.soi.city.ac.uk
Head of Department and Course Director, Information Studies Masters Scheme
Dr Vesna Brujic-Okretic (020 7040 8551; e-mail: vesna@soi.city.ac.uk)
Course Director, Information Science and Technology Masters Scheme
Dr Andrew MacFarlane BSc MSc PhD MBCS CEng CITP (020 7040 8386; e-mail: andym@soi.city.ac.uk)

UNIVERSITY COLLEGE DUBLIN

UCD School of Information and Library Studies, University College Dublin, Belfield, Dublin 4, Republic of Ireland
☎(00 353 1) 716 7055
Fax (00 353 1) 716 1161
e-mail: sils@ucd.ie

url: www.ucd.ie/sils
Head of Department Dr Ian Cornelius (e-mail: ian.cornelius@ucd.ie)

LEEDS METROPOLITAN UNIVERSITY

Innovation North, Leeds Metropolitan University, Headingley Campus, Priestley Hall, Leeds LS6 3QS
☎0113 812 7555
Fax 0113 812 6166
url: www.leedsmet.ac.uk/inn
Associate Dean John Blake BSc MSc CSTAT MBCS (e-mail: j.blake@leedsmet.ac.uk)

LIVERPOOL JOHN MOORES UNIVERSITY

Information Strategy Group, Liverpool Business School, Liverpool John Moores University, The John Foster Building, 98 Mount Pleasant, Liverpool L3 5UZ
☎0151 231 3596/3425
Fax 0151 707 0423
url: www.ljmu.ac.uk
Principal Lecturer and Subject Group Leader Ms Janet Farrow MA BA MCLIP (0151 231 3596; e-mail: a.j.farrow@ljmu.ac.uk)

LONDON METROPOLITAN UNIVERSITY

Media, Information and Communications, Department of Applied Social Sciences, London Metropolitan University, London Metropolitan University, London North Campus, Ladbroke House, 62-66 Highbury Grove, London N5 2AD
☎020 7423 0000 (main switchboard), 020 7133 5129 (postgraduate office)
Fax 020 7133 5203
url: www.londonmet.ac.uk
Head of Department Prof John Gabriel (e-mail: j.gabriel@londonmet.ac.uk)
Academic contact for Information Management Ms Sue Batley BA PhD (020 7133 5160; e-mail: s.batley@londonmet.ac.uk)

UNIVERSITY COLLEGE LONDON

School of Library, Archive and Information Studies, University College London, Gower Street, London WC1E 6BT
☎020 7679 7204
Fax 020 7383 0557
e-mail: slais-enquiries@ucl.ac.uk
url: www.slais.ucl.ac.uk
Director Prof David Nicholas MPhil PhD MCLIP

LOUGHBOROUGH UNIVERSITY

Department of Information Science, Loughborough University, Ashby Road, Loughborough, Leics LE11 3TU

☎(01509) 223051/2
Fax (01509) 223053
e-mail: dis@lboro.ac.uk
url: www.lboro.ac.uk/departments/dis/
Head of Department Prof Charles Oppenheim BSc PhD DSc HonFCLIP FCLIP (e-mail: c.oppenheim@lboro.ac.uk)
Director of LISU (Library & Information Statistics Unit) Ms Claire Creaser BSc CStat (e-mail: c.creaser@lboro.ac.uk)

(See also LISU in Key Library Agencies section)

MANCHESTER METROPOLITAN UNIVERSITY

Department of Information and Communications, Manchester Metropolitan University, Geoffrey Manton Building, Rosamond Street West, off Oxford Road, Manchester M15 6LL
☎0161 247 6144
Fax 0161 247 6351
e-mail: infcomms-hums@mmu.ac.uk
url: www.mmu.ac.uk/infocomms
Head of Department and Professor of Information Science Prof R J Hartley BSc MLib FCLIP
Professor of Information Management and Director of the Centre for Research in Library and Information Management (CERLIM) Prof Peter Brophy BSc HonFCLIP FCLIP
Professor of Information and Communications Prof Jenny Rowley BA MSc MSc DMS PhD FCLIP MBCS CEng MCMI

NAPIER UNIVERSITY

School of Computing, Napier University, 10 Colinton Road, Edinburgh EH10 5DT
☎0131 455 2700
Fax 0131 455 2727
e-mail: info@napier.ac.uk
url: www.soc.napier.ac.uk
Head of School Bob Rankin BSc(Eng) DipCS MBCS ILTM CEng (e-mail: b.rankin@napier.ac.uk)

NORTHUMBRIA UNIVERSITY

Division of Information and Communication Studies, School of Computing, Engineering and Information Sciences, Northumbria University, Pandon Building, Camden Street, Newcastle upon Tyne NE2 1XE
☎0191 227 3702
Fax 0191 227 3662
e-mail: il.admin@northumbria.ac.uk/sd/academic/ceis
url: http://northumbria.ac.uk/informatics
Dean Prof Alastair Sambell
Head of Subject Division Dr Alison Pickard

THE ROBERT GORDON UNIVERSITY

Department of Information Management, Aberdeen Business School, The Robert Gordon University, Garthdee Road, Aberdeen AB10 7QE
☎(01224) 262000 (University switchboard); (01224) 263800 (School Reception)
Fax (01224) 263838
e-mail: abs-enquiries@rgu.ac.uk
url: www.rgu.ac.uk/abs
Dean, Aberdeen Business School Prof Rita C Marcella MA DipEd DipLib PhD FCMI FCLIP (e-mail: r.c.marcella@rgu.ac.uk)
Associate Dean, Teaching Quality and Resources, Aberdeen Business School Prof Ian M Johnson BA FCLIP MIMgt (e-mail: i.m.johnson@rgu.ac.uk)
Associate Dean, Research, Aberdeen Business School Prof Robert Newton MA PGDipLib PhD MCLIP (e-mail: r.newton@rgu.ac.uk)
Subject Leader, Department of Information Management Dr Peter H Reid BA PhD (e-mail: p.reid@rgu.ac.uk)
Research Co-ordinator, Department of Information Management Prof Dorothy A Williams BSc PGDipLib PhD (e-mail: d.williams@rgu.ac.uk)

THE UNIVERSITY OF SHEFFIELD

Department of Information Studies, The University of Sheffield, Regent Court, 211 Portobello Street, Sheffield S1 4DP
☎0114 222 2630 (dept/administration)
Fax 0114 278 0300
e-mail: dis@shef.ac.uk
url: www.shef.ac.uk/is
Head of Department and Professor of Librarianship & Information Management Prof Sheila Corrall MA DipLib MBA MSc FCLIP FCMI FRSA (0114 222 2632; e-mail: s.m.corrall@sheffield.ac.uk)

STRATHCLYDE UNIVERSITY

Department of Computer and Information Sciences, Graduate School of Informatics, Strathclyde University, Livingstone Tower, 26 Richmond Street, Glasgow G1 1XH
☎0141 548 3700/2934 (direct); 0141 552 4400 (switchboard)
Fax 0141 548 4523
e-mail: ils-enquiries@cis.strath.ac.uk
url: www.cis.strath.ac.uk
Head of Department Prof Maria Fox BA(Hons) MSc PhD
Course Director Dr Paul Burton BA MA MPhil PhD FCLIP

THAMES VALLEY UNIVERSITY

Information Management, Faculty of Professional Studies, Thames Valley University, St Mary's Road, Ealing, London W5 5RF
☎020 8231 2180 (learning advice centre); 020 8231 2314 (faculty)
e-mail: management@tvu.ac.uk
url: www.tvu.ac.uk

Programme Leaders, MA Information Management (Library and Information Services) Dr Tony Olden (e-mail: tony.olden@tvu.ac.uk), Dr Stephen Roberts (e-mail: stephen.roberts@tvu.ac.uk)

UNIVERSITY OF THE WEST OF ENGLAND, BRISTOL

School of Information Systems, University of the West of England, Bristol, Faculty of Computing, Engineering and Mathematical Sciences, Frenchay Campus, Coldharbour Lane, Bristol
BS16 1QY
☎0870 901 0767
Fax 0117 328 3680
e-mail: admissions.cems@uwe.ac.uk
url: www.uwe.ac.uk/cems/
Head of Information Systems School Morris Williams
Programme Leader Ian Beeson MA MSc

Key Library Agencies and other relevant organizations

Note: Organizations are listed using their full names. If searching for an organization by its acronym, please use the general index

ADVISORY COUNCIL ON LIBRARIES (ACL)

Advisory Council on Libraries (ACL), Department for Culture, Media and Sport (Libraries Branch), 2–4 Cockspur Street, London SW1Y 5BG
☎020 7211 6287
Fax 020 7211 6195
url: www.culture.gov.uk/what_we_do/libraries/ac_libraries.htm
Secretary Craig Westwood (e-mail: craig.westwood@culture.gsi.gov.uk)
Chair Michael Thorne (e-mail: michael.thorne@anglia.ac.uk)
ACL is constituted under the Public Libraries and Museums Act 1964. Under the Act, it has a wide ranging remit but, in practice, it concentrates on advising DCMS Ministers, and the MLA (Museums, Libraries and Archives Council) on public library matters.

AFRICAN CARIBBEAN LIBRARY ASSOCIATION (ACLA)

African Caribbean Library Association (ACLA), c/o Ann Thompson, 133A Sydney Road, Hornsey, London N8 0ET
☎020 8496 1120/020 8245 5536/020 8496 1091
e-mail: acla_uk@yahoo.co.uk
url: www.cilip.org/interests/oils2.html
Secretary Ms Ann Thompson BA MA PGDip MCLIP (e-mail: libraryannie@yahoo.co.uk)
Founded in 1981 by Ann Thompson, ACLA is an independent fully constituted organization committed to the full implementation of race equality principles and policies throughout librarianship. It welcomes as members any library or information workers of African or Caribbean origin. ACLA is a founding member of the Diversity Council of CILIP.

ART LIBRARIES SOCIETY OF THE UK AND IRELAND (ARLIS)

Art Libraries Society of the UK and Ireland (ARLIS), Courtauld Institute of Art, Somerset House, The Strand, London WC2R 0RN
☎020 7848 2703
e-mail: arlis@courtauld.ac.uk
url: www.arlis.org.uk
Business Manager Ms Amy Donnison
Chair Elect Ms Vanessa Crane MBA MCLIP
The Society aims to promote all aspects of the librarianship of the visual arts, including architecture and design.

ASIAN LIBRARIANS AND ADVISERS GROUP (ALAG)

Asian Librarians and Advisers Group (ALAG), c/o Croydon Central Library, Croydon Clocktower Complex, Room B4, Katharine Street, Croydon CR9 1ET
☎020 8760 5400 ext 61052

url: www.cilip.org.uk/alag
Chair Mrs Krishna Ray (020 8686 4433 ext 61052; e-mail: krishna.ray@croydon.gov.uk)
Secretary Mrs Kamaljit Bedi (020 8489 5353)
ALAG was formed in 1982 by a group of Asian librarians to raise awareness and to serve library needs of the diverse Asian communities and, equally importantly, to support library professionals in delivering library services with vision and vigour. ALAG's mission is to promote Asian languages, history, culture and heritage through library and information services to Asians in particular and the population at large. ALAG is an active member of the Diversity Group of CILIP.

ASLIB, THE ASSOCIATION FOR INFORMATION MANAGEMENT

Aslib, The Association for Information Management, Holywell Centre, 1 Phipp Street, London EC2A 4PS
☎020 7613 3031
Fax 020 7613 5080
e-mail: aslib@aslib.com
url: www.aslib.com
Managing Director Roger Bowes
Aslib is a global corporate membership organization promoting best practice in resource management and lobbying on all aspects of management of and legislation concerning information at all levels.

ASSOCIATION OF SENIOR CHILDREN'S AND EDUCATION LIBRARIANS (ASCEL)

Association of Senior Children's and Education Librarians (ASCEL), c/o Helen Boothroyd, Adult and Community Services, Libraries, Archives and Information, Endeavour House, 8 Russell Road, Ipswich, Suffolk IP1 2BX
☎(01473) 264623
Fax (01473) 216824
url: www.ascel.org.uk
Secretary Ms Helen Boothroyd BA MCLIP (e-mail: helen.boothroyd@libher.suffolkcc.gov.uk)
Chair Ms Sharon Kirkpatrick BLS MCLIP (e-mail: s.d.kirkpatrick@dorsetcc.gov.uk)
ASCEL is a pro-active forum comprising heads of children's public and schools library services from across the UK. The Association, through its members, responds to initiatives, stimulates development, establishes best practice and works to support the provision of quality library and education services for children and young people.

ASSOCIATION OF UK MEDIA LIBRARIANS (AUKML)

Association of UK Media Librarians (AUKML), c/o Sara Margetts, Financial Times Library, 1 Southwark Bridge, London SE1 9HL

☎020 7873 3920
url: www.aukml.org.uk
Chair Richard Nelson
Membership Secretary Ms Sara Margetts (e-mail: membership@aukml.org.uk)
AUKML is the organization for information workers in the media industry, including print and broadcast news librarians, information researchers and broadcast archivists. It organizes a range of training and networking activities, publishes a newsletter and website and acts as a network and representative organization for anyone interested in media librarianship.

BAILER – THE INFORMATION EDUCATION AND RESEARCH ASSOCIATION

BAILER – the Information Education and Research Association, c/o Sheila Corrall, Department of Information Studies, University of Sheffield, Regent Court, 211 Portobello Street, Sheffield S1 4DP
☎0114 222 2632
Fax 0114 278 0300
url: www.bailer.org.uk
Chair Prof Sheila Corrall MA DipLib MBA MSc FCLIP FCMI FRSA (e-mail: s.m.corrall@sheffield.ac.uk)
BAILER includes the teaching and research staff of all the Information and Library Schools in the UK and Ireland. It aims to reflect and focus the evolution of the field of information and library studies through the development and encouragement of its members and by representing and promoting their interests. It acts as a forum within the UK for matters relating to information and library studies education and research, and maintains contact with organizations outside the UK concerned with education for information work. BAILER is recognized as the subject body for Librarianship and Information Management by the Funding Councils, the Quality Assurance Agency for Higher Education (QAA) and the Arts and Humanities Research Council (AHRC).

BOOK INDUSTRY COMMUNICATION (BIC)

Book Industry Communication (BIC), 39/41 North Road, London N7 9DP
☎020 7607 0021
Fax 020 7607 0415
url: www.bic.org.uk
Managing Agent Peter Kilborn (e-mail: peter@bic.org.uk)
Chairman Michael Holdsworth
Book Industry Communication was set up and sponsored by the Booksellers Association, the Publishers Association, The Library Association (now CILIP) and the British Library to develop and promote standards for electronic communication and supply chain efficiency in the book and serials industries.

BOOKTRUST

Booktrust, Book House, 45 East Hill, London SW18 2QZ

☎020 8516 2977
Fax 020 8516 2978
e-mail: query@booktrust.org.uk
url: www.booktrust.org.uk
Executive Director Chris Meade (e-mail: chris@booktrust.org.uk)
Booktrust is an independent national charity that encourages people of all ages and cultures to discover and enjoy reading.

BRITISH AND IRISH ASSOCIATION OF LAW LIBRARIANS (BIALL)

British and Irish Association of Law Librarians (BIALL), c/o The Boots Library, Nottingham Trent University, Goldsmith Street, Nottingham NG1 5LS
☎0115 848 2893
Fax 0115 848 2286
url: www.biall.org.uk
BIALL Hon Secretary Mrs Angela Donaldson BA MA MCLIP (e-mail: angela.donaldson@ntu.ac.uk)
Chair Ms Jennefer Aston
BIALL was formed in 1969 with the objectives of pursuing policies to bring benefits to its members, enhancing the status of the legal information profession and promoting better administration and exploitation of law libraries and legal information units nationwide.

BRITISH ASSOCIATION OF PICTURE LIBRARIES AND AGENCIES (BAPLA)

British Association of Picture Libraries and Agencies (BAPLA), 18 Vine Hill, London EC1R 5DZ
☎020 7713 1780
Fax 020 7713 1211
e-mail: enquiries@bapla.org.uk
url: www.bapla.org
Chief Executive Officer Ms Linda Royles
BAPLA represents over 450 member picture libraries and agencies. All members sign a code of conduct. The website provides details about BAPLA services and benefits to picture researchers, to photographers and of membership. The site also has a useful search engine facility.

BRITISH COMPUTER SOCIETY – INFORMATION RETRIEVAL SPECIALIST GROUP (BCS IRSG)

British Computer Society – Information Retrieval Specialist Group (BCS IRSG), c/o Andrew MacFarlane, Dept of Information Science, City University, Northampton Square, London EC1V 0HB
☎020 7040 8386
Fax 020 7040 8584

url: http://irsg.bcs.org
Secretary Dr Andrew MacFarlane BSc MSc PhD MBCS CEng CITP (e-mail: andym@soi.city.ac.uk)
Chair Leif Azzopardi (e-mail: leif@bcs.gla.ac.uk)
The BCS IRSG provides a forum for academic and industrial researchers and practitioners to discuss core issues involved in the representation, management, searching, retrieval and presentation of multimedia electronic information.

CENTRE FOR DIGITAL LIBRARY RESEARCH (CDLR)

(BUBL, CAIRNS, Glasgow Digital Library, HaIRST, HILT, SAPIENS, SCONE, SPEIR, Victorian Times)
Centre for Digital Library Research (CDLR), Department of Computer and Information Sciences, University of Strathclyde, 12.12 Livingstone Tower, 26 Richmond Street, Glasgow G1 1XH
☎0141 548 4752
Fax 0141 548 4523
e-mail: cdlr@strath.ac.uk
url: http://cdlr.strath.ac.uk/
Director Dennis Nicholson BSc MCLIP (e-mail: d.m.nicholson@strath.ac.uk)
Depute Director Gordon Dunsire BSc MCLIP (e-mail: g.dunsire@strath.ac.uk)
Research Co-ordinator Ms Emma McCulloch BA(Hons) (e-mail: e.mcculloch@strath.ac.uk)
CDLR seeks to combine theory with practice in innovative ways with the aim of being a centre of excellence on digital libraries issues ranging from information policy and information retrieval to document storage technologies and standards.

CENTRE FOR RESEARCH IN LIBRARY AND INFORMATION MANAGEMENT (CERLIM)

Centre for Research in Library and Information Management (CERLIM), Department of Information and Communications, Manchester Metropolitan University, Geoffrey Manton Building, Rosamond Street West, Manchester M15 6LL
☎0161 247 6142
Fax 0161 247 6979
e-mail: cerlim@mmu.ac.uk
url: www.cerlim.ac.uk
Director Prof Peter Brophy BSc HonFCLIP FCLIP FRSA FHEA
CERLIM undertakes research and consultancy in the library and information management field.

CHARTERED INSTITUTE OF LIBRARY AND INFORMATION PROFESSIONALS (CILIP)

Chartered Institute of Library and Information Professionals (CILIP), 7 Ridgmount Street, London WC1E 7AE

☎020 7255 0500
Fax 020 7255 0501
e-mail: info@cilip.org.uk
url: www.cilip.org.uk
Textphone 020 7255 0505
Chief Executive Bob McKee PhD MCLIP FRSA
CILIP (The Chartered Institute of Library and Information Professionals) is the leading professional body for librarians and information professionals in the UK, with members in all sectors, including business and industry, further and higher education, schools, central government departments and agencies, the health service, the voluntary sector and national and public libraries. CILIP is committed to enabling its members to achieve and maintain the highest professional standards, and encouraging them in the promotion of high-quality library and information services responsive to the needs of users.

CHARTERED INSTITUTE OF LIBRARY AND INFORMATION PROFESSIONALS IN SCOTLAND (CILIPS)

Chartered Institute of Library and Information Professionals in Scotland (CILIPS), First Floor, Building C, Brandon Gate, Leechlee Road, Hamilton, Lanarkshire ML3 6AU
☎(01698) 458888
Fax (01698) 283170
e-mail: cilips@slainte.org.uk
url: www.slainte.org.uk
Director Ms Elaine Fulton BA MCLIP (e-mail: e.fulton@slainte.org.uk)
Assistant Directors Ms Rhona Arthur BA FCLIP, Ms Catherine Kearney BA MEd DipLib DipEdTech MCLIP
CILIPS is the professional body for librarians and information personnel in Scotland, and represents personal members from all sectors – public, school, FE/HE libraries, and libraries/information services from both the voluntary and private sectors.

CHARTERED INSTITUTE OF LIBRARY AND INFORMATION PROFESSIONALS IRELAND (CILIP IRELAND)

Chartered Institute of Library and Information Professionals Ireland (CILIP Ireland), c/o Belfast Education and Library Board, 40 Academy Street, Belfast BT1 2NQ
☎028 9056 4011
url: www.cilip.org.uk/ireland
Executive Secretary and Chair Ms Elga Logue (e-mail: elgal@belb.co.uk)
The function of CILIP Ireland is to represent the interests of library staff across the sectors. It supports staff by providing access to expert advice on qualifications and continuing professional development. It identifies issues of concern to the profession, and where necessary provides intervention in the form of both advice and advocacy. CILIP Ireland works with relevant bodies such as LISC(NI) and the relevant departments of the Northern Ireland Assembly.

CHARTERED INSTITUTE OF LIBRARY AND INFORMATION PROFESSIONALS WALES (CILIP WALES)/SEFYDLIAD SIARTREDIG LLYFRGELLWYR A GWEITHWYR GWYBODAETH CYMRU (CILIP CYMRU)

Chartered Institute of Library and Information Professionals Wales (CILIP Wales)/Sefydliad Siartredig Llyfrgellwyr a Gweithwyr Gwybodaeth Cymru (CILIP Cymru), c/o Department of Information Studies, University of Wales Aberystwyth, Llanbadarn Fawr, Aberystwyth, Ceredigion SY23 3AS
☎(01970) 622174
Fax (01970) 622190
e-mail: cilip-wales@aber.ac.uk; cilip-cymru@aber.ac.uk
url: www.cilip.org.uk/wales
President Andrew Green MA DipLib MCLIP
Executive Officer Vacant
CILIP Wales promotes the professional development of individual members; seeks to influence the development of policies on the provision of information and library services at a local and national level, and provides and disseminates information about/promotes library and information services in Wales.

AN CHOMHAIRLE LEABHARLANNA (THE LIBRARY COUNCIL)

An Chomhairle Leabharlanna (The Library Council), 53–54 Upper Mount Street, Dublin 2, Republic of Ireland
☎(00 353 1) 676 1167/676 1963
Fax (00 353 1) 676 6721
e-mail: info@librarycouncil.ie
url: www.librarycouncil.ie
Director Ms Norma McDermott
An Chomhairle Leabharlanna/The Library Council is the statutory agency that advises the Minister for the Environment, Heritage and Local Government and public library authorities in Ireland on public library development. An Chomhairle also promotes policies, strategies and activities that foster co-operation and partnership between library and information services and other relevant agencies in Ireland, with the United Kingdom and within Europe.

CITY INFORMATION GROUP (CiG)

City Information Group (CiG), PO Box 13297, London SW19 8GH
☎020 8543 7339
Fax 020 8543 7639
e-mail: admin@cityinformation.org.uk
url: www.cityinformation.org.uk
Chair 2006 Ms Mandy Sullivan
Administrator Ms Phillipa Mills

The aim of the City Information Group is to promote, develop and advance the practice of collecting, collating, evaluating and disseminating financial and business information and to foster and promote education and training in these matters. The effective management of business information is seen as a critical function within a wide range of organizations, both public and private, and CiG aims to help its members to work together to share ideas and promote the ethical and effective use of information and knowledge. CiG carries this out by offering a regular programme of seminars, debates and networking events. Anyone with an interest in business information can join the Group. Information is also distributed through a website and a quarterly newsletter.

CONARLS

CONARLS, c/o Kate Holliday, Library HQ, Yorkshire Libraries and Information, Balne Lane, Wakefield, West Yorks WF2 0DQ
☎(01924) 302210
Fax (01924) 302245
url: www.conarls.org
Officer Ms Kate Holliday (e-mail: kholliday@wakefield.gov.uk)
CONARLS is a library sector co-operative concerned with the co-operation of strategic and operational affairs relating to the resource discovery and delivery of library and information collections in the UK and Ireland. Its website and e-list act as a conduit for dialogue on resource discovery.

CONSORTIUM OF RESEARCH LIBRARIES IN THE BRITISH ISLES (CURL)

Consortium of Research Libraries in the British Isles (CURL), Room 101B, The Old Gymnasium, University of Birmingham, Edgbaston, Birmingham B15 2TT
☎0121 415 8106
Fax 0121 415 8109
url: www.curl.ac.uk
Executive Director Robin Green BA MA DipLib (e-mail: robin.green@curl.ac.uk)
Deputy Executive Director and Data Services Manager Mike Mertens BA MA PhD (0121 415 8107; e-mail: mike.mertens@curl.ac.uk)
CURL's mission is to increase the ability of research libraries to share resources for the benefit of the local, national and international research community.

CONSTRUCTION INDUSTRY INFORMATION GROUP (CIIG)

Construction Industry Information Group (CIIG), c/o Max Fordham LLP, 42-43 Gloucester Crescent, London NW1 7PE
☎020 7267 5161
url: www.ciig.org.uk
Chair Mike Waring (e-mail: m.waring@maxfordham.com)
Vice-Chair Ms Vivienne Tregenza (e-mail: vivienne.tregenza@arup.com)
Secretary Clive Lacey (e-mail: clacey@estate.fco.gov.uk)

CIIG is an organization for professionals concerned with the provision, dissemination and use of information in the construction industry.

CONVENTION OF SCOTTISH LOCAL AUTHORITIES (COSLA)

Convention of Scottish Local Authorities (COSLA), Rosebery House, 9 Haymarket Terrace, Edinburgh EH12 5XZ
☎0131 474 9200
Fax 0131 474 9292
e-mail: carol@cosla.gov.uk
Chief Executive Rory Mair
President Pat Watters
COSLA is the representative voice of Scotland's unitary local authorities. Its main objectives are to promote the interests of its member councils and of local government; to liaise with the Scottish Parliament, Scottish Executive, UK Government, European institutions and appropriate partner organizations on issues of mutual interest; and to provide support for member councils in strengthening local democracy and raising awareness of and support for local government.

COUNCIL FOR LEARNING RESOURCES IN COLLEGES (COLRIC)

Council for Learning Resources in Colleges (CoLRiC), 122 Preston New Road, Blackburn, Lancs BB2 6BU
☎(01254) 662923
Fax (01254) 610979
e-mail: colric@colric.org.uk
url: www.colric.org.uk
Executive Director Jeff Cooper MA FCLIP
CoLRiC is an independent organization dedicated to enhancing and maintaining the quality of learning resources services in further education colleges throughout the United Kingdom and Ireland.

CYMAL: MUSEUMS ARCHIVES AND LIBRARIES WALES, WELSH ASSEMBLY GOVERNMENT

CyMAL: Museums Archives and Libraries Wales, Welsh Assembly Government, Unit 10, The Science Park, Aberystwyth, Ceredigion SY23 3AH
☎(01970) 610224
Fax (01970) 610223
e-mail: cymal@wales.gsi.gov.uk
url: www.cymal.wales.gov.uk
Director Ms Linda Tomos
CyMAL is a policy division of the Welsh Assembly Government established on 1 April 2004 to develop and implement policies for local museums, libraries and archives in Wales, and

to provide advice and support to the sector. An Advisory Council, chaired by the Minister for Education, Culture and the Welsh Language, has also been established.

DEPARTMENT FOR CULTURE, MEDIA AND SPORT (MUSEUMS, LIBRARIES AND CULTURAL PROPERTY DIVISION) (DCMS)

Department for Culture, Media and Sport (Museums, Libraries and Cultural Property Division) (DCMS), 2–4 Cockspur Street, London SW1Y 5DH
☎020 7211 6368
Fax 020 7211 6382
e-mail: enquiries@culture.gsi.gov.uk
url: www.culture.gov.uk
Head of Museums, Libraries and Cultural Property Division Keith Nichol (020 7211 6123; e-mail: keith.nichol@culture.gsi.gov.uk)
Head of Library Policy Craig Westwood (020 7211 6392; e-mail: craig.westwood@culture.gsi.gov.uk)
The Department for Culture, Media and Sport is the government department with overall policy responsibility for the public library sector in England.

DEPARTMENT OF CULTURE, ARTS AND LEISURE (DCAL)

Interpoint, Department of Culture, Arts and Leisure (DCAL), 20–24 York Street, Belfast BT15 1AQ
☎028 9025 8843
Fax 028 9025 8987
e-mail: dcalni@nics.gov.uk
url: www.dcalni.gov.uk
Director of Culture Division Colin Jack (e-mail: colin.jack@dcalni.gov.uk)
DCAL is responsible for the central administration of arts and culture, museums, libraries, sport and leisure visitor amenities, inland waterways and inland fisheries. It also has responsibility for Ordnance Survey, the Public Record Office, language policy, matters relating to National Lottery distribution, Millennium events and the Northern Ireland Events Company.

EVIDENCE BASE RESEARCH AND EVALUATION

Evidence Base Research and Evaluation, Library and Learning Resources, University of Central England in Birmingham, 84 Aldridge Road, Perry Barr, Birmingham B42 2SU
☎0121 331 7670
Fax 0121 331 6510
url: www.ebase.uce.ac.uk
Director Pete Dalton BA MA (e-mail: pete.dalton@uce.ac.uk)
Evidence Base undertakes research, consultancy and evaluation in the library and information management field.

THE INFORMATION COMMISSIONER'S OFFICE (ICO)

The Information Commissioner's Office (ICO), Wycliffe House, Water Lane, Wilmslow, Cheshire SK9 5AF
☎(08456) 306060/(01625) 545745 (Helpline); 020 7025 7580 (press and media enquiries)
Fax (01625) 524510 (Helpline); 020 7025 7588 (press and media enquiries)
e-mail: mail@ico.gsi.gov.uk; notification@ico.gsi.gov.uk (for notification under the Data Protection Act)
url: www.ico.gov.uk
Information Commissioner William Stewart (01625 545867; e-mail: william.stewart@ico.gsi.gov.uk)
The ICO is the UK's independent public body set up to promote access to official information and protect personal information by promoting good practice, ruling on eligible complaints, providing information to individuals and organizations, and taking appropriate action when the law is broken.

INTER-LIBRARY SERVICES – NATIONAL LIBRARY OF SCOTLAND (NLS-ILS)

Inter-Library Services – National Library of Scotland (NLS-ILS), Causewayside Building, 33 Salisbury Place, Edinburgh EH9 1SL
☎0131 623 3985 (direct), 0131 623 3700 (switchboard)
Fax 0131 623 3984
e-mail: ils@nls.uk
url: www.nls.uk; www.nls.uk/professional/interlibraryservices/index.html
Manager, Inter-Library Services Vacant
The Inter-Library Services (ILS) Division of the National Library of Scotland operates as the Scottish centre for interlibrary loans and represents Scotland in the interlending community. It has a lending collection of c.150,000 titles and provides electronic and postal document delivery. Additionally, ILS provides bibliographic verification and location services and maintains the Scottish Union Catalogue. It also operates the Scottish Book Exchange, an electronic service for Scottish libraries.

JIBS USER GROUP

JIBS User Group, c/o Science Faculty Librarian, University of Bath, Claverton Down, Bath BA2 7AY
☎(01225) 385248
url: www.jibs.ac.uk
Chair Ms Linda Humphreys (e-mail: l.j.humphreys@bath.ac.uk)
The JIBS User Group is one of the major means of feedback for end-users of the UK's networked resources. It encompasses users and librarians in higher education (HE), further education (FE) and the Research Councils. JIBS originated as the user group for BIDS ISI data service. With the growth in electronic library resources its remit asas extended beyond its core interest in resource discovery tools to encompass other electronic resources, primarily those licensed by JISC. JIBS is currently represented on all of

the JISC Collections Working Groups and has active Enhancement Groups for Web of Knowledge, Scopus, British Standards Online, Ovid and Intute. News of JIBS activities are communicated via the mailing list: lis-jibs-users@jiscmail.ac.uk and through a weblog: http://jibsnews.blogspot.com/.

JOINT INFORMATION SYSTEMS COMMITTEE (JISC)

Joint Information Systems Committee (JISC), Northavon House, Coldharbour Lane, Bristol BS16 1QD
☎0117 931 7403
Fax 0117 931 7255
url: www.jisc.ac.uk
Secretary Dr Malcolm Read (e-mail: m.read@jisc.ac.uk)
The Joint Information Systems Committee (JISC) promotes the innovative application and use of information systems and information technology in higher and further education across the UK.

LIBRARIES AND INFORMATION EAST MIDLANDS (LIEM)

Libraries and Information East Midlands (LIEM), c/o Lynn Hodgkins, Alfreton Library, Severn Square, Alfreton, Derbyshire DE55 7BQ
☎(01773) 835064
Fax (01773) 831359
e-mail: liem@derbyshire.gov.uk
url: www.liem.org.uk
Regional Librarian Ms Lynn Hodgkins BA(Hons) MCLIP (e-mail: lynn.hodgkins@derbyshire.gov.uk)
Chair Paul Chapman BSc DipILM MCLIP
Libraries and Information East Midlands is the strategic body for libraries across all sectors in the region. LIEM is funded entirely by membership subscriptions and its members include all the public and university libraries together with many of the further education and special libraries in the East Midlands. LIEM acts as an advocate for libraries on policy and strategic issues, and promotes awareness of libraries' role in the educational, cultural, social and economic vitality of the region. It continues to encourage and support regional co-operation and partnership working related to resource sharing.

LIBRARIES NORTH WEST (LNW)

Libraries North West (LNW), University of Chester, Parkgate Road, Chester CH1 4BJ
☎(01244) 511660 (direct line)
Fax (01244) 370927
e-mail: lnw.contactus@chester.ac.uk (Chester Office); lnw@lancscc.gov.uk (Interlibrary Loans Business Unit)
url: www.lnw.org.uk

Executive Officer Ms Sue Valentine BA(Hons) MCLIP FRSA
LNW represents the interests of all libraries based in the North West of England. It works closely with a range of organizations to provide a strategic voice at regional and national level. Its vision is 'to bring together all groups within the library domain in the North West to provide a strategic lead through the formulation of plans, policies, representations and expressions of view'. Its members enjoy the benefits of an organization specifically created to meet their needs through a range of activities such as advocacy, resource sharing, interlending and other services.

LIBRARY AND INFORMATION SERVICES COUNCIL (LISC(NI))

Library and Information Services Council (LISC(NI)), c/o 26 Glenkeen, Randalstown, Antrim, Co Antrim BT41 3JX
☎028 9447 2874
url: www.liscni.co.uk
Acting Executive Officer Ms Linda Houston BLS MCLIP MBA (e-mail: linda.houston2@btinternet.com)
LISC(NI)'s mission is to enhance the standard of library and information services by providing advice to the Department of Culture, Arts and Leisure (NI) and other government departments, providing a voice for the sector and acting as a catalyst for progress and development in all areas of provision.

LIBRARY ASSOCIATION OF IRELAND (CUMANN LEABHARLANN NA HÉIREANN)

Library Association of Ireland (Cumann Leabharlann na hÉireann), 53 Upper Mount Street, Dublin 2, Republic of Ireland
☎(00 353 21) 454 6499
url: www.libraryassociation.ie
President Ms Deirdre Ellis-King BA DipLib ALAI MPhil (e-mail: deirdre.ellis_king@dublincity.ie)
Hon Secretary Michael Plaice (e-mail: honsec@libraryassociation.ie)
The Library Association of Ireland is the professional body in Ireland for those engaged in librarianship and information management. It encourages professional training for library staff and acts as an educational and examining body whose fellowship diploma is a recognized qualification in librarianship.

THE LIBRARY CAMPAIGN

The Library Campaign, 22 Upper Woburn Place, London WC1H 0TB
☎0870 770 7946
Fax 0870 770 7947
e-mail: librarycam@aol.com
url: www.librarycampaign.com
Director Vacant
National Secretary Andrew Coburn (01245 356210)

The Library Campaign is a registered charity (no. 1102634) and is the UK organization representing and co-ordinating friends and user support groups for libraries of all kinds.

LIFELONG LEARNING (UK) LTD

Lifelong Learning (UK) Ltd, 5th Floor, St Andrews House, 18–20 St Andrews Street, London EC4A 3AY
☎0870 757 7890
Fax 0870 757 7889
e-mail: enquiries@lifelonglearninguk.org
url: www.lifelonglearninguk.org
Constituency Manager Ms Alix Craven (e-mail: alix@isnto.org.uk) (based at Leeds, see below)

Lifelong Learning (UK) Ltd, 4th Floor, 36 Park Row, Leeds LS1 5JL
☎0113 241 0420
Fax 0113 242 5897
e-mail: enquiries@lifelonglearninguk.org
url: www.lifelonglearninguk.org
Constituency Manager Ms Alix Craven (e-mail: alix@isnto.org.uk)
Lifelong Learning UK Ltd is the sector skills council for community learning and development, further education, higher education, libraries, archives and information services and work-based learning.

LISU

LISU, Loughborough University, Loughborough, Leics LE11 3TU
☎(01509) 635680
Fax (01509) 635699
e-mail: lisu@lboro.ac.uk
url: www.lboro.ac.uk/departments/dis/lisu
Director Ms Claire Creaser BSc CStat (e-mail: c.creaser@lboro.ac.uk)
LISU is an internationally renowned research and information centre for library and information services, based on the Department of Information Science at Loughborough University. It focuses on the analysis and interpretation of statistics and performance data to contribute to good management practice in the information economy.

LOCAL GOVERNMENT ASSOCIATION (LGA)

Local Government Association (LGA), Local Government House, Smith Square, Westminster, London SW1P 3HZ
☎020 7664 3131
Fax 020 7664 3030
url: www.lga.gov.uk
Document Management Team Leader Nick Georgiou (e-mail: nick.georgiou@lga.gov.uk)
The LGA's mission is to promote better local government. It works with and for its member authorities to realize a shared vision of local government that enables local people to shape a distinctive and better future for their locality and its communities.

LONDON LIBRARIES DEVELOPMENT AGENCY (LLDA)

London Libraries Development Agency (LLDA), 35 St Martin's Street, London WC2H 7HP
☎020 7641 5266 (tel/fax)
url: www.llda.org.uk
Director Michael Clarke (e-mail: michael.clarke@llda.org.uk)
Co-ordinator Ms Andy Hill (e-mail: andy.hill@llda.org.uk)
Development Manager Ms Fiona O'Brien (e-mail: fiona.o'brien@llda.org.uk)
The LLDA has been created to develop and realise a co-ordinated strategic vision for all library and information services across London.

MLA EAST MIDLANDS (MUSEUMS, LIBRARIES AND ARCHIVES EAST MIDLANDS)

MLA East Midlands (Museums, Libraries and Archives East Midlands), 56 King Street, Leicester LE1 6RL
☎0116 285 1350
Fax 0116 285 1351
e-mail: admin@mlaeastmidlands.org.uk
url: www.mlaeastmidlands.org.uk
Chief Executive Ms Samantha Bestwick
Chair Dr Helen Forde DAA PhD FSA RMSA
MLA East Midlands is the regional development agency for the East Midlands. Its mission is to provide strategic leadership for museums, archives and libraries in the East Midlands so that they provide a better service to the public. Its aim, working in partnership with the region's domain-specific bodies, is to ensure that the region's museums, libraries and archives play a full role in the social, educational, cultural and economic life of the region.

MLA EAST OF ENGLAND (MUSEUMS, LIBRARIES AND ARCHIVES EAST OF ENGLAND)

MLA East of England (Museums, Libraries and Archives East of England), 110 Northgate Street, Northgate Business Park, Bury St Edmunds, Suffolk IP33 1HP
☎(01284) 723100
Fax (01284) 701394
e-mail: info@mlaeastofengland.org.uk
url: www.mlaeastofengland.org.uk
Chief Executive Terry Turner
Regional Development Manager – Libraries Ms Sue Hughes
MLA East of England is the regional development agency for museum, library and archive activity in the East of England.

MLA LONDON (MUSEUMS, LIBRARIES AND ARCHIVES LONDON)

MLA London (Museums, Libraries and Archives London), Fourth Floor, 53–56 Great Sutton Street, London EC1V 0DG
☎020 7549 1700
Fax 020 7490 5225
e-mail: info@mlalondon.org.uk
url: www.mlalondon.org.uk
Chief Executive Graham Fisher (e-mail: graham.fisher@mlalondon.org.uk)
Chair Geoffrey Bond
MLA London is the strategic development agency for the sector in London. Its mission is to support and promote London's museums, libraries and archives. The agency works in partnership with a wide range of organizations to ensure that the unique cultural, knowledge and learning resources of the capital are made accessible for the benefit of all Londoners and contribute to London's status as a world-class city.

MLA NORTH EAST (MUSEUMS, LIBRARIES AND ARCHIVES NORTH EAST)

MLA North East (Museums, Libraries and Archives North East), House of Recovery, Bath Lane, Newcastle upon Tyne NE4 5SQ
☎0191 222 1661
Fax 0191 261 4725
e-mail: info@mlanortheast.co.uk
url: www.mlanortheast.co.uk
Chief Executive Ms Penny Wilkinson
MLA North East is the regional development agency for museums, libraries and archives in North East England. It will facilitate the sector's development across the region through strategic leadership, advocacy, advice, exemplar projects and service delivery.

MLA NORTH WEST (MUSEUMS, LIBRARIES AND ARCHIVES NORTH WEST)

MLA North West (Museums, Libraries and Archives North West), Ground Floor, The Malt Building, Wilderspool Park, Greenalls Avenue, Warrington, Cheshire WA4 6HL
☎(01925) 625050
Fax (01925) 243453
e-mail: info@mlanorthwest.org.uk
url: www.mlanorthwest.org.uk
Chief Executive Ms Clare Connor BA PGDipLIS FHEA
MLA North West is the regional strategic development agency for the museums, libraries and archives sector in the North West of England, working to promote and develop the social, cultural and economic potential of the sector, and its contribution to learning, inclusion and social cohesion.

MLA SOUTH EAST (MUSEUMS, LIBRARIES AND ARCHIVES SOUTH EAST)

MLA South East (Museums, Libraries and Archives South East), 15 City Business Centre, Hyde Street, Winchester, Hants SO23 7TA
☎(01962) 858844
Fax (01962) 878439
e-mail: info@mlasoutheast.org.uk
url: www.mlasoutheast.org.uk
Chief Executive Helen Jackson
MLA South East is the regional development agency for museum, library and archive activity in the South East of England.

MLA SOUTH WEST (MUSEUMS, LIBRARIES AND ARCHIVES SOUTH WEST)

MLA South West (Museums, Libraries and Archives South West), Creech Castle, Bathpool, Taunton, Somerset TA1 2DX
☎(01823) 259696
Fax (01823) 270933
e-mail: general@mlasouthwest.org.uk
url: www.mlasouthwest.org.uk
Chief Executive Bob Sharpe BSc MSc DMS
MLA South West is the regional strategic development agency for the South West, and aims to maximize the value that museums, libraries and archives add to the social, cultural, educational and economic well-being of the South West.

MLA WEST MIDLANDS (MUSEUMS, LIBRARIES AND ARCHIVES WEST MIDLANDS)

MLA West Midlands (Museums, Libraries and Archives West Midlands), 2nd Floor, Grosvenor House, 14 Bennetts Hill, Birmingham B2 5RS
☎0121 631 5800
Fax 0121 631 5825
e-mail: info@mlawestmidlands.org.uk
url: www.mlawestmidlands.org.uk
Chief Executive Jon Finch (0121 631 5801; e-mail: jon.finch@mlawestmidlands.org.uk)
Deputy Chief Executive Geoff Warren BA MCLIP (0121 631 5805; fax: 0121 631 5825; e-mail: geoff.warren@mlawestmidlands.org.uk)
MLA West Midlands is the regional development agency for museums, libraries and archives for the West Midlands.

MLA YORKSHIRE (MUSEUMS, LIBRARIES AND ARCHIVES YORKSHIRE)

MLA Yorkshire (Museums, Libraries and Archives Yorkshire), Ground Floor, Marshall Court, 1 Marshall Street, Leeds LS11 9YP
☎0113 394 4840
Fax 0113 243 9872
e-mail: info@mlayorkshire.org.uk
url: www.mlayorkshire.org.uk
Chief Executive Ms Annie Mauger BA(Hons) DipLib MCLIP MBA
MLA Yorkshire is the regional development agency for museum, library and archive activity in Yorkshire.

MUSEUMS ASSOCIATION (MA)

Museums Association (MA), 24 Calvin Street, London E1 6NW
☎020 7426 6970
Fax 020 7426 6961
e-mail: info@museumsassociation.org
url: www.museumsassociation.org
Director Mark Taylor
The Museums Association is the professional membership body for anyone involved in museums, galleries and related organizations.

MUSEUMS, LIBRARIES AND ARCHIVES COUNCIL (MLA)

Museums, Libraries and Archives Council (MLA), Victoria House, Southampton Row, London WC1B 4EA
☎020 7273 1458
url: www.mla.gov.uk
Chief Executive Roy Clare OBE
Communications and Events Officer Ms Viola Lewis (e-mail: viola.lewis@mla.gov.uk)
The Museums, Libraries and Archives Council (MLA) is the lead strategic agency for museums, libraries and archives. We are part of the wider MLA Partnership, working with the nine regional agencies to improve people's lives by building knowledge, supporting learning, inspiring creativity and celebrating identity. The Partnership acts collectively for the benefit of the sector and the public, leading the transformation of museums, libraries and archives for the future.

NATIONAL ACQUISITIONS GROUP (NAG)

National Acquisitions Group (NAG), 27 Belgrave Mount, Wakefield, West Yorks WF1 3SB
☎(01924) 383010
e-mail: nag1@btconnect.com
url: www.nag.org.uk
Administrator Ms Jane Butler MCLIP

Chair Mrs Maggie Sumner
NAG's mission is to recruit and unite members in common discussion of acquisitions policies and practices, and to promote knowledge and understanding of technological developments in publishing, bookselling and library and information work, and their use in acquisitions.

NATIONAL FORUM FOR INFORMATION PLANNING (NFIP)

National Forum for Information Planning (NFIP), Faculty of Computing, Information Systems and Mathematics, Kingston University, Kingston upon Thames, Surrey KT1 2EE
☎020 8547 2000
JISC mail: lis-nfip@jiscmail.ac.uk
url: www.bl.uk/concord/linc/nfip.html
Chair John Lindsay (e-mail: lindsay@kingston.ac.uk)
The National Forum for Information Planning (NFIP) is a forum for organizations involved in the practical implementation of information planning in the United Kingdom and Republic of Ireland. It promotes the Library and Information Plan (LIP) concept: intra-sectoral, cross-sectoral and cross-domain library and information planning on a geographical or subject basis at local, regional and national levels. It provides exchange of experience, advice and support, and is an active contributor to the policy debate on the development of a national information plan. Increasingly this involves working with museums, archives or cultural diversity, multiculturalism and sustainable development.The following information plans form part of the NFIP: Information Systems and Social Change (taxonomy@jiscmail.ac.uk); Transport Information Planning Forum (trip@jiscmail.ac.uk); and Information for Development Forum (eldis@jiscmail.ac.uk).

NATIONAL LITERACY TRUST

National Literacy Trust, Swire House, 68 South Lambeth Road, London SW8 1RL
☎020 7587 1842
Fax 020 7857 1411
e-mail: contact@literacytrust.org.uk
url: www.literacytrust.org.uk
Director Jonathan Douglas
The National Literacy Trust is an independent charity that creates literacy partnerships to change lives. By bringing together partners in education and the community in innovative ways, the Trust works towards a society in which all have the reading, writing, speaking and listening skills they need to fulfill their potential.

PIPA (PHARMACEUTICAL INFORMATION & PHARMACOVIGILANCE ASSOCIATION)

PIPA (Pharmaceutical Information & Pharmacovigilance Association), PO Box 254, Haslemere, Surrey GU27 9AF
☎(07726) 221239
e-mail: pipa@pipaonline.org

url: www.pipaonline.org
Administrator Mrs Sharon Braithwaite (e-mail: administrator@pipaonline.org)
Operations Support and Sponsor Liaison Mrs Anne Turnbull (07726 211148; e-mail: operationssupport@pipaonline.org)
President John Barber (e-mail: president@pipaonline.org)
PIPA is the professional organization for individuals in the pharmaceutical industry involved in the provision and management of information and those involved in the fulfillment of regulatory requirements relating to drug safety. The Association was formed in 1974 and was previously known as AIOPI (Association of Information Officers in the Pharmaceutical Industry). PIPA exists to support and assist its members in the development of their professional skills and responsibilities.

PUBLIC LENDING RIGHT (PLR)

Public Lending Right (PLR), Richard House, Sorbonne Close, Stockton-on-Tees TS17 6DA
☎(01642) 604699
Fax (01642) 615641
e-mail: theregistrar@plr.uk.com
url: www.plr.uk.com
Registrar Dr Jim Parker (e-mail: jim.parker@plr.uk.com)
PLR is a statutory scheme which makes payments to authors for the free lending of their books by public libraries in the UK.

THE PUBLISHERS ASSOCIATION (PA)

Academic and Professional Division, The Publishers Association (PA), 29B Montague Street, London WC1B 5BW
☎020 7691 9191
Fax 020 7691 9199
e-mail: mail@publishers.org.uk
url: www.publishers.org.uk
Director of Educational, Academic and Professional Publishing Graham Taylor
The Publishers Association is the leading trade organization serving book, journal and electronic publishers in the UK.The Educational Publishers Council (EPC) is a division of the Publishers Association, and provides a voice for school and college publishers. Contact details as above.

THE READING AGENCY

The Reading Agency, PO Box 96, St Albans, Herts AL1 3WP
url: www.readingagency.org.uk
Director Ms Miranda McKearney OBE
Head of Resources Ms Penny Shapland (e-mail: penny.shapland@readingagency.org.uk)
Head of Programme Support Ms Elizabeth Dubber BA MCLIP (e-mail: liz.dubber@readingagency.org.uk)
Head of Finance Ms Maureen McCulloch (e-mail: maureen.mcculloch@readingagency.org.uk)

TRA is an independent reading development agency, revenue funded by the Arts Council of England. TRA works with libraries and their partners to enrich everyone's lives and communities through free, democratic access to reading.

READING IS FUNDAMENTAL, UK

Reading Is Fundamental, UK, c/o The National Literacy Trust, 68 South Lambeth Road, London SW8 1RL
☎020 7587 1842
Fax 020 7587 1411
e-mail: rif@literacytrust.org.uk
url: www.rif.org.uk
Director Ms Viv Bird (e-mail: viv.bird@literacytrust.org.uk)
Reading Is Fundamental, UK (RIF) promotes a love of reading among children and young people (aged 0–19) in areas of disadvantage and gives them opportunities to choose free books to keep for themselves. RIF works through local volunteers who promote the fun of reading, the importance of book choice and the benefits of families sharing books at home. RIF is an initiative of the National Literacy Trust.

RECORDS MANAGEMENT SOCIETY OF GREAT BRITAIN (RMS)

Records Management Society of Great Britain (RMS), Woodside, Coleheath Bottom, Speen, Princes Risborough, Bucks HP27 0SZ
☎(01494) 488566
Fax (01494) 488590
e-mail: info@rms-gb.org.uk
url: www.rms-gb.org.uk
Administration Secretary Jude Awdry
Chair Dr Paul Duller
Records management is the system(s) by which an organization seeks to control the creation, distribution, filing, retrieval, storage and disposal of those records, regardless of media, which are created or received by that organization in the course of its business. Membership is open to all regardless of status, from students to corporate entities.

THE SCHOOL LIBRARY ASSOCIATION (SLA)

The School Library Association (SLA), Unit 2, Lotmead Business Village, Lotmead Farm, Wanborough, Swindon SN4 0UY
☎(01793) 791787; (0870) 777 0979
Fax (01793) 791786; (0870) 777 0987
e-mail: info@SLA.org.uk
url: www.SLA.org.uk
Chief Executive Ms Kathy Lemaire BA DipLib MCLIP FRSA
The SLA believes that every student is entitled to effective school library provision. It is committed to supporting everyone involved in school libraries, promoting high-quality learning and development opportunities for all, and provides advice, training, publications

and a quarterly journal, The School Librarian. The SLA School Librarian of the Year Award was inaugurated in 2004 at the suggestion of the SLA President, Aidan Chambers, with the first winner announced in May 2005. The Award honours and celebrates outstanding school librarians and is open to anyone who works as a school librarian from pre-school to sixth-form college.

SCOTTISH EXECUTIVE EDUCATION DEPARTMENT

Scottish Executive Education Department, Victoria Quay, Edinburgh EH6 6QQ
☎0131 244 0341
Fax 0131 244 0353
Head of Cultural Policy Division Ms Heather Jack
The Scottish Executive Education Department is responsible for sponsorship of the National Library of Scotland and development of policy on libraries in Scotland.

SCOTTISH LIBRARY AND INFORMATION COUNCIL (SLIC)

Scottish Library and Information Council (SLIC), 1st Floor, Building C, Brandon Gate, Leechlee Road, Hamilton, Lanarkshire ML3 6AU
☎(01698) 458888
Fax (01698) 283170
e-mail: slic@slainte.org.uk
url: www.slainte.org.uk
Director Ms Elaine Fulton BA MCLIP (e-mail: e.fulton@slainte.org.uk)
Assistant Directors Ms Rhona Arthur BA FCLIP, Ms Catherine Kearney BA MEd DipLib DipEdTech MCLIP
SLIC is an independent body that promotes the development of library and information services in Scotland. It advises Scottish Ministers, the Scottish Parliament and the Executive on library and information matters, provides support to library and information services and facilitates the co-ordination of services.

SHARE THE VISION (STV)

Share the Vision (STV), c/o RNIB National Library Service, Far Cromwell Road, Bredbury, Stockport SK6 2SG
☎0161 355 2003
Fax 0161 355 2098
url: www.rnib.org.uk
STV Co-ordinator Ms Helen Brazier MA MCLIP (e-mail: helen.brazier@rnib.org.uk)
Established in 1989, STV is a partnership of the main voluntary sector and publicly-funded library bodies, which aims to enhance LIS for visually impaired people via greater co-operation and co-ordination of service delivery, e.g. the Gateway Project at www.gateway-uk.org, and via campaigning services.

SINTO (THE INFORMATION PARTNERSHIP FOR SOUTH YORKSHIRE AND NORTH DERBYSHIRE)

SINTO (the Information Partnership for South Yorkshire and north Derbyshire), Learning Centre, Sheffield Hallam University, Collegiate Crescent, Sheffield S10 2BP
☎0114 225 5739/40
Fax 0114 225 2476
url: www.sinto.org.uk
Director Carl Clayton BA MCLIP DMS (e-mail: c.j.clayton@shu.ac.uk)
Assistant Ms Gilly Pearce
SINTO's mission is to promote library and information services in South Yorkshire and north Derbyshire through co-operation and partnership.

SOCIETY OF ARCHIVISTS

Society of Archivists, Prioryfield House, 20 Canon Street, Taunton, Somerset TA1 1SW
☎(01823) 327030
Fax (01823) 271719
e-mail: societyofarchivists@archives.org.uk
url: www.archives.org.uk
Executive Secretary Patrick Cleary
The principal aims of the Society are achieved both through the work of the Society's Council and its various committees, groups and regions, and by its position as spokesman for the profession, submitting evidence and comment on matters of professional concern to any official body which seeks advice or whose activities affect archives.

SOCIETY OF CHIEF LIBRARIANS (SCL)

Society of Chief Librarians (SCL), c/o Mrs Alison Bramley, Shade House, Fradley Junction, Alrewas, Burton-on-Trent, Staffs DE13 7DN
url: www.goscl.com
President Tony Durcan BLib MCLIP (e-mail: tony.durcan@newcastle.gov.uk)
SCL Development Officer Mrs Alison Bramley (e-mail: alison.bramley@virgin.net)
SCL aims to take a leading role in the development of public libraries by influencing statutory, financial and other decisions. The association represents the views of its member to the Department of Culture, Media and Sport (DCMS), the Welsh Assembly Government, Members of Parliament, MLA (the Museums, Libraries and Archives Council), the Advisory Council on Libraries (ACL), CILIP (the Chartered Institute of Library and Information Professionals), the Local Government Association, the Audit Commission and other government departments and bodies.

SOCIETY OF COLLEGE, NATIONAL AND UNIVERSITY LIBRARIES (SCONUL)

Society of College, National and University Libraries (SCONUL), 102 Euston Street, London NW1 2HA
☎020 7387 0317

Fax 020 7383 3197
url: www.sconul.ac.uk
Secretary A J C Bainton
SCONUL works to improve the quality and extend the influence of UK higher education libraries, of Irish university libraries, and of the national libraries of the UK and Ireland. Through its expert groups, SCONUL seeks to develop and promote policy at a national and international level. SCONUL's advisory groups also disseminate good practice and shared knowledge to strengthen the roles of senior library management. In August 2007 SCONUL approved the merger of the two access schemes, SCONUL Research Extra and UK Libraries Plus, to form a single scheme to be known as SCONUL Access.

SOCIETY OF INDEXERS

Society of Indexers, Woodburn Business Centre, 10 Jessell Street, Sheffield S9 3HY
☎0114 244 9561/07757 813134
Fax 0114 244 9563
e-mail: admin@indexers.org.uk
url: www.indexers.org.uk
Administrator Ms Wendy Burrow
Secretary Ms Judith Menes
The Society of Indexers is a non-profit organization, membership of which is open to any person who is, or intends to be, directly involved in indexing. Its formal objectives include promotion of standards and instruction on techniques for all forms of indexing, the training and continuing education of indexers, and publishing guidance, information and ideas about indexing.

SOUTH WESTERN REGIONAL LIBRARY SYSTEM (SWRLS)

South Western Regional Library System (SWRLS), c/o SWRLS Library Service, Civic Centre, High Street, Kingswood, South Glos BS15 9TR
url: www.swrls.org.uk
Hon Secretary Martin Burton BA MCLIP
SWRLS Chair Robert N Froud BLib DMS MIMgt FCLIP (e-mail: rnfroud@somerset.gov.uk) (Head of Cultural Services, Somerset County Council: refer to for strategic issues)
SWRLS is a co-operative of member libraries set up to promote co-operation and facilitate interlending.

SPRIG – PROMOTING INFORMATION IN LEISURE, TOURISM AND SPORT

SPRIG – Promoting Information in Leisure, Tourism and Sport, c/o Emma Butler, University of Derby Buxton, 1 Devonshire Road, Buxton, Derbyshire SK17 6RY
☎(01332) 594671
url: www.sprig.org.uk
Hon. Secretary Peter Drake (e-mail: secretary@sprig.org.uk)

Publicity Officer Ms Theresa Summerfield (e-mail: t.a.summerfield@bham.ac.uk)
Chair Ms Emma Butler (e-mail: chair@sprig.org.uk)
SPRIG promotes information sources in leisure, tourism, sport, recreation and hospitality management. It aims to: act as a special interest group for information managers; disseminate information to users; lobby information providers – such as government organizations – for better provision; and improve awareness of information sources to those outside the library and information profession.

THEATRE INFORMATION GROUP (TIG)

Theatre Information Group (TIG), c/o Claire Hudson, Membership Secretary, V&A Theatre Collections, Blythe House, 23 Blythe Road, London W14 0QX
☎020 7471 9860
Fax 020 7471 9864
e-mail: c.hudson@vam.ac.uk
Chair Guy Baxter (e-mail: g.baxter@vam.ac.uk)
Secretaries (Joint) Ms Kristy Davis (e-mail: kdavis@tcm.ac.uk), Ms Fran Birch (e-mail: fran.birch@theatrestrust.org.uk)
The Theatre Information Group is a support organization for libraries, archives, museums and other bodies dealing with performing arts information and collections. TIG is the UK branch of the international association for libraries and museums of the performing arts, SIBMS (www.sibmas.org).

UK LIBRARIES PLUS *see* SOCIETY OF COLLEGE, NATIONAL AND UNIVERSITY LIBRARIES (SCONUL)

UK SERIALS GROUP (UKSG)

UK Serials Group (UKSG), Hilltop, Heath End, Newbury, Berks RG20 0AP
☎(01635) 254292
Fax (01635) 253826
url: www.uksg.org
Chair Paul Harwood
Business Manager Ms Alison Whitehorn (e-mail: alison@uksg.org)
The UKSG exists to encourage the exchange and promotion of ideas on printed and electronic serials and the process of scholarly communication.The organization aims to increase professional awareness, to stimulate research and to provide a training and education programme, bringing together all parties in the serials information chain.

UKOLN

UKOLN, Library, University of Bath, Bath BA2 7AY
☎(01225) 386250
Fax (01225) 386838
e-mail: ukoln@ukoln.ac.uk

url: www.ukoln.ac.uk
Director Dr Elizabeth Lyon
A centre of expertise in digital information management, providing advice and services to the library, information, education and cultural heritage communities.

YORKSHIRE LIBRARIES AND INFORMATION (YLI)

Yorkshire Libraries and Information (YLI), Library HQ, Balne Lane, Wakefield, West Yorks WF2 0DQ
☎(01924) 302210
Fax (01924) 302245
e-mail: lib.admin@wakefield.gov.uk
url: www.yli.org.uk
Manager Ms Kate Holliday (e-mail: kholliday@wakefield.gov.uk)
YLI is the regional library system for Yorkshire and Humber.

The Regions of England

Public library authorities are arranged within the nine Government regions in England. (Upper Norwood Joint Library is included. This is not a public library authority but a service jointly managed by the London Boroughs of Croydon and Lambeth. However it has a separate entry). Full entries for these public library authorities will be found in the English Public Libraries section.

East

- Bedfordshire
- Cambridgeshire
- Essex
- Hertfordshire
- Luton
- Norfolk
- Peterborough
- Southend on Sea
- Suffolk
- Thurrock

East Midlands

- Derby
- Derbyshire
- Leicester
- Leicestershire
- Lincolnshire
- Northamptonshire
- Nottingham
- Nottinghamshire
- Rutland

London

- Barking and Dagenham
- Barnet
- Bexley
- Brent
- Bromley
- Camden
- City of London
- Croydon
- Ealing
- Enfield
- Greenwich
- Hackney
- Hammersmith and Fulham
- Haringey
- Harrow
- Havering
- Hillingdon
- Hounslow
- Islington
- Kensington and Chelsea
- Kingston upon Thames
- Lambeth
- Lewisham
- Merton
- Newham
- Redbridge
- Richmond upon Thames
- Southwark
- Sutton
- Tower Hamlets
- Upper Norwood Joint Library
- Waltham Forest
- Wandsworth
- Westminster

North East

- Darlington
- Durham
- Gateshead
- Hartlepool
- Middlesbrough
- Newcastle upon Tyne
- North Tyneside
- Northumberland
- Redcar and Cleveland
- South Tyneside
- Stockton-on-Tees
- Sunderland

North West and Merseyside

- Blackburn with Darwen
- Blackpool
- Bolton
- Bury
- Cheshire
- Cumbria
- Halton
- Knowsley

Lancashire
Liverpool
Manchester
Oldham
Rochdale
St Helens
Salford
Sefton
Stockport
Tameside
Trafford
Warrington
Wigan
Wirral

South East

Bracknell Forest
Brighton and Hove
Buckinghamshire
East Sussex
Hampshire
Isle of Wight
Kent
Medway
Milton Keynes
Oxfordshire
Portsmouth
Reading
Slough
Southampton
Surrey
West Berkshire
West Sussex
Windsor and Maidenhead
Wokingham

South West

Bath and North East Somerset
Bournemouth
Bristol
Cornwall
Devon
Dorset
Gloucestershire
North Somerset
Plymouth
Poole
Somerset
South Gloucestershire
Swindon
Torbay
Wiltshire

West Midlands

Birmingham
Coventry
Dudley
Herefordshire
Sandwell
Shropshire
Solihull
Staffordshire
Stoke-on-Trent
Telford and Wrekin
Walsall
Warwickshire
Wolverhampton
Worcestershire

Yorkshire and The Humber

Barnsley
Bradford
Calderdale
Doncaster
East Riding of Yorkshire
Kingston upon Hull
Kirklees
Leeds
North East Lincolnshire
North Lincolnshire
North Yorkshire
Rotherham
Sheffield
Wakefield
York

Name and place index

All page numbers from 3 to 212 refer to public libraries or public library authorities; page numbers from 215 to 413 refer to academic institutions and special libraries. Pages 417 to 442 refer to key library agencies.